THE BEST KNOWN WORKS OF
VOLTAIRE

THE
BEST KNOWN WORKS OF
VOLTAIRE

The Complete Romances, including *Candide*,
The Philosophy of History, *The Ignorant Philosopher*,
Dialogues and Philosophic Criticisms

DOUBLE

GARDEN CITY, NEW YORK

CONTENTS

ZADIG, OR FATE

CHAPTER | PAGE

I. THE BLIND OF ONE EYE 1

II. THE NOSE 3

III. THE DOG AND THE HORSE 4

IV. THE ENVIOUS MAN 7

V. THE GENEROUS 10

VI. THE MINISTER 11

VII. THE DISPUTES AND THE AUDIENCES 13

VIII. JEALOUSY 14

IX. THE WOMAN BEATER 17

X. SLAVERY 19

XI. THE FUNERAL PILE 21

XII. THE SUPPER 23

XIII. THE RENDEZVOUS 26

XIV. THE DANCE 28

XV. BLUE EYES 29

XVI. THE ROBBER 32

XVII. THE FISHERMAN 34

XVIII. THE BASILISK 37

XIX. THE COMBATS 41

XX. THE HERMIT 44

XXI. THE ENIGMAS 49

THE PRINCESS OF BABYLON

I. ROYAL CONTEST FOR THE HAND OF FORMOSANTA . . 52

II. THE KING OF BABYLON CONVENES HIS COUNCIL AND
CONSULTS THE ORACLE 58

CHAPTER   PAGE

III. Royal Festival Given in Honor of the Kingly Visitors. The Bird Converses Eloquently with Formosanta 60

IV. The Beautiful Bird Is Killed by the King of Egypt. Formosanta Begins a Journey. Aldea Elopes with the King of Scythia 64

V. Formosanta Visits China and Scythia in Search of Amazan 74

VI. The Princess Continues Her Journey 77

VII. Amazan Visits Albion 79

VIII. Amazan Leaves Albion 81

IX. An Unfortunate Adventure in Gaul 85

X. Amazan and Formosanta Become Reconciled . . 89

THE WHITE BULL

I. How the Princess Amasidia Meets a Bull . . . 96

II. How the Wise Mambres, Formerly Magician of Pharaoh, Knew Again the Old Woman, and Was Known by Her 98

III. How the Beautiful Amasidia Had a Secret Conversation with a Beautiful Serpent 100

IV. How They Wanted to Sacrifice the Bull and Exorcise the Princess 104

V. How the Wise Mambres Conducted Himself Wisely 106

VI. How Mambres Met Three Prophets and Gave Them a Good Dinner 109

VII. How King Amasis Wanted to Give the White Bull to Be Devoured by the Fish of Jonah, and Did Not Do It 111

CHAPTER PAGE

VIII. How the Serpent Told Stories to the Princess to Comfort Her 112

IX. How the Serpent Did Not Comfort the Princess . 113

X. How They Wanted to Behead the Princess and Did Not Do It 115

XI. Apotheosis of the White Bull. Triumph of the Wise Mambres. The Seven Years Proclaimed by Daniel Are Accomplished. Nebuchadnezzar Resumes the Human Form, Marries the Beautiful Amasidia, and Ascends the Throne of Babylon . 116

CANDIDE

I. How Candide Was Brought Up in a Fine Castle, and How He Was Expelled from Thence 119

II. What Became of Candide among the Bulgarians . 120

III. How Candide Made His Escape from the Bulgarians, and What Afterwards Befell Him 122

IV. How Candide Met His Old Master of Philosophy, Dr. Pangloss, and What Happened to Them . . 123

V. Tempest, Shipwreck, Earthquake, and What Became of Dr. Pangloss, Candide and James the Anabaptist 125

VI. How a Fine Inquisition Was Celebrated to Prevent Earthquakes, and How Candide Was Whipped . 127

VII. How an Old Woman Took Care of Candide, and How He Found the Object He Loved 128

VIII. The History of Cunegonde 129

IX. What Happened to Cunegonde, Candide, the Grand Inquisitor and the Jew 131

X. In What Distress Candide, Cunegonde, and the Old Woman Arrived at Cadiz and of Their Embarkation 132

CHAPTER   PAGE
   XI.   THE HISTORY OF THE OLD WOMAN 134

  XII.   THE SEQUEL OF THE OLD WOMAN'S ADVENTURES . . 136

 XIII.   HOW CANDIDE WAS OBLIGED TO PART FROM THE FAIR
         CUNEGONDE AND THE OLD WOMAN 138

 XIV.   HOW CANDIDE AND CACAMBO WERE RECEIVED BY THE
         CLERICS OF PARAGUAY 140

  XV.   HOW CANDIDE KILLED THE BROTHER OF HIS DEAR CUNE-
         GONDE 142

 XVI.   WHAT PASSED BETWEEN OUR TWO TRAVELLERS, AND
         TWO GIRLS, TWO MONKEYS, AND THE SAVAGES CALLED
         OREILLONS 143

XVII.   THE ARRIVAL OF CANDIDE AND HIS MAN AT THE COUNTRY
         OF ELDORADO 145

XVIII. WHAT THEY SAW IN THE COUNTRY OF ELDORADO . . 148

 XIX.   WHAT HAPPENED TO THEM AT SURINAM, AND HOW
         CANDIDE BECAME ACQUAINTED WITH MARTIN . . . 152

  XX.   WHAT HAPPENED TO CANDIDE AND MARTIN AT SEA . . 155

 XXI.   CANDIDE AND MARTIN DRAW NEAR TO THE COAST OF
         FRANCE AND CONTINUE TO DISCUSS 157

XXII.   WHAT HAPPENED IN FRANCE TO CANDIDE AND MARTIN . 158

XXIII. CANDIDE AND MARTIN GO TO THE ENGLISH COAST, AND
         WHAT THEY SAW THERE 164

XXIV.   CONCERNING PAQUETTA AND GIROFFLEE 165

 XXV.   THE VISIT TO SEIGNIOR POCOCURANTE, THE NOBLE
         VENETIAN 168

XXVI.   OF CANDIDE AND MARTIN SUPPING WITH SIX STRANGERS,
         AND WHO THEY WERE 172

XXVII. CANDIDE'S VOYAGE TO CONSTANTINOPLE 174

XXVIII. WHAT HAPPENED TO CANDIDE, CUNEGONDE, PANGLOSS,
         MARTIN, ETC. 176

CHAPTER   PAGE
XXIX.   How Candide Found Cunegonde and the Old Woman
        Again   178
XXX.   Conclusion   179

THE HURON, OR PUPIL OF NATURE

I.   The Huron Arrives in France   183
II.   The Huron, Called the Ingenu, Acknowledged by
        His Relations   187
III.   The Huron Converted   189
IV.   The Huron Baptized   191
V.   The Huron in Love   192
VI.   The Huron Flies to His Mistress, and Becomes
        Quite Furious   194
VII.   The Huron Repulses the English   196
VIII.   The Huron Goes to Court. Sups upon the Road with
        Some Huguenots   198
IX.   The Arrival of the Huron at Versailles. His Re-
        ception at Court   199
X.   The Huron Is Shut Up in the Bastile with a Jan-
        senist   202
XI.   How the Huron Discloses His Genius   205
XII.   The Huron's Sentiments upon Theatrical Pieces .   207
XIII.   The Beautiful Miss St. Yves Goes to Versailles .   208
XIV.   Rapid Progress of the Huron's Intellect .   .   .   211
XV.   The Beautiful Miss St. Yves Visits M. de St. Pouange   212
XVI.   Miss St. Yves Consults a Cleric   214
XVII.   The Cleric Triumphs   215
XVIII. Miss St. Yves Delivers Her Lover and a Jansenist .   216
XIX.   The Huron, the Beautiful Miss St. Yves, and Their
        Relations Are Convened   218

CHAPTER   PAGE

XX. THE DEATH OF THE BEAUTIFUL MISS ST. YVES, AND ITS CONSEQUENCES 222

MICROMEGAS

I. A VOYAGE TO THE PLANET SATURN BY A NATIVE OF SIRIUS 227

II. THE CONVERSATION BETWEEN MICROMEGAS AND THE IN-HABITANT OF SATURN 229

III. THE VOYAGE OF THESE INHABITANTS OF OTHER WORLDS 231

IV. WHAT BEFELL THEM UPON THIS OUR GLOBE . . . 232

V. THE TRAVELERS CAPTURE A VESSEL 234

VI. WHAT HAPPENED IN THEIR INTERCOURSE WITH MEN . 235

THE WORLD AS IT GOES 241

THE BLACK AND THE WHITE 252

MEMNON, THE PHILOSOPHER 262

ANDRE DES TOUCHES AT SIAM 266

THE BLIND PENSIONERS AT QUINZE VINGT 270

BABABEC 271

A CONVERSATION WITH A CHINESE 273

PLATO'S DREAM 275

AN ADVENTURE IN INDIA 277

JEANNOT AND COLIN 279

THE TRAVELS OF SCARMENTADO 286

THE GOOD BRAHMIN 291

THE TWO COMFORTERS 293

ANCIENT FAITH AND FABLE 295

THE STUDY OF NATURE

I. INTRODUCTION 298

II. THE STUDY OF NATURE 299

CONTENTS

CHAPTER   PAGE

III. GOOD ADVICE 299

IV. DIALOGUE UPON THE SOUL AND OTHER TOPICS . . . 300

THE MAN OF FORTY CROWNS

I. NATIONAL POVERTY 304

II. DISASTER OF THE MAN OF FORTY CROWNS 305

III. CONVERSATION WITH A GEOMETRICIAN 306

IV. AUDIENCE OF THE COMPTROLLER GENERAL . . . 314

V. ON TAXES PAID TO A FOREIGN POWER 316

VI. ON PROPORTIONS 318

VII. A GREAT QUARREL 321

VIII. A RASCAL REPULSED 322

IX. THE GOOD SENSE OF MR. ANDREW 323

X. THE GOOD SUPPER AT MR. ANDREW'S 324

THE SAGE AND THE ATHEIST

INTRODUCTION 329

CHAPTER

I. ADVENTURES OF JOHN, A YOUNG ENGLISHMAN, WRITTEN
BY DONNA LAS NALGAS 329

II. CONTINUATION OF THE ADVENTURES OF JOHN, THE YOUNG
ENGLISHMAN; ALSO THOSE OF HIS WORTHY FATHER,
D.D., M.P., AND F.R.S. 331

III. JOHN RETURNS TO LONDON, AND IS LED INTO BAD COM-
PANY 333

IV. THEY WANT TO GET JOHN MARRIED 335

V. A TERRIBLE ADVENTURE 337

VI. WHAT HAPPENED IN AMERICA 339

VII. DIALOGUE BETWEEN FREIND AND BIRTON ON ATHEISM . 344

VIII. ON ATHEISM 347

IX. ON ATHEISM 352

X. RETURN TO ENGLAND. JOHN'S MARRIAGE 356

THE PHILOSOPHY OF HISTORY

PAGE

DEDICATION 359

INTRODUCTION 361

CHAPTER

I. OF THE DIFFERENT RACES OF MEN 363

II. OF THE ANTIQUITY OF NATIONS 365

III. OF THE KNOWLEDGE OF THE SOUL 366

IV. OF THE RELIGION OF THE FIRST MEN 367

V. CUSTOMS AND OPINIONS OF ANCIENT NATIONS . . . 370

VI. OF SAVAGES 372

VII. OF AMERICA 376

VIII. OF THEOCRACY 378

IX. OF THE CHALDEANS 379

X. OF THE BABYLONIANS BECOME PERSIANS 382

XI. OF SYRIA 385

XII. OF THE PHŒNICIANS, AND OF SANCHONIATHON . . . 386

XIII. OF THE SCYTHIANS AND GOMERIANS 388

XIV. OF ARABIA 390

XV. OF BRAM, ABRAM, OR ABRAHAM 392

XVI. OF INDIA 393

XVII. OF CHINA 398

XVIII. OF EGYPT 401

XIX. THE EGYPTIAN LANGUAGE AND SYMBOLS 404

XX. EGYPTIAN MONUMENTS 405

XXI. OF THE GREEKS 406

XXII. OF THE JEWS, WHEN FIRST KNOWN 409

XXIII. OF THE JEWS IN EGYPT 410

XXIV. OF MOSES AS CHIEF OF A NATION 411

XXV. OF THE JEWS FROM MOSES TO SAUL 414

CHAPTER PAGE

XXVI. OF THE JEWS, AFTER SAUL 418

XXVII. OF THE ROMANS, THEIR EMPIRE, RELIGION AND TOL-
ERATION 419

THE IGNORANT PHILOSOPHER

I. THE FIRST DOUBT 422

II. OUR WEAKNESS 422

III. HOW AM I TO THINK? 423

IV. IS IT NECESSARY FOR ME TO KNOW? 423

V. ARISTOTLE, DESCARTES, AND GASSENDI 424

VI. BEASTS 424

VII. EXPERIENCE 425

VIII. SUBSTANCE 425

IX. NARROW LIMITS 426

X. IMPOSSIBLE DISCOVERIES 426

XI. THE FOUNDATION OF DESPAIR 427

XII. DOUBT 428

XIII. AM I FREE? 428

XIV. IS EVERY THING ETERNAL? 430

XV. INTELLIGENCE 431

XVI. ETERNITY 431

XVII. INCOMPREHENSIBILITY 431

XVIII. INFINITY 432

XIX. MY DEPENDENCE 432

XX. ETERNITY AGAIN 433

XXI. MY DEPENDENCE AGAIN 433

XXII. A FRESH DOUBT 434

XXIII. A SOLE SUPREME ARTIST 434

XXIV. SPINOZA 435

CHAPTER		PAGE
XXV.	ABSURDITIES	439
XXVI.	OF THE BEST OF WORLDS	440
XXVII.	OF MONADS	441
XXVIII.	OF PLASTIC FORMS	442
XXIX.	OF LOCKE	442
XXX.	WHAT HAVE I THUS FAR LEARNED?	445
XXXI.	IS THERE ANY MORALITY?	445
XXXII.	REAL UTILITY. THE NOTION OF JUSTICE	446
XXXIII.	IS UNIVERSAL CONSENT A PROOF OF TRUTH?	448
XXXIV.	AGAINST LOCKE	448
XXXV.	AGAINST LOCKE	449
XXXVI.	NATURE EVERYWHERE THE SAME	451
XXXVII.	OF HOBBES	451
XXXVIII.	UNIVERSAL MORALITY	452
XXXIX.	ZOROASTER	452
XL.	OF THE BRACHMANS	453
XLI.	OF CONFUCIUS	453
XLII.	OF THE GRECIAN PHILOSOPHERS AND FIRST OF PYTHAGORAS	454
XLIII.	OF ZALEUCUS	454
XLIV.	OF EPICURUS	455
XLV.	OF THE STOICS	455
XLVI.	PHILOSOPHY IS VIRTUE	456
XLVII.	OF AESOP	456
XLVIII.	OF PEACE, THE OFFSPRING OF PHILOSOPHY	457
XLIX.	QUESTIONS	457
L.	OTHER QUESTIONS	458
LI.	IGNORANCE	458
LII.	OTHER KINDS OF IGNORANCE	458
LIII.	GREATER IGNORANCE	459

CHAPTER   PAGE
LIV. RIDICULOUS IGNORANCE 459
LV. WORSE THAN IGNORANCE 460
LVI. THE DAWN OF REASON 460

DIALOGUES

I. THE CHINESE CATECHISM, OR, DIALOGUES BETWEEN CU-
SU, A DISCIPLE OF CONFUCIUS, AND PRINCE KOU, SON
OF THE KING OF LOU.
    FIRST DIALOGUE 461
    SECOND DIALOGUE 462
    THIRD DIALOGUE 463
    FOURTH DIALOGUE 466
    FIFTH DIALOGUE 468
    SIXTH DIALOGUE 470
II. THE JAPANESE CATECHISM, OR, AN INDIAN AND JAPANESE
DIALOGUE 472
III. THE GARDENER'S CATECHISM. A DIALOGUE BETWEEN
BASHAW TUCTAN AND KARPOS, THE GARDENER . . 475
IV. LIBERTY, A DIALOGUE BETWEEN A PHILOSOPHER AND HIS
FRIEND 477

PHILOSOPHIC CRITICISMS

OF THE EGYPTIAN RITES 479
MYSTERIES OF THE EGYPTIANS 480
OF ZALEUCUS 481
OF BACCHUS 482
GRECIAN METAMORPHOSES 484
OF IDOLATRY 485
OF ORACLES 487
OF THE GREEK SIBYLS 489
OF MIRACLES 493

ZADIG, OR FATE

I

THE BLIND OF ONE EYE

THERE lived at Babylon, in the reign of King Moabdar, a young man, named Zadig, of a good natural disposition, strengthened and improved by education. Though rich and young, he had learned to moderate his passions. He had nothing stiff or affected in his behavior. He did not pretend to examine every action by the strict rules of reason, but was always ready to make proper allowances for the weakness of mankind. It was a matter of surprise, that, notwithstanding his sprightly wit, he never exposed by his raillery those vague, incoherent, and noisy discourses; those rash censures, ignorant decisions, coarse jests, and all that empty jingle of words which at Babylon went by the name of conversation. He had learned, in the first book of Zoroaster, that self-love is a foot-ball swelled with wind, from which, when pierced, the most terrible tempests issue forth.

Above all, Zadig never boasted of his conquests among the women, nor affected to entertain a contemptible opinion of the fair sex. He was generous, and was never afraid of obliging the ungrateful; remembering the grand precept of Zoroaster, "When thou eatest, give to the dogs, should they even bite thee." He was as wise as it is possible for man to be; for he sought to live with the wise. Instructed in the sciences of the ancient Chaldeans, he understood the principles of natural philosophy, such as they were then supposed to be; and knew as much of metaphysics as hath ever been known in any age, that is, little or nothing at all. He was firmly persuaded, notwithstanding the new philosophy of the times, that the year consisted of three hundred and sixty-five days and six hours, and that the sun was the centre of the solar system. When the principal magi told him, with a haughty and contemptuous air, that his sentiments were of a dangerous tendency, and that it was to be an enemy to the state to believe that the sun revolved round its own axis, and that the year had twelve months, he held his tongue with great modesty and meekness.

Possessed as he was of great riches, and consequently of many friends, blessed with a good constitution, a handsome figure, a mind just and moderate, and a heart noble and sincere, he fondly imagined that he might easily be happy. He was going to be married to Semira, who, in point of beauty, birth, and fortune, was the first match in Babylon. He had a real and virtuous affection for this lady, and she loved him with the most passionate fondness. The happy moment was almost arrived that was to unite them for ever in the bands of wedlock, when happening to take a walk together toward one of the gates of Babylon, under the palm-trees that adorn the banks of the Euphrates, they saw some men approaching, armed with sabres and arrows. These were the attendants of young Orcan, the minister's nephew, whom his uncle's creatures had flattered into an opinion that he might do everything with impunity. He had none of the graces nor virtues of Zadig; but thinking himself a much more accomplished man, he was enraged to find that the other was preferred before him. This jealousy, which was merely the effect of his vanity, made him imagine that he was desperately in love with Semira; and accordingly he resolved to carry her off. The ravishers seized her; in the violence of the outrage, they wounded her, and made the blood flow from a person, the sight of which would have softened the tigers of mount Imaus. She pierced the heavens with her complaints. She cried out: "My dear husband! they tear me from the man I adore!"

Regardless of her own danger, she was only concerned for the fate of her dear Zadig, who, in the meantime, defended himself with all the strength that courage and love could inspire. Assisted only by two faithful slaves, he put the cowardly ravishers to flight, and carried home Semira, insensible and bloody as she was.

"O Zadig," said she, on opening her eyes, and beholding her deliverer, "I loved thee formerly as my intended husband, I now love thee as the preserver of my honor and my life!"

Never was heart more deeply affected than that of Semira. Never did a more charming mouth express more moving sentiments, in those glowing words inspired by a sense of the greatest of all favors, and by the most tender transports of a lawful passion. Her wound was slight, and was soon cured. Zadig was more dangerously wounded. An arrow had pierced him near his eye, and penetrated to a considerable depth. Semira wearied heaven with her prayers for the recovery of her lover. Her eyes were constantly bathed in tears; she anxiously waited the happy moment when those of Zadig should be able to meet her's; but an abscess growing on the wounded eye gave everything to fear. A messenger was immediately dispatched to Memphis, for the great physician Hermes, who came with a numerous retinue. He visited the patient, and declared that he would lose his eye. He even foretold the day and hour when this fatal event would happen.

"Had it been the right eye," said he, "I could easily have cured it; but the wounds of the left eye are incurable."

All Babylon lamented the fate of Zadig, and admired the profound knowledge of Hermes. In two days the abscess broke of its own accord, and Zadig was perfectly cured. Hermes wrote a book, to prove that it ought not to have been cured. Zadig did not read it: but, as soon as he was able to go abroad, he went to pay a visit to her in whom all his hopes of happiness were centred, and for whose sake alone he wished to have eyes. Semira had been in the country for three days past. He learned on the road, that that fine lady, having openly declared that she had an unconquerable aversion to one-eyed men, had the night before given her hand to Orcan. At this news he fell speechless to the ground. His sorrows brought him almost to the brink of the grave. He was long indisposed; but reason at last got the better of his affliction; and the severity of his fate served even to console him.

"Since," said he, "I have suffered so much from the cruel caprice of a woman educated at court, I must now think of marrying the daughter of a citizen."

He pitched upon Azora, a lady of the greatest prudence, and of the best family in town. He married her, and lived with her for three months in all the delights of the most tender union. He only observed that she had a little levity; and was too apt to find that those young men who had the most handsome persons were likewise possessed of the most wit and virtue.

II

THE NOSE

ONE morning Azora returned from a walk in a terrible passion and uttering the most violent exclamations.

"What aileth thee," said he, "my dear spouse? What is it that can thus have disturbed thee?"

"Alas!" said she, "thou wouldst have been as much enraged as I am, hadst thou seen what I have just beheld. I have been to comfort the young widow Cosrou, who, within these two days, hath raised a tomb to her young husband, near the rivulet that washes the skirts of this meadow. She vowed to heaven, in the bitterness of her grief, to remain at this tomb whilst the water of the rivulet should continue to run near it."

"Well," said Zadig, "she is an excellent woman, and loved her husband with the most sincere affection."

"Ah!" replied Azora, "didst thou but know in what she was employed when I went to wait upon her!"

"In what, pray tell me, beautiful Azora? Was she turning the course of the rivulet?"

Azora broke out into such long invectives, and loaded the young widow with such bitter reproaches, that Zadig was far from being pleased with this ostentation of virtue.

Zadig had a friend named Cador; one of those young men in whom his wife discovered more probity and merit than in others. He made him his confidant, and secured his fidelity as much as possible by a considerable present. Azora, having passed two days with a friend in the country, returned home on the third. The servants told her, with tears in their eyes, that her husband died suddenly the night before; that they were afraid to send her an account of this mournful event; and that they had just been depositing his corpse in the tomb of his ancestors, at the end of the garden. She wept, she tore her hair, and swore she would follow him to the grave. In the evening, Cador begged leave to wait upon her, and joined his tears with hers. Next day they wept less, and dined together. Cador told her, that his friend had left him the greater part of his estate; and that he should think himself extremely happy in sharing his fortune with her. The lady wept, fell into a passion, and at last became more mild and gentle. They sat longer at supper than at dinner. They now talked with greater confidence. Azora praised the deceased; but owned that he had many failings from which Cador was free.

During supper, Cador complained of a violent pain in his side. The lady, greatly concerned, and eager to serve him, caused all kinds of essences to be brought, with which she anointed him, to try if some of them might not possibly ease him of his pain. She lamented that the great Hermes was not still in Babylon. She even condescended to touch the side in which Cador felt such exquisite pain.

"Art thou subject to this cruel disorder?" said she to him, with a compassionate air.

"It sometimes brings me," replied Cador, "to the brink of the grave; and there is but one remedy that can give me relief—and that is, to apply to my side the nose of a man who is lately dead."

"A strange remedy, indeed!" said Azora.

"Not more strange," replied he, "than the satchels of Arnou, against the apoplexy."

This reason, added to the great merit of the young man, at last determined the lady.

"After all," says she, "when my husband shall cross the bridge Tchinavar in his journey to the other world, the angel Asrael will not refuse him a passage because his nose is a little shorter in the second life than it was in the first."

She then took a razor, went to her husband's tomb, bedewed it with her tears, and drew near to cut off the nose of Zadig, whom she found extended at full length in the tomb. Zadig arose, holding his nose with one hand, and putting back the razor with the other.

"Madam," said he, "don't exclaim so violently against the widow Cosrou. The project of cutting off my nose is equal to that of turning the course of a rivulet."

III

The Dog and the Horse

Zadig found by experience, that the first month of marriage, as it is written in the book of Zend, is the moon of honey, and that the second is the moon of wormwood. He was some time after obliged to repudiate Azora, who became too difficult to be pleased; and he then sought for happiness in the study of nature.

"No man," said he, "can be happier than a philosopher, who reads in this great book, which God hath placed before our eyes. The truths he discovers are his own; he nourishes and exalts his soul; he lives in peace; he fears nothing from men; and his tender spouse will not come to cut off his nose."

Possessed of these ideas, he retired to a country house on the banks of the Euphrates. There he did not employ himself in calculating how many inches of water flow in a second of time under the arches of a bridge, or whether there fell a cube-line of rain in the month of the mouse more than in the month of the sheep. He never dreamed of making silk of cobwebs, or porcelain of broken bottles: but he chiefly studied the properties of plants and animals; and soon acquired a sagacity that made him discover a thousand differences where other men see nothing but uniformity.

One day, as he was walking near a little wood, he saw one of the queen's eunuchs running toward him, followed by several officers, who appeared to be in great perplexity, and who ran to and fro like men distracted, eagerly searching for something they had lost of great value.

"Young man," said the first eunuch, "hast thou seen the queen's dog?"

"It is a bitch," replied Zadig, with great modesty, "and not a dog."

"Thou art in the right," returned the first eunuch.

"It is a very small she-spaniel," added Zadig; "she has lately whelped; she limps on the left fore-foot, and has very long ears."

"Thou has seen her," said the first eunuch, quite out of breath.

"No," replied Zadig, "I have not seen her, nor did I so much as know that the queen had a bitch."

Exactly at the same time, by one of the common freaks of fortune, the finest horse in the king's stable had escaped from the jockey in the plains of Babylon. The principal huntsman, and all the other officers, ran after him with as much eagerness and anxiety as the first eunuch had done after the bitch. The principal huntsman addressed himself to Zadig, and asked him if he had not seen the king's horse passing by.

"He is the fleetest horse in the king's stable," replied Zadig; "he is five feet high, with very small hoofs, and a tail three feet and an half in length; the studs on his bit are gold, of twenty-three carats, and his shoes are silver of eleven penny-weights."

"What way did he take? where is he?" demanded the chief huntsman.

"I have not seen him," replied Zadig, "and never heard talk of him before."

The principal huntsman and the first eunuch never doubted but that Zadig had stolen the king's horse and the queen's bitch. They therefore had him conducted before the assembly of the grand desterham, who condemned him to the knout, and to spend the rest of his days in Siberia. Hardly was the sentence passed, when the horse and the bitch were both found. The judges were reduced to the disagreeable necessity of reversing their sentence; but they condemned Zadig to pay four hundred ounces of gold for having said that he had not seen what he had seen. This fine he was obliged to pay; after which, he was permitted to plead his cause before the counsel of the grand desterham, when he spoke to the following effect:

"Ye stars of justice, abyss of sciences, mirrors of truth, who have the weight of lead, the hardness of iron, the splendor of the diamond, and many of the properties of gold; since I am permitted to speak before this august assembly, I swear to you by Oromazes, that I have never seen the queen's respectable bitch, nor the sacred horse of the king of kings. The truth of the matter is as follows: I was walking toward the little wood, where I afterward met the venerable eunuch, and the most illustrious chief huntsman. I observed on the sand the traces of an animal, and could easily perceive them to be those of a little dog. The light and long furrows impressed on little eminences of sand between the marks of the paws, plainly discovered that it was a bitch, whose dugs were hanging down, and that therefore she must have whelped a few days before. Other traces of a different kind, that always appeared to have gently brushed the surface of the sand near the marks of the forefeet, showed me that she had very long ears; and as I remarked that there was always a slighter impression made on the sand by one foot than by the other three, I found that the bitch of our august queen was a little lame, if I may be allowed the expression. With regard to the horse of the king of kings, you will be pleased to know, that walking in the lanes of this wood, I observed the marks of a horse's shoes, all at equal distances. This must be a horse, said I to myself, that gallops excellently. The dust on the trees in a narrow road that was but seven feet wide was a little brushed off, at the distance of three feet and a half from the middle of the road. This horse, said I, has a tail three feet and a half long, which, being whisked to the right and left, has swept away the dust. I observed under the trees that formed an arbor five feet in height, that the leaves of the branches were newly fallen, from whence I inferred that the horse had touched them, and that he must therefore be five feet high. As to his bit, it must be gold of twenty-three carats, for he had rubbed its bosses against a stone which I knew to be a touchstone, and which I have tried. In a word, from a mark made by his shoes on flints of another kind, I concluded that he was shod with silver eleven deniers fine."

All the judges admired Zadig for his acute and profound discernment. The news of this speech was carried even to the king and queen. Nothing was talked of but Zadig in the antechambers, the chambers, and the cabinet; and though many of the magi were of opinion that he ought to be burnt as a sorcerer, the king ordered his officers to restore him the four hundred ounces of gold which he had been obliged to pay. The register, the attorneys, and bailiffs went to his house with great formality to carry him back his four hundred ounces. They only retained three hundred and ninety-eight of them to defray the expenses of justice; and then their servants demanded their fees.

Zadig saw how extremely dangerous it sometimes is to appear too knowing, and therefore resolved, that on the next occasion of the like nature he would not tell what he had seen.

Such an opportunity soon offered. A prisoner of state made his escape and passed under the windows of Zadig's house. Zadig was examined and made no answer. But it was proved that he had looked at the prisoner from this window. For this crime he was condemned to pay five hundred ounces of gold; and, according to the polite custom of Babylon, he thanked his judges for their indulgence.

"Great God!" said he to himself, "what a misfortune it is to walk in a wood through which the queen's bitch or the king's horse have passed! how dangerous to look out at a window! and how difficult to be happy in this life!"

IV

THE ENVIOUS MAN

ZADIG resolved to comfort himself by philosophy and friendship for the evils he had suffered from fortune. He had in the suburbs of Babylon a house elegantly furnished, in which he assembled all the arts and all the pleasures worthy the pursuit of a gentleman. In the morning his library was open to the learned. In the evening his table was surrounded by good company. But he soon found what very dangerous guests these men of letters are. A warm dispute arose on one of Zoroaster's laws, which forbids the eating of a griffin.

"Why," said some of them, "prohibit the eating of a griffin, if there is no such animal in nature?"

"There must necessarily be such an animal," said the others, "since Zoroaster forbids us to eat it."

Zadig would fain have reconciled them by saying:

"If there are no griffins, we cannot possibly eat them; and thus either way we shall obey Zoroaster."

A learned man, who had composed thirteen volumes on the properties of the griffin, and was besides the chief theurgite, hasted away to accuse Zadig before one of the principal magi, named Yebor, the greatest blockhead, and therefore the greatest fanatic among the Chaldeans. This man would have empaled Zadig to do honor to the sun, and would then have recited the breviary of Zoroaster with greater satisfaction. The friend Cador (a friend is better than a hundred priests) went to Yebor, and said to him:

"Long live the sun and the griffins; beware of punishing Zadig; he is a saint; he has griffins in his inner court, and does not eat them; and his accuser is an heretic, who dares to maintain that rabbits have cloven feet, and are not unclean."

"Well," said Yebor, shaking his bald pate, "we must empale Zadig for having thought contemptuously of griffins, and the other party for having spoken disrespectfully of rabbits."

Cador hushed up the affair by appealing to a person who had great interest in the college of the magi. Nobody was empaled. This lenity occasioned a great murmuring among some of the doctors, who from thence predicted the fall of Babylon.

"Upon what does happiness depend?" said Zadig; "I am persecuted by everything in the world, even on account of beings that have no existence."

He cursed those men of learning, and resolved for the future to live with none but good company.

He assembled at his house the most worthy men, and the most beautiful ladies of Babylon. He gave them delicious suppers, often preceded by concerts of music, and always animated by polite conversation, from which he knew how to banish that affectation of wit, which is the surest method of preventing it entirely, and of spoiling the pleasure of the most agreeable society. Neither the choice of his friends, nor that of the dishes, was made by vanity; for in everything he preferred the substance to the shadow; and by these means he procured that real respect to which he did not aspire.

Opposite to his house lived one Arimazes, a man whose deformed countenance was but a faint picture of his still more deformed mind. His heart was a mixture of malice, pride, and envy. Having never been able to succeed in any of his undertakings, he revenged himself on all around him, by loading them with the blackest calumnies. Rich as he was, he found it difficult to procure a set of flatterers. The rattling of the chariots that entered Zadig's court in the evening filled him with uneasiness; the sound of his praises enraged him still more. He sometimes went to Zadig's house, and sat down at table without being desired; where he spoiled all the pleasure of the company, as the harpies are said to infect the viands they touch.

It happened that one day he took it in his head to give an entertainment to a lady, who, instead of accepting it, went to sup with Zadig. At another time, as he was talking with Zadig at court, a minister of state came up to them, and invited Zadig to supper, without inviting Arimazes. The most implacable hatred has seldom a more solid foundation. This man, who in Babylon was called the *envious*, resolved to ruin Zadig, because he was called the *happy*. "The opportunity of doing mischief occurs a hundred times in a day, and that of doing good but once a year," as sayeth the wise Zoroaster.

The envious man went to see Zadig, who was walking in his garden with two friends and a lady, to whom he said many gallant things, without any other intention than that of saying them. The conversation turned upon a war which the king had just brought to a happy conclusion against the prince of Hircania, his vassal. Zadig, who had signalized his courage in this short war, bestowed great praises on the king, but greater still on the lady. He took out his pocket-book, and wrote four lines extempore, which he gave to this amiable person to read. His friends begged they might see them; but modesty, or rather a well-regulated self-love, would not allow him to grant their request. He knew that extemporary verses are never approved by any but by the person in whose honor they are written. He therefore tore in two the leaf on which he had written them, and threw both the pieces into a thicket of rose busnes where the rest of the company sought for them in vain. A slight shower falling soon after obliged them to return to the house.

The envious man, who remained in the garden, continued to search, till at last he found a piece of the leaf. It had been torn in such a manner, that each half of a line formed a complete sense, and even a verse of a shorter measure; but what was still more surprising, these short verses were found to contain the most injurious reflections on the king. They ran thus:

> To flagrant crimes
> His crown he owes,
> To peaceful times
> The worst of foes.

The envious man was now happy for the first time in his life. He had it in his power to ruin a person of virtue and merit. Filled with this fiend-like joy, he found means to convey to the king the satire written by the hand of Zadig, who was immediately thrown into prison, together with the lady and Zadig's two friends.

His trial was soon finished without his being permitted to speak for himself. As he was going to receive his sentence, the envious man threw himself in his way, and told him with a loud voice, that his verses were good for nothing. Zadig did not value himself on being a good poet; but it filled him with inexpressible concern to find that he was condemned for high treason; and that the fair lady and his two friends were confined in prison for a crime of which they were not guilty. He was not allowed to speak, because his writing spoke for him. Such was the law of Babylon. Accordingly he was conducted to the place of execution through an immense crowd of spectators, who durst not venture to express their pity for him, but who carefully examined his countenance to see if he died with a good grace. His relations alone were inconsolable; for they could not succeed to his estate. Three-fourths of his wealth were confiscated into the king's treasury, and the other fourth was given to the envious man.

Just as he was preparing for death, the king's parrot flew from its cage, and alighted on a rose bush in Zadig's garden. A peach had been driven thither by the wind from a neighboring tree, and had fallen on a piece of the written leaf of the pocket-book to which it stuck. The bird carried off the peach and the paper, and laid them on the king's knee. The king took up the paper with great eagerness, and read the words, which formed no sense, and seemed to be the endings of verses. He loved poetry; and there is always some mercy to be expected from a prince of that disposition. The adventure of the parrot caused him to reflect.

The queen, who remembered what had been written on the piece of Zadig's pocket-book, ordered it to be brought. They compared the two pieces together, and found them to tally exactly. They then read the verses as Zadig had written them.

> Tyrants are prone to flagrant crimes;
> To clemency his crown he owes;
> To concord and to peaceful times
> Love only is the worst of foes.

The king gave immediate orders that Zadig should be brought before him, and that his two friends and the lady should be set at liberty. Zadig fell prostrate on the ground before the king and queen, humbly begged their pardon for having made such bad verses, and spoke with so much propriety, wit, and good sense, that their majesties desired they might see him again. He did himself that honor, and insinuated himself still farther into their good graces. They gave him all the wealth of the envious man; but Zadig restored him back the whole of it; and this instance of generosity gave no other pleasure to the envious man than that of having preserved his estate. The king's esteem for Zadig increased every day. He admitted him into all his parties of pleasure, and consulted him in all affairs of state. From that time the queen began to regard him with an eye of tenderness, that might one day prove dangerous to herself, to the king her august consort, to Zadig, and to the kingdom in general. Zadig now began to think that happiness was not so unattainable as he had formerly imagined.

V

The Generous

THE time had now arrived for celebrating a grand festival, which returned every five years. It was a custom in Babylon solemnly to declare, at the end of every five years, which of the citizens had performed the most generous action. The grandees and the magi were the judges. The first satrap, who was charged with the government of the city, published the most noble actions that had passed under his administration. The competition was decided by votes; and the king pronounced the sentence. People came to this solemnity from the extremities of the earth. The conqueror received from the monarch's hands a golden cup adorned with precious stones, his majesty at the same time making him this compliment: "Receive this reward of thy generosity, and may the gods grant me many subjects like to thee."

This memorable day having come, the king appeared on his throne, surrounded by the grandees, the magi, and the deputies of all the nations that came to these games, where glory was acquired not by the swiftness of horses, nor by strength of body, but by virtue. The first satrap recited, with an audible voice, such actions as might entitle the authors of them to this invaluable prize. He did not mention the greatness of soul with which Zadig had restored the envious man his fortune, because it was not judged to be an action worthy of disputing the prize.

He first presented a judge, who having made a citizen lose a considerable cause by a mistake, for which, after all, he was not accountable, had given him the whole of his own estate, which was just equal to what the other had lost.

He next produced a young man, who, being desperately in love with a lady whom he was going to marry, had yielded her up to his friend, whose passion for her had almost brought him to the brink of the grave, and at the same time had given him the lady's fortune.

He afterwards produced a soldier, who, in the wars of Hircania, had given a still more noble instance of generosity. A party of the enemy having seized his mistress, he fought in her defence with great intrepidity. At that very instant he was informed that another party, at the distance of a few paces, was carrying off his mother; he therefore left his mistress with tears in his eyes, and flew to the assistance of his mother. At last he returned to the dear object of his love, and found her expiring. He was just going to plunge his sword in his own bosom; but his mother remonstrating against such a desperate deed, and telling him that he was the only support of her life, he had the courage to endure to live.

The judges were inclined to give the prize to the soldier. But the king took up the discourse, and said:

"The action of the soldier, and those of the other two, are doubtless very great, but they have nothing in them surprising. Yesterday, Zadig performed an action that filled me with wonder. I had a few days before disgraced Coreb, my minister and favorite. I complained of him in the most violent and bitter terms; all my courtiers assured me that I was too gentle, and seemed to vie with each other in speaking ill of Coreb. I asked Zadig what he thought of him, and he had the courage to commend him. I have read in our histories of many people who have atoned for an error by the surrender of their fortune; who have resigned a mistress; or preferred a mother to the object of their affection; but never before did I hear of a courtier who spoke favorably of a disgraced minister, that labored under the displeasure of his sovereign. I give to each of those whose generous actions have been now recited, twenty thousand pieces of gold; but the cup I give to Zadig."

"May it please your majesty," said Zadig, "thyself alone deservest the cup. Thou hast performed an action of all others the most uncommon and meritorious, since, notwithstanding thy being a powerful king, thou wast not offended at thy slave, when he presumed to oppose thy passion."

The king and Zadig were equally the object of admiration. The judge who had given his estate to his client; the lover who had resigned his mistress to his friend, and the soldier, who had preferred the safety of his mother to that of his mistress, received the king's presents, and saw their names enrolled in the catalogue of generous men. Zadig had the cup, and the king acquired the reputation of a good prince, which he did not long enjoy. The day was celebrated by feasts that lasted longer than the law enjoined; and the memory of it is still preserved in Asia. Zadig said: "Now I am happy at last." But he found himself fatally deceived.

VI

THE MINISTER

THE king had lost his first minister, and chose Zadig to supply his place. All the ladies in Babylon applauded the choice; for, since the foundation of the empire, there had never been such a young minister. But all the courtiers were filled with jealousy and vexation. The envious man, in particular, was troubled with a spitting of blood, and a prodigious inflammation in his nose. Zadig, having thanked the king and queen for their goodness, went likewise to thank the parrot.

"Beautiful bird," said he, " 'tis thou that hast saved my life, and made me first minister. The queen's bitch and the king's horse did me a great deal of mischief; but thou hast done me much good. Upon such slender threads as these do the fates of mortals hang! but," added he, "this happiness perhaps will vanish very soon."

"Soon," replied the parrot.

Zadig was somewhat startled at this word. But as he was a good natural philosopher, and did not believe parrots to be prophets, he quickly recovered his spirits, and resolved to execute his duty to the best of his power.

He made every one feel the sacred authority of the laws, but no one felt the weight of his dignity. He never checked the deliberations of the divan; and every vizier might give his opinion without fear of incurring the minister's displeasure. When he gave judgment, it was not he that gave it; it was the law; the rigor of which, however, whenever it was too severe, he always took care to soften; and when laws were wanting, the equity of his decisions was such as might easily have made them pass for those of Zoroaster.

It is to him that the nations are indebted for this grand principle, to wit, that it is better to run the risk of sparing the guilty than to condemn the innocent. He imagined that laws were made as well to secure the people from the suffering of injuries as to restrain them from the commission of crimes. His chief talent consisted in discovering the truth, which all men seek to obscure. This great talent he put in practice from the very beginning of his administration.

A famous merchant of Babylon, who died in the Indies, divided his estate equally between his two sons, after having disposed of their sister in marriage, and left a present of thirty thousand pieces of gold to that son who should be found to have loved him best. The eldest raised a tomb to his memory; the youngest increased his sister's portion, by giving her a part of his inheritance. Every one said that the eldest son loved his father best, and the youngest his sister; and that the thirty thousand pieces belonged to the eldest.

Zadig sent for both of them, the one after the other. To the eldest he said: "Thy father is not dead; but has survived his last illness, and is returning to Babylon."

"God be praised," replied the young man; "but his tomb cost me a considerable sum."

Zadig afterwards repeated the same story to the youngest son.

"God be praised," said he; "I will go and restore to my father all that I have; but I could wish that he would leave my sister what I have given her."

"Thou shalt restore nothing," replied Zadig, "and thou shalt have the thirty thousand pieces, for thou art the son who loves his father best."

A widow, having a young son, and being possessed of a handsome fortune, had given a promise of marriage to two magi; who were both desirous of marrying her.

"I will take for my husband," said she, "the man who can give the best education to my beloved son."

The two magi contended who should bring him up, and the cause was carried before Zadig. Zadig summoned the two magi to attend him.

"What will you teach your pupil?" said he to the first.

"I will teach him," said the doctor, "the eight parts of speech, logic, astrology, pneumatics, what is meant by substance and accident, abstract and concrete, the doctrine of the monads, and the pre-established harmony."

"For my part," said the second, "I will endeavor to give him a sense of justice, and to make him worthy the friendship of good men."

Zadig then cried:

"Whether thou art the child's favorite or not, thou shalt have his mother."

VII

THE DISPUTES AND THE AUDIENCES

In this manner he daily discovered the subtlety of his genius and the goodness of his heart. The people at once admired and loved him. He passed for the happiest man in the world. The whole empire resounded with his name. All the ladies ogled him. All the men praised him for his justice. The learned regarded him as an oracle; and even the priests confessed that he knew more than the old arch-magi Yebor. They were now so far from prosecuting him on account of the griffins, that they believed nothing but what he thought credible.

There had continued at Babylon, for the space of fifteen hundred years, a violent contest that had divided the empire into two sects. The one pretended that they ought to enter the temple of Mithra with the left foot foremost; the other held this custom in detestation, and always entered with the right foot first. The people waited with great impatience for the day on which the solemn feast of the sacred fire was to be celebrated, to see which sect Zadig would favor. All the world had their eyes fixed on his two feet, and the whole city was in the utmost suspense and perturbation. Zadig jumped into the temple with his feet joined together; and afterward proved, in an eloquent discourse, that the Sovereign of heaven and earth, who accepteth not the persons of men, maketh no distinction between the right and the left foot. The envious man and his wife alleged that his discourse was not figurative enough, and that he did not make the rocks and mountains dance with sufficient agility.

"He is dry," said they, "and void of genius. He does not make the sea to fly, and stars to fall, nor the sun to melt like wax. He has not the true oriental style."

Zadig contended himself with having the style of reason. All the world favored him, not because he was in the right road, or followed the dictates of reason, or was a man of real merit, but because he was prime vizier.

He terminated with the same happy address the grand dispute between the black and the white magi. The former maintained that it was the height of impiety to pray to God with the face turned toward the east in winter; the latter asserted that God abhorred the prayers of those who turned toward the west in summer. Zadig decreed that every man should be allowed to turn as he pleased.

Thus he found out the happy secret of finishing all affairs, whether of a private or a public nature, in the morning. The rest of the day he employed in superintending and promoting the embellishments of Babylon. He exhibited tragedies that drew tears from the eyes of the spectators, and comedies that shook their sides with laughter—a custom which had long been disused, and which his good taste now induced him to revive. He never affected to be more knowing in the polite arts than the artists themselves. He encouraged them by rewards and honors, and was never jealous of their talents. In the evening the king was highly entertained with his conversation, and the queen still more.

"Great minister!" said the king.

"Amiable minister!" said the queen; and both of them added, "It would have been a great loss to the state had such a man been hanged."

Meanwhile Zadig perceived that his thoughts were always distracted, as well when he gave audience as when he sat in judgment. He did not know to what to attribute this absence of mind, and that was his only sorrow.

He had a dream, in which he imagined that he laid himself down upon a heap of dry herbs, among which there were many prickly ones that gave him great uneasiness, and that he afterward reposed himself on a soft bed of roses, from which there sprang a serpent that wounded him to the heart with its sharp venomed fangs. "Alas," said he, "I have long lain on these dry and prickly herbs, I am now on the bed of roses; but what shall be the serpent?"

VIII

Jealousy

Zadig's calamities sprang even from his happiness, and especially from his merit. He every day conversed with the king and his august consort. The charms of Zadig's conversation were greatly heightened by that desire of pleasing which is to the mind what dress is to beauty. His youth and graceful appearance insensibly made an impression on Astarte, which she did not at first perceive. Her passion grew and flourished in the bosom of innocence. Without fear or scruple, she indulged the pleasing satisfaction of seeing and hearing a man who was so dear to her husband, and to the empire in general. She was continually praising him to the king. She talked of him to her women, who were always sure to improve on her praises. And thus everything contributed to pierce her heart with a dart, of which she did not seem to be sensible. She made several presents to Zadig, which discovered a greater spirit of gallantry than she imagined. She intended to speak to him only as a queen satisfied with his services; and her expressions were sometimes those of a woman in love.

Astarte was much more beautiful than that Semira who had such a strong aversion to one-eyed men, or that other woman who had resolved to cut off her husband's nose. Her unreserved familiarity, her tender expressions, at

which she began to blush; and her eyes, which, though she endeavored to
divert them to other objects, were always fixed upon his, inspired Zadig with
a passion that filled him with astonishment. He struggled hard to get the
better of it. He called to his aid the precepts of philosophy, which had always
stood him instead; but from thence, though he could derive the light of
knowledge, he could procure no remedy to cure the disorders of his love-sick
heart. Duty, gratitude, and violated majesty presented themselves to his mind,
as so many avenging gods. He struggled; he conquered. But this victory, which
he was obliged to purchase afresh every moment, cost him many sighs and
tears. He no longer dared to speak to the queen with that sweet and charming
familiarity which had been so agreeable to them both. His countenance was
covered with a cloud. His conversation was constrained and incoherent. His
eyes were fixed on the ground; and when, in spite of all his endeavors to the
contrary, they encountered those of the queen, they found them bathed in
tears, and darting arrows of flame. They seemed to say, We adore each other,
and yet are afraid to love: we are consumed with a passion which we both
condemn.

Zadig left the royal presence full of perplexity and despair, and having his
heart appressed with a burden which he was no longer able to bear. In the
violence of his perturbation he involuntarily betrayed the secret to his friend
Cador, in the same manner as a man, who, having long endured a cruel
disease, discovers his pain by a cry extorted from him by a more severe
attack, and by the cold sweat that covers his brow.

"I have already discovered," said Cador, "the sentiments which thou wouldst
fain conceal from thyself. The symptoms by which the passions show themselves are certain and infallible. Judge, my dear Zadig, since I have read thy
heart, whether the king will not discover something in it that may give him
offence. He has no other fault but that of being the most jealous man in the
world. Thou canst resist the violence of thy passion with greater fortitude
than the queen, because thou art a philosopher, and because thou art Zadig.
Astarte is a woman. She suffers her eyes to speak with so much the more
imprudence, as she does not as yet think herself guilty. Conscious of her own
innocence, she unhappily neglects those external appearances which are so
necessary. I shall tremble for her so long as she has nothing wherewithal to
reproach herself. A growing passion which we endeavor to suppress discovers
itself in spite of all our efforts to the contrary."

Meanwhile, the queen mentioned the name of Zadig frequently, and with
such a blushing and downcast look. She was sometimes so lively, and sometimes so perplexed, when she spoke to him in the king's presence, and was
seized with such a deep thoughtfulness at his going away, that the king began
to be troubled. He believed all that he saw, and imagined all that he did not
see. He particularly remarked that his wife's shoes were blue, and that Zadig's
shoes were blue; that his wife's ribbons were yellow, and that Zadig's bonnet
was yellow; and these were terrible symptoms to a prince of so much delicacy.
In his jealous mind suspicion was turned into certainty.

All the slaves of kings and queens are so many spies over their hearts. They soon observed that Astarte was tender, and that Moabdar was jealous. The envious man persuaded his wife to send anonymously to the king her garter, which resembled those of the queen; and to complete the misfortune, this garter was blue. The monarch now thought of nothing but in what manner he might best execute his vengeance. He one night resolved to poison the queen, and in the morning to put Zadig to death by the bowstring. The orders were given to a merciless eunuch, who commonly executed his acts of vengeance.

There happened at that time to be in the king's chamber a little dwarf, who, though dumb, was not deaf. He was allowed, on account of his insignificance, to go wherever he pleased; and, as a domestic animal, was a witness of what passed in the most profound secrecy.

This little mute was strongly attached to the queen and Zadig. With equal horror and surprise, he heard the cruel orders given; but how could he prevent the fatal sentence that in a few hours was to be carried into execution? He could not write, but he could paint; and excelled particularly in drawing a striking resemblance. He employed a part of the night in sketching out with his pencil what he meant to impart to the queen. The piece represented the king in one corner, boiling with rage, and giving orders to the eunuch; a blue bowstring, and a bowl on a table, with blue garters and yellow ribbons; the queen in the middle of the picture, expiring in the arms of her woman, and Zadig strangled at her feet. The horizon represented a rising sun, to express that this shocking execution was to be performed in the morning. As soon as he had finished the picture, he ran to one of Astarte's women, awoke her, and made her understand that she must immediately carry it to the queen.

At midnight a messenger knocks at Zadig's door, awakes him, and gives him a note from the queen. He doubts whether it is not a dream; and opens the letter with a trembling hand. But how great was his surprise, and who can express the consternation and despair into which he was thrown upon reading these words? "Fly, this instant, or thou art a dead man! Fly, Zadig, I conjure thee by our mutual love and my yellow ribbons. I have not been guilty, but I find that I must die like a criminal."

Zadig was hardly able to speak. He sent for Cador, and, without uttering a word, gave him the note. Cador forced him to obey, and forthwith to take the road to Memphis.

"Shouldst thou dare," said he, "to go in search of the queen, thou wilt hasten her death. Shouldst thou speak to the king, thou wilt infallibly ruin her. I will take upon me the charge of her destiny; follow thy own. I will spread a report that thou hast taken the road to India. I will soon follow thee, and inform thee of all that shall have passed in Babylon."

At that instant, Cador caused two of the swiftest dromedaries to be brought to a private gate of the palace. Upon one of these he mounted Zadig, whom he was obliged to carry to the door, and who was ready to expire with grief. He was accompanied by a single domestic; and Cador, plunged in sorrow and astonishment, soon lost sight of his friend.

This illustrious fugitive arriving on the side of a hill, from whence he could take a view of Babylon, turned his eyes toward the queen's palace, and fainted away at the sight; nor did he recover his senses but to shed a torrent of tears, and to wish for death. At length, after his thoughts had been long engrossed in lamenting the unhappy fate of the loveliest woman and the greatest queen in the world, he for a moment turned his views on himself, and cried:

"What then is human life? O virtue, how hast thou served me? Two women have basely deceived me; and now a third, who is innocent, and more beautiful than both the others, is going to be put to death! Whatever good I have done hath been to me a continual source of calamity and affliction; and I have only been raised to the height of grandeur, to be tumbled down the most horrid precipice of misfortune."

Filled with these gloomy reflections, his eyes overspread with the veil of grief, his countenance covered with the paleness of death, and his soul plunged in an abyss of the blackest despair, he continued his journey toward Egypt.

IX

THE WOMAN BEATER

ZADIG directed his course by the stars. The constellation of Orion, and the splendid Dogstars, guided his steps toward the pole of Canopæa. He admired those vast globes of light which appear to our eyes as so many little sparks, while the earth, which in reality is only an imperceptible point in nature, appears to our fond imaginations as something so grand and noble. He then represented to himself the human species, as it really is, as a parcel of insects devouring one another on a little atom of clay. This true image seemed to annihilate his misfortunes, by making him sensible of the nothingness of his own being, and that of Babylon. His soul launched out into infinity, and detached from the senses, contemplated the immutable order of the universe. But when afterward, returning to himself, and entering into his own heart, he considered that Astarte had perhaps died for him, the universe vanished from his sight, and he beheld nothing in the whole compass of nature but Astarte expiring, and Zadig unhappy.

While he thus alternately gave up his mind to this flux and reflux of sublime philosophy and intolerable grief, he advanced toward the frontiers of Egypt; and his faithful domestic was already in the first village, in search of a lodging.

Meanwhile, as Zadig was walking toward the gardens that skirted the village, he saw, at a small distance from the highway, a woman bathed in tears and calling heaven and earth to her assistance, and a man in a furious passion pursuing her.

This madman had already overtaken the woman, who embraced his knees, notwithstanding which he loaded her with blows and reproaches. Zadig judged by the frantic behavior of the Egyptian, and by the repeated pardons which the lady asked him, that the one was jealous, and the other unfaithful. But when he surveyed the woman more narrowly, and found her to be a lady of exquisite beauty, and even to have a strong resemblance to the unhappy Astarte, he felt himself inspired with compassion for her, and horror toward the Egyptian.

"Assist me," cried she to Zadig, with the deepest sighs, "deliver me from the hands of the most barbarous man in the world. Save my life."

Moved by these pitiful cries, Zadig ran and threw himself between her and the barbarian. As he had some knowledge of the Egyptian language, he addressed him in that tongue:

"If," said he, "thou hast any humanity, I conjure thee to pay some regard to her beauty and weakness. How canst thou behave in this outrageous manner to one of the masterpieces of nature, who lies at thy feet, and hath no defence but her tears?"

"Ah, ah!" replied the madman, "thou art likewise in love with her. I must be revenged on thee too."

So saying, he left the lady, whom he had hitherto held with his hand twisted in her hair, and taking his lance, attempted to stab the stranger. Zadig, who was in cold blood, easily eluded the blow aimed by the frantic Egyptian. He seized the lance near the iron with which it was armed. The Egyptian strove to draw it back; Zadig to wrest it from the Egyptian; and in the struggle it was broken in two. The Egyptian draws his sword; Zadig does the same. They attack each other. The former gives a hundred blows at random; the latter wards them off with great dexterity. The lady, seated on a turf, readjusts her head-dress, and looks at the combatants. The Egyptian excelled in strength: Zadig in address. The one fought like a man whose arm was directed by his judgment; the other like a madman, whose blind rage made him deal his blows at random. Zadig closes with him, and disarms him; and while the Egyptian, now become more furious, endeavors to throw himself upon him, he seizes him, presses him close, and throws him down; and then holding his sword to his breast, offers him his life. The Egyptian, frantic with rage, draws his poniard, and wounds Zadig at the very instant that the conqueror was granting a pardon. Zadig, provoked at such brutal behavior, plunged his sword in the bosom of the Egyptian, who, giving a horrible shriek and a violent struggle, instantly expired. Zadig then approached the lady, and said to her with a gentle tone:

"He hath forced me to kill him. I have avenged thy cause. Thou are now delivered from the most violent man I ever saw. What further, madam, wouldst thou have me do for thee?"

"Die, villain," replied she, "thou hast killed my lover. O that I were able to tear out thy heart!"

"Why truly, madam," said Zadig, "thou hadst a strange kind of a man for a lover; he beat thee with all his might, and would have killed thee, because thou hadst entreated me to give thee assistance."

"I wish he were beating me still," replied the lady with tears and lamentation. "I well deserved it; for I had given him cause to be jealous. Would to heaven that he was now beating me, and that thou wast in his place."

Zadig, struck with surprise, and inflamed with a higher degree of resent- ment than he had ever felt before, said:

"Beautiful as thou art, madam, thou deservest that I should beat thee in my turn for thy perverse and impertinent behavior. But I shall not give myself the trouble."

So saying, he remounted his camel, and advanced toward the town. He had proceeded but a few steps, when he turned back at the noise of four Baby- lonian couriers, who came riding at full gallop. One of them, upon seeing the woman, cried:

"It is the very same. She resembles the description that was given us."

They gave themselves no concern about the dead Egyptian, but instantly seized the lady. She called out to Zadig:

"Help me once more, generous stranger. I ask pardon for having complained of thy conduct. Deliver me again, and I will be thine for ever."

Zadig was no longer in the humor of fighting for her.

"Apply to another," said he, "thou shalt not again ensnare me in thy wiles."

Besides, he was wounded; his blood was still flowing, and he himself had need of assistance; and the sight of four Babylonians, probably sent by King Moabdar, filled him with apprehension. He therefore hastened toward the village, unable to comprehend why four Babylonian couriers should come and seize this Egyptian woman, but still more astonished at the lady's behavior.

X

SLAVERY

As HE ENTERED the Egyptian village, he saw himself surrounded by the people. Every one said:

"This is the man who carried off the beautiful Missouf, and assassinated Clitofis."

"Gentlemen," said he, "God preserve me from carrying off your beautiful Missouf. She is too capricious for me. And with regard to Clitofis, I did not assassinate him. I only fought with him in my own defence. He endeavored to kill me, because I humbly interceded for the beautiful Missouf, whom he beat most unmercifully. I am a stranger, come to seek refuge in Egypt; and it is not likely, that in coming to implore your protection, I should begin by carrying off a woman, and assassinating a man."

The Egyptians were then just and humane. The people conducted Zadig to the town-house. They first of all ordered his wound to be dressed, and then examined him and his servant apart, in order to discover the truth. They found that Zadig was not an assassin; but as he was guilty of having killed a man, the law condemned him to be a slave. His two camels were sold for the benefit of the town; all the gold he had brought with him was distributed among the inhabitants; and his person, as well as that of the companion of his journey, was exposed for sale in the market-place. An Arabian merchant, named Setoc, made the purchase; but as the servant was fitter for labor than the master, he was sold at a higher price. There was no comparison between the two men. Thus Zadig became a slave subordinate to his own servant. They were linked together by a chain fastened to their feet, and in this condition they followed the Arabian merchant to his house.

By the way Zadig comforted his servant, and exhorted him to patience; but he could not help making, according to his usual custom, some reflections on human life. "I see," said he, "that the unhappiness of my fate hath an influence on thine. Hitherto everything has turned out to me in a most unaccountable manner. I have been condemned to pay a fine for having seen the marks of a bitch's feet. I thought that I should once have been empaled alive on account of a griffin. I have been sent to execution for having made some verses in praise of the king. I have been on the point of being strangled, because the queen had yellow ribbons; and now I am a slave with thee, because a brutal wretch beat his mistress. Come, let us keep a good heart; all this will perhaps have an end. The Arabian merchants must necessarily have slaves; and why not me as well as another, since, as well as another, I am a man? This merchant will not be cruel. He must treat his slaves well if he expects any advantage from them."

But while he spoke thus, his heart was entirely engrossed by the fate of the queen of Babylon.

Two days after, the merchant Setoc set out for Arabia Deserta, with his slaves and his camels. His tribe dwelt near the desert of Oreb. The journey was long and painful. Setoc set a much greater value on the servant than the master, because the former was more expert in loading the camels, and all the little marks of distinction were shown to him. A camel having died within two days journey of Oreb, his burden was divided and laid on the backs of the servants; and Zadig had his share among the rest. Setoc laughed to see all his slaves walking with their bodies inclined. Zadig took the liberty to explain to him the cause, and inform him of the laws of balance. The merchant was astonished, and began to regard him with other eyes. Zadig, finding he had raised his curiosity, increased it still further by acquainting him with many things that related to commerce; the specific gravity of metals and commodities under an equal bulk; the properties of several useful animals; and the means of rendering those useful that are not naturally so.

At last Setoc began to consider Zadig as a sage, and preferred him to his companion, whom he had formerly so much esteemed. He treated him well, and had no cause to repent of his kindness.

As soon as Setoc arrived among his own tribe he demanded the payment of five hundred ounces of silver, which he had lent to a Jew in presence of two witnesses; but as the witnesses were dead, and the debt could not be proved, the Hebrew appropriated the merchant's money to himself, and piously thanked God for putting it in his power to cheat an Arabian. Setoc imparted this troublesome affair to Zadig, who had now become his counsel.

"In what place," said Zadig, "didst thou lend the five hundred ounces to· this infidel?"

"Upon a large stone," replied the merchant, "that lies near the mountain of Oreb."

"What is the character of thy debtor?" said Zadig.

"That of a knave," returned Setoc.

"But I ask thee, whether he is lively or phlegmatic; cautious or imprudent?"

"He is, of all bad payers," said Setoc, "the most lively fellow I ever knew."

"Well," resumed Zadig, "allow me to plead thy cause."

In effect, Zadig having summoned the Jew to the tribunal, addressed the judge in the following terms:

"Pillar of the throne of equity, I come to demand of this man, in the name of my master, five hundred ounces of silver, which he refuses to repay."

"Hast thou any witnesses?" said the judge.

"No, they are dead; but there remains a large stone upon which the money was counted; and if it please thy grandeur to order the stone to be sought for, I hope that it will bear witness. The Hebrew and I will tarry here till the stone arrives. I will send for it at my master's expense."

"With all my heart," replied the judge, and immediately applied himself to the discussion of other affairs.

When the court was going to break up, the judge said to Zadig:

"Well, friend, hath not thy stone yet arrived?"

The Hebrew replied with a smile:

"Thy grandeur may stay here till to-morrow, and after all not see the stone. It is more than six miles from hence; and it would require fifteen men to move it."

"Well," cried Zadig, "did I not say that the stone would bear witness? Since this man knows where it is, he thereby confesses that it was upon it that the money was counted."

The Hebrew was disconcerted, and was soon after obliged to confess the truth. The judge ordered him to be fastened to the stone, without meat or drink, till he should restore the five hundred ounces, which were soon after paid.

The slave Zadig and the stone were held in great repute in Arabia.

XI

THE FUNERAL PILE

SETOC, charmed with the happy issue of this affair, made his slave his intimate friend. He had now conceived as great an esteem for him as ever the king of Babylon had done; and Zadig was glad that Setoc had no wife. He discovered in his master a good natural disposition, much probity of heart, and a great share of good sense; but he was sorry to see that, according to the ancient custom of Arabia. he adored the host of heaven; that is, the sun, moon, and stars. He sometimes spoke to him on this subject with great prudence and discretion. At last he told him that these bodies were like all other bodies in the universe, and no more deserving of our homage than a tree or a rock.

"But," said Setoc, "they are eternal beings; and it is from them we derive all we enjoy. They animate nature; they regulate the seasons; and, besides, are removed at such an immense distance from us, that we cannot help revering them."

"Thou receivest more advantage," replied Zadig, "from the waters of the Red Sea, which carry thy merchandise to the Indies. Why may not it be as ancient as the stars? and if thou adorest what is placed at a distance from thee, thou shouldst adore the land of Gangarides, which lies at the extremity of the earth."

"No," said Setoc, "the brightness of the stars commands my adoration."

At night Zadig lighted up a great number of candles in the tent where he was to sup with Setoc; and the moment his patron appeared, he fell on his knees before these lighted tapers, and said:

"Eternal and shining luminaries! be ye always propitious to me."

Having thus said, he sat down at the table, without taking the least notice of Setoc.

"What art thou doing?" said Setoc in amaze.

"I act like thee," replied Zadig, "I adore these candles, and neglect their master and mine."

Setoc comprehended the profound sense of this apologue. The wisdom of his slave sunk deep into his soul. He no longer offered incense to the creatures, but he adored the eternal Being who made them.

There prevailed at that time in Arabia a shocking custom, sprung originally from Scythia, and which, being established in the Indies by the credit of the Brahmins, threatened to overrun all the East. When a married man died, and his beloved wife aspired to the character of a saint, she burned herself publicly on the body of her husband. This was a solemn feast, and was called the Funeral Pile of Widowhood; and that tribe in which most women had been burned was the most respected. An Arabian of Setoc's tribe being dead, his widow, whose name was Almona, and who was very devout, published the day and hour when she intended to throw herself into the fire, amidst the sound of drums and trumpets.

Zadig remonstrated against this horrible custom. He showed Setoc how inconsistent it was with the happiness of mankind to suffer young widows to burn themselves—widows who were capable of giving children to the state, or at least of educating those they already had; and he convinced him that it was his duty to do all that lay in his power to abolish such a barbarous practice.

"The women," said Setoc, "have possessed the right of burning themselves for more than a thousand years; and who shall dare to abrogate a law which time hath rendered sacred? Is there anything more respectable than ancient abuses?"

"Reason is more ancient," replied Zadig: "meanwhile, speak thou to the chiefs of the tribes, and I will go to wait on the young widow."

Accordingly, he was introduced to her, and after having insinuated himself into her good graces by some compliments on her beauty, and told her what a pity it was to commit so many charms to the flames, he at last praised her for her constancy and courage.

"Thou must surely have loved thy husband," said he to her, "with the most passionate fondness."

"Who, I?" replied the lady, "I loved him not at all. He was a brutal, jealous, and insupportable wretch; but I am firmly resolved to throw myself on his funeral pile."

"It would appear then," said Zadig, "that there must be a very delicious pleasure in being burnt alive."

"Oh! it makes me shudder," replied the lady, "but that must be overlooked. I am a devotee; I should lose my reputation; and all the world would despise me, if I did not burn myself."

Zadig having made her acknowledge that she burned herself to gain the good opinion of others, and to gratify her own vanity, entertained her with a long discourse calculated to make her a little in love with life, and even went so far as to inspire her with some degree of good will for the person who spoke to her.

"And what will thou do at last," said he, "if the vanity of burning thyself should not continue?"

"Alas!" said the lady, "I believe I should desire thee to marry me."

Zadig's mind was too much engrossed with the idea of Astarte not to elude this declaration; but he instantly went to the chiefs of the tribes, told them what had passed, and advised them to make a law by which a widow should not be permitted to burn herself, till she had conversed privately with a young man for the space of an hour. Since that time not a single widow had burned herself in Arabia. They were indebted to Zadig alone for destroying in one day a cruel custom that had lasted for so many ages; and thus he became the benefactor of Arabia.

XII

THE SUPPER

SETOC, who could not separate himself from this man in whom dwelt wisdom, carried Zadig to the great fair of Balzora, whither the richest merchants of the earth resorted. Zadig was highly pleased to see so many men of different countries united in the same place. He considered the whole universe as one large family assembled at Balzora. The second day he sat at table with an Egyptian, an Indian, an inhabitant of Cathay, a Greek, a Celtic, and several other strangers, who, in their frequent voyages to the Arabian Gulf, had learned enough of the Arabic to make themselves understood.

The Egyptian seemed to be in a violent passion. "What an abominable country," said he, "is Balzora! They refuse me a thousand ounces of gold on the best security in the world!"

"How!" said Setoc. "On what security have they refused thee this sum?"

"On the body of my aunt," replied the Egyptian. "She was the most notable woman in Egypt; she always accompanied me in my journeys; she died on the road. I have converted her into one of the finest mummies in the world; and in my own country I could obtain any amount by giving her as a pledge. It is very strange that they will not here lend me a thousand ounces of gold on such a solid security."

Angry as he was, he was going to help himself to a bit of excellent boiled fowl, when the Indian, taking him by the hand, cried out in a sorrowful tone, "Ah! what art thou going to do?"

"To eat a bit of this fowl," replied the man who owned the mummy.

"Take care that thou dost not," replied the Indian. "It is possible that the soul of the deceased may have passed into this fowl; and thou wouldst not, surely, expose thyself to the danger of eating thy aunt? To boil fowls is a manifest outrage on nature."

"What dost thou mean by thy nature and thy fowls?" replied the choleric Egyptian. "We adore a bull, and yet we eat heartily of beef."

"You adore a bull! Is it possible?" said the Indian.

"Nothing is more possible," returned the other; "we have done so for these hundred and thirty-five thousand years; and nobody amongst us has ever found fault with it."

"A hundred and thirty-five thousand years!" said the Indian. "This account is a little exaggerated. It is but eighty thousand years since India was first peopled, and we are surely more ancient than you are. Brahma prohibited our eating of ox-flesh before you thought of putting it on your spits or altars."

"This Brahma of yours," said the Egyptian, "is a pleasant sort of an animal, truly, to compare with our Apis. What great things hath your Brahma done?"

"It was he," replied the Brahmin, "that taught mankind to read and write, and to whom the world is indebted for the game of chess."

"Thou art mistaken," said a Chaldean who sat near him. "It is to the fish Oannes that we owe these great advantages; and it is just that we should render homage to none but him. All the world will tell thee that he is a divine being, with a golden tail, and a beautiful human head: and that for three hours every day he left the water to preach on dry land. He had several children, who were kings, as every one knows. I have a picture of him at home, which I worship with becoming reverence. We may eat as much beef as we please; but it is surely a great sin to dress fish for the table. Besides, you are both of an origin too recent and ignoble to dispute with me. The Egyptians reckon only a hundred and thirty-five thousand years, and the Indians but eighty thousand, while we have almanacs of four thousand ages. Believe me; renounce your follies; and I will give to each of you a beautiful picture of Oannes."

The man of Cathay took up the discourse, and said:

"I have a great respect for the Egyptians, the Chaldeans, the Greeks, the Celtics, Brahma, the bull Apis, and the beautiful fish Oannes; but I could think that Li, or Tien, as he is commonly called, is superior to all the bulls on the earth, or all the fish in the sea. I shall say nothing of my native country; it is as large as Egypt, Chaldea, and the Indies put together. Neither shall I dispute about the antiquity of our nation; because it is of little consequence whether we are ancient or not; it is enough if we are happy. But were it necessary to speak of almanacs, I could say that all Asia takes ours, and that we had very good ones before arithmetic was known in Chaldea."

"Ignorant men, as ye all are," said the Greek; "do you not know that Chaos is the father of all; and that form and matter have put the world in its present condition?"

The Greek spoke for a long time, but was at last interrupted by the Celtic, who, having drank pretty deeply while the rest were disputing, imagined he was now more knowing than all the others, and said, with an oath, that there were none but Teutat and the mistletoe of the oak that were worth the trouble of a dispute; that, for his own part, he had always some mistletoe in his pocket; and that the Scythians, his ancestors, were the only men of merit that had ever appeared in the world; that it was true they had sometimes eaten human flesh, but that, notwithstanding this circumstance, his nation deserved to be held in great esteem; and that, in fine, if any one spoke ill of Teutat, he would teach him better manners.

The quarrel had now become warm, and Setoc feared the table would be stained with blood.

Zadig, who had been silent during the whole dispute, arose at last. He first addressed himself to the Celtic, as the most furious of the disputants. He told him that he had reason on his side, and begged a few mistletoes. He then praised the Greek for his eloquence, and softened all their exasperated spirits. He said but little to the man of Cathay, because he had been the most reasonable of them all. At last he said:

"You were going, my friends, to quarrel about nothing; for you are all of one mind."

At this assertion they all cried out in dissent.

"Is it not true," said he to the Celtic, "that you adore not this mistletoe, but him that made both the mistletoe and the oak?"

"Most undoubtedly," replied the Celtic.

"And thou, Mr. Egyptian, dost not thou revere, in a certain bull, him who created the bulls?"

"Yes," said the Egyptian.

"The fish Oannes," continued he, "must yield to him who made the sea and the fishes. The Indian and the Cathaian," added he, "acknowledge a first principle. I did not fully comprehend the admirable things that were said by the Greek; but I am sure he will admit a superior being on whom form and matter depend."

The Greek, whom they all admired, said that Zadig had exactly taken his meaning.

"You are all then," replied Zadig, "of one opinion and have no cause to quarrel."

All the company embraced him.

Setoc, after having sold his commodities at a very high price, returned to his own tribe with his friend Zadig; who learned, upon his arrival, that he had been tried in his absence and was now going to be burned by a slow fire.

XIII

THE RENDEZVOUS

DURING his journey to Balzora the priests of the stars had resolved to punish Zadig. The precious stones and ornaments of the young widows whom they sent to the funeral pile belonged to them of right; and the least they could now do was to burn Zadig for the ill office he had done them. Accordingly they accused him of entertaining erroneous sentiments of the heavenly host. They deposed against him, and swore that they had heard him say that the stars did not set in the sea. This horrid blasphemy made the judges tremble; they were ready to tear their garments upon hearing these impious words; and they would certainly have torn them had Zadig had wherewithal to pay them for new ones. But in the excess of their zeal and indignation, they contented themselves with condemning him to be burnt by a slow fire. Setoc, filled with despair at this unhappy event, employed all his interest to save his friend, but in vain. He was soon obliged to hold his peace. The young widow, Almona, who had now conceived a great fondness for life, for which she was obliged to Zadig, resolved to deliver him from the funeral pile, of the abuse of which he had fully convinced her. She resolved the scheme in her own mind, without imparting it to any person whatever. Zadig was to be executed the next day. If she could save him at all, she must do it that very night; and the method taken by this charitable and prudent lady was as follows:

She perfumed herself; she heightened her beauty by the richest and gayest apparel, and went to demand an audience of the chief priest of the stars. As soon as she was introduced to the venerable old man, she addressed him in these terms: "Eldest son of the great bear, brother of the bull, and cousin of the great dog, (such were the titles of this pontiff,) I come to acquaint thee with my scruples. I am much afraid that I have committed a heinous crime in not burning myself on the funeral pile of my dear husband; for, indeed, what had I worth preserving? Perishable flesh, thou seest, that is already entirely withered." So saying, she drew up her long sleeves of silk, and showed her naked arms, which were of an elegant shape and a dazzling whiteness. "Thou seest," said she, "that these are little worth." The priest found in his heart that they were worth a great deal. He swore that he had never in his life seen such beautiful arms. "Alas!" said the widow, "my arms, perhaps, are not so bad as the rest; but thou wilt confess that my neck is not worthy of the least regard." She then discovered the most charming neck that nature had ever formed. Compared to it a rose-bud on an apple of ivory would have appeared like madder on the box-tree, and the whiteness of new-washed lambs would have seemed of a dusky yellow. Her large black eyes, languishing with the gentle lustre of a tender fire; her cheeks animated with the finest pink, mixed with the whiteness of milk; her nose, which had no resemblance to the tower of Mount Lebanon; her lips, like two borders of coral, inclosing the finest pearls in the Arabian Sea; all conspired to make the old man fancy and believe that he was young again. Almona, seeing his admiration, now entreated him to pardon Zadig. "Alas!" said he, "my charming lady, should I grant thee his pardon, it would be of no service, as it must necessarily be signed by three others, my brethren." "Sign it, however," said Almona. "With all my heart," said the priest. "Be pleased to visit me," said Almona, "when the bright star of Sheat shall appear in the horizon."

Almona then went to the second pontiff. He assured her that the sun, the moon, and all the luminaries of heaven, were but glimmering meteors in comparison to her charms. She asked the same favor of him, and he also granted it readily. She then appointed the second pontiff to meet her at the rising of the star Algenib. From thence she went to the third and fourth priest, always taking their signatures, and making an appointment from star to star. She then sent a message to the judges, entreating them to come to her house on an affair of great importance. They obeyed her summons. She showed them the four names, and told them that the priests had granted the pardon of Zadig. Each of the pontiffs arrived at the hour appointed. Each was surprised at finding his brethren there, but still more at seeing the judges also present. Zadig was saved; and Setoc was so charmed with the skill and address of Almona that he at once made her his wife.

Business affairs now required Setoc's presence in the island of Serendib; but during the first month of his marriage—the month which is called the honeymoon—he could not permit himself to leave Almona, nor even to think he could ever leave her, and he requested Zadig to make the journey in his place. "Alas!" said Zadig, "must I put a still greater distance between the beautiful Astarte and myself? But it would be ungrateful not to serve my friend, and I will endeavor to do my duty."

Setoc and Zadig now took leave of each other with tears in their eyes, both swearing an eternal friendship, and promising to always share their fortunes with each other. Zadig then, after having thrown himself at the feet of his fair deliverer, set out on his journey to Serendib, still musing on the unhappy Astarte, and meditating on the severity of fortune, which seemed to persistently make him the sport of her cruelty and the object of her persecution.

"What!" said he to himself, "fined four hundred ounces of gold for having observed a bitch! condemned to lose my head for four bad verses in praise of the king! sentenced to be strangled because the queen had shoes the color of my turban! reduced to slavery for having succored a woman who was beaten! and on the point of being burned for having saved the lives of all the young widows of Arabia!"

XIV

The Dance

Arriving in due time at the island of Serendib, Zadig's merits were at once recognized, and he was popularly regarded as an extraordinary man. He became the friend of the wise and learned, the arbitrator of disputes, and the advisor of the small number of those who were willing to take advice. He was duly presented to the king, who was pleased with his affability, and soon chose him for his friend. But this royal favor caused Zadig to tremble; for he well remembered the misfortunes which the kindness of king Moabdar had formerly brought upon him. "I please the king," said he; "shall I not therefore be lost?" Still he could not refuse the king's friendship, for it must be confessed that Nabussan, king of Serendib, son of Nassanab, son of Nabassau, son of Sanbusna, was one of the most amiable princes in Asia.

But this good prince was always flattered, deceived and robbed. It was a contest who should most pillage the royal treasury. The example set by the receiver-general of Serendib was universally followed by the inferior officers. This the king knew. He had often changed his treasurers, but had never been able to change the established custom of dividing the revenues into two unequal parts, of which the smaller came to his majesty, and the larger to his officers.

This custom Nabussan explained to Zadig. "You, whose knowledge embraces so many subjects," said he, "can you not tell me how to select a treasurer who will not rob me?"

"Assuredly," said Zadig; "I know a sure method for finding you a man who will keep his hands clean."

The king was charmed, and asked, while he embraced him, how this was to be done.

"You have only," said Zadig, "to cause all those who apply for the office of treasurer to dance. He who dances the lightest will surely prove to be the most honest man."

"You jest," said the king. "A strange way, certainly, of choosing a receiver of my revenues. What! do you pretend that he who cuts the neatest caper will be the most just and skillful financier?"

"I will not answer," returned Zadig, "for his being the most skillful, but I assure you he will be the most honest."

Zadig spoke with so much confidence that the king imagined he had some supernatural test for selecting honest financiers.

"I do not like the supernatural," said Zadig: "people and books dealing in prodigies have always displeased me. If your majesty will permit me to make the test, you will be convinced it is the easiest and simplest thing possible."

Nabussan consented, and was more astonished to hear that the test was simple, than if it had been claimed as a miracle.

"Leave all the details to me," said Zadig. "You will gain more by this trial than you imagine."

The same day he made proclamation in the king's name, that all candidates for the office of receiver-in-chief of the revenues of his gracious majesty Nabussan, son of Nassanab must present themselves in dresses of light silk, on the first day of the month of the crocodile, in the king's ante-chamber. The candidates came, accordingly, to the number of sixty-four. Musicians were placed in an adjoining room, and all was prepared for the dance. As the door of the saloon was closed, it was necessary, in order to enter it, to pass through a small gallery which was slightly darkened. An usher directed each candidate in succession through this obscure passage, in which he was left alone for some moments. The king, being aware of the plan, had temptingly spread out in this gallery many of his choicest treasures. When all the candidates were assembled in the saloon, the king ordered the band to play and the dance to begin. Never had dancers performed more unwillingly or with less grace. Their heads were down, their backs bent, their hands pressed to their sides.

"What rascals!" murmured Zadig.

One alone danced with grace and agility—his head up, his look assured, his body erect, his arms free, his motions natural.

"Ah, the honest man, the excellent man!" cried Zadig.

The king embraced this upright dancer, appointed him treasurer, and punished all the others with the utmost justice, for each one had, while passing through the gallery, filled his pockets till he could hardly walk. His majesty was distressed at this exhibition of dishonesty, and regretted that among these sixty-four dancers there should be sixty-three thieves. This dark gallery was then named the Corridor of Temptation.

In Persia these sixty-three lords would have been impaled; in other countries a chamber of justice would have consumed in costs three times the money stolen, replacing nothing in the king's coffers; in yet another kingdom they would have been honorably acquitted, and the light dancer disgraced; in Serendib they were only sentenced to add to the public treasure, for Nabussan was very indulgent.

He was also very grateful, and willingly gave Zadig a larger sum than any treasurer had ever stolen from the revenue. This wealth Zadig used to send a courier ·to Babylon to learn the fate of queen Astarte. His voice trembled when directing the courier. His blood seemed to stagnate in his veins. His heart almost ceased to beat. His eyes were suffused with tears.

XV

BLUE EYES

AFTER the courier had gone, Zadig returned to the palace; and forgetting that he was not in his own room, almost unconsciously uttered the word LOVE.

"Ah! love," exclaimed the king, "that is indeed the cause of my unhappiness. You have divined what it is that causes me pain. You are indeed a great man. I hope you will assist me in my search for a woman, perfect in all respects, and of whose affection I may feel assured. You have proved your ability for this service by selecting for me an honest financier, and I have entire confidence in your success."

Zadig, having recovered his composure, promised to serve the king in love as he had in finance, although the task seemed to him far more difficult.

"The body and the heart——" said the king.

At these words Zadig could not refrain from interrupting his majesty: "You show good taste," said he, "by not saying the mind and the heart; for we hear nothing but these words in the talk of Babylon. We see nothing but books which treat of the heart and mind, written by people who have neither the one nor the other: but pardon me, sire, and deign to continue."

"I have in my palace," said the king, "one hundred women who are all called charming, graceful, beautiful, affectionate even, or pretending to be so when in my company; but I have too often realized that it is to the king of Serendib they pay court, and that they care very little for Nabussan. This pretended affection does not satisfy my desires. I would find a consort that loves me for myself, and who would willingly be all my own. For such a treasure I would joyfully barter the hundred beauties whose forced smiles afford me no delight. Let us see if out of these hundred queens you can select one true woman to bless me with her love."

Zadig replied to him as he had previously done in regard to the finances: "Sire, allow me to make the attempt, and permit me to again use the treasure formerly displayed in the Corridor of Temptation. I will render you a faithful account."

The king willingly acceded to this request, and permitted Zadig to do as he desired. He first chose thirty-three of the ugliest little hunchbacks that could be procured in Serendib, then thirty-three of the handsomest pages to be found, and, lastly, thirty-three bonzes (priests), the most eloquent and robust he could select. He gave them all liberty to enter the king's private apartments in the palace, and secure a partner if they so desired. Each little hunchback had four thousand gold pieces given to him: and on the first day each had secured a companion. The pages, who had nothing to give but themselves, did not succeed in many cases until the end of two or three days. The priests had still more trouble in obtaining partners, but, finally, thirty-three devotees joined their fortunes with these pious suitors. The king, through the blinds which opened into his apartments, saw all these trials, and was astounded. Of these hundred women, ninety-nine discarded his protection. There still remained one, however, still quite young, with whom his majesty had never conversed. They sent to her one, two, three hunchbacks, who displayed before her twenty thousand pieces of gold. She still remained firm, and could not refrain from laughing at the idea of these cripples, that wealth could change their appearance. They then presented before her the two most beautiful pages. She said she thought the king was still more beautiful. They attacked her with the most eloquent of the priests, and after-ward with the most audacious. She found the first a prattler, and could not perceive any merit in the second.

"The heart," said she, "is everything. I will never yield to the hunchbacks' gold, the pages' vanity, or the pompous prattle of the priests. I love only Nabussan, son of Nassanab, and I will wait until he condescends to love me in return."

The king was transported with joy, astonishment, and love. He took back all the money that had brought success to the hunchbacks, and made a present of it to the beautiful Falide, which was the name of this charming lady. He gave her his heart, which she amply deserved, for never were glances from female eyes more brilliant than her own, nor the charms of youthful beauty more enchanting. Envy, it is true, asserted that she courtesied awkwardly; but candor compels the admission that she danced like the fairies, acted like the graces, sang like the sirens, and that she was in truth the very embodiment of intelligence and virtue. Nabussan loved and adored her: but, alas! she had BLUE EYES, and this apparently trivial fact was the cause of the gravest mis-fortunes.

There was an old law in Serendib forbidding the kings to marry those to whom the Greeks applied the word βοωπις. A high-priest had established this law thousands of years ago. He had anathematized blue eyes in order that he might secure for himself the hand of the king's favorite. The various orders of the empire now remonstrated with Nabussan for disregarding this organic law and loving the beautiful Falide. They publicly asserted that the last days of the kingdom had arrived—that this act of royal love was the height of sacrilege—that all nature was threatened with a sinister ending—and all because Nabussan, son of Nassanab, loved two magnificent blue eyes. The cripples, the capitalists, the bonzes, and the brunettes filled the kingdom with their complaints.

The barbarians of the northern provinces profited by the general discontent. They invaded the territory of the good Nabussan and demanded a tribute from his subjects. The priests, who possessed half the revenues of the state, contented themselves with raising their hands to heaven, and refused to put them in their coffers to aid the king. They chanted beautiful prayers, and left the state a prey to the invaders.

"Oh! my dear Zadig," sadly cried Nabussan, "can you not rescue me from this impending danger?"

"Very willingly," replied Zadig. "You shall have for your defence as much money from the priests as you may desire. Leave, I pray you, without guard the property of the bonzes, and defend only your own possessions."

Nabussan wisely followed this advice. The priests became alarmed, threw themselves at his feet and implored his protection. The king replied with agreeable music, and chanted forth prayers and invocations to heaven with much sweetness and melody. Finally, the priests reluctantly contributed the money, and the king brought the war to a happy termination.

Thus Zadig by his sensible advice and judicious services drew upon himself the enmity of the most powerful parties in the state. The bonzes and the brunettes swore to destroy him; the capitalists and the cripples did not spare him. They caused the good Nabussan to suspect him. "Services rendered often remain in the antechamber, and distrust enters into the cabinet." So said Zoroaster. Every day there were fresh accusations: the first is repelled; the second is lightly thought of; the third wounds; the fourth kills.

Zadig was dismayed, and having now satisfactorily arranged Setoc's affairs, he only thought of leaving the island in safety.

"But where shall I go?" said he. "If I remain in Serendib the priests will doubtless have me impaled; in Egypt I would probably be enslaved; burnt, according to all appearance, in Arabia; strangled in Babylon. However, I must learn what has become of queen Astarte, and will go on and see what sad fate destiny has still in store for me."

XVI

THE ROBBER

ARRIVING on the frontiers which divide Arabia Petræa from Syria, he passed by a very strong castle from which a party of armed Arabians sallied forth. They instantly surrounded him and cried:

"All thou hast belongs to us, and thy person is the property of our master."

Zadig replied by drawing his sword; his servant, who was a man of courage, did the same. They killed the first Arabians that presumed to lay hands on them; and though the number was redoubled, they were not dismayed, but resolved to perish in the conflict. Two men defended themselves against a multitude; but such a combat could not last long. The master of the castle, whose name was Arbogad, having observed from a window the prodigies of valor performed by Zadig, conceived a high esteem for this heroic stranger. He descended in haste, and went in person to call off his men and deliver the two travelers.

"All that passes over my lands," said he, "belongs to me, as well as what I find upon the lands of others; but thou seemest to be a man of such undaunted courage, that I will exempt thee from the common law."

He then conducted him to his castle, ordering his men to treat him well; and in the evening Arbogad supped with Zadig. The lord of the castle was one of those Arabians who are commonly called robbers; but he now and then performed some good actions amidst a multitude of bad ones. He robbed with a furious rapacity, and granted favors with great generosity. He was intrepid in action; affable in company; a debauchee at table, but gay in his debauchery; and particularly remarkable for his frank and open behavior. He was highly pleased with Zadig, whose lively conversation lengthened the repast. At last Arbogad said to him:

"I advise thee to enroll thy name in my catalogue. Thou canst not do better. This is not a bad trade, and thou mayest one day become what I am at present."

"May I take the liberty of asking thee," said Zadig, "how long thou hast followed this noble profession?"

"From my most tender youth," replied the lord, "I was servant to a petty, good-natured Arabian, but could not endure the hardships of my situation. I was vexed to find that fate had given me no share of the earth which equally belongs to all men. I imparted the cause of my uneasiness to an old Arabian, who said to me:

" 'My son, do not despair; there was once a grain of sand that lamented that it was no more than a neglected atom in the deserts; at the end of a few years it became a diamond, and it is now the brightest ornament in the crown of the king of the Indies.'

"This discourse made a deep impression on my mind. I was the grain of sand, and I resolved to become the diamond. I began by stealing two horses. I soon got a party of companions. I put myself in a condition to rob small caravans; and thus, by degrees, I destroyed the difference which had formerly subsisted between me and other men. I had my share of the good things of this world; and was even recompensed with usury for the hardships I had suffered. I was greatly respected, and became the captain of a band of robbers. I seized this castle by force. The satrap of Syria had a mind to dispossess me of it; but I was too rich to have any thing to fear. I gave the satrap a handsome present, by which means I preserved my castle, and increased my possessions. He even appointed me treasurer of the tributes which Arabia Petræa pays to the king of kings. I perform my office of receiver with great punctuality; but take the freedom to dispense with that of paymaster.

"The grand Desterham of Babylon sent hither a petty satrap in the name of king Moabdar, to have me strangled. This man arrived with his orders. I was apprised of all. I caused to be strangled in his presence the four persons he had brought with him to draw the noose; after which I asked him how much his commission of strangling me might be worth. He replied that his fees would amount to about three hundred pieces of gold. I then convinced him that he might gain more by staying with me. I made him an inferior robber; and he is now one of my best and richest officers. If thou wilt take my advice, thy success may be equal to his. Never was there a better season for plunder, since king Moabdar is killed, and all Babylon thrown into confusion."

"Moabdar killed!" said Zadig, "and what has become of queen Astarte?"

"I know not," replied Arbogad. "All I know is, that Moabdar lost his senses and was killed; that Babylon is a scene of disorder and bloodshed; that all the empire is desolated; that there are some fine strokes to be made yet; and that, for my own part, I have struck some that are admirable."

"But the queen," said Zadig; "for heaven's sake, knowest thou nothing of the queen's fate?"

"Yes," replied he, "I have heard something of a prince of Hircania. If she was not killed in the tumult, she is probably one of his concubines. But I am fonder of booty than news. I have taken several women in my excursions; but I keep none of them. I sell them at a high price when they are beautiful, without enquiring who they are. In commodities of this kind rank makes no difference, and a queen that is ugly will never find a merchant. Perhaps I may have sold queen Astarte; perhaps she is dead; but, be it as it will, it is of little consequence to me, and I should imagine of as little to thee."

So saying, he drank a large draught, which threw all his ideas into such confusion that Zadig could obtain no farther information.

Zadig remained for some time without speech, sense, or motion. Arbogad continued drinking; constantly repeated that he was the happiest man in the world; and exhorted Zadig to put himself in the same condition. At last the soporiferous fume of the wine lulled him into a gentle repose. Zadig passed the night in the most violent perturbation.

"What," said he, "did the king lose his senses? and is he killed? I cannot help lamenting his fate. The empire is rent in pieces: and this robber is happy. O fortune! O destiny! A robber is happy, and the most beautiful of nature's works hath perhaps perished in a barbarous manner, or lives in a state worse than death. O Astarte! what has become of thee?"

At day break, he questioned all those he met in the castle; but they were all busy and he received no answer. During the night they had made a new capture, and they were now employed in dividing the spoil. All he could obtain in this hurry and confusion was an opportunity of departing, which he immediately embraced, plunged deeper than ever in the most gloomy and mournful reflections.

Zadig proceeded on his journey with a mind full of disquiet and perplexity, and wholly employed on the unhappy Astarte, on the king of Babylon, on his faithful friend Cador, on the happy robber, Arbogad, on that capricious woman whom the Babylonians had seized on the frontiers of Egypt. In a word, on all the misfortunes and disappointments he had hitherto suffered.

XVII

The Fisherman

At a few leagues distance from Arbogad's castle he came to the banks of a small river, still deploring his fate, and considering himself as the most wretched of mankind. He saw a fisherman lying on the bank of the river, scarcely holding in his weak and feeble hand a net which he seemed ready to drop, and lifting up his eyes to heaven.

"I am certainly," said the fisherman, "the most unhappy man in the world. I was universally allowed to be the most famous dealer in cream-cheese in Babylon, and yet I am ruined. I had the most handsome wife that any man in my situation could have; and by her I have been betrayed. I had still left a paltry house, and that I have seen pillaged and destroyed. At last I took refuge in this cottage, where I have no other resource than fishing, and yet I cannot catch a single fish. Oh, my net! no more will I throw thee into the water; I will throw myself in thy place."

So saying, he arose and advanced forward, in the attitude of a man ready to throw himself into the river, and thus to finish his life.

"What," said Zadig, "are there men as wretched as I?"

His eagerness to save the fisherman's life was as sudden as this reflection. He runs to him, stops him, and speaks to him with a tender and compassionate air. It is commonly supposed that we are less miserable when we have companions in our misery. This, according to Zoroaster, does not proceed from malice, but necessity. We feel ourselves insensibly drawn to an unhappy person as to one like ourselves. The joy of the happy would be an insult; but two men in distress are like two slender trees, which, mutually supporting each other, fortify themselves against the tempest.

"Why," said Zadig to the fisherman, "dost thou sink under thy misfortunes?"

"Because," replied he, "I see no means of relief. I was the most considerable man in the village of Derlback, near Babylon, and with the assistance of my wife I made the best cream-cheese in the empire. Queen Astarte, and the famous minister, Zadig, were extremely fond of them. I had sent them six hundred cheeses, and one day went to the city to receive my money; but, on my arrival at Babylon, was informed that the queen and Zadig had disappeared. I ran to the house of Lord Zadig, whom I had never seen; and found there the inferior officers of the grand Desterham, who being furnished with a royal license, were plundering it with great loyalty and order. From thence I flew to the queen's kitchen, some of the lords of which told me that the queen was dead; some said she was in prison; and others pretended that she had made her escape; but they all agreed in assuring me that I would not be paid for my cheese. I went with my wife to the house of Lord Orcan, who was one of my customers, and begged his protection in my present distress. He granted it to my wife, but refused it to me. She was whiter than the cream-cheeses that began my misfortune, and the lustre of the Tyrian purple was not more bright than the carnation which animated this whiteness. For this reason Orcan detained her, and drove me from his house. In my despair I wrote a letter to my dear wife. She said to the bearer, 'Ha, ha! I know the writer of this a little. I have heard his name mentioned. They say he makes excellent cream-cheeses. Desire him to send me some and he shall be paid.'

"In my distress I resolved to apply to justice. I had still six ounces of gold remaining. I was obliged to give two to the lawyer whom I consulted, two to the procurator who undertook my cause, and two to the secretary of the first judge. When all this was done, my business was not begun; and I had already expended more money than my cheese and my wife were worth. I returned to my own village, with an intention to sell my house, in order to enable me to recover my wife.

"My house was well worth sixty ounces of gold; but as my neighbors saw that I was poor and obliged to sell it, the first to whom I applied offered me thirty ounces, the second twenty, and the third ten. Bad as these offers were, I was so blind that I was going to strike a bargain, when a prince of Hircania came to Babylon, and ravaged all in his way. My house was first sacked and then burned.

"Having thus lost my money, my wife, and my house, I retired into this country, where thou now seest me. I have endeavored to gain a subsistance by fishing; but the fish make a mock of me as well as the men. I catch none; I die with hunger; and had it not been for thee, august comforter, I should have perished in the river."

The fisherman was not allowed to give this long account without interruption; at every moment, Zadig, moved and transported, said:

"What! knowest thou nothing of the queen's fate?"

"No my lord," replied the fisherman; "but I know that neither the queen nor Zadig have paid me for my cream-cheeses; that I have lost my wife, and am now reduced to despair."

"I flatter myself," said Zadig, "that thou wilt not lose all thy money. I have heard of this Zadig; he is an honest man; and if he return to Babylon, as he expects, he will give thee more than he owes thee. But with regard to thy wife, who is not so honest, I advise thee not to seek to recover her. Believe me, go to Babylon; I shall be there before thee, because I am on horseback, and thou art on foot. Apply to the illustrious Cador. Tell him thou hast met his friend. Wait for me at his house. Go, perhaps thou wilt not always be unhappy.

"O powerful Oromazes!" continued he, "thou employest me to comfort this man. Whom wilt thou employ to give me consolation?"

So saying, he gave the fisherman half the money he had brought from Arabia. The fisherman, struck with surprise and ravished with joy, kissed the feet of the friend of Cador, and said:

"Thou art surely an angel sent from heaven to save me!" Meanwhile Zadig continued to make fresh inquiries and to shed tears. "What! my lord," cried the fisherman, "and art thou then so unhappy, thou who bestowest favors?"

"A hundred times more unhappy than thee," replied Zadig.

"But how is it possible," said the good man, "that the giver can be more wretched than the receiver?"

"Because," replied Zadig, "thy greatest misery arose from poverty, and mine is seated in the heart."

"Did Orcan take thy wife from thee?" said the fisherman.

This word recalled to Zadig's mind the whole of his adventures. He repeated the catalogue of his misfortunes, beginning with the queen's bitch and ending with his arrival at the castle of the robber Arbogad.

"Ah!" said he to the fisherman, "Orcan deserves to be punished: but it is commonly such men as those that are the favorites of fortune. However, go thou to the house of Lord Cador, and there await my arrival."

They then parted: the fisherman walked, thanking heaven for the happiness of his condition; and Zadig rode, accusing fortune for the hardness of his lot.

XVIII

THE BASILISK

ARRIVING in a beautiful meadow, he there saw several women, who were searching for something with great application. He took the liberty to approach one of them, and to ask if he might have the honor to assist them in their search.

"Take care that thou dost not," replied the Syrian. "What we are searching for can be touched only by women."

"Strange," said Zadig. "May I presume to ask thee what it is that women only are permitted to touch?"

"It is a basilisk," said she.

"A basilisk, madam! and for what purpose, pray, dost thou seek for a basilisk?"

"It is for our lord and master, Ogul, whose castle thou seest on the bank of that river, at the end of that meadow. We are his most humble slaves. The Lord Ogul is sick. His physician hath ordered him to eat a basilisk, stewed in rose-water; and as it is a very rare animal, and can only be taken by women, the Lord Ogul hath promised to choose for his well-beloved wife the woman that shall bring him a basilisk. Let me go on in my search; for thou seest what I shall lose if I am forestalled by my companions."

Zadig left her and the other Assyrians to search for their basilisk, and continued his journey through the meadow; when coming to the brink of a small rivulet, he found a lady lying on the grass, and who was not searching for any thing. Her person seemed majestic; but her face was covered with a veil. She was inclined toward the rivulet, and profound sighs proceeded from her bosom. In her hand she held a small rod with which she was tracing characters on the fine sand that lay between the turf and the brook.

Zadig had the curiosity to examine what this woman was writing. He drew near. He saw the letter Z, then an A; he was astonished: then appeared a D; he started. But never was surprise equal to his, when he saw the two last letters of his name. He stood for some time immovable. At last breaking silence with a faltering voice:

"Oh! generous lady! pardon a stranger, an unfortunate man, for presuming to ask thee by what surprising adventure I here find the name of Zadig traced out by thy divine hand?"

At this voice and these words, the lady lifted up the veil with a trembling hand, looked at Zadig, sent forth a cry of tenderness, surprise, and joy, and sinking under the various emotions which at once assaulted her soul, fell speechless into his arms. It was Astarte herself; it was the queen of Babylon, it was she whom Zadig adored, and whom he had reproached himself for adoring; it was she whose misfortunes he had so deeply lamented, and for whose fate he had been so anxiously concerned. He was for a moment deprived of the use of his senses, when he had fixed his eyes on those of Astarte, which now began to open again with a languor mixed with confusion and tenderness:

"O ye immortal powers!" cried he, "who preside over the fates of weak mortals; do ye indeed restore Astarte to me? At what a time, in what a place, and in what a condition do I again behold her?"

He fell on his knees before Astarte, and laid his face in the dust at her feet. The queen of Babylon raised him up, and made him sit by her side on the brink of the rivulet. She frequently wiped her eyes, from which the tears continued to flow afresh. She twenty times resumed her discourse, which her sighs as often interrupted. She asked by what strange accident they were brought together; and suddenly prevented his answer by other questions. She waived the account of her own misfortunes, and desired to be informed of those of Zadig. At last, both of them having a little composed the tumult of their souls, Zadig acquainted her in a few words by what adventure he was brought into that meadow.

"But, O unhappy and respectable queen! by what means do I find thee in this lonely place, clothed in the habit of a slave, and accompanied by other female slaves, who are searching for a basilisk, which by order of the physician, is to be stewed in rose-water?"

"While they are searching for their basilisk," said the fair Astarte, "I will inform thee of all I have suffered, for which heaven has sufficiently recompensed me, by restoring thee to my sight. Thou knowest that the king, my husband, was vexed to see thee, the most amiable of mankind; and that for this reason he one night resolved to strangle thee and poison me. Thou knowest how heaven permitted my little mute to inform me of the orders of his sublime majesty. Hardly had the faithful Cador obliged thee to depart, in obedience to my command, when he ventured to enter my apartment at midnight by a secret passage. He carried me off, and conducted me to the temple of Oromazes, where the magi, his brother, shut me up in that huge statue, whose base reaches to the foundation of the temple, and whose top rises to the summit of the dome. I was there buried in a manner; but was served by the magi, and supplied with all the necessaries of life. At break of day his majesty's apothecary entered my chamber with a potion composed of a mixture of henbane, opium, hemlock, black hellebore, and aconite; and another officer went to thine with a bow-string of blue silk. Neither of us were to be found. Cador, the better to deceive the king, pretended to come and accuse us both. He said that thou hadst taken the road to the Indies, and I that to Memphis; on which the king's guards were immediately dispatched in pursuit of us both.

"The couriers who pursued me did not know me. I had hardly ever shown my face to any but thee, and to thee only in the presence and by the order of my husband. They conducted themselves in the pursuit by the description that had been given of my person. On the frontiers of Egypt they met with a woman of the same stature with me, and possessed perhaps of greater charms. She was weeping and wandering. They made no doubt but that this woman was the queen of Babylon, and accordingly brought her to Moabdar. Their mistake at first threw the king into a violent passion; but having viewed this woman more attentively, he found her extremely handsome, and was comforted. She was called Missouf. I have since been informed that this name in the Egyptian language signifies the capricious fair one. She was so in reality; but she had as much cunning as caprice. She pleased Moabdar, and gained such an ascendency over him as to make him choose her for his wife. Her character then began to appear in its true colors. She gave herself up, without scruple, to all the freaks of a wanton imagination. She would have obliged the chief of the magi, who was old and gouty, to dance before her; and on his refusal, she persecuted him with the most unrelenting cruelty. She ordered her master of the horse to make her a pie of sweetmeats. In vain did he represent that he was not a pastry-cook. He was obliged to make it, and lost his place because it was baked a little too hard. The post of master of the horse she gave to her dwarf, and that of chancellor to her page. In this manner did she govern Babylon. Every body regretted the loss of me. The king, who till the moment of his resolving to poison me and strangle thee had been a tolerably good kind of man, seemed now to have drowned all his virtues in his immoderate fondness for this capricious fair one. He came to the temple on the great day of the feast held in honor of the sacred fire. I saw him implore the gods in behalf of Missouf, at the feet of the statue in which I was inclosed. I raised my voice; I cried out:

" 'The gods reject the prayers of a king who is now become a tyrant, and who attempted to murder a reasonable wife, in order to marry a woman remarkable for nothing but her folly and extravagance.'

"At these words Moabdar was confounded and his head became disordered. The oracle I had pronounced, and the tyranny of Missouf, conspired to deprive him of his judgment, and in a few days his reason entirely forsook him.

"His madness, which seemed to be the judgment of heaven, was the signal for a revolt. The people rose, and ran to arms, and Babylon, which had been so long immersed in idleness and effeminacy, became the theatre of a bloody civil war. I was taken from the heart of my statue and placed at the head of a party. Cador flew to Memphis to bring thee back to Babylon. The prince of Hircania, informed of these fatal events, returned with his army and made a third party in Chaldea. He attacked the king, who fled before him with his capricious Egyptian. Moabdar died pierced with wounds. Missouf fell into the hands of the conqueror. I myself had the misfortune to be taken by a party of Hircanians, who conducted me to their prince's tent, at the very moment that Missouf was brought before him. Thou wilt doubtless be pleased to hear that the prince thought me more beautiful than the Egyptian; but thou wilt be sorry to be informed that he designed me for his seraglio. He told me, with a blunt and resolute air, that as soon as he had finished a military expedition, which he was just going to undertake, he would come to me. Judge how great must have been my grief. My ties with Moabdar were already dissolved; I might have been the wife of Zadig; and I was fallen into the hands of a barbarian. I answered him with all the pride which my high rank and noble sentiment could inspire. I had always heard it affirmed that heaven stamped on persons of my condition a mark of grandeur, which, with a single word or glance, could reduce to the lowliness of the most profound respect those rash and forward persons who presume to deviate from the rules of politeness. I spoke like a queen, but was treated like a maid-servant. The Hircanian, without even deigning to speak to me, told his black eunuch that I was impertinent, but that he thought me handsome. He ordered him to take care of me and to put me under the regimen of favorites, that, so my complexion being improved, I might be the more worthy of his favors when he should be at leisure to honor me with them. I told him, that rather than submit to his desires, I would put an end to my life. He replied with a smile, that women, he believed, were not so bloodthirsty, and that he was accustomed to such violent expressions; and then left me with the air of a man who had just put another parrot into his aviary. What a state for the first queen in the universe, and, what is more, for a heart devoted to Zadig!"

At these words Zadig threw himself at her feet, and bathed them with his tears. Astarte raised him with great tenderness, and thus continued her story:

"I now saw myself in the power of a barbarian, and rival to the foolish woman with whom I was confined. She gave me an account of her adventures in Egypt. From the description she gave of your person, from the time, from the dromedary on which you were mounted, and from every other circumstance, I inferred that Zadig was the man who had fought for her. I doubted not but that you were at Memphis, and therefore resolved to repair thither. 'Beautiful Missouf,' said I, 'thou art more handsome than I, and will please the prince of Hircania much better. Assist me in contriving the means of my escape. Thou wilt then reign alone. Thou wilt at once make me happy and rid thyself of a rival.'

"Missouf concerted with me the means of my flight; and I departed secretly with a female slave. As I approached the frontiers of Arabia, a famous robber, named Arbogad, seized me and sold me to some merchants who brought me to this castle where Lord Ogul resides. He bought me without knowing who I was. He is a voluptuary, ambitious of nothing but good living, and thinks that God sent him into the world for no other purpose than to sit at table. He is so extremely corpulent, that he is always in danger of suffocation. His physician, who has but little credit with him when he has a good digestion, governs him with a despotic sway when he has eaten too much. He has persuaded him that a basilisk stewed in rose-water will effect a complete cure. The Lord Ogul hath promised his hand to the female slave that brings him a basilisk. Thou seest that I leave them to vie with each other in meriting this honor; and never was I less desirous of finding the basilisk than since heaven hath restored thee to my sight."

This account was succeeded by a long conversation between Astarte and Zadig, consisting of every thing that their long suppressed sentiments, their great sufferings, and their mutual love could inspire into hearts the most noble and tender; and the genii who preside over love carried their words to the sphere of Venus.

The women returned to Ogul without having found the basilisk. Zadig was introduced to this mighty lord, and spoke to him in the following terms: "May immortal health descend from heaven to bless all thy days! I am a physician. At the first report of thy indisposition I flew to thy castle, and have now brought thee a basilisk stewed in rose-water. Not that I pretend to marry thee. All I ask is the liberty of a Babylonian slave, who hath been in thy possession for a few days; and, if I should not be so happy as to cure thee, magnificent Lord Ogul, I consent to remain a slave in her place."

The proposal was accepted. Astarte set out for Babylon with Zadig's servant, promising, immediately upon her arrival, to send a courier to inform him of all that had happened. Their parting was as tender as their meeting. The moment of meeting, and that of parting are the two greatest epochas of life, as sayeth the great book of Zend. Zadig loved the queen with as much ardor as he professed; and the queen loved Zadig more than she thought proper to acknowledge.

Meanwhile Zadig spoke thus to Ogul:

"My lord, my basilisk is not to be eaten; all its virtues must enter through thy pores. I have inclosed it in a little ball, blown up and covered with a fine skin. Thou must strike this ball with all thy might, and I must strike it back for a considerable time; and by observing this regimen for a few days, thou wilt see the effects of my art."

The first day Ogul was out of breath, and thought he should have died with fatigue. The second, he was less fatigued, and slept better. In eight days he recovered all the strength, all the health, all the agility and cheerfulness of his most agreeable years.

"Thou hast played at ball, and hast been temperate," said Zadig. "Know that there is no such thing in nature as a basilisk; that temperance and exercise are the two great preservatives of health; and that the art of reconciling intemperance and health is as chimerical as the philosopher's stone, judicial astrology, or the theology of the magi."

Ogul's first physician observing how dangerous this man might prove to the medical art, formed a design, in conjunction with the apothecary, to send Zadig to search for a basilisk in the other world. Thus, after having suffered such a long train of calamities on account of his good actions, he was now upon the point of losing his life for curing a gluttonous lord. He was invited to an excellent dinner, and was to have been poisoned in the second course; but, during the first, he happily received a courier from the fair Astarte.

"When one is beloved by a beautiful woman," says the great Zoroaster, "he hath always the good fortune to extricate himself out of every kind of difficulty and danger."

XIX

The Combats

THE queen was received at Babylon with all those transports of joy which are ever felt on the return of a beautiful princess who hath been involved in calamities. Babylon was now in greater tranquillity. The prince of Hircania had been killed in battle. The victorious Babylonians declared that the queen should marry the man whom they should choose for their sovereign. They were resolved that the first place in the world, that of being husband to Astarte and king of Babylon, should not depend on cabals and intrigues. They swore to acknowledge for king the man who, upon trial, should be found to be possessed of the greatest valor and the greatest wisdom. Accordingly, at the distance of a few leagues from the city, a spacious place was marked out for the list, surrounded with magnificent amphitheatres. Thither the combatants were to repair in complete armor. Each of them had a separate apartment behind the amphitheatre, where they were neither to be seen nor known by any one. Each was to encounter four knights; and those that were so happy as to conquer four were then to engage with one another: so that he who remained the last master of the field, would be proclaimed conqueror at the games. Four days after he was to return to the same place, and to explain the enigmas proposed by the magi. If he did not explain the enigmas, he was not king; and the running at the lances was to begin afresh, till a man should be found who was conqueror in both these combats; for they were absolutely determined to have a king possessed of the greatest wisdom and the most invincible courage. The queen was all the while to be strictly guarded. She was only allowed to be present at the games, and even there she was to be covered with a veil; but was not allowed to speak to any of the competitors, that so they might neither receive favor, nor suffer injustice.

These particulars Astarte communicated to her lover, hoping that, in order to obtain her, he would show himself possessed of greater courage and wisdom than any other person.

Zadig set out on his journey, beseeching Venus to fortify his courage and enlighten his understanding. He arrived on the banks of the Euphrates on the eve of this great day. He caused his device to be inscribed among those of the combatants, concealing his face and his name, as the law ordained; and then went to repose himself in the apartment that fell to him by lot. His friend, Cador, who after the fruitless search he had made for him in Egypt, had now returned to Babylon, sent to his tent a complete suit of armor, which was a present from the queen; as also from himself, one of the finest horses in Persia. Zadig presently perceived that these presents were sent by Astarte; and from thence his courage derived fresh strength, and his love the most animating hopes.

Next day, the queen being seated under a canopy of jewels, and the amphitheatres filled with all the gentlemen and ladies of rank in Babylon, the combatants appeared in the circus. Each of them came and laid his device at the feet of the grand magi. They drew their devices by lot; and that of Zadig was the last. The first who advanced was a certain lord, named Itobad, very rich and very vain, but possessed of little courage, of less address, and scarcely of any judgment at all. His servants had persuaded him that such a man as he ought to be king. He had said in reply, "Such a man as I ought to reign"; and thus they had armed him cap-a-pie. He wore an armor of gold enameled with green, a plume of green feathers, and a lance adorned with green ribbons. It was instantly perceived by the manner in which Itobad managed his horse, that it was not for such a man as him that heaven reserved the sceptre of Babylon. The first knight that ran against him threw him out of his saddle: the second laid him flat on his horse's buttocks, with his legs in the air, and his arms extended. Itobad recovered himself, but with so bad a grace, that the whole amphitheatre burst out a-laughing. The third knight disdained to make use of his lance; but, making a pass at him, took him by the right leg, and wheeling him half round, laid him prostrate on the sand. The squires of the games ran to him laughing, and replaced him in his saddle. The fourth combatant took him by the left leg, and tumbled him down on the other side. He was conducted back with scornful shouts to his tent, where, according to the law, he was to pass the night; and as he limped along with great difficulty, he said: "What an adventure for such a man as I!"

The other knights acquitted themselves with greater ability and success. Some of them conquered two combatants; a few of them vanquished three; but none but prince Otamus conquered four. At last Zadig fought in his turn. He successively threw four knights off their saddles with all the grace imaginable. It then remained to be seen who should be conqueror, Otamus or Zadig. The arms of the first were gold and blue, with a plume of the same color; those of the last were white. The wishes of all the spectators were divided between the knight in blue and the knight in white. The queen, whose heart was in a violent palpitation, offered prayers to heaven for the success of the white color.

The two champions made their passes and vaults with so much agility, they mutually gave and received such dexterous blows with their lances, and sat so firmly in their saddles, that every body but the queen wished there might be two kings in Babylon. At length, their horses being tired and their lances broken, Zadig had recourse to this stratagem: He passed behind the blue prince; springs upon the buttocks of his horse; seizes him by the middle; throws him on the earth; places himself in the saddle, and wheels around Otamus as he lay extended on the ground. All the amphitheatre cried out, "Victory to the white knight!" Otamus rises in a violent passion, and draws his sword; Zadig leaps from his horse with his sabre in his hand. Both of them are now on the ground, engaged in a new combat, where strength and agility triumph by turns. The plumes of their helmets, the studs of their bracelets, and the rings of their armor are driven to a great distance by the violence of a thousand furious blows. They strike with the point and the edge; to the right, to the left; on the head, on the breast; they retreat; they advance; they measure swords; they close; they seize each other; they bend like serpents; they attack like lions; and the fire every moment flashes from their blows. At last Zadig, having recovered his spirits, stops; makes a feint; leaps upon Otamus; throws him on the ground and disarms him; and Otamus cries out:

"It is thou alone, O white knight, that oughtest to reign over Babylon!"

The queen was now at the height of her joy. The knight in blue armor, and the knight in white, were conducted each to his own apartment, as well as all the others, according to the intention of the law. Mutes came to wait upon them, and to serve them at table. It may be easily supposed that the queen's little mute waited upon Zadig. They were then left to themselves to enjoy the sweets of repose till next morning, at which time the conqueror was to bring his device to the grand magi, to compare it with that which he had left, and make himself known.

Zadig, though deeply in love, was so much fatigued that he could not help sleeping. Itobad, who lay near him, never closed his eyes. He arose in the night, entered his apartment, took the white arms and the device of Zadig, and put his green armor in their place. At break of day, he went boldly to the grand magi, to declare that so great a man as he was conqueror. This was little expected; however, he was proclaimed while Zadig was still asleep. Astarte, surprised and filled with despair, returned to Babylon. The amphitheatre was almost empty when Zadig awoke; he sought for his arms but could find none but the green armor. With this he was obliged to cover himself, having nothing else near him. Astonished and enraged, he put it on in a furious passion and advanced in this equipage.

The people that still remained in the amphitheatre and the circus received him with hoots and hisses. They surrounded him, and insulted him to his face. Never did man suffer such cruel mortifications. He lost his patience; with his sabre he dispersed such of the populace as dared to affront him; but he knew not what course to take. He could not see the queen; he could not claim the white armor she had sent him without exposing her; and thus, while she was plunged in grief, he was filled with fury and distraction. He walked on the banks of the Euphrates, fully persuaded that his star had destined him to inevitable misery; and revolving in his mind all his misfortunes, from the adventure of the woman who hated one-eyed men, to that of his armor:

"This," said he, "is the consequence of my having slept too long. Had I slept less, I should now have been king of Babylon, and in possession of Astarte. Knowledge, virtue, and courage, have hitherto served only to make me miserable."

He then let fall some secret murmurings against providence, and was tempted to believe that the world was governed by a cruel destiny, which oppressed the good, and prospered knights in green armor.

XX

The Hermit

One of Zadig's greatest mortifications was his being obliged to wear that green armor which had exposed him to such contumelious treatment. A merchant happening to pass by, he sold it to him for a trifle, and bought a gown and a long bonnet. In this garb he proceeded along the banks of the Euphrates, filled with despair, and secretly accusing providence, which thus continued to persecute him with unremitting severity.

While he was thus sauntering along, he met a hermit whose white and venerable beard hung down to his girdle. He held a book in his hand, which he read with great attention. Zadig stopped, and made him a profound obeisance. The hermit returned the compliment with such a noble and engaging air, that Zadig had the curiosity to enter into conversation with him. He asked him what book it was that he had been reading.

"It is the book of destinies," said the hermit. "Wouldst thou choose to look into it?"

He put the book into the hands of Zadig, who, thoroughly versed as he was in several languages, could not decipher a single character of it. This only redoubled his curiosity.

"Thou seemest," said the good father, "to be in great distress."

"Alas!" replied Zadig, "I have but too much reason."

"If thou wilt permit me to accompany thee," resumed the old man, "perhaps I may be of some service to thee. I have often poured the balm of consolation into the bleeding heart of the unhappy."

Zadig felt himself inspired with respect for the dignity, the beard, and the book of the hermit. He found, in the course of the conversation, that he was possessed of superior degrees of knowledge. The hermit talked of fate, of justice, of morals, of the chief good, of human weakness, and of virtue and vice, with such a spirited and moving eloquence, that Zadig felt himself drawn toward him by an irresistible charm. He earnestly entreated the favor of his company till their return to Babylon.

"I ask the same favor of thee," said the old man. "Swear to me by Oromazes that, whatever I do, thou wilt not leave me for some days."

Zadig swore, and they set out together. In the evening the two travelers arrived at a superb castle. The hermit entreated a hospitable reception for himself and the young man who accompanied him. The porter, whom one might have mistaken for a great lord, introduced them with a kind of disdainful civility. He presented them to a principle domestic, who showed them his master's magnificent apartments. They were admitted to the lower end of the table, without being honored with the least mark of regard by the lord of the castle; but they were served, like the rest, with delicacy and profusion. They were then presented, in a golden basin adorned with emeralds and rubies, with water to wash their hands. At last they were conducted to bed in a beautiful apartment; and in the morning a domestic brought each of them a piece of gold, after which they took their leave and departed.

"The master of the house," said Zadig, as they were proceeding on the journey, "appears to be a generous man, though somewhat too proud. He nobly performs the duties of hospitality."

At that instant he observed that a kind of large pocket, which the hermit had, was filled and distended; and upon looking more narrowly, he found that it contained the golden basin adorned with precious stones, which the hermit had stolen. He durst not then take any notice of it; but he was filled with a strange surprise.

About noon the hermit came to the door of a paltry house, inhabited by a rich miser, and begged the favor of an hospitable reception for a few hours. An old servant, in a tattered garb, received them with a blunt and rude air, and led them into the stable, where he gave them some rotten olives, sour wine, and mouldy bread. The hermit ate and drank with as much seeming satisfaction as he had done the evening before, and then addressing himself to the old servant who watched them both to prevent them stealing anything, and had rudely pressed them to depart, he gave him the two pieces of gold he had received in the morning, and thanked him for his great civility.

"Pray," added he, "allow me to speak to thy master."

The servant, filled with astonishment, introduced the two travelers.

"Magnificent lord!" said the hermit, "I cannot but return thee my most humble thanks for the noble manner in which thou hast entertained us. Be pleased to accept of this golden basin as a small mark of my gratitude."

The miser started, and was ready to fall backwards; but the hermit, without giving him time to recover from his surprise, instantly departed with his young fellow traveler.

"Father," said Zadig, "what is the meaning of all this? Thou seemest to me to be entirely different from other men. Thou stealest a golden basin adorned with precious stones, from a lord who received thee magnificently, and givest it to a miser who treats thee with indignity."

"Son," replied the old man, "this magnificent lord, who receives strangers only from vanity and ostentation, will hereby be rendered more wise; and the miser will learn to practice the duties of hospitality. Be surprised at nothing, but follow me."

Zadig knew not as yet whether he was in company with the most foolish or the most prudent of mankind; but the hermit spoke with such an ascendency that Zadig, who was moreover bound by his oath, could not refuse to follow him.

In the evening they arrived at a house built with equal elegance and simplicity, where nothing savored either of prodigality or avarice. The master of it was a philosopher who had retired from the world, and who cultivated in peace the study of virtue and wisdom, without any of that rigid and morose severity so commonly found in men of his character. He had chosen to build this fine house in which he received strangers with a generosity free from ostentation. He went himself to meet the two travelers, whom he led into a commodious apartment, and desired them to repose themselves. Soon after he came and invited them to a decent and well ordered repast, during which he spoke with great judgment of the last revolutions in Babylon. He seemed to be strongly attached to the queen, and wished that Zadig had appeared in the lists to contend for the crown.

"But the people," added he, "do not deserve to have such a king as Zadig."

Zadig blushed and felt his griefs redoubled. They agreed, in the course of the conversation, that the things of this world did not always answer the wishes of the wise. The hermit maintained that the ways of providence were inscrutable; and that men were in the wrong to judge of a whole, of which they understood but the smallest part. They talked of the passions:

"Ah," said Zadig, "how fatal are their effects!"

"They are the winds," replied the hermit, "that swell the sails of the ship; it is true, they sometimes sink her, but without them she could not sail at all. The bile makes us sick and choleric; but without the bile we could not live. Everything in this world is dangerous, and yet everything in it is necessary."

The conversation turned on pleasure; and the hermit proved that it was a present bestowed by the deity.

"For," said he, "man cannot either give himself sensations or ideas: he receives all; and pain and pleasure proceed from a foreign cause as well as his being."

Zadig was surprised to see a man who had been guilty of such extravagant actions, capable of reasoning with so much judgment and propriety. At last, after a conversation equally entertaining and instructive, the host led back his two guests to their apartment, blessing heaven for having sent him two men possessed of so much wisdom and virtue. He offered them money with such an easy and noble air that it could not possibly give any offence. The hermit refused it, and said that he must now take his leave of him, as he proposed to set out for Babylon in the morning before it was light. Their parting was tender. Zadig especially felt himself filled with esteem and affection for a man of such an amiable character.

When he and the hermit were alone in their apartment they spent a long time in praising their host. At break of day the old man awakened his companion.

"We must now depart," said he; "but while all the family are still asleep, I will leave this man a mark of my esteem and affection."

So saying he took a candle and set fire to the house. Zadig, struck with horror, cried aloud, and endeavored to hinder him from committing such a barbarous action; but the hermit drew him away by a superior force, and the house was soon in flames. The hermit, who, with his companion, was already at a considerable distance, looked back to the conflagration with great tranquillity.

"Thanks be to God," said he, "the house of my dear host is entirely destroyed! Happy man!"

At these words Zadig was at once tempted to burst out in laughing, to reproach the reverend father, to beat him, and to run away. But he did none of all these; for still subdued by the powerful ascendancy of the hermit, he followed him, in spite of himself, to the next stage.

This was at the house of a charitable and virtuous widow, who had a nephew fourteen years of age, a handsome and promising youth, and her only hope. She performed the honors of the house as well as she could. Next day, she ordered her nephew to accompany the strangers to a bridge, which being lately broken down, was become extremely dangerous in passing. The young man walked before them with great alacrity. As they were crossing the bridge, the hermit said to the youth:

"Come, I must show my gratitude to thy aunt."

He then took him by the hair, and plunged him into the river. The boy sank, appeared again on the surface of the water, and was swallowed up by the current.

"O monster! O thou most wicked of mankind!" cried Zadig.

"Thou promised to behave with greater patience," said the hermit, interrupting him. "Know, that under the ruins of that house which providence hath set on fire, the master hath found an immense treasure: know, that this young man, whose life providence hath shortened, would have assassinated his aunt in the space of a year, and thee in that of two."

"Who told thee so, barbarian?" cried Zadig, "and though thou hadst read this event in thy book of destinies, art thou permitted to drown a youth who never did thee any harm?"

While the Babylonian was thus exclaiming, he observed that the old man had no longer a beard, and that his countenance assumed the features and complexion of youth. The hermit's habit disappeared, and four beautiful wings covered a majestic body resplendent with light.

"O sent of heaven! O divine angel!" cried Zadig, humbly prostrating himself on the ground. "Hast thou then descended from the empyrean to teach a weak mortal to submit to the eternal decrees of providence?"

"Men," said the angel Jesrad, "judge of all without knowing anything: and, of all men, thou best deservest to be enlightened."

Zadig begged to be permitted to speak:

"I distrust myself," said he, "but may I presume to ask the favor of thee to clear up one doubt that still remains in my mind? Would it not have been better to have corrected this youth, and made him virtuous, than to have drowned him?"

"Had he been virtuous," replied Jesrad, "and enjoyed a longer life, it would have been his fate to have been assassinated himself, together with the wife he would have married, and the child he would have had by her."

"But why," said Zadig, "is it necessary that there should be crimes and misfortunes, and that these misfortunes should fall on the good?"

"The wicked," replied Jesrad, "are always unhappy. They serve to prove and try the small number of the just that are scattered through the earth; and there is no evil that is not productive of some good."

"But," said Zadig, "suppose there was nothing but good and no evil at all."

"Then," replied Jesrad, "this earth would be another earth: the chain of events would be ranged in another order and directed by wisdom. But this other order, which would be perfect, can exist only in the eternal abode of the Supreme Being, to which no evil can approach. The Deity hath created millions of worlds, among which there is not one that resembles another. This immense variety is the effect of his immense power. There are not two leaves among the trees of the earth, nor two globes in the unlimited expanse of heaven, that are exactly similar: and all that thou seest on the little atom in which thou art born, ought to be, in its proper time and place, according to the immutable decrees of him who comprehends all. Men think that this child, who hath just perished, is fallen into the water by chance; and that it is by the same chance that this house is burned. But there is no such thing as chance.

All is either a trial, or a punishment, or a reward, or a foresight. Remember the fisherman, who thought himself the most wretched of mankind. Oromazes sent thee to change his fate. Cease then, frail mortal, to dispute against what thou oughtest to adore."

"But," said Zadig—

As he pronounced the word "But," the angel took his flight toward the tenth sphere. Zadig on his knees adored providence, and submitted. The angel cried to him from on high:

"Direct thy course toward Babylon."

XXI

The Enigmas

Zadig, entranced as it were, and like a man about whose head the thunder had burst, walked at random. He entered Babylon on the very day when those who had fought at the tournaments were assembled in the grand vestibule of the palace to explain the enigmas, and to answer the questions of the grand magi. All the knights were already present, except the knight in green armor. As soon as Zadig appeared in the city, the people crowded around him; every eye was fixed on him, every mouth blessed him, and every heart wished him the empire. The envious man saw him pass; he frowned and turned aside. The people conducted him to the place where the assembly was held. The queen, when informed of his arrival, became a prey to the most violent agitations of hope and fear. She was filled with anxiety and apprehension. She could not comprehend why Zadig was without arms, nor why Itobad wore the white armor.

When the knights who had fought were directed to appear in the assembly, Zadig said: "I have fought as well as the other knights, but another here wears my arms; and while I wait for the honor of proving the truth of my assertion, I demand the liberty of presenting myself to explain the enigmas.

The question was put to vote, and his reputation for probity was so well established, that they admitted him without scruple.

The first question proposed by the grand magi, was: "What, of all things in the world, is the longest and the shortest, the swiftest and the slowest, the most divisible and the most extended, the most neglected and the most regretted, without which nothing can be done, which devours all that is little, and enlivens all that is great?"

Itobad was to speak. He replied, that so great a man as he did not understand enigmas; and that it was sufficient for him to have conquered by his strength and valor. Some said that the meaning of the enigma was fortune; some, the earth; and others, the light. Zadig said that it was time.

"Nothing," added he, "is longer, since it is the measure of eternity. Nothing is shorter, since it is insufficient for the accomplishment of our projects. Nothing more slow to him that expects, nothing more rapid to him that enjoys. In greatness it extends to infinity, in smallness it is infinitely divisible. All men neglect it, all regret the loss of it; nothing can be done without it. It consigns to oblivion whatever is unworthy of being transmitted to posterity, and it immortalizes such actions as are truly great."

The assembly acknowledged that Zadig was in the right.

The next question was: "What is the thing which we receive without thanks, which we enjoy without knowing how, and which we lose without perceiving it?"

Every one gave his own explanation. Zadig alone guessed that it was life; and he explained all the other enigmas with the same facility. Itobad always said that nothing was more easy, and that he could have answered them with the same readiness, had he chosen to have given himself the trouble. Questions were then proposed on justice, on the sovereign good, and on the art of government. Zadig's answers were judged to be the most solid, and the people exclaimed:

"What a pity it is, that so great a genius should be so bad a knight!"

"Illustrious lords," said Zadig, "I have had the honor of conquering in the tournaments. It is to me that the white armor belongs. Lord Itobad took possession of it during my sleep. He probably thought it would fit him better than the green. I am now ready to prove in your presence, with my gown and sword, against all that beautiful white armor which he took from me, that it is I who have had the honor of conquering the brave Otamus."

Itobad accepted the challenge with the greatest confidence. He never doubted but that, armed as he was with a helmet, a cuirass, and brassarts, he would obtain an easy victory over a champion in a cap and a night-gown. Zadig drew his sword, saluting the queen, who looked at him with a mixture of fear and joy. Itobad drew his, without saluting any one. He rushed upon Zadig, like a man who had nothing to fear; he was ready to cleave him in two. Zadig knew how to ward off his blows, by opposing the strongest part of his sword to the weakest of that of his adversary, in such a manner that Itobad's sword was broken. Upon which Zadig, seizing his enemy by the waist, threw him on the ground; and fixing the point of his sword at the extremity of his breast-plate, exclaimed: "Suffer thyself to be disarmed, or thou art a dead man."

Itobad, greatly surprised at the disgrace that happened to such a man as he, was obliged to yield to Zadig, who took from him, with great composure, his magnificent helmet, his superb cuirass, his fine brassarts, his shining cuisses; clothed himself with them, and in this dress ran to throw himself at the feet of Astarte. Cador easily proved that the armor belonged to Zadig. He was acknowledged king by the unanimous consent of the whole nation, and especially by that of Astarte, who, after so many calamities, now tasted the exquisite pleasure of seeing her lover worthy, in the eyes of the world, to be her husband. Itobad went home to be called lord in his own house. Zadig was king, and was happy. He recollected what the angel Jesrad had said to him. He even remembered the grain of sand that became a diamond. He sent in search of the robber Arbogad, to whom he gave an honorable post in his army, promising to advance him to the first dignities, if he behaved like a true warrior; and threatening to hang him, if he followed the profession of a robber.

Setoc, with the fair Almona, was called from the heart of Arabia, and placed at the head of the commerce of Babylon. Cador was preferred and distinguished according to his great services. He was the friend of the king; and the king was then the only monarch on earth that had a friend. The little mute was not forgotten. A fine house was given to the fisherman; and Orcan was condemned to pay him a large sum of money, and to restore him his wife; but the fisherman, who had now become wise, took only the money.

The beautiful Semira could not be comforted for having believed that Zadig would be blind of an eye; nor did Azora cease to lament her attempt to cut off his nose: their griefs, however, he softened by his presents. The capricious beauty, Missouf, was left unnoticed. The envious man died of rage and shame. The empire enjoyed peace, glory, and plenty. This was the happiest age of the earth. It was governed by love and justice. The people blessed Zadig, and Zadig blessed heaven.

THE PRINCESS OF BABYLON

I

ROYAL CONTEST FOR THE HAND OF FORMOSANTA

THE aged Belus, king of Babylon, thought himself the first man upon earth; for all his courtiers told him so, and his historians proved it. We know that his palace and his park, situated at a few parafangs from Babylon, extended between the Euphrates and the Tigris, which washed those enchanted banks. His vast house, three thousand feet in front, almost reached the clouds. The platform was surrounded with a balustrade of white marble, fifty feet high, which supported colossal statues of all the kings and great men of the empire. This platform, composed of two rows of bricks, covered with a thick surface of lead from one extremity to the other, bore twelve feet of earth; and upon the earth were raised groves of olive, orange, citron, palm, cocoa, and cinnamon trees, and stock gillyflowers, which formed alleys that the rays of the sun could not penetrate.

The waters of the Euphrates running, by the assistance of pumps, in a hundred canals, formed cascades of six thousand feet in length in the park, and a hundred thousand *jets d'eau*, whose height was scarce perceptible. They afterward flowed into the Euphrates, from whence they came. The gardens of Semiramis, which astonished Asia several ages after, were only a feeble imitation of these ancient prodigies; for in the time of Semiramis, every thing began to degenerate amongst men and women.

But what was more admirable in Babylon, and eclipsed every thing else, was the only daughter of the king, named Formosanta. It was from her pictures and statues, that in succeeding times Praxiteles sculptured his Aphrodita, and the Venus of Medicis. Heavens! what a difference between the original and the copies! so that king Belus was prouder of his daughter than of his kingdom. She was eighteen years old. It was necessary she should have a husband worthy of her; but where was he to be found? An ancient oracle had ordained that Formosanta could not belong to any but him who could bend the bow of Nimrod.

This Nimrod, "a mighty hunter before the Lord," had left a bow seventeen Babylonian feet in length, made of ebony, harder than the iron of mount Caucasus, which is wrought in the forges of Derbent; and no mortal since Nimrod could bend this astonishing bow.

It was again said, "that the arm which should bend this bow would kill the most terrible and ferocious lion that should be let loose in the Circus of Babylon." This was not all. The bender of the bow, and the conqueror of the lion, should overthrow all his rivals; but he was above all things to be very sagacious, the most magnificent and most virtuous of men, and possess the greatest curiosity in the whole universe.

Three kings appeared, who were bold enough to claim Formosanta. Pharaoh of Egypt, the Shah of India, and the great Khan of the Scythians. Belus appointed the day and place of combat, which was to be at the extremity of his park, in the vast expanse surrounded by the joint waters of the Euphrates and the Tigris. Round the lists a marble amphitheatre was erected, which might contain five hundred thousand spectators. Opposite the amphitheatre was placed the king's throne. He was to appear with Formosanta, accompanied by the whole court; and on the right and left between the throne and the amphitheatre, there were other thrones and seats for the three kings, and for all the other sovereigns who were desirous to be present at this august ceremony.

The king of Egypt arrived the first, mounted upon the bull Apis, and holding in his hand the cithern of Isis. He was followed by two thousand priests, clad in linen vestments whiter than snow, two thousand eunuchs, two thousand magicians, and two thousand warriors.

The king of India came soon after in a car drawn by twelve elephants. He had a train still more numerous and more brilliant than Pharaoh of Egypt.

The last who appeared was the king of the Scythians. He had none with him but chosen warriors, armed with bows and arrows. He was mounted upon a superb tiger, which he had tamed, and which was as tall as any of the finest Persian horses. The majestic and important mien of this king effaced the appearance of his rivals; his naked arms, as nervous as they were white, seemed already to bend the bow of Nimrod.

These three lovers immediately prostrated themselves before Belus and Formosanta. The king of Egypt presented the princess with two of the finest crocodiles of the Nile, two sea horses, two zebras, two Egyptian rats, and two mummies, with the books of the great Hermes, which he judged to be the scarcest things upon earth.

The king of India offered her a hundred elephants, each bearing a wooden gilt tower, and laid at her feet the *vedam*, written by the hand of Xaca himself.

The king of the Scythians, who could neither write nor read, presented a hundred warlike horses with black fox skin housings.

The princess appeared with a downcast look before her lovers, and reclined herself with such a grace as was at once modest and noble.

Belus ordered the kings to be conducted to the thrones that were prepared for them. "Would I had three daughters," said he to them, "I should make six people this day happy!" He then made the competitors cast lots which should try Nimrod's bow first. Their names inscribed were put into a golden casque. That of the Egyptian king came out first, then the name of the king of India appeared. The king of Scythia, viewing the bow and his rivals, did not complain at being the third.

Whilst these brilliant trials were preparing, twenty thousand pages and twenty thousand youthful maidens distributed, without any disorder, refreshments to the spectators between the rows of seats. Every one acknowledged that the gods had instituted kings for no other cause than every day to give festivals, upon condition they should be diversified—that life is too short for any other purpose—that lawsuits, intrigues, wars, the altercations of theologists, which consume human life, are horrible and absurd—that man is born only for happiness—that he would not passionately and incessantly pursue pleasure, were he not designed for it—that the essence of human nature is to enjoy ourselves, and all the rest is folly. This excellent moral was never controverted but by facts.

Whilst preparations were making for determining the fate of Formosanta, a young stranger, mounted upon an unicorn, accompanied by his valet, mounted on a like animal, and bearing upon his hand a large bird, appeared at the barrier. The guards were surprised to observe in this equipage, a figure that had an air of divinity. He had, as hath been since related, the face of Adonis upon the body of Hercules; it was majesty accompanied by the graces. His black eye-brows and flowing fair tresses wore a mixture of beauty unknown at Babylon, and charmed all observers. The whole amphitheatre rose up, the better to view the stranger. All the ladies of the court viewed him with looks of astonishment. Formosanta herself, who had hitherto kept her eyes fixed upon the ground, raised them and blushed. The three kings turned pale. The spectators, in comparing Formosanta with the stranger, cried out, "There is no other in the world, but this young man, who can be so handsome as the princess."

The ushers, struck with astonishment, asked him if he was a king? The stranger replied that he had not that honor, but that he had come from a distant country, excited by curiosity, to see if there were any king worthy of Formosanta. He was introduced into the first row of the amphitheatre, with his valet, his two unicorns, and his bird. He saluted, with great respect, Belus, his daughter, the three kings, and all the assembly. He then took his seat, not without blushing. His two unicorns lay down at his feet; his bird perched upon his shoulder; and his valet, who carried a little bag, placed himself by his side.

The trials began. The bow of Nimrod was taken out of its golden case. The first master of the ceremonies, followed by fifty pages, and preceded by twenty trumpets, presented it to the king of Egypt, who made his priests bless it; and supporting it upon the head of the bull Apis, he did not question his gaining this first victory. He dismounted, and came into the middle of the circus. He tries, exerts all his strength, and makes such ridiculous contortions, that the whole amphitheatre re-echoes with laughter, and Formosanta herself could not help smiling.

His high almoner approached him:

"Let your majesty give up this idle honor, which depends entirely upon the nerves and muscles. You will triumph in every thing else. You will conquer the lion, as you are possessed of the favor of Osiris. The princess of Babylon is to belong to the prince who is most sagacious, and you have solved enigmas. She is to wed the most virtuous: you are such, as you have been educated by the priests of Egypt. The most generous is to marry her, and you have presented her with two of the handsomest crocodiles, and two of the finest rats in all the Delta. You are possessed of the bull Apis, and the books of Hermes, which are the scarcest things in the universe. No one can hope to dispute Formosanta with you."

"You are in the right," said the king of Egypt, and resumed his throne.

The bow was then put in the hands of the king of India. It blistered his hands for a fortnight; but he consoled himself in presuming that the Scythian king would not be more fortunate than himself.

The Scythian handled the bow in his turn. He united skill with strength. The bow seemed to have some elasticity in his hands. He bent it a little, but he could not bring it near a curve. The spectators, who had been prejudiced in his favor by his agreeable aspect, lamented his ill success, and concluded that the beautiful princess would never be married.

The unknown youth leaped into the arena and addressing himself to the king of Scythia said:

"Your majesty need not be surprised at not having entirely succeeded. These ebony bows are made in my country. There is a peculiar method in using them. Your merit is greater in having bent it, than if I were to curve it."

He then took an arrow and, placing it upon the string, bent the bow of Nimrod, and shot the arrow beyond the gates. A million hands at once applauded the prodigy. Babylon re-echoed with acclamations; and all the ladies agreed it was fortunate for so handsome a youth to be so strong.

He then took out of his pocket a small ivory tablet, wrote upon it with a golden pencil, fixed the tablet to the bow, and then presented it to the princess with such a grace as charmed every spectator. He then modestly returned to his place between his bird and his valet. All Babylon was in astonishment; the three kings were confounded; whilst the stranger did not seem to pay the least attention to what had happened.

Formosanta was still more surprised to read upon the ivory tablet, tied to the bow, these lines, written in the best Chaldean:

> L'arc de Nembrod est celui de la guerre;
> L'arc de l'amour est celui du bonheur;
> Vous le portez. Par vous ce Dieu vainqueur
> Est devenu le maitre de la terre.
> Trois Rois puissants, trois rivaux aujourd'hui,
> Osent pretendre a l'honneur de vous plaire.
> Je ne sais pas qui votre cœur prefere,
> Mais l'univers sera jaloux de lui.

> [The bow of Nimrod is that of war;
> The bow of love is that of happiness—
> Which you possess. Through you this conquering God
> Has become master of the earth.
> Three powerful kings—three rivals now
> Dare aspire to the honor of pleasing you.
> I know not whom your heart may prefer,
> But the universe will be jealous of him.]

This little madrigal did not displease the princess; but it was criticised by some of the lords of the ancient court, who said that, in former times, Belus would have been compared to the sun, and Formosanta to the moon; his neck to a tower, and her breast to a bushel of wheat. They said the stranger had no sort of imagination, and that he had lost sight of the rules of true poetry, but all the ladies thought the verses very gallant. They were astonished that a man who handled a bow so well should have so much wit. The lady of honor to the princess said to her:

"Madam, what great talents are here entirely lost? What benefit will this young man derive from his wit, and his skill with Nimrod's bow?"

"Being admired!" said Formosanta.

"Ah!" said the lady, "one more madrigal, and he might well be beloved."

The king of Babylon, having consulted his sages, declared that though none of these kings could bend the bow of Nimrod, yet, nevertheless, his daughter was to be married, and that she should belong to him who could conquer the great lion, which was purposely kept in training in his great menagerie.

The king of Egypt, upon whose education all the wisdom of Egypt had been exhausted, judged it very ridiculous to expose a king to the ferocity of wild beasts in order to be married. He acknowledged that he considered the possession of Formosanta of inestimable value; but he believed that if the lion should strangle him, he could never wed this fair Babylonian. The king of India held similar views to the king of Egypt. They both concluded that the king of Babylon was laughing at them, and that they should send for armies to punish him—that they had many subjects who would think themselves highly honored to die in the service of their masters, without it costing them a single hair of their sacred heads—that they could easily dethrone the king of Babylon, and then they would draw lots for the fair Formosanta.

This agreement being made, the two kings sent each an express into his respective country, with orders to assemble three hundred thousand men to carry off Formosanta.

However, the king of Scythia descended alone into the arena, scimitar in hand. He was not distractedly enamored with Formosanta's charms. Glory till then had been his only passion, and it had led him to Babylon. He was willing to show that if the kings of India and Egypt were so prudent as not to tilt with lions, he was courageous enough not to decline the combat, and he would repair the honor of diadems. His uncommon valor would not even allow him to avail himself of the assistance of his tiger. He advanced singly, slightly armed with a shell casque ornamented with gold, and shaded with three horses' tails as white as snow.

One of the most enormous and ferocious lions that fed upon the Antilibanian mountains was let loose upon him. His tremendous paws appeared capable of tearing the three kings to pieces at once, and his gullet to devour them. The two proud champions fled with the utmost precipitancy and in the most rapid manner to each other. The courageous Scythian plunged his sword into the lion's mouth; but the point, meeting with one of those thick teeth that nothing can penetrate, was broken; and the monster of the woods, more furious from his wound, had already impressed his fearful claws into the monarch's sides.

The unknown youth, touched with the peril of so brave a prince, leaped into the arena swift as lightning, and cut off the lion's head with as much dexterity as we have lately seen, in our carousals, youthful knights knock off the heads of black images.

Then drawing out a small box, he presented it to the Scythian king, saying to him:

"Your majesty will here find the genuine dittany, which grows in my coun- try. Your glorious wounds will be healed in a moment. Accident alone pre- vented your triumph over the lion. Your valor is not the less to be admired."

The Scythian king, animated more with gratitude than jealousy, thanked his benefactor; and, after having tenderly embraced him, returned to his seat to apply the dittany to his wounds.

The stranger gave the lion's head to his valet, who, having washed it at the great fountain which was beneath the amphitheatre, and drained all the blood, took an iron instrument out of his little bag, with which having drawn the lion's forty teeth, he supplied their place with forty diamonds of equal size.

His master, with his usual modesty, returned to his place; he gave the lion's head to his bird:—"Beauteous bird," said he, "carry this small homage, and lay it at the feet of Formosanta."

The bird winged its way with the dreadful triumph in one of its talons, and presented it to the princess; bending with humility his neck, and crouching before her. The sparkling diamonds dazzled the eyes of every beholder. Such magnificence was unknown even in superb Babylon. The emerald, the topaz, the sapphire, and the pyrope, were as yet considered as the most precious ornaments. Belus and the whole court were struck with admiration. The bird which presented this present surprised them still more. It was of the size of an eagle, but its eyes were as soft and tender as those of the eagle are fierce and threatening. Its bill was rose color, and seemed somewhat to resemble Formosanta's handsome mouth. Its neck represented all the colors of Iris, but still more striking and brilliant. Gold, in a thousand shades, glittered upon its plumage. Its feet resembled a mixture of silver and purple. And the tails of those beautiful birds, which have since drawn Juno's car, did not equal the splendor of this incomparable bird.

The attention, curiosity, astonishment, and ecstasy of the whole court were divided between the jewels and the bird. It had perched upon the balustrade between Belus and his daughter Formosanta. She petted it, caressed it, and kissed it. It seemed to receive her attentions with a mixture of pleasure and respect. When the princess gave the bird a kiss, it returned the embrace, and then looked upon her with languishing eyes. She gave it biscuits and pistachios, which it received in its purple-silvered claw, and carried to its bill with in- expressible grace.

Belus, who had attentively considered the diamonds, concluded that scarce any one of his provinces could repay so valuable a present. He ordered that more magnificent gifts should be prepared for the stranger than those des- tined for the three monarchs. "This young man," said he, "is doubtless son to the emperor of China; or of that part of the world called Europe, which I have heard spoken of; or of Africa, which is said to be in the vicinity of the kingdom of Egypt."

He immediately sent his first equerry to compliment the stranger, and ask him whether he was himself the sovereign, or son to the sovereign of one of those empires; and why, being possessed of such surprising treasures, he had come with nothing but his valet and a little bag?

Whilst the equerry advanced toward the amphitheatre to execute his commission, another valet arrived upon an unicorn. This valet, addressing himself to the young man, said: "Ormar, your father is approaching the end of his life: I am come to acquaint you with it."

The stranger raised his eyes to heaven, whilst tears streamed from them, and answered only by saying, "*Let us depart.*"

The equerry, after having paid Belus's compliments to the conqueror of the lion, to the giver of the forty diamonds, and to the master of the beautiful bird, asked the valet, "Of what kingdom was the father of this young hero sovereign?"

The valet replied:

"His father is an old shepherd, who is much beloved in his district."

During this conversation, the stranger had already mounted his unicorn. He said to the equerry:

"My lord, vouchsafe to prostrate me at the feet of King Belus and his daughter. I must entreat her to take particular care of the bird I leave with her, as it is a nonpareil like herself."

In uttering these last words he set off, and flew like lightning. The two valets followed him, and in an instant he was out of sight.

Formosanta could not refrain from shrieking. The bird, turning toward the amphitheatre where his master had been seated, seemed greatly afflicted to find him gone; then viewing steadfastly the princess, and gently rubbing her beautiful hand with his bill, he seemed to devote himself to her service.

Belus, more astonished than ever, hearing that this very extraordinary young man was the son of a shepherd, could not believe it. He dispatched messengers after him; but they soon returned with the information, that the three unicorns, upon which these men were mounted, could not be overtaken; and that, according to the rate they went, they must go a hundred leagues a day.

Every one reasoned upon this strange adventure, and wearied themselves with conjectures. How can the son of a shepherd make a present of forty large diamonds? How comes it that he is mounted upon an unicorn? This bewildered them, and Formosanta, whilst she caressed her bird, was sunk into a profound reverie.

II

THE KING OF BABYLON CONVENES HIS COUNCIL AND CONSULTS THE ORACLE

PRINCESS ALDEA, Formosanta's cousin-german, who was very well shaped, and almost as handsome as the king's daughter, said to her:

"Cousin, I know not whether this demi-god be the son of a shepherd, but methinks he has fulfilled all the conditions stipulated for your marriage. He has bent Nimrod's bow; he has conquered the lion; he has a good share of sense, having written for you extempore a very pretty madrigal. After having presented you with forty large diamonds, you cannot deny that he is the most generous of men. In his bird he possessed the most curious thing upon earth. His virtue cannot be equaled, since he departed without hesitation as soon as he learned his father was ill, though he might have remained and enjoyed the pleasure of your society. The oracle is fulfilled in every particular, except that wherein he is to overcome his rivals. But he has done more; he has saved the life of the only competitor he had to fear; and when the object is to surpass the other two, I believe you cannot doubt but that he will easily succeed."

"All that you say is very true," replied Formosanta: "but is it possible that the greatest of men, and perhaps the most amiable too, should be the son of a shepherd?"

The lady of honor, joining in the conversation, said that the title of shepherd was frequently given to kings—that they were called shepherds because they attended very closely to their flocks—that this was doubtless a piece of ill-timed pleasantry in his valet—that this young hero had not come so badly equipped, but to show how much his personal merit alone was above the fastidious parade of kings. The princess made no answer, but in giving her bird a thousand tender kisses.

A great festival was nevertheless prepared for the three kings, and for all the princes who had come to the feast. The king's daughter and niece were to do the honors. The king distributed presents worthy the magnificence of Babylon. Belus, during the time the repast was being served, assembled his council to discuss the marriage of the beautiful Formosanta, and this is the way he delivered himself as a great politician:

"I am old: I know not what is best to do with my daughter, or upon whom to bestow her. He who deserves her is nothing but a mean shepherd. The kings of India and Egypt are cowards. The king of the Scythians would be very agreeable to me, but he has not performed any one of the conditions imposed. I will again consult the oracle. In the meantime, deliberate among you, and we will conclude agreeably to what the oracle says; for a king should follow nothing but the dictates of the immortal gods."

He then repaired to the temple: the oracle answered in few words according to custom: *Thy daughter shall not be married until she hath traversed the globe.* In astonishment, Belus returned to the council, and related this answer.

All the ministers had a profound respect for oracles. They therefore all agreed, or at least appeared to agree, that they were the foundation of religion —that reason should be mute before them—that it was by their means that kings reigned over their people—that without oracles there would be neither virtue nor repose upon earth.

At length, after having testified the most profound veneration for them, they almost all concluded that this oracle was impertinent, and should not be obeyed—that nothing could be more indecent for a young woman, and particularly the daughter of the great king of Babylon, than to run about, without any particular destination—that this was the most certain method to prevent her being married, or else engage her in a clandestine, shameful, and ridiculous union—that, in a word, this oracle had not common sense.

The youngest of the ministers, named Onadase, who had more sense than the rest, said that the oracle doubtless meant some pilgrimage of devotion, and offered to be the princess's guide. The council approved of his opinion, but every one was for being her equerry. The king determined that the princess might go three hundred parasangs upon the road to Arabia, to the temple whose saint had the reputation of procuring young women happy marriages, and that the dean of the council should accompany her. After this determination they went to supper.

III

Royal Festival Given in Honor of the Kingly Visitors. The Bird Converses Eloquently with Formosanta

In the centre of the gardens, between two cascades, an oval saloon three hundred feet in diameter was erected, whose azure roof, intersected with golden stars, represented all the constellations and planets, each in its proper station; and this ceiling turned about, as well as the canopy, by machines as invisible as those which direct the celestial spheres. A hundred thousand flambeaux, inclosed in rich crystal cylinders, illuminated the gardens and the dining-hall. A buffet, with steps, contained twenty thousand vases and golden dishes; and opposite the buffet, upon other steps, were seated a great number of musicians. Two other amphitheatres were decked out; the one with the fruits of each season, the other with crystal decanters, that sparkled with the choicest wines.

The guests took their seats round a table divided into compartments that resembled flowers and fruits, all in precious stones. The beautiful Formosanta was placed between the kings of India and Egypt—the amiable Aldea next the king of Scythia. There were about thirty princes, and each was seated next one of the handsomest ladies of the court. The king of Babylon, who was in the middle, opposite his daughter, seemed divided between the chagrin of being yet unable to effect her marriage, and the pleasure of still beholding her. Formosanta asked leave to place her bird upon the table next her; the king approved of it.

The music, which continued during the repast, furnished every prince with an opportunity of conversing with his female neighbor. The festival was as agreeable as it was magnificent. A ragout was served before Formosanta, which her father was very fond of. The princess said it should be carried to his majesty. The bird immediately took hold of it, and carried it in a miraculous manner to the king. Never was any thing more astonishing witnessed. Belus caressed it as much as his daughter had done. The bird afterward took its flight to return to her. It displayed, in flying, so fine a tail, and its extended wings set forth such a variety of brilliant colors—the gold of its plumage made such a dazzling eclat, that all eyes were fixed upon it. All the musicians were struck motionless, and their instruments afforded harmony no longer. None ate, no one spoke, nothing but a buzzing of admiration was to be heard. The princess of Babylon kissed it during the whole supper, without considering whether there were any kings in the world. Those of India and Egypt felt their spite and indignation rekindle with double force, and they resolved speedily to set their three hundred thousand men in motion to obtain revenge.

As for the king of Scythia, he was engaged in entertaining the beautiful Aldea. His haughty soul despising, without malice, Formosanta's inattention, had conceived for her more indifference than resentment. "She is handsome," said he, "I acknowledge; but she appears to me one of those women who are entirely taken up with their own beauty, and who fancy that mankind are greatly obliged to them when they deign to appear in public. I should prefer an ugly complaisant woman, that exhibited some amiability, to that beautiful statue. You have, madam, as many charms as she possesses, and you, at least, condescend to converse with strangers. I acknowledge to you with the sincerity of a Scythian, that I prefer you to your cousin."

He was, however, mistaken in regard to the character of Formosanta. She was not so disdainful as she appeared. But his compliments were very well received by the princess Aldea. Their conversation became very interesting. They were well contented, and already certain of one another before they left the table. After supper the guests walked in the groves. The king of Scythia and Aldea did not fail to seek for a place of retreat. Aldea, who was sincerity itself thus declared herself to the prince:

"I do not hate my cousin, though she be handsomer than myself, and is destined for the throne of Babylon. The honor of pleasing you may very well stand in the stead of charms. I prefer Scythia with you, to the crown of Babylon without you. But this crown belongs to me by right, if there be any right in the world; for I am of the elder branch of the Nimrod family, and Formosanta is only of the younger. Her grandfather dethroned mine, and put him to death."

"Such, then, are the rights of inheritance in the royal house of Babylon!" said the Scythian. "What was your grandfather's name?"

"He was called Aldea, like me. My father bore the same name. He was banished to the extremity of the empire with my mother, and Belus, after their death, having nothing to fear from me, was willing to bring me up with his daughter. But he has resolved that I shall never marry."

"I will avenge the cause of your grandfather—of your father—and also your own cause," said the king of Scythia. "I am responsible for your being married. I will carry you off the day after to-morrow by daybreak—for we must dine to-morrow with the king of Babylon—and I will return and support your rights with three hundred thousand men."

"I agree to it," said the beauteous Aldea: and, after having mutually pledged their words of honor, they separated.

The incomparable Formosanta, before retiring to rest, had ordered a small orange tree, in a silver case, to be placed by the side of her bed, that her bird might perch upon it. Her curtains had long been drawn, but she was not in the least disposed to sleep. Her heart was agitated, and her imagination excited. The charming stranger was ever in her thoughts. She fancied she saw him shooting an arrow with Nimrod's bow. She contemplated him in the act of cutting off the lion's head. She repeated his madrigal. At length, she saw him retiring from the crowd upon his unicorn. Tears, sighs, and lamentations overwhelmed her at this reflection. At intervals, she cried out: "Shall I then never see him more? Will he never return?"

"He will surely return," replied the bird from the top of the orange tree. "Can one have seen you once, and not desire to see you again?"

"Heavens! eternal powers! my bird speaks the purest Chaldean." In uttering these words she drew back the curtain, put out her hand to him, and knelt upon her bed, saying:

"Art thou a god descended upon earth? Art thou the great Oromasdes concealed under this beautiful plumage? If thou are, restore me this charming young man."

"I am nothing but a winged animal," replied the bird; "but I was born at the time when all animals still spoke; when birds, serpents, asses, horses, and griffins conversed familiarly with man. I would not speak before company, lest your ladies of honor should have taken me for a sorcerer. I would not discover myself to any but you."

Formosanta was speechless, bewildered, and intoxicated with so many wonders. Desirous of putting a hundred questions to him at once, she at length asked him how old he was.

"Only twenty-seven thousand nine hundred years and six months. I date my age from the little revolution of the equinoxes, and which is accomplished in about twenty-eight thousand of your years. There are revolutions of a much greater extent, so are there beings much older than me. It is twenty-two thousand years since I learnt Chaldean in one of my travels. I have always had a very great taste for the Chaldean language, but my brethren, the other animals, have renounced speaking in your climate."

"And why so, my divine bird?"

"Alas! because men have accustomed themselves to eat us, instead of conversing and instructing themselves with us. Barbarians! should they not have been convinced, that having the same organs with them, the same sentiments, the same wants, the same desires, we have also what is called a soul, the same as themselves—that we are their brothers, and that none should be dressed and eaten but the wicked? We are so far your brothers, that the Supreme Being, the Omnipotent and Eternal Being, having made a compact with men, expressly comprehended us in the treaty. He forbade you to nourish yourselves with our blood, and we to suck yours.

"The fables of your ancient Locman, translated into so many languages, will be a testimony eternally subsisting of the happy commerce you formerly carried on with us. They all begin with these words: 'In the time when beasts spoke.' It is true, there are many families among you who keep up an incessant conversation with their dogs; but the dogs have resolved not to answer, since they have been compelled by whipping to go a hunting, and become accomplices in the murder of our ancient and common friends, stags, deers, hares, and partridges.

"You still have some ancient poems in which horses speak, and your coachmen daily address them in words; but in so barbarous a manner, and in uttering such infamous expressions, that horses, though formerly entertaining so great a kindness for you, now detest you.

"The country which is the residence of your charming stranger, the most perfect of men, is the only one in which your species has continued to love ours, and to converse with us; and this is the only country in the world where men are just."

"And where is the country of my dear incognito? What is the name of his empire? For I will no more believe he is a shepherd than that you are a bat."

"His country is that of the Gangarids, a wise, virtuous, and invincible people, who inhabit the eastern shore of the Ganges. The name of my friend is Amazan. He is no king; and I know not whether he would so humble himself as to be one. He has too great a love for his fellow countrymen. He is a shepherd like them. But do not imagine that those shepherds resemble yours; who, covered with rags and tatters, watch their sheep, who are better clad than themselves; who groan under the burden of poverty, and who pay to an extortioner half the miserable stipend of wages which they receive from their masters. The Gangaridian shepherds are all born equal, and own the innumerable herds which cover their vast fields and subsist on the abundant verdure. These flocks are never killed. It is a horrid crime, in that favored country, to kill and eat a fellow creature. Their wool is finer and more brilliant than the finest silk, and constitutes the greatest traffic of the East. Besides, the land of the Gangarids produces all that can flatter the desires of man. Those large diamonds that Amazan had the honor of presenting you with, are from a mine that belongs to him. An unicorn, on which you saw him mounted, is the usual animal the Gangarids ride upon. It is the finest, the proudest, most terrible, and at the same time most gentle animal that ornaments the earth. A hundred Gangarids with as many unicorns would be sufficient to disperse innumerable armies. Two centuries ago, a king of India was mad enough to attempt to conquer this nation. He appeared, followed by ten thousand elephants and a million of warriors. The unicorns pierced the elephants, just as I have seen upon your table beads pierced in golden brochets. The warriors fell under the sabres of the Gangarids like crops of rice mowed by the people of the East. The king was taken prisoner, with upwards of six thousand men. He was bathed in the salutary water of the Ganges, and followed the regimen of the country, which consists only of vegetables, of which nature hath there been amazingly liberal to nourish every breathing creature. Men who are fed with carnivorous aliments, and drenched with spirituous liquors, have a sharp adust blood, which turns their brains a hundred different ways. Their chief rage is a fury to spill their brothers' blood, and, laying waste fertile plains, to reign over churchyards. Six full months were taken up in curing the king of India of his disorder. When the physicians judged that his pulse had become natural, they certified this to the council of the Gangarids. The council then followed the advice of the unicorns and humanely sent back the king of India, his silly court, and impotent warriors, to their own country. This lesson made them wise, and from that time the Indians respected the Gangarids; as ignorant men, willing to be instructed, revere the philosophers they cannot equal."

"Apropos, my dear bird," said the princess to him, "do the Gangarids profess any religion? Have they one?"

"Yes, we meet to return thanks to God on the days of the full moon; the men in a great temple made of cedar, and the women in another, to prevent their devotion being diverted. All the birds assemble in a grove, and the quadrupeds on a fine down. We thank God for all the benefits he had bestowed upon us. We have in particular some parrots *that preach wonderfully well.*

"Such is the country of my dear Amazan; there I reside. My friendship for him is as great as the love with which he has inspired you. If you will credit me, we will set out together, and you shall pay him a visit."

"Really, my dear bird, this is a very pretty invitation of yours," replied the princess smiling, and who flamed with desire to undertake the journey, but did not dare say so.

"I serve my friend," said the bird; "and, after the happiness of loving you, the greatest pleasure is to assist you."

Formosanta was quite fascinated. She fancied herself transported from earth. All she had seen that day, all she then saw, all she heard, and particularly what she felt in her heart, so ravished her as far to surpass what those fortunate Mussulmans now feel, who, disencumbered from their terrestrial ties, find themselves in the ninth heaven in the arms of their Houris, surrounded and penetrated with glory and celestial felicity.

IV

THE BEAUTIFUL BIRD IS KILLED BY THE KING OF EGYPT. FORMOSANTA
BEGINS A JOURNEY. ALDEA ELOPES WITH THE KING OF SCYTHIA

FORMOSANTA passed the whole night in speaking of Amazan. She no longer called him any thing but her shepherd; and from this time it was that the names of shepherd and lover were indiscriminately used throughout every nation.

Sometimes she asked the bird whether Amazan had had any other mistresses. It answered, "No," and she was at the summit of felicity. Sometimes she asked how he passed his life; and she, with transport, learned that it was employed in doing good, in cultivating arts, in penetrating into the secrets of nature, and improving himself. She at times wanted to know if the soul of her lover was of the same nature as that of her bird; how it happened that it had lived twenty thousand years, when her lover was not above eighteen or nineteen She put a hundred such questions, to which the bird replied with such discretion as excited her curiosity. At length sleep closed her eyes, and yielded up Formosanta to the sweet delusion of dreams sent by the gods, which sometimes surpass reality itself, and which all the philosophy of the Chaldeans can scarce explain.

Formosanta did not awaken till very late. The day was far advanced when the king, her father, entered her chamber. The bird received his majesty with respectful politeness, went before him, fluttered his wings, stretched his neck, and then replaced himself upon his orange tree. The king seated himself upon his daughter's bed, whose dreams had made her still more beautiful. His large beard approached her lovely face, and after having embraced her, he spoke to her in these words:

"My dear daughter, you could not yesterday find a husband agreeable to my wishes; you nevertheless must marry; the prosperity of my empire requires it. I have consulted the oracle, which you know never errs, and which directs all my conduct. His commands are, that you should traverse the globe. You must therefore begin your journey."

"Ah! doubtless to the Gangarids," said the princess; and in uttering these words, which escaped her, she was sensible of her indiscretion. The king, who was utterly ignorant of geography, asked her what she meant by the Gangarids. She easily diverted the question. The king told her she must go on a pilgrimage, that he had appointed the persons who were to attend her— the dean of the counsellors of state, the high almoner, a lady of honor, a physician, an apothecary, her bird, and all necessary domestics.

Formosanta, who had never been out of her father's palace, and who, till the arrival of the three kings and Amazan, had led a very insipid life, according to the *etiquette* of rank and the parade of pleasure, was charmed at setting out upon a pilgrimage. "Who knows," said she, whispering to her heart, "if the gods may not inspire Amazan with the like desire of going to the same chapel, and I may have the happiness of again seeing the pilgrim?" She affectionately thanked her father, saying she had always entertained a secret devotion for the saint she was going to visit.

Belus gave an excellent dinner to his guests, who were all men. They formed a very ill assorted company—kings, ministers, princes, pontiffs—all jealous of each other; all weighing their words, and equally embarrassed with their neighbors and themselves. The repast was very gloomy, though they drank pretty freely. The princesses remained in their apartments, each meditating upon her respective journey. They dined at their little cover. Formosanta afterward walked in the gardens with her dear bird, which, to amuse her, flew from tree to tree, displaying his superb tail and divine plumage.

The king of Egypt, who was heated with wine, not to say drunk, asked one of his pages for a bow and arrow. The prince was, in truth, the most unskillful archer in his whole kingdom. When he shot at a mark, the place of the greatest safety was generally the spot he aimed at. But the beautiful bird, flying as swiftly as the arrow, seemed to court it, and fell bleeding in the arms of Formosanta. The Egyptian, bursting into a foolish laugh, retired to his place. The princess rent the skies with her moans, melted into tears, tore her hair, and beat her breast. The dying bird said to her, in a low voice: "Burn me, and fail not to carry my ashes to the east of the ancient city of Aden or Eden, and expose them to the sun upon a little pile of cloves and cinnamon." After having uttered these words it expired. Formosanta was for a long time in a swoon, and revived again only to burst into sighs and groans. Her father, partaking of her grief, and imprecating the king of Egypt, did not doubt but this accident foretold some fatal event. He immediately went to consult the oracle, which replied: *A mixture of everything—life and death, infidelity and constancy, loss and gain, calamities and good fortune.* Neither he nor his council could comprehend any meaning in this reply; but, at length, he was satisfied with having fulfilled the duties of devotion.

His daughter was bathed in tears, whilst he consulted the oracle. She paid the funeral obsequies to the bird, which it had directed, and resolved to carry its remains into Arabia at the risk of her life. It was burned in incombustible flax, with the orange tree on which it used to perch. She gathered up the ashes in a little golden vase, set with rubies, and the diamonds taken from the lion's mouth. Oh! that she could, instead of fulfilling this melancholy duty, have burned alive the detestable king of Egypt! This was her sole wish. She, in spite, put to death the two crocodiles, his two sea horses, his two zebras, his two rats, and had his two mummies thrown into the Euphrates. Had she possessed his bull Apis, she would not have spared him.

The king of Egypt, enraged at this affront, set out immediately to forward his three hundred thousand men. The king of India, seeing his ally depart, set off also on the same day, with a firm intention of joining his three hundred thousand Indians to the Egyptian army. The king of Scythia decamped in the night with the princess Aldea, fully resolved to fight for her at the head of three hundred thousand Scythians, and to restore to her the inheritance of Babylon, which was her right, as she had descended from the elder branch of the Nimrod family.

As for the beautiful Formosanta, she set out at three in the morning with her caravan of pilgrims, flattering herself that she might go into Arabia, and execute the last will of her bird; and that the justice of the gods would restore her the dear Amazan, without whom life had become insupportable.

When the king of Babylon awoke, he found all the company gone.

"How mighty festivals terminate," said he; "and what a surprising vacuum they leave when the hurry is over."

But he was transported with a rage truly royal, when he found that the princess Aldea had been carried off. He ordered all his ministers to be called up, and the council to be convened. Whilst they were dressing, he failed not to consult the oracle; but the only answer he could obtain was in these words, so celebrated since throughout the universe: *When girls are not provided for in marriage by their relatives, they marry themselves.*

Orders were immediately issued to march three hundred thousand men against the king of Scythia. Thus was the torch of a most dreadful war lighted up, which was caused by the amusements of the finest festival ever given upon earth. Asia was upon the point of being overrun by four armies of three hundred thousand men each. It is plain that the war of Troy, which astonished the world some ages after, was mere child's play in comparison to this: but it should also be considered, that in the Trojans' quarrel, the object was nothing more than a very immoral old woman, who had contrived to be twice run away with; whereas, in this case, the cause was tripartite—two girls and a bird.

The king of India went to meet his army upon the large fine road which then led straight to Babylon, at Cachemir. The king of Scythia flew with Aldea by the fine road which led to Mount Imaus. Owing to bad government, all these fine roads have disappeared in the lapse of time. The king of Egypt had marched to the west, along the coast of the little Mediterranean sea, which the ignorant Hebrews have since called the Great Sea.

As to the charming Formosanta, she pursued the road to Bassora, planted with lofty palm trees, which furnished a perpetual shade, and fruit at all seasons. The temple in which she was to perform her devotions, was in Bassora itself. The saint to whom this temple had been dedicated was somewhat in the style of him who was afterward adored at Lampsacus, and was generally successful in procuring husbands for young ladies. Indeed, he was the holiest saint in all Asia.

Formosanta had no sort of inclination for the saint of Bassora. She only invoked her dear Gangaridian shepherd, her charming Amazan. She proposed embarking at Bassora, and landing in Arabia Felix, to perform what her deceased bird had commanded.

At the third stage, scarce had she entered into a fine inn, where her harbingers had made all the necessary preparations for her, when she learned that the king of Egypt had arrived there also. Informed by his emissaries of the princess's route, he immediately altered his course, followed by a numerous escort. Having alighted, he placed sentinels at all the doors; then repaired to the beautiful Formosanta's apartment, when he addressed her by saying:

"Miss, you are the lady I was in quest of. You paid me very little attention when I was at Babylon. It is just to punish scornful capricious women. You will, if you please, be kind enough to sup with me to-night; and I shall behave to you according as I am satisfied with you."

Formosanta saw very well that she was not the strongest. She judged that good sense consisted in knowing how to conform to one's situation. She resolved to get rid of the king of Egypt by an innocent stratagem. She looked at him through the corners of her eyes (which in after ages has been called ogling), and then she spoke to him, with a modesty, grace, and sweetness, a confusion, and a thousand other charms, which would have made the wisest man a fool, and deceived the most discerning:

"I acknowledge, sir, I always appeared with a downcast look, when you did the king, my father, the honor of visiting him. I had some apprehensions for my heart. I dreaded my too great simplicity. I trembled lest my father and your rivals should observe the preference I gave you, and which you so highly deserved. I can now declare my sentiments. I swear by the bull Apis, which after you is the thing I respect the most in the world, that your proposals have enchanted me. I have already supped with you at my father's, and I will sup with you again, without his being of the party. All that I request of you is that your high almoner should drink with us. He appeared to me at Babylon to be an excellent guest. I have some Chiras wine remarkably good. I will make you both taste it. I consider you as the greatest of kings, and the most amiable of men."

This discourse turned the king of Egypt's head. He agreed to have the almoner's company.

"I have another favor to ask of you," said the princess, "which is to allow me to speak to my apothecary. Women have always some little ails that require attention, such as vapors in the head, palpitations of the heart, colics, and the like, which often require some assistance. In a word, I at present stand in need of my apothecary, and I hope you will not refuse me this slight testimony of confidence."

Miss," replied the king of Egypt, "I know life too well to refuse you so just a demand. I will order the apothecary to attend you whilst supper is preparing. I imagine you must be somewhat fatigued by the journey; you will also have occasion for a chambermaid; you may order her you like best to attend you. I will afterward wait your commands and convenience."

He then retired, and the apothecary and the chambermaid, named Irla, entered. The princess had an entire confidence in her. She ordered her to bring six bottles of Chiras wine for supper, and to make all the sentinels, who had her officers under arrest, drink the same. Then she recommended her apothecary to infuse in all the bottles certain pharmaceutic drugs, which make those who take them sleep twenty-four hours, and with which he was always provided. She was implicitly obeyed. The king returned with his high almoner in about half an hour's time. The conversation at supper was very gay. The king and the priest emptied the six bottles, and acknowledged there was not such good wine in Egypt. The chambermaid was attentive to make the servants in waiting drink. As for the princess, she took great care not to drink any herself, saying that she was ordered by her physician a particular regimen. They were all presently asleep.

The king of Egypt's almoner had one of the finest beards that a man of his rank could wear. Formosanta lopped it off very skillfully; then sewing it to a ribbon, she put it on her own chin. She then dressed herself in the priest's robes, and decked herself in all the marks of his dignity, and her waiting maid clad herself like the sacristan of the goddess Isis. At length, having furnished herself with his urn and jewels, she set out from the inn amidst the sentinels, who were asleep like their master. Her attendant had taken care to have two horses ready at the door. The princess could not take with her any of the officers of her train. They would have been stopped by the great guard.

Formosanta and Irla passed through several ranks of soldiers, who, taking the princess for the high priest, called her, "My most Reverend Father in God," and asked his blessing. The two fugitives arrived in twenty-four hours at Bassora, before the king awoke. They then threw off their disguise, which might have created some suspicion. They fitted out with all possible expedition a ship, which carried them, by the Straits of Ormus, to the beautiful banks of Eden in Arabia Felix. This was that Eden, whose gardens were so famous, that they have since been the residence of the best of mankind. They were the model of the Elysian fields, the gardens of the Hesperides, and also those of the Fortunate Islands. In those warm climates men imagined there could be no greater felicity than shades and murmuring brooks. To live eternally in heaven with the Supreme Being, or to walk in the garden of paradise, was the same thing to those who incessantly spoke without understanding one another, and who could scarce have any distinct ideas or just expressions.

As soon as the princess found herself in this land, her first care was to pay her dear bird the funeral obsequies he had required of her. Her beautiful hands prepared a small quantity of cloves and cinnamon. What was her surprise, when, having spread the ashes of the bird upon this funeral pyre, she saw it blaze of itself! All was presently consumed. In the place of the ashes there appeared nothing but a large egg, from whence she saw her bird issue more brilliant than ever. This was one of the most happy moments the princess had ever experienced in her whole life. There was but another that could ever be dearer to her; it was the object of her wishes, but almost beyond her hopes.

"I plainly see," said she, to the bird, "you are the phœnix which I have heard so much spoken of. I am almost ready to expire with joy and astonishment. I did not believe in your resurrection; but it is my good fortune to be convinced of it."

"Resurrection, in fact," said the phœnix to her, "is one of the most simple things in the world. There is nothing more in being born twice than once. Every thing in this world is the effect of resurrection. Caterpillars are regenerated into butterflies; a kernel put into the earth is regenerated into a tree. All animals buried in the earth regenerate into vegetation, herbs, and plants, and nourish other animals, of which they speedily compose part of the substance. All particles which compose bodies are transformed into different beings. It is true, that I am the only one to whom Oromasdes has granted the favor of regenerating in my own form."

Formosanta, who from the moment she first saw Amazan and the phœnix, had passed all her time in a round of astonishment, said to him:

"I can easily conceive that the Supreme Being may form out of your ashes a phœnix nearly resembling yourself but that you should be precisely the same person—that you should have the same soul, is a thing, I acknowledge, I cannot very clearly comprehend. What became of your soul when I carried you in my pocket after your death?"

"Reflect one moment! Is it not as easy for the great Oromasdes to continue action upon a single atom of my being, as to begin afresh this action? He had before granted me sensation, memory, and thought. He grants them to me again. Whether he united this favor to an atom of elementary fire, latent within me, or to the assemblage of my organs, is, in reality, of no consequence. Men, as well as phœnixes, are entirely ignorant how things come to pass; but the greatest favor the Supreme Being has bestowed upon me is to regenerate me for you. Oh! that I may pass the twenty-eight thousand years which I have still to live before my next resurrection, with you and my dear Amazan."

"My dear phœnix, remember what you first told me at Babylon, which I shall never forget, and which flattered me with the hope of again seeing my dear shepherd, whom I idolize; 'we must absolutely pay the Gangarids a visit together,' and I must carry Amazan back with me to Babylon."

"This is precisely my design," said the phœnix. "There is not a moment to lose. We must go in search of Amazan by the shortest road, that is, through the air. There are in Arabia Felix two griffins who are my particular friends, and who live only a hundred and fifty thousand leagues from here. I am going to write to them by the pigeon post, and they will be here before night. We shall have time to make you a convenient palankeen, with drawers, in which you may place your provisions. You will be quite at your ease in this vehicle, with your maid. These two griffins are the most vigorous of their kind. Each of them will support one of the poles of the canopy between their claws. But, once for all, time is very precious."

He instantly went with Formosanta to order the carriage at an upholsterer's of his acquaintance. It was made complete in four hours. In the drawers were placed small fine loaves, biscuits superior to those of Babylon, large lemons, pine-apples, cocoa, and pistachio nuts, Eden wine, which is as superior to that of Chiras, as Chiras is to that of Surinam.

The two griffins arrived at Eden at the appointed time. The vehicle was as light as it was commodious and solid, and Formosanta and Irla placed themselves in it. The two griffins carried it off like a feather. The phœnix sometimes flew after it, and sometimes perched upon its roof. The two griffins winged their way toward the Ganges with the velocity of an arrow which rends the air. They never stopped but a moment at night for the travelers to take some refreshment, and the carriers to take a draught of water.

They at length reached the country of the Gangarids. The princess's heart palpitated with hope, love, and joy. The phœnix stopped the vehicle before Amazan's house; but Amazan had been absent from home three hours, without any one knowing whither he had gone.

There are no words, even in the Gangaridian language, that could express Formosanta's extreme despair.

"Alas! this is what I dreaded," said the phœnix: "the three hours which you passed at the inn, upon the road to Bassora, with that wretched king of Egypt, have perhaps been at the price of the happiness of your whole life. I very much fear we have lost Amazan, without the possibility of recovering him."

He then asked the servants if he could salute the mother of Amazan. They answered, that her husband had died only two days before, and she could speak to no one. The phœnix, who was not without influence in the house, introduced the princess of Babylon into a saloon, the walls of which were covered with orange-tree wood inlaid with ivory. The inferior shepherds and shepherdesses, who were dressed in long white garments, with gold colored trimmings, served up, in a hundred plain porcelain baskets, a hundred various delicacies, amongst which no disguised carcasses were to be seen. They consisted of rice, sago, vermicelli, macaroni, omelets, milk, eggs, cream, cheese, pastry of every kind, vegetables, fruits, peculiarly fragrant and grateful to the taste, of which no idea can be formed in other climates; and they were accompanied with a profusion of refreshing liquors superior to the finest wine.

Whilst the princess regaled herself, seated upon a bed of roses, four peacocks, who were luckily mute, fanned her with their brilliant wings; two hundred birds, one hundred shepherds and shepherdesses, warbled a concert in two different choirs; the nightingales, thistlefinches, linnets, chaffinches, sung the higher notes with the shepherdesses, and the shepherds sung the tenor and bass. The princess acknowledged that if there was more magnificence at Babylon, nature was infinitely more agreeable among the Gangarids; but whilst this consolatory and voluptuous music was playing tears flowed from her eyes, whilst she said to the damsel Irla:

"These shepherds and shepherdesses, these nightingales, these linnets, are making love; and for my part, I am deprived of the company of the Gangaridian hero, the worthy object of my most tender thoughts."

Whilst she was taking this collation, her tears and admiration kept pace with each other, and the phœnix addressed himself to Amazan's mother, saying:

"Madam, you cannot avoid seeing the princess of Babylon; you know——"

"I know every thing," said she, "even her adventure at the inn, upon the road to Bassora. A blackbird related the whole to me this morning; and this cruel blackbird is the cause of my son's going mad, and leaving his paternal abode."

"You have not been informed, then, that the princess regenerated me?"

"No, my dear child, the blackbird told me you were dead, and this made me inconsolable. I was so afflicted at this loss, the death of my husband, and the precipitate flight of my son, that I ordered my door to be shut to every one. But since the princess of Babylon has done me the honor of paying me a visit, I beg she may be immediately introduced. I have matters of great importance to acquaint her with, and I choose you should be present."

She then went to meet the princess in another saloon. She could not walk very well. This lady was about three hundred years old; but she had still some agreeable vestiges of beauty. It might be conjectured, that about her two hundred and fortieth, or two hundred and fiftieth year, she must have been a most charming woman. She received Formosanta with a respectful nobleness, blended with an air of interest and sorrow, which made a very lively impression upon the princess.

Formosanta immediately paid her the compliments of condolence upon her husband's death.

"Alas!" said the widow, "you have more reason to lament his death than you imagine."

"I am, doubtless, greatly afflicted," said Formosanta; "he was father to ————." Here a flood of tears prevented her from going on. "For his sake only I undertook this journey, and which I have so narrowly escaped many dangers. For him I left my father, and the most splendid court in the universe. I was detained by a king of Egypt, whom I detest. Having escaped from this tyrant, I have traversed the air in search of the only man I love. When I arrive, he flies from me!" Here sighs and tears stopped her impassioned harangue.

His mother then said to her:

"When the king of Egypt made you his prisoner—when you supped with him at an inn upon the road to Bassora, when your beautiful hands filled him bumpers of Chiras wine, did you observe a blackbird that flew about the room?"

"Yes, really," said the princess, "I now recollect there was such a bird, though at that time I did not pay it the least attention. But in collecting my ideas, I now remember well, that at the instant when the king of Egypt rose from the table to give me a kiss, the blackbird flew out at the window giving a loud cry, and never appeared after."

"Alas! madam," resumed Amazan's mother, "this is precisely the cause of all our misfortunes; my son had dispatched this blackbird to gain intelligence of your health, and all that passed at Babylon. He proposed speedily to return, throw himself at your feet, and consecrate to you the remainder of his life. You know not to what a pitch he adores you. All the Gangarids are both loving and faithful; but my son is the most passionate and constant of them all. The blackbird found you at an inn, drinking very cheerfully with the king of Egypt and a vile priest; he afterward saw you give this monarch who had killed the phœnix—the man my son holds in utter detestation—a fond embrace. The blackbird, at the sight of this, was seized with a just indignation. He flew away imprecating your fatal error. He returned this day, and has related every thing. But, just heaven, at what a juncture! At the very time that my son was deploring with me the loss of his father and that of the wise phœnix, the very instant I had informed him that he was your cousin-german——"

"Oh heavens! my cousin, madam, is it possible? How can this be? And am I so happy as to be thus allied to him, and yet so miserable as to have offended him?"

"My son is, I tell you," said the Gangaridian lady, "your cousin, and I shall presently convince you of it; but in becoming my relation, you rob me of my son. He cannot survive the grief that the embrace you gave to the king of Egypt has occasioned him."

"Ah! my dear aunt," cried the beautiful Formosanta, "I swear by him and the all-powerful Oromasdes, that this embrace, so far from being criminal, was the strongest proof of love your son could receive from me. I disobeyed my father for his sake. For him I went from the Euphrates to the Ganges. Having fallen into the hands of the worthless Pharaoh of Egypt, I could not escape his clutches but by artifice. I call the ashes and soul of the phœnix, which were then in my pocket, to witness. He can do me justice. But how can your son, born upon the banks of the Ganges, be my cousin? I, whose family have reigned upon the banks of the Euphrates for so many centuries?"

"You know," said the venerable Gangaridian lady to her, "that your grand uncle, Aldea, was king of Babylon, and that he was dethroned by Belus's father?"

"Yes, madam."

"You know that this Aldea had in marriage a daughter named Aldea, brought up in your court? It was this prince, who, being persecuted by your father, took refuge under another name in our happy country. He married me, and is the father of the young prince Aldea Amazan, the most beautiful, the most courageous, the strongest, and most virtuous of mortals; and at this hour the most unhappy. He went to the Babylonian festival upon the credit of your beauty; since that time he idolizes you, and now grieves because he believes that you have proved unfaithful to him. Perhaps I shall never again set eyes upon my dear son."

She then displayed to the princess all the titles of the house of Aldea. Formosanta scarce deigned to look at them.

"Ah! madam, do we examine what is the object of our desire? My heart sufficiently believes you. But where is Aldea Amazan? Where is my kinsman, my lover, my king? Where is my life? What road has he taken? I will seek for him in every sphere the Eternal Being hath framed, and of which he is the greatest ornament. I will go into the star Canope, into Sheath, into Aldebaran; I will go and tell him of my love and convince him of my innocence."

The phœnix justified the princess with regard to the crime that was imputed to her by the blackbird, of fondly embracing the king of Egypt; but it was necessary to undeceive Amazan and recall him. Birds were dispatched on every side. Unicorns sent forward in every direction. News at length arrived that Amazan had taken the road toward China.

"Well, then," said the princess, "let us set out for China. I will seek him in defiance of both difficulty and danger. The journey is not long, and I hope I shall bring you back your son in a fortnight at farthest."

At these words tears of affection streamed from his mother's eyes and also from those of the princess. They most tenderly embraced, in the great sensibility of their hearts.

The phœnix immediately ordered a coach with six unicorns. Amazan's mother furnished two thousand horsemen, and made the princess, her niece, a present of some thousands of the finest diamonds of her country. The phœnix, afflicted at the evil occasioned by the blackbird's indiscretion, ordered all the blackbirds to quit the country; and from that time none have been met with upon the banks of the Ganges.

V

FORMOSANTA VISITS CHINA AND SCYTHIA IN SEARCH OF AMAZAN

THE unicorns, in less than eight days, carried Formosanta, Irla, and the phœnix, to Cambalu, the capital of China. This city was larger than that of Babylon, and in appearance quite different. These fresh objects, these strange manners, would have amused Formosanta could any thing but Amazan have engaged her attention.

As soon as the emperor of China learned that the princess of Babylon was at the city gates, he dispatched four thousand Mandarins in ceremonial robes to receive her. They all prostrated themselves before her, and presented her with an address written in golden letters upon a sheet of purple silk. Formosanta told them, that if she were possessed of four thousand tongues, she would not omit replying immediately to every Mandarin; but that having only one, she hoped they would be satisfied with her general thanks. They conducted her, in a respectful manner, to the emperor.

He was the wisest, most just and benevolent monarch upon earth. It was he who first tilled a small field with his own imperial hands, to make agriculture respectable to his people. Laws in all other countries were shamefully confined to the punishment of crimes: he first allotted premiums to virtue. This emperor had just banished from his dominions a gang of foreign Bonzes, who had come from the extremities of the West, with the frantic hope of compelling all China *to think like themselves;* and who, under pretence of teaching truths, had already acquired honors and riches. In expelling them, he delivered himself in these words, which are recorded in the annals of the empire:

"You may here do as much harm as you have elsewhere. You have come to preach dogmas of intolerance, to the most tolerant nation upon earth. I send you back, that I may never be compelled to punish you. You will be honorably conducted to my frontiers. You will be furnished with every thing necessary to return to the confines of the hemisphere from whence you came. Depart in peace, if you can be at peace, and never return."

The princess of Babylon heard with pleasure of this speech and determination. She was the more certain of being well received at court, as she was very far from entertaining any dogmas of intolerance. The emperor of China, in dining with her *tête-à-tête,* had the politeness to banish all disagreeable *etiquette.* She presented the phœnix to him, who was gently caressed by the emperor, and who perched upon his chair. Formosanta, toward the end of the repast, ingenuously acquainted him with the cause of her journey, and entreated him to search for the beautiful Amazan in the city of Cambalu; and in the meanwhile she acquainted the emperor with her adventures, without concealing the fatal passion with which her heart burned for this youthful hero.

"He did me the honor of coming to my court," said the emperor of China. "I was enchanted with this amiable Amazan. It is true that he is deeply afflicted; but his graces are thereby the more affecting. Not one of my favorites has more wit. There is not a gown Mandarin who has more knowledge—not a military one who has a more martial or heroic air. His extreme youth adds an additional value to all his talents. If I were so unfortunate, so abandoned by the Tien and Changti, as to desire to be a conqueror, I would wish Amazan to put himself at the head of my armies, and I should be sure of conquering the whole universe. It is a great pity that his melancholy sometimes disconcerts him."

"Ah! sir," said Formosanta, with much agitation and grief, blended with an air of reproach, "why did you not request me to dine with him? This is a cruel stroke you have given me. Send for him immediately, I entreat you."

"He set out this very morning," replied the emperor, "without acquainting me with his destination."

Formosanta, turning toward the phœnix, said to him:

"Did you ever know so unfortunate a damsel as myself?" Then resuming the conversation, she said:

"Sir, how came he to quit in so abrupt a manner, so polite a court, in which, methinks, one might pass one's life?"

"The case was as follows," said he. "One of the most amiable of the princesses of the blood, falling desperately in love with him, desired to meet him at noon. He set out at day-break, leaving this billet for my kinswoman, whom it hath cost a deluge of tears:

"Beautiful princess of the mongolian race. You are deserving of a heart that was never offered up at any other altar. I have sworn to the immortal gods never to love any other than Formosanta, princess of Babylon, and to teach her how to conquer one's desires in traveling. She has had the misfortune to yield to a worthless king of Egypt. I am the most unfortunate of men; having lost my father, the phœnix, and the hope of being loved by Formosanta. I left my mother in affliction, forsook my home and country, being unable to live a moment in the place where I learned that Formosanta loved another than me. I swore to traverse the earth, and be faithful. You would despise me, and the gods punish me, if I violated my oath. Choose another lover, madam, and be as faithful as I am."

"Ah! give me that miraculous letter," said the beautiful Formosanta; "it will afford me some consolation. I am happy in the midst of my misfortunes. Amazan loves me! Amazan, for me, renounces the society of the princesses of China. There is no one upon earth but himself endowed with so much fortitude. He sets me a most brilliant example. The phœnix knows I did not stand in need of it. How cruel it is to be deprived of one's lover for the most innocent embrace given through pure fidelity. But, tell me, whither has he gone? What road has he taken? Deign to inform me, and I will immediately set out."

The emperor of China told her, that, according to the reports he had received, her lover had taken the road toward Scythia. The unicorns were immediately harnessed, and the princess, after the most tender compliments, took leave of the emperor, and resumed her journey with the phœnix, her chambermaid Irla, and all her train.

As soon as she arrived in Scythia, she was more convinced than ever how much men and governments differed, and would continue to differ, until noble and enlightened minds should by degrees remove that cloud of darkness which has covered the earth for so many ages; and until there should be found in barbarous climes, heroic souls, who would have strength and perseverance enough to transform brutes into men. There are no cities in Scythia, consequently no agreeable arts. Nothing was to be seen but extensive fields, and whole tribes whose sole habitations were tents and chars. Such an appearance struck her with terror. Formosanta enquired in what tent or char the king was lodged? She was informed that he had set out eight days before with three hundred thousand cavalry to attack the king of Babylon, whose niece, the beautiful princess Aldea, he had carried off.

"What! did he run away with my cousin?" cried Formosanta. "I could not have imagined such an incident. What! has my cousin, who was too happy in paying her court to me, become a queen, and I am not yet married?" She was immediately conducted, by her desire, to the queen's tent.

Their unexpected meeting in such distant climes—the uncommon occurrences they mutually had to impart to each other, gave such charms to this interview, as made them forget they never loved one another. They saw each other with transport; and a soft illusion supplied the place of real tenderness. They embraced with tears, and there was a cordiality and frankness on each side that could not have taken place in a palace.

Aldea remembered the phœnix and the waiting maid Irla. She presented her cousin with zibelin skins, who in return gave her diamonds. The war between the two kings was spoken of. They deplored the fate of soldiers who were forced into battle, the victims of the caprice of princes, when two honest men might, perhaps, settle the dispute in less than an hour, without a single throat being cut. But the principal topic was the handsome stranger, who had conquered lions, given the largest diamonds in the universe, written madrigals, and had now become the most miserable of men from believing the statements of a blackbird.

"He is my dear brother," said Aldea. "He is my lover," cried Formosanta. "You have, doubtless, seen him. Is he still here? for, cousin, as he knows he is your brother, he cannot have left you so abruptly as he did the king of China."

"Have I seen him? good heavens! yes. He passed four whole days with me. Ah! cousin, how much my brother is to blame. A false report has absolutely turned his brain. He roams about the world, without knowing whither he is destined. Imagine to yourself his distraction of mind, which is so great, that he has refused to meet the handsomest lady in all Scythia. He set out yesterday, after writing her a letter which has thrown her into despair. As for him, he has gone to visit the Cimmerians."

"God be thanked!" cried Formosanta; "another refusal in my favor. My good fortune is beyond my hopes, as my misfortunes surpass my greatest apprehensions. Procure me this charming letter, that I may set out and follow him, loaded with his sacrifices. Farewell, cousin. Amazan is among the Cimmerians, and I fly to meet him."

Aldea judged that the princess, her cousin, was still more frantic than her brother Amazan. But as she had herself been sensible of the effects of this epidemic contagion, having given up the delights and magnificence of Babylon for a king of Scythia; and as the women always excuse those follies that are the effects of love, she felt for Formosanta's affliction, wished her a happy journey, and promised to be her advocate with her brother, if ever she was so fortunate as to see him again.

VI

THE PRINCESS CONTINUES HER JOURNEY

FROM Scythia the princess of Babylon, with her phœnix, soon arrived at the empire of the Cimmerians, now called Russia; a country indeed much less populous than Scythia, but of far greater extent.

After a few days' journey, she entered a very large city, which has of late been greatly improved by the reigning sovereign. The empress, however, was not there at that time, but making a journey through her dominions, on the frontiers of Europe and Asia, in order to judge of their state and condition with her own eyes—to enquire into their grievances, and to provide the proper remedies for them.

The principal magistrate of that ancient capital, as soon as he was informed of the arrival of the Babylonian lady and the phœnix, lost no time in paying her all the honors of his country; being certain that his mistress, the most polite and generous empress in the world, would be extremely well pleased to find that he had received so illustrious a lady with all that respect which she herself, if on the spot, would have shown her.

The princess was lodged in the palace, and entertained with great splendor and elegance. The Cimmerian lord, who was an excellent natural philosopher, diverted himself in conversing with the phœnix, at such times as the princess chose to retire to her own apartment. The phœnix told him that he had formerly traveled among the Cimmerians, but that he should not have known the country again.

"How comes it," said he, "that such prodigious changes have been brought about in so short a time? Formerly, when I was here, about three hundred years ago, I saw nothing but savage nature in all her horrors. At present, I perceive industry, arts, splendor, and politeness."

"This mighty revolution," replied the Cimmerian, "was begun by one man, and is now carried to perfection by one woman—a woman who is a greater legislator than the Isis of the Egyptians, or the Ceres of the Greeks. Most lawgivers have been, unhappily, of a narrow genius and an arbitrary disposition, which confined their views to the countries they governed. Each of them looked upon his own race as the only people existing upon the earth, or as if they ought to be an enmity with all the rest. They formed institutions, introduced customs, and established religions exclusively for themselves. Thus the Egyptians, so famous for those heaps of stones called pyramids, have dishonored themselves with their barbarous superstitions. They despise all other nations as profane; refuse all manner of intercourse with them; and, excepting those conversant in the court, who now and then rise above the prejudices of the vulgar, there is not an Egyptian who will eat off a plate that has ever been used by a stranger. Their priests are equally cruel and absurd. It were better to have no laws at all, and to follow those notions of right and wrong engraven on our hearts by nature, than to subject society to institutions so inhospitable.

"Our empress has adopted quite a different system. She considers her vast dominions, under which all the meridians on the globe are united, as under an obligation of correspondence with all the nations dwelling under those meridians. The first and most fundamental of her laws, is an universal toleration of all religions, and an unbounded compassion for every error. Her penetrating genius perceives, that though the modes of religious worship differ, yet morality is every where the same. By this principle, she has united her people to all the nations on earth, and the Cimmerians will soon consider the Scandinavians and the Chinese as their brethren. Not satisfied with this, she has resolved to establish this invaluable toleration, the strongest link of society, among her neighbors. By these means, she obtained the title of the parent of her country; and, if she persevere, will acquire that of the benefactress of mankind.

"Before her time, the men, who were unhappily possessed of power, sent out legions of murderers to ravage unknown countries, and to water with the blood of the children the inheritance of their fathers. Those assassins were called heroes, and their robberies accounted glorious achievements. But our sovereign courts another sort of glory. She has sent forth her armies to be the messengers of peace; not only to prevent men from being the destroyers, but to oblige them to be the benefactors of one another. Her standards are the ensigns of public tranquillity."

The phœnix was quite charmed with what he heard from this nobleman. He told him, that though he had lived twenty-seven thousand nine hundred years and seven months in this world, he had never seen any thing like it. He then enquired after his friend Amazan. The Cimmerian gave the same account of him that the princess had already heard from the Chinese and the Scythians. It was Amazan's constant practice to run away from all the courts he visited, the instant any lady noticed him in particular and seemed anxious to make his acquaintance. The phœnix soon acquainted Formosanta with this fresh instance of Amazan's fidelity—a fidelity so much the more surprising, since he could not imagine his princess would ever hear of it.

Amazan had set out for Scandinavia, where he was entertained with sights still more surprising. In this place, he beheld monarchy and liberty subsisting together in a manner thought incompatible in other states; the laborers of the ground shared in the legislature with the grandees of the realm. In another place he saw what was still more extraordinary; a prince equally remarkable for his extreme youth and uprightness, who possessed a sovereign authority over his country, acquired by a solemn contract with his people.

Amazan beheld a philosopher on the throne of Sarmatia, who might be called a king of anarchy; for he was the chief of a hundred thousand petty kings, one of whom with his single voice could render ineffectual the resolution of all the rest. Eolus had not more difficulty to keep the warring winds within their proper bounds, than this monarch to reconcile the tumultuous discordant spirits of his subjects. He was the master of a ship surrounded with eternal storms. But the vessel did not founder, for he was an excellent pilot.

In traversing those various countries, so different from his own, Amazan perservered in rejecting all the advances made to him by the ladies, though incessantly distracted with the embrace given by Formosanta to the king of Egypt, being resolved to set Formosanta an amazing example of an unshaken and unparalleled fidelity.

The princess of Babylon was constantly close at his heels, and scarcely ever missed of him but by a day or two; without the one being tired of roaming, or the other losing a moment in pursuing him.

Thus he traversed the immense continent of Germany, where he beheld with wonder the progress which reason and philosophy had made in the north. Even their princes were enlightened, and had become the patrons of freedom of thought. Their education had not been trusted to men who had an interest in deceiving them, or who were themselves deceived. They were brought up in the knowledge of universal morality, and in the contempt of superstition.

They had banished from all their estates a senseless custom which had enervated and depopulated the southern countries. This was to bury alive in immense dungeons, infinite numbers of both sexes who were eternally separated from one another, and sworn to have no communication together. This madness had contributed more than the most cruel wars to lay waste and depopulate the earth.

In opposing these barbarous institutions, so inimical to the laws of nature and the best interests of society, the princes of the north had become the benefactors of their race. They had likewise exploded other errors equally absurd and pernicious. In short, men had at last ventured to make use of their reason in those immense regions; whereas it was still believed almost every where else, that they could not be governed but in proportion to their ignorance.

VII

AMAZAN VISITS ALBION

FROM Germany, Amazan arrived at Batavia; where his perpetual chagrin was in a good measure alleviated, by perceiving among the inhabitants a faint resemblance to his happy countrymen, the Gangarids. There he saw liberty, security, and equality—with toleration in religion; but the ladies were so indifferent, that none made him any advances; an experience he had not met with before. It is true, however, that had he been inclined to address them, they would not have been offended; though, at the same time, not one would have been the least in love; but he was far from any thoughts of making conquests.

Formosanta had nearly caught him in this insipid nation. He had set out but a moment before her arrival.

Amazan had heard so much among the Batavians in praise of a certain island called Albion, that he was led by curiosity to embark with his unicorns on board a ship, which, with a favorable easterly wind, carried him in a few hours to that celebrated country, more famous than Tyre, or Atlantis.

The beautiful Formosanta, who had followed him, as it were on the scent, to the banks of the Volga, the Vistula, the Elbe, and the Weser, and had never been above a day or two behind him, arrived soon after at the mouth of the Rhine, where it disembogues its waters into the German Ocean.

Here she learned that her beloved Amazan had just set sail for Albion. She thought she saw the vessel on board of which he was, and could not help crying out for joy; at which the Batavian ladies were greatly surprised, not imagining that a young man could possibly occasion so violent a transport. They took, indeed, but little notice of the phœnix, as they reckoned his feathers would not fetch near so good a price as those of their own ducks, and other water fowl. The princess of Babylon hired two vessels to carry herself and her retinue to that happy island, which was soon to possess the only object of her desires, the soul of her life, and the god of her idolatry.

An unpropitious wind from the west suddenly arose, just as the faithful and unhappy Amazan landed on Albion's sea-girt shore, and detained the ships of the Babylonian princess just as they were on the point of sailing. Seized with a deep melancholy, she went to her room, determined to remain there till the wind should change; but it blew for the space of eight days, with an unremitting violence. The princess, during this tedious period, employed her maid of honor, Irla, in reading romances; which were not indeed written by the Batavians; but as they are the factors of the universe, they traffic in the wit as well as commodities of other nations. The princess purchased of Mark Michael Rey, the bookseller, all the novels which had been written by the Ausonians and the Welch, the sale of which had been wisely prohibited among those nations to enrich their neighbors, the Batavians. She expected to find in those histories some adventure similar to her own, which might alleviate her grief. The maid of honor read, the phœnix made comments, and the princess, finding nothing in the *Fortunate Country Maid,* in *Tansai,* or in the *Sopha,* that had the least resemblance to her own affairs, interrupted the reader every moment, by asking how the wind stood.

VIII

AMAZAN LEAVES ALBION

In the mean time Amazan was on the road to the capital of Albion, in his coach and six unicorns, all his thoughts employed on his dear princess. At a small distance he perceived a carriage overturned in a ditch. The servants had gone in different directions in quest of assistance, but the owner kept his seat, smoking his pipe with great tranquillity, without manifesting the smallest impatience. His name was my lord What-then, in the language from which I translate these memoirs.

Amazan made all the haste possible to help him, and without assistance set the carriage to rights, so much was his strength superior to that of other men. My lord What-then took no other notice of him, than saying, "a stout fellow, by Jove!" In the meantime the neighboring people, having arrived, flew into a great passion at being called out to no purpose, and fell upon the stranger. They abused him, called him an outlandish dog, and challenged him to strip and box.

Amazan seized a brace of them in each hand, and threw them twenty paces from him; the rest, seeing this, pulled off their hats, and bowing with great respect, asked his honor for something to drink. His honor gave them more money than they had ever seen in their lives before. My lord What-then now expressed great esteem for him, and asked him to dinner at his country house, about three miles off. His invitation being accepted, he went into Amazan's coach, his own being out of order from the accident.

After a quarter of an hour's silence, my lord What-then, looking upon Amazan for a moment, said: "How d'ye do?" which, by the way, is a phrase without any meaning; adding, "You have got six fine unicorns there." After which he continued smoking as usual.

The traveler told him his unicorns were at his service, and that he had brought them from the country of the Gangarids. From thence he took occasion to inform him of his affair with the princess of Babylon, and the unlucky kiss she had given the king of Egypt; to which the other made no reply, being very indifferent whether there were any such people in the world, as a king of Egypt, or a princess of Babylon.

He remained dumb for another quarter of an hour; after which he asked his companion a second time how he did, and whether they had any good roast beef among the Gangarids.

Amazan answered with his wonted politeness, "that they did not eat their brethren on the banks of the Ganges." He then explained to him that system which many ages afterward was surnamed the Pythagorean philosophy. But my lord fell asleep in the meantime, and made but one nap of it till he came to his own house.

He was married to a young and charming woman, on whom nature had bestowed a soul as lively and sensible as that of her husband was dull and stupid. A few gentlemen of Albion had that day come to dine with her; among whom there were characters of all sorts; for that country having been almost always under the government of foreigners, the families that had come over with these princes had imported their different manners. There were in this company some persons of an amiable disposition, others of superior genius, and a few of profound learning.

The mistress of the house had none of that awkward stiffness, that false modesty, with which the young ladies of Albion were then reproached. She did not conceal by a scornful look and an affected taciturnity her deficiency of ideas and the embarrassing humility of having nothing to say. Never was a woman more engaging. She received Amazan with a grace and politeness that were quite natural to her. The extreme beauty of this young stranger, and the involuntary comparison she could not help making between him and her prosaic husband, did not increase her happiness or content.

Dinner being served, she placed Amazan at her side, and helped him to a variety of puddings, he having informed her that the Gangarids never dined upon any thing which had received from the gods the celestial gift of life. The events of his early life, the manners of the Gangarids, the progress of arts, religion, and government, were the subjects of a conversation equally agreeable and instructive all the time of the entertainment, which lasted till night: during which my lord What-then did nothing but push the bottle about, and call for the toast.

After dinner, while my lady was pouring out the tea, still feeding her eyes on the young stranger, he entered into a long conversation with a member of parliament; for every one knows that there was, even then, a parliament called Wittenagenot, or the assembly of wise men. Amazan enquired into the constitution, laws, manners, customs, forces, and arts, which made this country so respectable; and the member answered him in the following manner.

"For a long time we went stark naked, though our climate is none of the hottest. We were likewise for a long time enslaved by a people who came from the ancient country of Saturn, watered by the Tiber. But the mischief we have done one another has greatly exceeded all that we ever suffered from our first conquerors.

"To those times of infamy and debasement, succeeded the ages of barbarity and confusion. Our country, more tempestuous than the surrounding ocean, has been ravaged and drenched in blood by our civil discords. Many of our crowned heads have perished by a violent death. Above a hundred princes of the royal blood have ended their days on the scaffold, whilst the hearts of their adherents have been torn from their breasts, and thrown in their faces. In short, it is the province of the hangman to write the history of our island, seeing that this personage has finally determined all our affairs of moment.

"But to crown these horrors, it is not very long since some fellows wearing black mantles, and others who cast white shirts over their jackets, having become aggressive and intolerant, succeeded in communicating their madness to the whole nation. Our country was then divided into two parties, the murderers and the murdered, the executioners and the sufferers, plunderers and slaves; and all in the name of God, and whilst they were seeking the Lord.

"Who would have imagined, that from this horrible abyss, this chaos of dissension, cruelty, ignorance, and fanaticism, a government should at last spring up, the most perfect, it may be said, now in the world; yet such has been the event. A prince, honored and wealthy, all-powerful to do good, but without power to do evil, is at the head of a free, warlike, commercial, and enlightened nation. The nobles on one hand, and the representatives of the people on the other, share the legislature with the monarch.

"We have seen, by a singular fatality of events, disorder, civil wars, anarchy and wretchedness, lay waste the country, when our kings aimed at arbitrary power: whereas tranquillity, riches, and universal happiness, have only reigned among us, when the prince has remained satisfied with a limited authority. All order had been subverted whilst we were disputing about mysteries, but was re-established the moment we grew wise enough to despise them. Our victorious fleets carry our flag on every ocean; our laws place our lives and fortunes in security; no judge can explain them in an arbitrary manner, and no decision is ever given without the reasons assigned for it. We should punish a judge as an assassin, who should condemn a citizen to death without declaring the evidence which accused him, and the law upon which he was convicted.

"It is true, there are always two parties among us, who are continually writing and intriguing against each other; but they constantly re-unite, whenever it is needful to arm in defence of liberty and our country. These two parties watch over one another, and mutually prevent the violation of the sacred *deposit* of the laws. They hate one another, but they love the state. They are like those jealous lovers, who pay court to the same mistress, with a spirit of emulation.

"From the same fund of genius by which we discovered and supported the natural rights of mankind, we have carried the sciences to the highest pitch to which they can attain among men. Your Egyptians, who pass for such great mechanics—your Indians, who are believed to be such great philosophers—your Babylonians, who boast of having observed the stars for the course of four hundred and thirty thousand years—the Greeks, who have written so much, and said so little, know in reality nothing in comparison to our inferior scholars, who have studied the discoveries of our great masters. We have ravished more secrets from nature in the space of an hundred years, than the human species had been able to discover in as many ages.

"This is a true account of our present state. I have concealed from you neither the good nor the bad; neither our shame nor our glory; and I have exaggerated nothing."

At this discourse Amazan felt a strong desire to be instructed in those sublime sciences his friend had spoken of; and if his passion for the princess of Babylon, his filial duty to his mother whom he had quitted, and his love for his native country had not made strong remonstrances to his distempered heart, he would willingly have spent the remainder of his life in Albion. But that unfortunate kiss his princess had given the king of Egypt, did not leave his mind at sufficient ease to study the abstruse sciences.

"I confess," said he, "having made a solemn vow to roam about the world, and to escape from myself."

Amazan had spoken in so agreeable a manner; his voice was so charming; his whole behavior so noble and engaging, that the mistress of the house could not resist the pleasure of having a little private chat with him in her turn. She accordingly sent him a little billet-doux intimating her wishes in the most agreeable language. Amazan had once more the courage to resist the fascination of female society, and, according to custom, wrote the lady an answer full of respect—representing to her the sacredness of his oath, and the strict obligation he was under to teach the princess of Babylon to conquer her passions by his example; after which he harnessed his unicorns and departed for Batavia, leaving all the company in deep admiration of him, and the lady in profound astonishment. In her confusion she dropped Amazan's letter. My lord What-then read it next morning:

"D—n it," said he, shrugging up his shoulders, "what stuff and nonsense have we got here?" and then rode out a fox hunting with some of his drunken neighbors.

Amazan was already sailing upon the sea, possessed of a geographical chart, with which he had been presented by the learned Albion he had conversed with at lord What-then's. He was extremely astonished to find the greatest part of the earth upon a single sheet of paper.

His eyes and imagination wandered over this little space; he observed the Rhine, the Danube, the Alps of Tyrol, there specified under their different names, and all the countries through which he was to pass. But he more particularly fixed his eyes upon the country of the Gangarids, upon Babylon, where he had seen his dear princess, and upon the country of Bassora, where she had given a fatal kiss to the king of Egypt. He sighed, and tears streamed from his eyes at the unhappy remembrance. He agreed with the Albion who had presented him with the universe in epitome, when he averred that the inhabitants of the banks of the Thames were a thousand times better instructed than those upon the banks of the Nile, the Euphrates, and the Ganges.

As he returned into Batavia, Formosanta proceeded toward Albion with her two ships at full sail. Amazan's ship and the princess's crossed one another and almost touched; the two lovers were close to each other, without being conscious of the fact. Ah! had they but known it! But this great consolation tyrannic destiny would not allow.

IX

An Unfortunate Adventure in Gaul

In all the provinces through which Amazan passed, he remained ever faithful to the princess of Babylon, though incessantly enraged at the king of Egypt. This model of constancy at length arrived at the new capital of the Gauls. This city, like many others, had alternately submitted to barbarity, ignorance, folly, and misery. The first name it bore was Dirt and Mire; it then took that of Isis, from the worship of Isis, which had reached even here. Its first senate consisted of a company of watermen. It had long been in bondage, and submitted to the ravages of the heroes of the Seven Mountains; and some ages after, some other heroic thieves who came from the farther banks of the Rhine had seized upon its little lands.

Time, which changes all things, had formed it into a city, half of which was very noble and very agreeable, the other half somewhat barbarous and ridiculous: this was the emblem of its inhabitants. There were within its walls at least a hundred thousand people, who had no other employment than play and diversion. These idlers were the judges of those arts which the others cultivated. They were ignorant of all that passed at court; though they were only four short miles distant from it: but it seemed to them at least six hundred thousand miles off. Agreeableness in company, gaiety and frivolity, formed the important and sole considerations of their lives. They were governed like children, who are extravagantly supplied with gewgaws, to prevent their crying. If the horrors were discussed, which two centuries before had laid waste their country, or if those dreadful periods were recalled, when one half of the nation massacred the other for sophisms, they, indeed, said, "this was not well done," then, presently, they fell to laughing again, or singing of catches.

In proportion as the idlers were polished, agreeable, and amiable, it was observed that there was a greater and more shocking contrast between them and those who were engaged in business.

Among the latter, or such as pretended so to be, there was a gang of melancholy fanatics, whose absurdity and knavery divided their character—whose appearance alone diffused misery—and who would have overturned the world, had they been able to gain a little credit. But the nation of idlers, by dancing and singing, forced them into obscurity in their caverns, as the warbling birds drive the croaking bats back to their holes and ruins.

A smaller number of those who were occupied, were the preservers of ancient barbarous customs, against which nature, terrified, loudly exclaimed. They consulted nothing but their worm-eaten registers. If they there discovered a foolish or horrid custom, they considered it as a sacred law. It was from this vile practice of not daring to think for themselves, but extracting their ideas from the ruins of those times when no one thought at all, that in the metropolis of pleasure there still remained some shocking manners. Hence it was that there was no proportion between crimes and punishments. A thousand deaths were sometimes inflicted upon an innocent victim, to make him acknowledge a crime he had not committed.

The extravagancies of youth were punished with the same severity as murder or parricide. The idlers screamed loudly at these exhibitions, and the next day thought no more about them, but were buried in the contemplation of some new fashion.

This people saw a whole age elapse, in which the fine arts attained a degree of perfection that far surpassed the most sanguine hopes. Foreigners then repaired thither, as they did to Babylon, to admire the great monuments of architecture, the wonders of gardening, the sublime efforts of sculpture and painting. They were charmed with a species of music that reached the heart without astonishing the ears.

True poetry, that is to say, such as is natural and harmonious, that which addresses the heart as well as the mind, was unknown to this nation before this happy period. New kinds of eloquence displayed sublime beauties. The theatres in particular re-echoed with masterpieces that no other nation ever approached. In a word, good taste prevailed in every profession to that degree, that there were even good writers among the Druids.

So many laurels that had branched even to the skies soon withered in an exhausted soil. There remained but a very small number, whose leaves were of a pale dying verdure. This decay was occasioned by the facility of producing; laziness preventing good productions, and by a satiety of the brilliant, and a taste for the whimsical. Vanity protected arts that brought back times of barbarity; and this same vanity, in persecuting persons of real merit, forced them to quit their country. The hornets banished the bees.

There were scarce any real arts, scarce any real genius. Talent now consisted in reasoning right or wrong upon the merit of the last age. The dauber of a sign-post criticised with an air of sagacity the works of the greatest painters; and the blotters of paper disfigured the works of the greatest writers. Ignorance and bad taste had other daubers in their pay. The same things were repeated in a hundred volumes under different titles. Every work was either a dictionary or a pamphlet. A Druid gazetteer wrote twice a week of obscure annals of an unknown people possessed with the devil, and of celestial prodigies operated in garrets by little beggars of both sexes. Other Ex-Druids, dressed in black, ready to die with rage and hunger, set forth their complaints in a hundred different writings, that they were no longer allowed to cheat mankind—this privilege being conferred on some goats clad in grey; and some Arch-Druids were employed in printing defamatory libels.

Amazan was quite ignorant of all this, and even if he had been acquainted with it, he would have given himself very little concern about it, having his head filled with nothing but the princess of Babylon, the king of Egypt, and the inviolable vow he had made to despise all female coquetry in whatevei country his despair should drive him.

The gaping ignorant mob, whose curiosity exceeds all the bounds of nature and reason, for a long time thronged about his unicorns. The more sensible women forced open the doors of his *hotel* to contemplate his person.

He at first testified some desire of visiting the court; but some of the idlers, who constituted good company and casually went thither, informed him that it was quite out of fashion, that times were greatly changed, and that all amusements were confined to the city. He was invited that very night to sup with a lady whose sense and talents had reached foreign climes, and who had traveled in some countries through which Amazan had passed. This lady gave him great pleasure, as well as the society he met at her house. Here reigned a decent liberty, gaiety without tumult, silence without pedantry, and wit without asperity. He found that *good company* was not quite ideal, though the title was frequently usurped by pretenders. The next day he dined in a society far less amiable, but much more voluptuous. The more he was satisfied with the guests, the more they were pleased with him. He found his soul soften and dissolve, like the aromatics of his country, which gradually melt in a moderate heat, and exhale in delicious perfumes.

After dinner he was conducted to a place of public entertainment which was enchanting; but condemned, however, by the Druids, because it deprived them of their auditors, which, therefore, excited their jealousy. The representation here consisted of agreeable verses, delightful songs, dances which expressed the movements of the soul, and perspectives that charmed the eye in deceiving it. This kind of pastime, which included so many kinds, was known only under a foreign name. It was called an *Opera*, which formerly signified, in the language of work, care, occupation, industry, enterprise, business. This exhibition enchanted him. A female singer, in particular, charmed him by her melodious voice, and the graces that accompanied her. This child of genius, after the performance, was introduced to him by his new friends. He presented her with a handful of diamonds; for which she was so grateful, that she could not leave him all the rest of the day. He supped with her and her companions, and during the delightful repast he forgot his sobriety and became heated and oblivious with wine. * * * What an instance of human frailty!

The beautiful princess of Babylon arrived at this juncture, with her phœnix, her chambermaid Irla, and her two hundred Gangaridian cavaliers mounted on their unicorns. It was a long while before the gates were opened. She immediately asked, if the handsomest, the most courageous, the most sensible, and the most faithful of men was still in that city. The magistrates readily concluded that she meant Amazan. She was conducted to his *hotel*. How great was the palpitation of her heart!—the powerful operation of the tender passion. Her whole soul was penetrated with inexpressible joy, to see once more in her lover the model of constancy. Nothing could prevent her entering his chamber; the curtains were open; and she saw the beautiful Amazan asleep and stupefied with drink.

Formosanta expressed her grief with such screams as made the house echo.
She swooned into the arms of Irla. As soon as she had recovered her senses, she
retired from this fatal chamber with grief blended with rage.

"Oh! just heaven; oh, powerful Oromasdes!" cried the beautiful princess of
Babylon, bathed in tears. "By whom, and for whom am I thus betrayed? He
that could reject for my sake so many princesses, to abandon me for the company of a strolling Gaul! No! I can never survive this affront."

"This is the disposition of all young people," said Irla to her, "from one end
of the world to the other. Were they enamoured with a beauty descended from
heaven, they would at certain moments forget her entirely."

"It is done," said the princess, "I will never see him again whilst I live. Let us
depart this instant, and let the unicorns be harnessed."

The phœnix conjured her to stay at least till Amazan awoke, that he might
speak with him.

"He does not deserve it," said the princess. "You would cruelly offend me.
He would think that I had desired you to reproach him, and that I am willing
to be reconciled to him. If you love me, do not add this injury to the insult he
has offered me."

The phœnix, who after all owed his life to the daughter of the king of
Babylon, could not disobey her. She set out with all her attendants.

"Whither are you going?" said Irla to her.

"I do not know," replied the princess; "we will take the first road we find.
Provided I fly from Amazan for ever, I am satisfied."

The phœnix, who was wiser than Formosanta, because he was divested of
passion, consoled her upon the road. He gently insinuated to her that it was
shocking to punish one's self for the faults of another; that Amazan had given
her proofs sufficiently striking and numerous of his fidelity, so that she should
forgive him for having forgotten himself for one moment in social company;
that this was the only time in which he had been wanting of the grace of
Oromasdes; that it would render him only the more constant in love and virtue
for the future; that the desire of expiating his fault would raise him beyond
himself; that it would be the means of increasing her happiness; that many great
princesses before her had forgiven such slips, and had had no reason to be sorry
afterward; and he was so thoroughly possessed of the art of persuasion, that
Formosanta's mind grew more calm and peaceable. She was now sorry she had
set out so soon. She thought her unicorns went too fast, but she did not dare
return. Great was the conflict between her desire of forgiving and that of
showing her rage—between her love and vanity. However, her unicorns pursued
their pace; and she traversed the world, according to the prediction of her
father's oracle.

When Amazan awoke, he was informed of the arrival and departure of
Formosanta and the phœnix. He was also told of the rage and distraction of
the princess, and that she had sworn never to forgive him.

"Then," said he, "there is nothing left for me to do, but follow her, and kill
myself at her feet."

The report of this adventure drew together his festive companions, who all remonstrated with him. They said that he had much better stay with them; that nothing could equal the pleasant life they led in the centre of arts and refined delicate pleasures; that many strangers, and even kings, preferred such an agreeable enchanting repose to their country and their thrones. Moreover, his vehicle was broken, and another was being made for him according to the newest fashion; that the best tailor of the whole city had already cut out for him a dozen suits in the latest style; that the most vivacious, amiable, and fashionable ladies, at whose houses dramatic performances were represented, had each appointed a day to give him a regale. The girl from the opera was in the meanwhile drinking her chocolate, laughing, singing, and ogling the beautiful Amazan—who by this time clearly perceived she had no more sense than a goose.

A sincerity, cordiality, and frankness, as well as magnanimity and courage, constituted the character of this great prince; he related his travels and misfortunes to his friends. They knew that he was cousin-german to the princess. They were informed of the fatal kiss she had given the king of Egypt. "Such little tricks," said they, "are often forgiven between relatives, otherwise one's whole life would pass in perpetual uneasiness."

Nothing could shake his design of pursuing Formosanta; but his carriage not being ready, he was compelled to remain three days longer among the idlers, who were still feasting and merry-making. He at length took his leave of them, by embracing them and making them accept some of his diamonds that were the best mounted, and recommending to them a constant pursuit of frivolity and pleasure, since they were thereby made more agreeable and happy.

"The Germans," said he, "are the greyheads of Europe; the people of Albion are men formed; the inhabitants of Gaul are the children—and I love to play with children."

X

AMAZAN AND FORMOSANTA BECOME RECONCILED

THE guides had no difficulty in following the route the princess had taken. There was nothing else talked of but her and her large bird. All the inhabitants were still in a state of fascination. The banks of the Loire, of the Dordogue—the Garonne, and the Gironde, still echoed with acclamation.

When Amazan reached the foot of the Pyrenees, the magistrates and Druids of the country made him dance, whether he would or not, a *Tambourin;* but as soon as he cleared the Pyrenees, nothing presented itself that was either gay or joyous. If he here and there heard a peasant sing, it was a doleful ditty. The inhabitants stalked with much gravity, having a few strung beads and a girted poniard. The nation dressed in black, and appeared to be in mourning.

If Amazan's servants asked passengers any questions, they were answered by signs; if they went into an inn, the host acquainted his guests in three words, that there was nothing in the house, but that the things they so pressingly wanted might be found a few miles off.

When these votaries to taciturnity were asked if they had seen the beautiful princess of Babylon pass, they answered with less brevity than usual: "We have seen her—she is not so handsome—there are no beauties that are not tawny—she displays a bosom of alabaster, which is the most disgusting thing in the world, and which is scarce known in our climate."

Amazan advanced toward the province watered by the Betis. The Tyrians discovered this country about twelve thousand years ago, about the time they discovered the great Atlantic Isle, inundated so many centuries after. The Tyrians cultivated Betica, which the natives of the country had never done, being of opinion that it was not their place to meddle with anything, and that their neighbors, the Gauls, should come and reap their harvests. The Tyrians had brought with them some Palestines, or Jews, who, from that time, have wandered through every clime where money was to be gained. The Palestines, by extraordinary usury, at fifty per cent., had possessed themselves of almost all the riches of the country. This made the people of Betica imagine the Palestines were sorcerers; and all those who were accused of witchcraft were burnt, without mercy.

The princess of Babylon alighted in that city which has since been called Sevilla. Her design was to embark upon the Betis to return by Tyre to Babylon, and see again king Belus, her father; and forget, if possible, her perfidious lover —or, at least, to ask him in marriage. She sent for two Palestines, who transacted all the business of the court. They were to furnish her with three ships. The phœnix made all the necessary contracts with them, and settled the price after some little dispute.

The hostess was a great devotee, and her husband, who was no less religious, was a Familiar: that is to say, a spy of the Inquisitors or *Anthropokaies.*

He failed not to inform them, that in his house was a sorceress and two Palestines, who were entering into a compact with the devil, disguised like a large gilt bird.

The Inquisitors having learned that the lady possessed a large quantity of diamonds, swore point blank that she was a sorceress. They waited till night to imprison the two hundred cavaliers and the unicorns (which slept in very extensive stables), for the Inquisitors are cowards.

Having strongly barricaded the gates, they seized the princess and Irla; but they could not catch the phœnix, who flew away with great swiftness. He did not doubt of meeting with Amazan upon the road from Gaul to Sevilla.

He met him upon the frontiers of Betica, and acquainted him with the disaster that had befallen the princess.

Amazan was struck speechless with rage. He armed himself with a steel cuirass damasquined with gold, a lance twelve feet long, two javelins, and an edged sword called the Thunderer, which at one single stroke would rend trees, rocks, and Druids. He covered his beautiful head with a golden casque, shaded with heron and ostrich feathers. This was the ancient armor of Magog, which his sister Aldea gave him when upon his journey in Scythia. The few attendants he had with him all mounted their unicorns.

Amazan, in embracing his dear phœnix, uttered only these melancholy expressions: "I am guilty! Had I not dined with the child of genius from the opera, in the city of the idlers, the princess of Babylon would not have been in this alarming situation. Let us fly to the *Anthropokaies.*" He presently entered Sevilla. Fifteen hundred Alguazils guarded the gates of the inclosure in which the two hundred Gangarids and their unicorns were shut up, without being allowed anything to eat. Preparations were already made for sacrificing the princess of Babylon, her chambermaid Irla, and the two rich Palestines.

The high *Anthropokaie,* surrounded by his subaltern *Anthropokaies,* was already seated upon his sacred tribunal. A crowd of Sevillians joined their two hands, without uttering a syllable, when the beautiful princess, the maid Irla, and the two Palestines were brought forth, with their hands tied behind their backs and dressed in masquerade habits.

The phœnix entered the prison by a dormer window, whilst the Gangarids began to break open the doors. The invincible Amazan shattered them without. They all sallied forth armed, upon their unicorns, and Amazan put himself at their head. He had no difficulty in overthrowing the Alguazils, the Familiars, or *Anthropokaies.* Each unicorn pierced dozens at a time. The thundering Amazan cut to pieces all he met.

Amazan collared the high Inquisitor upon his tribunal, and threw him upon the pile, which was prepared about forty paces distant; and he also cast upon it the other Inquisitors, one after the other. He then prostrated himself at Formosanta's feet. "Ah! how amiable you are," said she; "and how I should adore you, if you had not forsaken me for the company of an opera singer."

Whilst Amazan was making his peace with the princess, whilst his Gangarids cast upon the pile the bodies of all the *Anthropokaies,* and the flames ascended to the clouds, Amazan saw an army that approached him at a distance. An aged monarch, with a crown upon his head, advanced upon a car drawn by eight mules harnessed with ropes. An hundred other cars followed. They were accompanied by grave looking men mounted upon very fine horses. A multitude of people, with greasy hair, followed silently on foot.

Amazan immediately drew up his Gangarids about him, and advanced with his lance couched. As soon as the king perceived him, he took off his crown, alighted from his car, and embraced Amazan's stirrup, saying to him: "Man sent by the gods, you are the avenger of human kind, the deliverer of my country. These monsters, of which you have purged the earth, were my masters. I was forced to submit to their criminal power. My people would have deserted me, if I had only been inclined to moderate their abominable crimes. From this moment I breathe, I reign, and am indebted to you for it."

He afterward respectfully kissed Formosanta's hand, and entreated her to get into his coach (drawn by eight mules) with Amazan, Irla, and the phœnix.

The two Palestine bankers, who still remained prostrate on the ground through fear and terror, now raised their heads. The troops of unicorns followed the king of Betica into his palace.

As the dignity of a king who reigned over a people of characteristic brevity required that his mules should go at a very slow pace, Amazan and Formosanta had time to relate to him their adventures. He also conversed with the phœnix, admiring and frequently embracing him. He easily comprehended how brutal and barbarous the people of the West should be considered, who ate animals, and did not understand their language; that the Gangarids alone had preserved the nature and dignity of primitive man; but he particularly agreed, that the most barbarous of mortals were the *Anthropokaies,* of whom Amazan had just purged the earth. He incessantly blessed and thanked him. The beautiful Formosanta had already forgotten the affair in Gaul, and had her soul filled with nothing but the valor of the hero who had preserved her life. Amazan being made acquainted with the innocence of the embrace she had given to the king of Egypt, and being told of the resurrection of the phœnix, tasted the purest joy, and was intoxicated with the most violent love.

They dined at the palace, but had a very indifferent repast. The cooks of Betica were the worst in Europe. Amazan advised the king to send for some from Gaul. The king's musicians performed, during the repast, that celebrated air which has since been called the *Follies of Spain.* After dinner, matters of business came upon the carpet.

The king enquired of the handsome Amazan, the beautiful Formosanta, and the charming phœnix what they proposed doing. "For my part," said Amazan, "my intention is to return to Babylon, of which I am the presumptive heir, and to ask of my uncle Belus the hand of my cousin-german, the incomparable Formosanta."

"My design certainly is," said the princess, "never to separate from my cousin-german. But I imagine he will agree with me, that I should return first to my father, because he only gave me leave to go upon a pilgrimage to Bassora, and I have wandered all over the world."

"For my part," said the phœnix, "I will follow every where these two tender, generous lovers."

"You are in the right," said the king of Betica; "but your return to Babylon is not so easy as you imagine. I receive daily intelligence from that country by Tyrian ships, and my Palestine bankers, who correspond with all the nations of the earth. The people are all in arms toward the Euphrates and the Nile. The king of Scythia claims the inheritance of his wife, at the head of three hundred thousand warriors on horseback. The kings of Egypt and India are also laying waste the banks of the Tigris and the Euphrates, each at the head of three hundred thousand men, to revenge themselves for being laughed at. The king of Ethiopia is ravaging Egypt with three hundred thousand men, whilst the king of Egypt is absent from his country. And the king of Babylon has as yet only six hundred thousand men to defend himself.

"I acknowledge to you," continued the king, "when I hear of those prodigious armies which are disembogued from the East, and their astonishing magnificence—when I compare them to my trifling bodies of twenty or thirty thousand soldiers, which it is so difficult to clothe and feed; I am inclined to think the Eastern subsisted long before the Western hemisphere. It seems as if we sprung only yesterday from chaos and barbarity."

"Sire," said Amazan, "the last comers frequently outstrip those who first began the career. It is thought in my country that man was first created in India; but this I am not certain of."

"And," said the king of Betica to the phœnix, "what do you think?"

"Sire," replied the phœnix, "I am as yet too young to have any knowledge concerning antiquity. I have lived only about twenty-seven thousand years; but my father, who had lived five times that age, told me he had learned from his father, that the Eastern country had always been more populous and rich than the others. It had been transmitted to him from his ancestors, that the generation of all animals had begun upon the banks of the Ganges. For my part, said he, I have not the vanity to be of this opinion. I cannot believe that the foxes of Albion, the marmots of the Alps, and the wolves of Gaul are descended from my country. In the like manner, I do not believe that the firs and oaks of your country descended from the palm and cocoa trees of India."

"But from whence are we descended, then?" said the king.

"I do not know," said the phœnix; "all I want to know is, whither the beautiful princess of Babylon and my dear Amazan may repair."

"I very much question," said the king, "whether with his two hundred unicorns he will be able to destroy so many armies of three hundred thousand men each."

"Why not?" said Amazan. The king of Betica left the force of this sublime question, "Why not?" but he imagined sublimity alone was not sufficient against innumerable armies.

"I advise you," said he, "to seek the king of Ethiopia. I am related to that black prince through my Palestines. I will give you recommendatory letters to him. As he is at enmity with the king of Egypt, he will be but too happy to be strengthened by your alliance. I can assist you with two thousand sober, brave men; and it will depend upon yourself to engage as many more of the people who reside, or rather skip, about the foot of the Pyrenees, and who are called Vasques or Vascons. Send one of your warriors upon an unicorn, with a few diamonds. There is not a Vascon that will not quit the castle, that is, the thatched cottage of his father, to serve you. They are indefatigable, courageous, and agreeable; and whilst you wait their arrival, we will give you festivals, and prepare your ships. I cannot too much acknowledge the service you have done me."

Amazan realized the happiness of having recovered Formosanta, and enjoyed in tranquillity her conversation, and all the charms of reconciled love—which are almost equal to a growing passion.

A troop of proud, joyous Vascons soon arrived, dancing a *Tambourin*. The haughty and grave Betician troops were now ready. The old sun-burnt king tenderly embraced the two lovers. He sent great quantities of arms, beds, chests, boards, black clothes, onions, sheep, fowls, flour, and particularly garlic, on board the ships, and wished them a happy voyage, invariable love, and many victories.

Proud Carthage was not then a seaport. There were at that time only a few Numidians there, who dried fish in the sun. They coasted along Bizacenes, the Syrthes, the fertile banks where since arose Cyrene and the great Chersonese.

They at length arrived toward the first mouth of the sacred Nile. It was at the extremity of this fertile land that the ships of all commercial nations were already received in the port of Canope, without knowing whether the god Canope had founded this port, or whether the inhabitants had manufactured the god—whether the star Canope had given its name to the city, or whether the city had bestowed it upon the star. All that was known of this matter was, that the city and the star were both very ancient; and this is all that can be known of the origin of things, of what nature soever they may be.

It was here that the king of Ethiopia, having ravaged all Egypt, saw the invincible Amazan and the adorable Formosanta come on shore. He took one for the god of war, and the other for the goddess of beauty. Amazan presented to him the letter of recommendation from the king of Spain. The king of Ethiopia immediately entertained them with some admirable festivals, according to the indispensable custom of heroic times. They then conferred about their expedition to exterminate the three hundred thousand men of the king of Egypt, the three hundred thousand of the emperor of the Indies, and the three hundred thousand of the great Khan of the Scythians, who laid siege to the immense, proud, voluptuous city of Babylon.

The two hundred Spaniards, whom Amazan had brought with him, said that they had nothing to do with the king of Ethiopia's succoring Babylon; that it was sufficient their king had ordered them to go and deliver it; and that they were formidable enough for this expedition.

The Vascons said they had performed many other exploits; that they would alone defeat the Egyptians, the Indians, and the Scythians; and that they would not march unless the Spaniards were placed in the rear-guard.

The two hundred Gangarids could not refrain from laughing at the pretensions of their allies, and they maintained that with only one hundred unicorns, they could put to flight all the kings of the earth. The beautiful Formosanta appeased them by her prudence, and by her enchanting discourse. Amazan introduced to the black monarch his Gangarids, his unicorns, his Spaniards, his Vascons, and his beautiful bird.

Every thing was soon ready to march by Memphis, Heliopolis, Arsinoe, Petra, Artemitis, Sora, and Apamens, to attack the three kings, and to prosecute this memorable war, before which all the wars ever waged by man sink into insignificance.

Fame with her hundred tongues has proclaimed the victories Amazan gained over the three kings, with his Spaniards, his Vascons, and his unicorns. He restored the beautiful Formosanta to her father. He set at liberty all his mistress's train, whom the king of Egypt had reduced to slavery. The great

Khan of the Scythians declared himself his vassal; and his marriage was confirmed with princess Aldea. The invincible and generous Amazan was acknowledged the heir to the kingdom of Babylon, and entered the city in triumph with the phœnix, in the presence of a hundred tributary kings. The festival of his marriage far surpassed that which king Belus had given. The bull Apis was served up roasted at table. The kings of Egypt and India were cup-bearers to the married pair; and these nuptials were celebrated by five hundred illustrious poets of Babylon.

THE WHITE BULL

I

How the Princess Amasidia Meets a Bull

The princess Amasidia, daughter of Amasis, King of Tanis in Egypt, took a walk upon a highway of Peluaium with the ladies of her train. She was sunk in deep melancholy. Tears gushed from her beautiful eyes. The cause of her grief was known, as well as the fears she entertained lest that grief should displease the king, her father. The old man, Mambres, ancient magician and eunuch of the Pharaohs, was beside her, and seldom left her. He was present at her birth. He had educated her, and taught her all that a fair princess was allowed to know of the sciences of Egypt. The mind of Amasidia equaled her beauty. Her sensibility and tenderness rivaled the charms of her person; and it was this sensibility which cost her so many tears.

The princess was twenty-four years old; the magician, Mambres, about thirteen hundred. It was he, as every one knows, who had that famous dispute with Moses, in which the victory was so long doubtful between these two profound philosophers. If Mambres yielded, it was owing to the visible protection of the celestial powers, who favored his rival. It required gods to overcome Mambres!

Amasis made him superintendent of his daughter's household, and he acquitted himself in this office with his usual prudence. His compassion was excited by the sighs of the beautiful Amasidia.

"O, my lover!" said she to herself, "my young, my dear lover! O, greatest of conquerors, most accomplished, most beautiful of men! Almost seven years hast thou disappeared from the world. What God hath snatched thee from thy tender Amasidia? Thou art not dead. The wise Egyptian prophets confess this. But thou art dead to me. I am alone in the world. To me it is a desert. By what extraordinary prodigy hast thou abandoned thy throne and thy mistress?—thy throne, which was the first in the world—however, that is a matter of small consequence; but to abandon me, who adores thee! O, my dear Ne——"

She was going on.

"Tremble to pronounce that fatal name," said Mambres, the ancient eunuch and magician of the Pharaohs. "You would perhaps be discovered by some of the ladies of your court. They are all very much devoted to you, and all fair ladies certainly make it a merit to serve the noble passions of fair princesses. But there may be one among them indiscreet, and even treacherous. You know that your father, although he loves you, has sworn to put you to death, should you pronounce the terrible name always ready to escape your lips. This law is severe; but you have not been educated in Egyptian wisdom to be ignorant of the government of the tongue. Remember that Hippocrates, one of our greatest gods, has always his finger upon his mouth."

The beautiful Amasidia wept, and was silent.

As she pensively advanced toward the banks of the Nile she perceived at a distance, under a thicket watered by the river, an old woman in a tattered gray garment, seated on a hillock. This old woman had beside her a she-ass, a dog, and a he-goat. Opposite to her was a serpent, which was not like the common serpents; for its eyes were mild, its physiognomy noble and engaging, while its skin shone with the liveliest and brightest colors. A huge fish, half immersed in the river, was not the least astonishing figure in the group; and on a neighboring tree were perched a raven and a pigeon. All these creatures seemed to carry on a very animated conversation.

"Alas!" said the princess in a low tone, "these animals undoubtedly speak of their loves, and it is not so much as allowed me to mention the name of mine."

The old woman held in her hand a slender steel chain a hundred fathoms long, to which was fastened a bull who fed in the meadow. This bull was white, perfectly well-made, plump, and at the same time agile, which is a thing seldom to be found. He was indeed the most beautiful specimen that was ever seen of his kind. Neither the bull of Pasiphæ, nor that in whose shape Jupiter appeared when he carried off Europa, could be compared to this noble animal. The charming young heifer into which Isis was changed, would have scarce been worthy of his company.

As soon as the bull saw the princess he ran toward her with the swiftness of a young Arabian horse, who pricks up his ears and flies over the plains and rivers of the ancient Saana to approach the lovely consort whose image reigns in his heart. The old woman used her utmost efforts to restrain the bull. The serpent wanted to terrify him by its hissing. The dog followed him and bit his beautiful limbs. The she-ass crossed his way and kicked him to make him return. The great fish remounted the Nile and, darting himself out of the water, threatened to devour him. The he-goat remained immovable, apparently struck with fear. The raven fluttered round his head as if it wanted to tear out his eyes. The pigeon alone accompanied him from curiosity, and applauded him by a sweet murmur.

So extraordinary a sight threw Mambres into serious reflections. In the meanwhile, the white bull, dragging after him his chain and the old woman, had already reached the princess, who was struck with astonishment and fear. He threw himself at her feet. He kissed them. He shed tears. He looked upon her with eyes in which there was a strange mixture of grief and joy. He dared not to low, lest he should terrify the beautiful Amasidia. He could not speak. A weak use of the voice, granted by heaven to certain animals, was denied him; but all his actions were eloquent. The princess was delighted with him. She perceived that a trifling amusement could suspend for some moments even the most poignant grief.

"Here," said she, "is a most amiable animal. I could wish much to have him in my stable."

At these words the bull bent himself on his knees and kissed the ground.

"He understands me," cried the princess. "He shows me that he wants to be mine. Ah, heavenly magician! ah, divine eunuch! Give me this consolation. Purchase this beautiful bovine. Settle the price with the old woman, to whom he no doubt belongs. This animal must be mine. Do not refuse me this innocent comfort."

All the ladies joined their requests to the entreaties of the princess. Mambres yielded to them, and immediately went to speak to the old woman.

II

How the Wise Mambres, Formerly Magician of Pharaoh, Knew Again the Old Woman, and Was Known by Her

"Madam," said Mambres to her, "you know that ladies, and particularly princesses, have need of amusement. The daughter of the king is distractedly . fond of your bull. I beg that you will sell him to us. You shall be paid in ready money."

"Sir," answered the old woman, "this precious animal does not belong to me. I am charged, together with all the beasts which you see, to keep him with care, to watch all his motions, and to give an exact account of them. God forbid that I should ever have any inclination to sell this invaluable animal."

Mambres, upon this discourse, began to have a confused remembrance of something which he could not yet properly distinguish. He eyed the old woman in the gray cloak with greater attention.

"Respectable lady," said he to her, "I either mistake, or I have seen you formerly."

"I make no mistake, sir," replied the old woman. "I have seen you seven hundred years ago, in a journey which I made from Syria into Egypt some months after the destruction of Troy, when Hiram the second reigned at Tyre, and Nephel Keres in ancient Egypt."

"Ah! madam," cried the old man, "you are the remarkable witch of Endor."

"And you, sir," said the sorceress, embracing him, "are the great Mambres of Egypt."

"O, unforeseen meeting! memorable day! eternal decrees!" said Mambres. "It certainly is not without permission of the universal providence that we meet again in this meadow upon the banks of the Nile near the noble city of Tanis. What, is it indeed you," continued Mambres, "who are so famous upon the banks of your little Jordan, and the first person in the world for raising apparitions?"

"What, is it you, sir," replied Miss Endor, "who are so famous for changing rods into serpents, the day into darkness, and rivers into blood?"

"Yes, madam, but my great age has in part deprived me of my knowledge and power. I am ignorant from whence you have this beautiful bull, and who these animals are that, together with you, watch round him."

The old woman, recollecting herself, raised her eyes to heaven, and then replied:

"My dear Mambres. We are of the same profession, but it is expressly forbidden me to tell you who this bull is. I can satisfy you with regard to the other animals. You will easily know them by the marks which characterize them. The serpent is that which persuaded Eve to eat an apple, and to make her husband partake of it. The ass, that which spoke to your contemporary, Balaam, in a remarkable discourse. The fish, which always carries its head above water, is that which swallowed Jonah a few years ago. The dog is he who followed Raphael and the young Tobit in their journey to Ragusa in Media, in the time of the great Salamanzar. This goat is he who expiates all the sins of your nation. The raven and the pigeon, those which were in the ark of Noah. Great event! universal catastrophe! of which almost all the world is still ignorant. You are now informed. But of the bull you can know nothing."

Mambres, having listened with respect, said:

"The Eternal, O illustrious witch! reveals and conceals what he thinks proper. All these animals who, together with you, are entrusted with the custody of the white bull, are only known to your generous and agreeable nation, which is itself unknown to almost all the world. The miracles which you and yours, I and mine, have performed, shall one day be a great subject of doubt and scandal to inquisitive philosophers. But happily these miracles shall find belief with the devout sages, who shall prove submissive to the enlightened in one corner of the world; and this is all that is necessary."

As he spoke these words, the princess pulled him by the sleeve, and said to him:

"Mambres, will you not buy my bull?"

The magician, plunged into a deep reverie, made no reply, and Amasidia poured forth her tears.

She then addressed herself to the old woman.

"My good woman," said she, "I conjure you, by all you hold most dear in the world, by your father, by your mother, by your nurse, who are certainly still alive, to sell me not only your bull, but likewise your pigeon, which seems very much attached to him.

"As for the other animals, I do not want them; but I shall catch the vapors if you do not sell me this charming bull, who will be all the happiness of my life."

The old woman respectfully kissed the fringe of her gauze robe, and replied:

"Princess, my bull is not to be sold. Your illustrious magician is acquainted with this. All that I can do for your service is to permit him to feed every day near your palace. You may caress him, give him biscuits, and make him dance about at your pleasure; but he must always be under the eyes of all these animals who accompany me, and who are charged with the keeping of him. If he does not endeavor to escape from them, they will prove peaceable; but if he attempt once more to break his chain, as he did upon seeing you, woe be unto him. I would not then answer for his life. This large fish, which you see, will certainly swallow him, and keep him longer than *three* days in his belly; or this serpent, who appears to you so mild, will give him a mortal sting."

The white bull, who understood perfectly the old woman's conversation, but was unable to speak, humbly accepted all the proposals. He laid himself down at her feet; he lowed softly; and, looking tenderly at Amasidia, seemed to say to her,

"Come and see me sometimes upon the lawn."

The serpent now took up the conversation:

"Princess," said he, "I advise you to act implicitly as mademoiselle of Endor has told you."

The she-ass likewise put in her word, and was of the opinion of the serpent.

Amasidia was afflicted that this serpent and this ass should speak so well; while a beautiful bull, who had such noble and tender sentiments, was unable to express them.

"Alas," said she, in a low voice, "nothing is more common at court. One sees there every day fine lords who cannot converse, and contemptible wretches who speak with assurance."

"This serpent," said Mambres, "is not a contemptible wretch. He is perhaps the personage of the greatest importance."

The day now declined, and the princess was obliged to return home, after having promised to come back next day at the same hour. Her ladies of the palace were astonished, and understood nothing of what they had seen or heard. Mambres made reflections. The princess, recollecting that the serpent called the old woman Miss, concluded at random that she was still unmarried, and felt some affliction that such was also her own condition. Respectable affliction! which she concealed, however, with as much care as the name of her lover.

III

How the Beautiful Amasidia Had a Secret Conversation with a Beautiful Serpent

The beautiful princess recommended secrecy to her ladies with regard to what they had seen. They all promised it, and kept their promise for a whole day.

We may believe that Amasidia slept little that night. An inexplicable charm continually recalled the idea of her beautiful bull. As soon, therefore, as she was at freedom with her wise Mambres, she said to him:

"O, sage! this animal turns my head."

"He employs mine very much," said Mambres. "I see plainly that this bovine is very much superior to those of his species. I see that there is a great mystery, and I suspect a fatal event. Your father Amasis is suspicious and violent; and this affair requires that you conduct yourself with the greatest precaution."

"Ah!" said the princess, "I have too much curiosity to be prudent. It is the only sentiment which can unite in my heart with that which preys upon me on account of the lover I have lost. Can I not know who this white bull is that gives me such strange disquiet?"

Mambres replied:

"I have already confessed to you, frankly, that my knowledge declines in proportion as my age advances; but I mistake much if the serpent is not informed of what you are so very desirous of knowing. He does not want sense. He expresses himself with propriety. He has been long accustomed to interfere in the affairs of the ladies."

"Ah! undoubtedly," said Amasidia, "this is the beautiful serpent of Egypt, who, by fixing his tail into his mouth, becomes the emblem of eternity; who enlightens the world when he opens his eyes, and darkens it when he shuts them."

"No, Miss."

"It is then the serpent of Esculapius?"

"Still less."

"It is perhaps Jupiter under the figure of a serpent?"

"Not at all."

"Ah, now I see, I see. It is the rod which you formerly changed into a serpent?"

"No, indeed, it is not; but all these serpents are of the same family. This one has a very high character in his own country. He passes there for the most extraordinary serpent that was ever seen. Address yourself to him. However, I warn you it is a dangerous undertaking. Were I in your place, I would hardly trouble myself either with the bull, the she-ass, the he-goat, the serpent, the fish, the raven, or the pigeon. But passion hurries you on; and all I can do is to pity you, and tremble."

The princess conjured him to procure her a *tête-à-tête* with the serpent. Mambres, who was obliging, consented, and making profound reflections, he went and communicated to the witch in so insinuating a manner the whim of the princess, that the old woman told him Amasidia might lay her commands upon her; that the serpent was perfectly well bred, and so polite to the ladies, that he wished for nothing more than to oblige them, and would not fail to keep the princess's appointment.

The ancient magician returned to inform the princess of this good news; but he still dreaded some misfortune, and made reflections.

"You desire to speak with the serpent, mademoiselle. This you may accomplish whenever your highness thinks proper. But remember you must flatter him; for every animal has a great deal of self-love, and the serpent in particular. It is said he was formerly driven out of heaven for excessive pride."

"I have never heard of it," replied the princess.

"I believe it," said the old man.

He then informed her of all the reports which had been spread about this famous serpent.

"But, my dear princess, whatever singular adventures may have happened to him, you never can extort these secrets from him but by flattery. Having formerly deceived women, it is equitable that a woman in her turn should deceive him."

"I will do my utmost," said the princess; and departed with her maids of honor. The old woman was feeding the bull at a considerable distance.

Mambres left Amasidia to herself, and went and discoursed with the witch. One lady of honor chatted with the she-ass, the others amused themselves with the goat, the dog, the raven, and the pigeon. As for the large fish that frightened every body, he plunged himself into the Nile by order of the old woman.

The serpent then attended the beautiful Amasidia into the grove, where they had the following conversation:

SERPENT.—You cannot imagine, mademoiselle, how much I am flattered with the honor which your highness deigns to confer upon me.

PRINCESS.—Your great reputation, sir, the beauty of your countenance, and the brilliancy of your eyes, have emboldened me to seek for this conversation. I know by public report (if it be not false) that you were formerly a very great lord in the empyrean heaven.

SERPENT.—It is true, miss, I had there a very distinguished place. It is pretended I am a disgraced favorite. This is a report which once went abroad in India. The Brahmins were the first who gave a history of my adventures. And I doubt not but one day or other the poets of the north will make them the subject of an extravagant epic poem, for in truth it is all that can be made of them. Yet I am not so much fallen, but that I have left in this globe a very extensive dominion. I might venture to assert that the whole earth belongs to me.

PRINCESS.—I believe it; for they tell me that your powers of persuasion are irresistible, and to please is to reign.

SERPENT.—I feel, mademoiselle, while I behold and listen to you, that you have over me the same power which you ascribe to me over so many others.

PRINCESS.—You are, I believe, an amiable conqueror. It is said that your conquests among the fair sex have been numerous, and that you began with our common mother, whose name I have unfortunately forgotten.

SERPENT.—They do me injustice. She honored me with her confidence, and I gave her the best advice. I desired that she and her husband should eat heartily of the fruit of the tree of knowledge. I imagined in doing so necessary to the human race was this that I should please the ruler of all things. It seemed to me that a tree not planted to be entirely useless. Would the supreme being have wished to have been served by fools and idiots? Is not the mind formed for the acquisition of knowledge and for improvement? Is not the knowledge of good and evil necessary for doing the one and avoiding the other? I certainly merited their thanks.

PRINCESS.—Yet, they tell me that you have suffered for it. Probably it is since this period that so many ministers have been punished for giving good advice, and so many real philosophers and men of genius persecuted for their writings that were useful to mankind.

SERPENT.—It is my enemies who have told you these stories. They say that I am out of favor at court. But a proof that my influence there has not declined is their own confession that I entered into the council when it was in agitation to try the good man Job: and I was again called upon when the resolution was taken to deceive a certain petty king called Ahab. I alone was charged with this honorable commission.

PRINCESS.—Ah, sir! I do not believe that you are formed to deceive. But since you are always in the ministry, may I beg a favor of you? I hope so amiable a lord will not deny me.

SERPENT.—Mademoiselle, your requests are laws; name your commands.

PRINCESS.—I entreat that you will tell me who this white bull is, for whom I feel such extraordinary sentiments, which both affect and alarm me. I am told that you would deign to inform me.

SERPENT.—Curiosity is necessary to human nature, and especially to your amiable sex. Without it they would live in the most shameful ignorance. I have always satisfied, as far as lay in my power, the curiosity of the ladies. I am accused indeed of using this complaisance only to vex the ruler of the world. I swear to you, that I could propose nothing more agreeable to myself than to obey you; but the old woman must have informed you that the revealing of this secret will be attended with some danger to you.

PRINCESS.—Ah! it is that which makes me still more curious.

SERPENT.—In this I discover the sex to whom I have formerly done service.

PRINCESS.—If you possess any feeling; if rational beings should mutually assist each other; if you have compassion for an unfortunate creature, do not refuse my request.

SERPENT.—You affect me. I must satisfy you; but do not interrupt me.

PRINCESS.—I promise you I will not.

SERPENT.—There was a young king, beautiful, charming, in love, beloved——

PRINCESS.—A young king! beautiful, charming, in love, beloved! And by whom? And who was this king? How old was he? What has become of him? Where is his kingdom? What is his name?

SERPENT.—See, I have scarce begun, and you have already interrupted me. Take care. If you have not more command over yourself, you are undone.

PRINCESS.—Ah, pardon me, sir. I will not repeat my indiscretion. Go on, I beseech you.

SERPENT.—This great king, the most valiant of men, victorious wherever he carried his arms, often dreamed when asleep, and forgot his dreams when awake. He wanted his magicians to remember and inform him what he had dreamed, otherwise he declared he would hang them; for that nothing was more equitable. It is now near seven years since he dreamed a fine dream, which he entirely forgot when he awoke; and a young Jew, full of experience, having revealed it to him, this amiable king was immediately changed into an ox for——

PRINCESS.—Ah! it is my dear Neb——

She could not finish, she fainted away. Mambres, who listened at a distance, saw her fall, and believed her dead.

IV

How They Wanted to Sacrifice the Bull and Exorcise the Princess

Mambres runs to her weeping. The serpent is affected. He, alas, cannot weep; but he hisses in a mournful tone. He cries out, "She is dead." The ass repeats, "She is dead." The raven tells it over again. All the other animals appeared afflicted, except the fish of Jonah, which has always been merciless. The lady of honor, the ladies of the court, arrive and tear their hair. The white bull, who fed at a distance and heard their cries, ran to the grove dragging the old woman after him, while his loud bellowings made the neighboring echoes resound. To no purpose did the ladies pour upon the expiring Amasidia their bottles of rose-water, of pink, of myrtle, of benzoin, of balm of Gilead, of amomum, of gilly-flower, of ambergris. She had not as yet given the smallest signs of life. But as soon as she perceived that the beautiful white bull was beside her, she came to herself, more blooming, more beautiful and lively than ever. A thousand times did she kiss this charming animal, who languishingly leaned his head on her snowy bosom. She called him, "My master, my king, my dear, my life!" She throws her fair arms around his neck, which was whiter than the snow. The light straw does not adhere more closely to the amber, the vine to the elm, nor the ivy to the oak. The sweet murmur of her sighs was heard. Her eyes were seen, now sparkling with a tender flame, and now obscured by those precious tears which love makes us shed.

We may easily judge into what astonishment the lady of honor and ladies of her train were thrown. As soon as they entered the palace, they related to their lovers this extraordinary adventure, and every one with different circumstances, which increased its singularity, and which always contributes to the variety of all histories.

No sooner was Amasis, king of Tanis, informed of these events, than his royal breast was inflamed with just indignation. Such was the wrath of Minos, when he understood that his daughter Pasiphæ lavished her tender favors upon the father of the Minotaur. Thus raged Juno, when she beheld Jupiter caressing the beautiful cow Io, daughter of the river Inachus. Following the dictates of passion, the stern Amasis imprisoned his unhappy daughter, the beautiful Amasidia, in her chamber and placed over her a guard of black eunuchs. He then assembled his privy council.

The grand magician presided there, but had no longer the same influence as formerly. All the ministers of state concluded that this white bull was a sorcerer. It was quite the contrary. He was bewitched. But in delicate affairs they are always mistaken at court.

It was carried by a great majority that the princess should be exorcised, and the old woman and the bull sacrificed.

The wise Mambres contradicted not the opinion of the king and council. The right of exorcising belonged to him. He could delay it under some plausible pretence. The god Apis had died lately at Memphis. A god ox dies just like another ox. And it was not allowed to exorcise any person in Egypt until a new ox was found to replace the deceased.

It was decreed in the council to wait until the nomination should be made of a new god at Memphis.

The good old man, Mambres, perceived to what danger his dear princess was exposed. He knew who her lover was. The syllables NEBU——, which nad escaped her, laid open the whole mystery to the eyes of this sage.

The dynasty of Memphis belonged at that time to the Babylonians. They preserved this remainder of the conquests they had gained under the greatest king of the world, to whom Amasis was a mortal enemy. Mambres had occasion for all his wisdom to conduct himself properly in the midst of so many difficulties. If the king Amasis should discover the lover of his daughter, her death would be inevitable. He had sworn it. The great, the young, the beautiful king of whom she was enamoured, had dethroned the king her father, and Amasis had only recovered his kingdom about seven years. From that time it was not known what had become of the adorable monarch—the conqueror and idol of the nations—the tender and generous lover of the charming Amasidia. Sacrificing the white bull would inevitably occasion the death of the beautiful princess.

What could Mambres do in such critical circumstances? He went, after the council had broken up, to find his dear foster-daughter.

"My dear child," he says, "I will serve you; but I repeat it, they will behead you if ever you pronounce the name of your lover."

"Ah! what signifies my neck," replied the beautiful Amasidia, "if I cánnot embrace that of Nebu——? My father is a cruel man. He not only refuses to give me a charming prince whom I adore, but he declares war against him; and after he was conquered by my lover, he has found the secret of changing him into an ox. Did one ever see more frightful malice? If my father were not my father, I do not know what I should do to him."

"It is not your father who played him this cruel trick," said the wise Mambres. "It was a native of Palestine, one of our ancient enemies, an inhabitant of a little country comprehended in that crowd of kingdoms which your lover subdued in order to polish and refine them.

"Such metamorphoses must not surprise you. You know that formerly I performed more extraordinary. Nothing was at that time more common than those changes which at present astonish philosophers. True history, which we have read together, informs us that Lycaon, king of Arcadia, was changed into a wolf; the beautiful Calista, his daughter, into a bear; Io, the daughter of Inachus, our venerable Isis, into a cow; Daphne into a laurel; Sirinx into a flute; the fair Edith, wife of Lot—the best and most affectionate husband and father ever known in the world—has she not become, in our neighborhood, a pillar of salt, very sharp tasted, which has preserved both her likeness and form, as the great men attest who have seen it? I was witness to this change in my youth. I saw seven powerful cities in the most dry and parched situation in

the world, all at once transformed into a beautiful lake. In the early part of
my life, the whole world was full of metamorphoses.

"In fine, madam, if examples can soothe your grief, remember that Venus
changed Cerastes into an ox."

"I do not know," said the princess, "that examples comfort us. If my lover
were dead, could I comfort myself by the idea that all men die?"

"Your pain may at least be alleviated," replied the sage; "and since your lover
has become an ox, it is possible from an ox he may become a man. As for
me, I should deserve to be changed into a tiger or a crocodile, if I did not employ the little power I have in the service of a princess worthy of the adoration of the world—if I did not labor for the beautiful Amasidia, whom I have
nursed upon my knees, and whom fatal destiny exposes to such rude trials."

V

How the Wise Mambres Conducted Himself Wisely

The sage Mambres having said every thing he could to comfort the princess,
but without succeeding in so doing, ran to the old woman.

"My companion," said he to her, "ours is a charming profession, but a very
dangerous one. You run the risk of being hanged, and your ox of being burned,
drowned or devoured. I don't know what they will do with your other animals; for, prophet as I am, I know very little; but do you carefully conceal the
serpent, and the fish. Let not the one show his head above water, nor the
other venture out of his hole. I will place the ox in one of my stables in the
country. You shall be there with him, since you say that you are not allowed
to abandon him. The good scape-goat may upon this occasion serve as an
expiation. We will send him into the desert loaded with the sins of all the
rest. He is accustomed to this ceremony, which does him no harm; and every
one knows that sin is expiated by means of a he-goat, who walks about for his
own amusement. I only beg of you to lend me immediately Tobit's dog, who
is a very swift greyhound; Balaam's ass, who runs better than a dromedary;
the raven and the pigeon of the ark, who fly with amazing swiftness. I want
to send them on an embassy to Memphis. It is an affair of great consequence."

The old woman replied to the magician:

"You may dispose as you please of Tobit's dog, of Balaam's ass, of the raven
and the pigeon of the ark, and of the scape-goat; but my ox cannot enter a
stable. It is said that he must be always made fast to an iron chain, be always
wet with the dew of heaven, and eat the grass of the field, and his portion be
with the wild beasts.

"He is entrusted to me, and I must obey. What would Daniel, Ezekiel, and
Jeremiah think of me, if I trusted my ox to any other than to myself? I see you
know the secret of this extraordinary animal, but I have not to reproach myself

with having revealed it to you. I am going to conduct him far from this pol-
luted land, toward the lake Sirbon, where he will be sheltered from the cruelties
of the king of Tanis. My fish and my serpent will defend me. I fear nobody
when I serve my master."

"My good woman," answered the wise Mambres, "let the will of God be
done! Provided I can find your white bull again, the lake Sirbon, the lake
Maris, or the lake of Sodom, are to me perfectly indifferent. I want to do nothing but good to him and to you. But why have you spoken to me of Daniel,
Ezekiel, and Jeremiah?"

"Ah! sir," answered the old woman, "you know as well as I what concern
they have in this important affair. But I have no time to lose. I don't desire to
be hanged. I want not that my bull should be burned, drowned, or devoured.
I go to the lake Sirbon by Canopus, with my serpent and my fish. Adieu."

The bull followed her pensively, after having testified his gratitude to the
beneficent Mambres.

The wise Mambres was greatly troubled. He saw that Amasis, king of Tanis,
distracted by the strange passion of his daughter for this animal, and believing
her bewitched, would pursue everywhere the unfortunate bull, who would
infallibly be burned as a socerer in the public place of Tanis, or given to the fish
of Jonah, or be roasted and served up for food. Mambres wanted at all events
to save the princess from this cruel disaster.

He wrote a letter in sacred characters, to his friend, the high priest of Memphis, upon the paper of Egypt, which was not yet in use. Here are the identical
words of this letter:

"Light of the world, lieutenant of Isis, Osiris, and Horus, chief of the circumcised,
you whose altar is justly raised above all thrones! I am informed that your god, the ox
Apis, is dead. I have one at your service. Come quickly with your priests to acknowledge, to worship him, and to conduct him into the stable of your temple. May Isis,
Osiris, and Horus, keep you in their holy and worthy protection, and likewise the
priests of Memphis in their holy care.

"Your affectionate friend,
"Mambres."

He made four copies of this letter for fear of accidents, and enclosed them
in cases of the hardest ebony. Then calling to him his four couriers, whom he
had destined for this employment, (these were the ass, the dog, the raven, and
the pigeon,) he said to the ass:

"I know with what fidelity you served Balaam my brother. Serve me as faithfully. There is not an unicorn who equals you in swiftness. Go, my dear friend,
and deliver this letter to the person himself to whom it is directed, and return."

The ass answered:

"Sir, as I served Balaam, I will serve you. I will go, and I will return."

The sage put the box of ebony into her mouth, and she swiftly departed.
He then called Tobit's dog.

"Faithful dog," said Mambres, "more speedy in thy course than the nimble-footed Achilles, I know what you performed for Tobit, son of Tobit, when you and the angel Raphael accompanied him from Nineveh to Ragusa in Medea, and from Ragusa to Nineveh, and that he brought back to his father ten talents, which the slave Tobit, the father, had lent to the slave Gabellus; for the slaves at that time were very rich. Carry this letter as it is directed. It is much more valuable than ten talents of silver."

The dog then replied:

"Sir, if I formerly followed the messenger Raphael, I can with equal ease execute your commission."

Mambres put the letter into his mouth.

He next spoke in the same manner to the pigeon, who replied:

"Sir, if I brought back a bough into the ark, I will likewise bring you back an answer."

She took the letter in her bill, and the three messengers were out of sight in a moment. Then Mambres addressed the raven:

"I know that you fed the great prophet Elijah, when he was concealed near the torrent of Cherith, so much celebrated in the world. You brought him every day good bread and fat pullets. I only ask of you to carry this letter to Memphis."

The raven answered in these words:

"It is true, sir, that I carried every day a dinner to the great prophet Elijah the Tishbite. I saw him mount in a chariot of fire drawn by fiery horses, although this is not the usual method of traveling. But I always took care to eat half the dinner myself. I am very well pleased to carry your letter, provided you make me certain of two good meals every day, and that I am paid money in advance for my commission."

Mambres, angry, replied:

"Gluttonous and malicious creature, I am not astonished that Apollo has made you black as a mole, after being white as a swan, as you was formerly before you betrayed in the plains of Thessaly the beautiful Coronis, the unfortunate mother of Esculapius. Tell me, did you eat ribs of beef and pullets every day when you were ten whole months in the ark?"

"Sir," said the raven, "we had there very good cheer. They served up roast meat twice a-day to all the fowls of my species who live upon nothing but flesh, such as the vultures, kites, eagles, buzzards, sparrow-hawks, owls, tarsels, falcons, great owls, and an innumerable crowd of birds of prey. They furnished, with the most plentiful profusion, the tables of the lions, leopards, tigers, panthers, hyænas, wolves, bears, foxes, polecats, and all sorts of carnivorous quadrupeds. There were in the ark eight persons of distinction (and the only ones who were then in the world), continually employed in the care of our table and our wardrobe; Noah and his wife, who were about six hundred years old, their three sons and their three wives. It was charming to see with what care, what dexterity, what cleanliness, our eight domestics served four thousand of the most ravenous guests, without reckoning the amazing

trouble which about ten or twelve thousand other animals required, from the
elephant and the giraffe, to the silk-worm and fly. What astonishes me is that
our purveyor Noah is unknown to all the nations of whom he is the stem, but
I don't much mind it. I had already been present at a similar entertainment with
Xesustres, king of Thrace. Such things as these happen from time to time for
the instruction of ravens. In a word, I want to have good cheer, and to be paid
in ready money."

The wise Mambres took care not to give his letter to such a discontented and
babbling animal; and they separated very much dissatisfied with each other.

But it is necessary to know what became of the white bull, and not to lose
sight of the old woman and the serpent. Mambres ordered his intelligent and
faithful domestics to follow them; and as for himself, he advanced in a litter by
the side of the Nile, always making reflections.

"How is it possible," said he to himself, "that a serpent should be master of
almost all the world, as he boasts, and as so many learned men acknowledge,
and that he nevertheless obeys an old woman? How is it, that he is sometimes
called to the council of the Most High, while he creeps upon earth? In what
manner can he enter by his power alone into the bodies of men, and that so
many men pretend to dislodge him by means of words? In short, why does he
pass with a small neighboring people, for having ruined the human race? And
how is it that the human race are entirely ignorant of this? I am old, I have
studied all my life, but I see a crowd of inconsistencies which I cannot reconcile.
I cannot account for what has happened to myself, neither for the great things
which I long ago performed, nor those of which I have been witness. Every
thing well considered, I begin to think that this world subsists by contradictions,
rerum concordia discors, as my master Zoroaster formerly said."

While he was plunged in this obscure metaphysical reasoning—obscure like
all metaphysics—a boatman, singing a jovial song, made fast a small boat by the
side of the river, and three grave personages, half clothed in dirty tattered garments, landed from it; but preserved, under the garb of poverty, the most
majestic and august air. These strangers were Daniel, Ezekiel, and Jeremiah.

VI

How Mambres Met Three Prophets and Gave Them a Good Dinner

These three great men who had the prophetic light in their countenance knew
the wise Mambres to be one of their brethren by some marks of the same light
which he had still remaining, and prostrated themselves before his litter. Mambres likewise knew them to be prophets, more by their uncouth dress, than by
those gleams of fire which proceeded from their august heads. He conjectured
that they came to learn news of the white bull; and conducting himself with
his usual propriety, he alighted from his carriage and advanced a few steps

toward them, with dignified politeness. He raised them up, caused tents to be erected, and prepared a dinner, of which he rightly judged that the prophets had very great need.

He invited the old woman to it, who was only about five hundred paces from them. She accepted the invitation, and arrived leading her white bull.

Two soups were served up, one *de Bisque*, and the other *à la reine*. The first course consisted of a carp's tongue pie, livers of eel-pouts, and pikes; fowls dressed with pistachios, pigeons with truffles and olives; two young turkeys with gravy of cray fish, mushrooms, and morels; and a chipotata. The second course was composed of pheasants, partridges, quails, and ortalons, with four salads; the epergne was in the highest taste; nothing could be more delicious than the side dishes; nothing more brilliant and more ingenious than the dessert. But the wise Mambres took great care to have no boiled beef, nor short ribs, nor tongue, nor palate of an ox, nor cow's udder, lest the unfortunate monarch near at hand should think that they insulted him.

This great and unfortunate prince was feeding near the tent; and never did he feel in a more cruel manner the fatal revolution which had deprived him of his throne for seven long years.

"Alas!" said he, to himself, "this Daniel who has changed me into a bull, and this sorceress my keeper, make the best cheer in the world; while I, the sovereign of Asia, am reduced to the necessity of eating grass, and drinking water."

When they had drunk heartily of the wine of Engaddi, of Tadmor, and of Schiras, the prophets and the witch conversed with more frankness than at the first course.

"I must acknowledge," said Daniel, "that I did not live so well in the lion's den."

"What, sir," said Mambres, "did they put you into a den of lions? How came you not to be devoured?"

"Sir," said Daniel, "you know very well that lions never eat prophets."

"As for me," said Jeremiah, "I have passed my whole life starving of hunger. This is the only day I ever ate a good meal; and were I to spend my life over again, and had it in my power to choose my condition, I must own I would much rather be comptroller-general or bishop of Babylon, than prophet at Jerusalem."

Ezekiel cried, "I was once ordered to sleep three hundred and ninety days upon my left side, and to eat all that time bread of wheat, and barley, and beans, and lentils, cooked in the strangest manner. Still I must own that the cookery of Seigneur Mambres is much more delicate. However, the prophetic trade has its advantages, and the proof is that there are many who follow it."

After they had spoken thus freely, Mambres entered upon business. He asked the three pilgrims the reason of their journey into the dominions of the king of Tanis. Daniel replied, "That the kingdom of Babylon had been all in a flame since Nebuchadnezzar had disappeared; that according to the custom of the court, they had persecuted all the prophets, who passed their lives in sometimes seeing kings humbled at their feet, and sometimes receiving a hundred lashes from them; that at length they had been obliged to take refuge in Egypt for fear of being starved."

Ezekiel and Jeremiah likewise spoke a long time in such fine terms that it was almost impossible to understand them. As for the witch, she had always a strict eye over her charge. The fish of Jonah continued in the Nile, opposite to the tent, and the serpent sported upon the grass. After drinking coffee, they took a walk by the side of the Nile; and the white bull, perceiving the three prophets, his enemies, bellowed most dreadfully, ran furiously at them, and gored them with his horns. As prophets never have anything but skin upon their bones, he would certainly have run them through; but the ruler of the world, who sees all and remedies all, changed them immediately into magpies; and they continued to chatter as before. The same thing happened since to the Pierides; so much has fable always imitated sacred history.

This incident caused new reflections in the mind of Mambres.

"Here," said he, "are three great prophets changed into magpies. This ought to teach us never to speak too much, and always to observe a suitable discretion."

He concluded that wisdom was better than eloquence, and thought profoundly as usual when a great and terrible spectacle presented itself to his eyes.

VII .

How King Amasis Wanted to Give the White Bull to be Devoured by the Fish of Jonah, and Did Not Do It

Clouds of dust floated from south to north. The noise of drums, fifes, psalteries, harps, and sackbuts was heard. Several squadrons and battalions advanced, and Amasis, king of Tanis, was at their head upon an Arabian horse caparisoned with scarlet trappings embroidered with gold. The heralds proclaimed that they should seize the white bull, bind him, and throw him into the Nile, to be devoured by the fish of Jonah; "for the king our lord, who is just, wants to revenge himself upon the white bull, who has bewitched his daughter."

The good old man Mambres made more reflections than ever. He saw very plainly that the malicious raven had told all to the king, and that the princess ran a great risk of being beheaded.

"My dear friend," he said to the serpent, "go quickly and comfort the fair Amasidia, my foster-daughter. Bid her fear nothing whatever may happen, and tell her stories to alleviate her inquietude; for stories always amuse the ladies, and it is only by interesting them that one can succeed in the world."

Mambres next prostrated himself before Amasis, king of Tanis, and thus addressed him:

"O king, live for ever! The white bull should certainly be sacrificed, for your majesty is always in the right; but the ruler of the world has said, this bull must not be swallowed up by the fish of Jonah till Memphis shall have found a god to supply the place of him who is dead. Then thou shalt be revenged, and thy daughter exorcised, for she is possessed. Your piety is too great not to obey the commands of the ruler of the universe."

Amasis, king of Tanis, remained for some time silent and in deep thought.

"The god Apis," said he, at length, "is dead! God rest his soul! When do you think another ox will be found to reign over the fruitful Egypt?"

"Sire," replied Mambres, "I ask but eight days."

"I grant them to you," replied the king, who was very religious, "and I will remain here the eight days. At the expiration of that time I will sacrifice the enemy of my daughter."

Amasis immediately ordered that his tents, cooks, and musicians should be brought, and remained here eight days, as it is related in Manethon.

The old woman was in despair that the bull she had in charge had but eight days to live. She raised phantoms every night, in order to dissuade the king from his cruel resolution; but Amasis forgot in the morning the phantoms he had seen in the night; similar to Nebuchadnezzar, who had always forgotten his dreams.

VIII

How the Serpent Told Stories to the Princess to Comfort Her

MEANWHILE the serpent told stories to the fair Amasidia to soothe her. He related to her how he had formerly cured a whole nation of the bite of certain little serpents, only by showing himself at the end of a staff. He informed her of the conquests of a hero who made a charming contrast with Amphibion, architect of Thebes. Amphibion assembled hewn stones by the sound of his violin. To build a city he had only to play a rigadoon and a minuet; but the other hero destroyed them by the sound of rams' horns. He executed thirty-one powerful kings in a country of four leagues in length and four in breadth. He made stones rain down from heaven upon a battalion of routed Amorites; and having thus exterminated them, he stopped the sun and moon at noon-day between Gibeon and Ajalon, in the road to Beth-horon, to exterminate them still more, after the example of Bacchus, who had stopped the sun and the moon in his journey to the Indies.

The prudence which every serpent ought to have did not allow him to tell the fair Amasidia of the powerful Jepthah, who made a vow and beheaded his daughter, because he had gained a battle. This would have struck terror into the mind of the fair princess. But he related to her the adventures of the great Sampson, who killed a thousand Philistines with the jaw-bone of an ass, who tied together three hundred foxes by the tail, and who fell into the snares of a lady, less beautiful, less tender, and less faithful than the charming Amasidia. He related to her the story of the unfortunate Sechem and Dinah, as well as the more celebrated adventures of Ruth and Boaz; those of Judah and Tamar; those even of Lot's two daughters; those of Abraham and Jacob's servant maids;

those of Reuben and Bilhah; those of David and Bath-sheba; and those of the great king Solomon. In short, every thing which could dissipate the grief of a fair princess.

IX

How the Serpent Did Not Comfort the Princess

"ALL these stories tire me," said Amasidia, for she had understanding and taste. "They are good for nothing but to be commented upon among the Irish by that madman Abbadie, or among the Welsh by that prattler d'Houteville. Stories which might have amused the great, great, great grandmother of my grandmother, appear insipid to me who have been educated by the wise Mambres, and who have read *Human Understanding* by the Egyptian philosopher named Locke, and the *Matron of Ephesus*. I choose that a story should be founded on probability, and not always resemble a dream. I desire to find nothing in it trivial or extravagant; and desire above all, that under the appearance of fable there may appear some latent truth, obvious to the discerning eye, though it escape the observation of the vulgar."

"I am weary of a sun and of a moon which an old beldam disposes of at her pleasure, of mountains which dance, of rivers which return to their sources, and of dead men who rise again; but I am above measure disgusted when such insipid stories are written in a bombastic and unintelligible manner. A lady who expects to see her lover swallowed up by a great fish, and who is apprehensive of being beheaded by her own father, has need of amusement; but suit my amusement to my taste."

"You impose a difficult task upon me," replied the serpent. "I could have formerly made you pass a few hours agreeably enough, but for some time past I have lost both my imagination and memory. Alas! what has become of those faculties with which I formerly amused the ladies? Let me try, however, if I can recollect one moral tale for your entertainment.

"Five and twenty thousand years ago king Gnaof and queen Patra reigned in Thebes with its hundred gates. King Gnaof was very handsome, and queen Patra still more beautiful. But their home was unblest with children, and no heirs were born to continue the royal race.

"The members of the faculty of medicine and of the academy of surgery wrote excellent treatises upon this subject. The queen was sent to drink mineral waters; she fasted and prayed; she made magnificent presents to the temple of Jupiter Ammon, but all was to no purpose. At length a——"

"Mon Dieu!" said the princess, "but I see where this leads. This story is too common, and I must likewise tell you that it offends my modesty. Relate some very true and moral story, which I have never yet heard, to complete the improvement of my understanding and my heart, as the Egyptian professor Lenro says."

"Here then, madam," said the beautiful serpent, "is one most incontestably authentic.

"There were three prophets all equally ambitious and discontented with their condition. They had in common the folly to wish to be kings: for there is only one step from the rank of a prophet to that of a monarch, and man always aspires to the highest step in the ladder of fortune. In other respects, their inclinations and their pleasures were totally different. The first preached admirably to his assembled brethren, who applauded him by clapping their hands; the second was distractedly fond of music; and the third was a passionate lover of the fair sex.

"The angel Ithuriel presented himself one day to them when they were at table discoursing on the sweets of royalty.

" 'The ruler of the world,' said the angel to them, 'sends me to you to reward your virtue. Not only shall you be kings, but you shall constantly satisfy your ruling passions. You, first prophet, I make king of Egypt, and you shall continually preside in your council, who shall applaud your eloquence and your wisdom; and you, second prophet, I make king over Persia, and you shall continually hear most heavenly music; and you, third prophet, I make king of India, and I give you a charming mistress who shall never forsake you.'

"He to whose lot Egypt fell, began his reign by assembling his council, which was composed only of two hundred sages. He made them a long and eloquent speech, which was very much applauded, and the monarch enjoyed the pleasing satisfaction of intoxicating himself with praises uncorrupted by flattery.

"The council for foreign affairs succeeded to the privy council. This was much more numerous; and a new speech received still greater encomiums. And it was the same in the other councils. There was not a moment of intermission in the pleasures and glory of the prophet king of Egypt. The fame of his eloquence filled the world.

"The prophet king of Persia began his reign by an Italian opera, whose choruses were sung by fifteen hundred eunuchs. Their voices penetrated his soul even to the very marrow of the bones, where it resides. To this opera succeeded another, and to the second a third, without interruption.

"The king of India shut himself up with his mistress, and enjoyed perfect pleasure in her society. He considered the necessity of always flattering her as the highest felicity, and pitied the wretched situation of his two brethren, of whom one was obliged always to convene his council and the other to be continually at an opera.

"It happened at the end of a few days, that each of these kings became disgusted with his occupation, and beheld from his window certain wood-cutters who came from an ale-house, and who were going to work in a neighboring forest. They walked arm in arm with their sweet-hearts, with whom they were happy. The kings begged of the angel Ithuriel, that he would intercede with the ruler of the world, and make them wood-cutters."

"I do not know whether the ruler of the world granted their request or not," interrupted the tender Amasidia, "and I do not care much about it; but I know very well that I should ask for nothing of any one, were I with my lover, with my dear Nebuchadnezzar!"

The vaults of the palace resounded this mighty name. At first Amasidia had only pronounced Ne—, afterwards Neb—, then Nebu—. At length passion hurried her on, and she pronounced entire the fatal name, notwithstanding the oath she had sworn to the king, her father. All the ladies of the court repeated Nebuchadnezzar, and the malicious raven did not fail to carry the tidings to the king. The countenance of Amasis, king of Tanis, sank, because his heart was troubled. And thus it was that the serpent, the wisest and most subtle of animals, always beguiled the women, thinking to do them service.

Amasis, in a fury, sent twelve alguazils for his daughter. These men are always ready to execute barbarous orders, because they are paid for it.

X

How They Wanted to Behead the Princess and Did Not Do It

No sooner had the princess entered the camp of the king, than he said to her: "My daughter, you know that all princesses who disobey their fathers are put to death; without which it would be impossible that a kingdom could be well governed. I charged you never to mention the name of your lover, Nebuchadnezzar, my mortal enemy, who dethroned me about seven years ago, and disappeared. In his place, you have chosen a white bull, and you have cried, 'Nebuchadnezzar.' It it just that I behead you."

The princess replied: "My father, thy will be done: but grant me some time to bewail my sad fate."

"That is reasonable," said King Amasis; "and it is a rule established among the most judicious princes. I give you a whole day to bewail your destiny, since it is your desire. To-morrow, which is the eighth day of my encampment, I will cause the white bull to be swallowed up by the fish, and I will behead you precisely at nine o'clock in the morning."

The beautiful Amasidia then went forth in sorrow, to bewail her father's cruelty, and wandered by the side of the Nile, accompanied with the ladies of her train.

The wise Mambres pondered beside her, and reckoned the hours and the moments.

"Well! my dear Mambres," said she to him, "you have changed the waters of the Nile into blood, according to custom, and cannot you change the heart of Amasis, king of Tanis, my father? Will you suffer him to behead me to-morrow, at nine o'clock in the morning?"

"That depends," replied the reflecting Mambres, "upon the speed and diligence of my couriers."

The next day, as soon as the shadows of the obelisks and pyramids marked upon the ground the ninth hour of the day, the white bull was securely bound, to be thrown to the fish of Jonah; and they brought to the king his large sabre.

"Alas! alas!" said Nebuchadnezzar to himself, "I, a king, have been a bull for near seven years; and scarcely have I found the mistress I have lost when I am condemned to be devoured by a fish."

Never had the wise Mambres made such profound reflections; and he was quite absorbed in his melancholy thoughts when he saw at a distance all he expected. An innumerable crowd drew nigh. Three figures of Isis, Osiris, and Horus, joined together, advanced, drawn in a carriage of gold and precious stones, by a hundred senators of Memphis, preceded by a hundred girls, playing upon the sacred sistrums. Four thousand priests, with their heads shaved, were each mounted upon a hippopotamus.

At a great distance appeared with the same pomp, the sheep of Thebes, the dog of Babastes, the cat of Phœbe, the crocodile of Arsinoe, the goat of Mendez, and all the inferior gods of Egypt, who came to pay homage to the great ox, to the mighty Apis, as powerful as Isis, Osiris, and Horus, united together.

In the midst of the demigods, forty priests carried an enormous basket, filled with sacred onions. These were, it is true, gods, but they resembled onions very much.

On both sides of this aisle of gods, people, marched forty thousand warriors, with helmets on their heads, scimitars upon their left thighs, quivers at their shoulders, and bows in their hands.

All the priests sang in chorus, with a harmony which ravished the soul, and which melted it,

> *"Alas! alas! our ox is dead—*
> *We'll have a finer in its stead."*

And at every pause was heard the sound of the sistrums, of cymbals, of tabors, of psalteries, of bagpipes, harps, and sackbuts.

Amasis, king of Tanis, astonished at this spectacle, beheaded not his daughter. He sheathed his scimitar.

XI

APOTHEOSIS OF THE WHITE BULL. TRIUMPH OF THE WISE MAMBRES. THE SEVEN YEARS PROCLAIMED BY DANIEL ARE ACCOMPLISHED. NEBUCHADNEZZAR RESUMES THE HUMAN FORM, MARRIES THE BEAUTIFUL AMASIDIA, AND ASCENDS THE THRONE OF BABYLON

"GREAT king," said Mambres to him, "the order of things is now changed. Your majesty must set the example. O king! quickly unbind the white bull, and be the first to adore him."

Amasis obeyed, and prostrated himself with all his people. The high priest of Memphis presented to the new god Apis the first handful of hay; the Princess Amasidia tied to his beautiful horns festoons of roses, anemonies, ranunculuses, tulips, pinks, and hyacinths. She took the liberty to kiss him, but with profound respect. The priests strewed palms and flowers on the road by which they were to conduct him to Memphis. And the wise Mambres, still making reflections, whispered to his friend, the serpent:

.."*Daniel changed this monarch into a bull, and I have changed this bull into a god!*"

They returned to Memphis in the same order, and the king of Tanis, in some confusion, followed the band. Mambres, with a serene and diplomatic air, walked by his side. The old woman came after, much amazed. She was accompanied by the serpent, the dog, the she-ass, the raven, the pigeon, and the scape-goat. The great fish mounted up the Nile. Daniel, Ezekiel, and Jeremiah, changed into magpies, brought up the rear.

When they had reached the frontiers of the kingdom, which are not far distant, King Amasis took leave of the bull Apis, and said to his daughter:

"My daughter, let us return into my dominions, that I may behead you, as it has been determined in my royal breast, because you have pronounced the name of Nebuchadnezzar, my enemy, who dethroned me seven years ago. When a father has sworn to behead his daughter, he must either fulfill his oath, or sink into hell for ever; and I will not damn myself out of love for you."

The fair princess Amasidia replied to the King Amasis:

"My dear father, whom it pleases you go and behead, but it shall not be me. I am now in the territories of Isis, Osiris, Horus, and Apis. I will never forsake my beautiful white bull, and I will continue to kiss him, till I have seen his apotheosis in his stable in the holy city of Memphis. It is a weakness pardonable in a young lady of high birth."

Scarce had she spoken these words, when the ox Apis cried out:

"My dear Amasidia, I will love you whilst I live!"

This was the first time that the god Apis had been heard to speak during the forty thousand years that he had been worshipped.

The serpent and the she-ass cried out, "the seven years are accomplished!" And the three magpies repeated, "the seven years are accomplished!"

All the priests of Egypt raised their hands to heaven.

The god on a sudden was seen to lose his two hind legs, his two fore legs were changed into two human legs; two white strong muscular arms grew from his shoulders; his taurine visage was changed to the face of a charming hero; and he once more became the most beautiful of mortals.

"I choose," cried he, "rather to be the lover of the beautiful Amasidia than a god. I am Nebuchadnezzar, KING OF KINGS!"

This metamorphosis astonished all the world, except the wise Mambres. But what surprised nobody was that Nebuchadnezzar immediately married the fair Amasidia in the presence of this assembly.

He left his father-in-law in quiet possession of the kingdom of Tanis; and made noble provision of the she-ass, the serpent, the dog, the pigeon, and even for the raven, the three magpies, and the large fish; showing to all the world that he knew how to forgive as well as to conquer.

The old woman had a considerable pension placed at her disposal.

The scape-goat was sent for a day into the wilderness, that all past sins might be expiated; and had afterwards twelve sprightly goats for his companions.

The wise Mambres returned to his palace, and made reflections.

Nebuchadnezzar, after having embraced the magician, his benefactor, governed in tranquillity the kingdoms of Memphis, Babylon, Damascus, Balbec, Tyre, Syria, Asia Minor, Scythia, the countries of Thiras, Mosok, Tubal, Madai, Gog, Magog, Javan, Sogdiana, Aroriana, the Indes, and the Isles; and the people of this vast empire cried out aloud every morning at the rising of the sun:

"Long live great Nebuchadnezzar, king of kings, who is no longer an ox!"

Since that time it has been custom in Babylon, when the sovereign, deceived by his satraps, his magicians, treasurers or wives, at length to acknowledge his errors, and amends his conduct, for all the people to cry out at his gate:

"Long live our great king, who is no longer an ox."

CANDIDE

I

How Candide Was Brought Up in a Fine Castle, and How He Was Expelled From Thence

There lived in Westphalia, in the castle of my Lord the Baron of Thunder-ten-tronckh, a young man, on whom nature had bestowed the most agreeable manners. His face was the index to his mind. He had an upright heart, with an easy frankness; which, I believe, was the reason he got the name of *Candide*. He was suspected, by the old servants of the family, to be the son of my Lord the Baron's sister, by a very honest gentleman of the neighborhood, whom the young lady declined to marry, because he could only produce seventy-one armorial quarterings; the rest of his genealogical tree having been destroyed through the injuries of time.

The Baron was one of the most powerful lords in Westphalia; his castle had both a gate and windows; and his great hall was even adorned with tapestry. The dogs of his outer yard composed his hunting pack upon occasion, his grooms were his huntsmen, and the vicar of the parish was his chief almoner. He was called My Lord by everybody, and everyone laughed when he told his stories.

My Lady the Baroness, who weighed about three hundred and fifty pounds, attracted, by that means, very great attention, and did the honors of the house with a dignity that rendered her still more respectable. Her daughter Cunegonde, aged about seventeen years, was of a ruddy complexion, fresh, plump, and well calculated to excite the passions. The Baron's son appeared to be in every respect worthy of his father. The preceptor, Pangloss, was the oracle of the house, and little Candide listened to his lectures with all the simplicity that was suitable to his age and character.

Pangloss taught metaphysico-theologo-cosmolonigology. He proved most admirably, that there could not be an effect without a cause; that, in this best of possible worlds, my Lord the Baron's castle was the most magnificent of castles, and my Lady the best of Baronesses that possibly could be.

"It is demonstrable," said he, "that things cannot be otherwise than they are: for all things having been made for some end, they must necessarily be for the best end. Observe well, that the nose has been made for carrying spectacles; therefore we have spectacles. The legs are visibly designed for stockings, and therefore we have stockings. Stones have been formed to be hewn, and make castles; therefore my Lord has a very fine castle; the greatest baron of the province ought to be the best accommodated. Swine were made to be eaten; therefore we eat pork all the year round: consequently, those who have merely asserted that all is good have said a very foolish thing; they should have said all is the best possible."

Candide listened attentively, and believed implicitly; for he thought Miss Cunegonde extremely handsome, though he never had the courage to tell her so. He concluded, that next to the good fortune of being Baron of Thunder-ten-tronckh, the second degree of happiness was that of being Miss Cunegonde, the third to see her every day, and the fourth to listen to the teachings of Master Pangloss, the greatest philosopher of the province, and consequently of the whole world.

One day Cunegonde having taken a walk in the environs of the castle, in a little wood, which they called a park, espied Doctor Pangloss giving a lesson in experimental philosophy to her mother's chambermaid; a little brown wench, very handsome, and very docile. As Miss Cunegonde had a strong inclination for the sciences, she observed, without making any noise, the reiterated experiments that were going on before her eyes; she saw very clearly the sufficient reason of the Doctor, the effects and the causes; and she returned greatly flurried, quite pensive, and full of desire to be learned; imagining that she might be a sufficient reason for young Candide, who also, might be the same to her.

On her return to the castle, she met Candide, and blushed; Candide also blushed; she wished him good morrow with a faltering voice, and Candide answered her, hardly knowing what he said. The next day, after dinner, as they arose from table, Cunegonde and Candide happened to get behind the screen. Cunegonde dropped her handkerchief, and Candide picked it up; she, not thinking any harm, took hold of his hand; and the young man, not thinking any harm either, kissed the hand of the young lady, with an eagerness, a sensibility, and grace, very particular; their lips met, their eyes sparkled, their knees trembled, their hands strayed.—— The Baron of Thunder-ten-tronckh happening to pass close by the screen, and observing this cause and effect, thrust Candide out of the castle, with lusty kicks. Cunegonde fell into a swoon and as soon as she came to herself, was heartily cuffed on the ears by my Lady the Baroness. Thus all was thrown into confusion in the finest and most agreeable castle possible.

II

What Became of Candide among the Bulgarians

Candide being expelled the terrestrial paradise, rambled a long while without knowing where, weeping, and lifting up his eyes to heaven, and sometimes turning them towards the finest of castles, which contained the handsomest of baronesses. He laid himself down, without his supper, in the open fields, between two furrows, while the snow fell in great flakes. Candide, almost frozen to death, crawled next morning to the neighboring village, which was called Walber-ghoff-trarbk-dikdorff. Having no money, and almost dying with hunger and fatigue, he stopped in a directed posture before the gate of an inn. Two men, dressed in blue, observing him in such a situation, "Brother," says one of them to the other, "there is a young fellow well built, and of a proper height." They accosted Candide, and invited him very civilly to dinner.

"Gentlemen," replied Candide, with an agreeable modesty, "you do me much honor, but I have no money to pay my shot."

"O sir," said one of the blues, "persons of your appearance and merit never pay anything; are you not five feet five inches high?"

"Yes, gentlemen, that is my height," returned he, making a bow.

"Come, sir, sit down at table; we will not only treat you, but we will never let such a man as you want money; men are made to assist one another."

"You are in the right," said Candide; "that is what Pangloss always told me, and I see plainly that everything is for the best."

They entreated him to take a few crowns, which he accepted, and would have given them his note; but they refused it, and sat down to table.

"Do not you tenderly love——?"

"O yes," replied he, "I tenderly love Miss Cunegonde."

"No," said one of the gentlemen; "we ask you if you do tenderly love the King of the Bulgarians?"

"Not at all," said he, "for I never saw him."

"How! he is the most charming of kings, and you must drink his health."

"O, with all my heart, gentlemen," and drinks.

"That is enough," said they to him; "you are now the bulwark, the support, the defender, the hero of the Bulgarians; your fortune is made, and you are certain of glory." Instantly they put him in irons, and carried him to the regiment. They made him turn to the right, to the left, draw the rammer, return the rammer, present, fire, step double; and they gave him thirty blows with a cudgel. The next day, he performed his exercises not quite so badly, and received but twenty blows; the third day the blows were restricted to ten, and he was looked upon by his fellow-soldiers as a kind of prodigy.

Candide, quite stupefied, could not well conceive how he had become a hero. One fine Spring day he took it into his head to walk out, going straight forward, imagining that the human, as well as the animal species, were entitled to make whatever use they pleased of their limbs. He had not travelled two leagues, when four other heroes, six feet high, came up to him, bound him, and put him into a dungeon. He is asked by a Court-martial, whether he chooses to be whipped six and thirty times through the whole regiment, or receive at once twelve bullets through the forehead? He in vain argued that the will is free, and that he chose neither the one nor the other; he was obliged to make a choice; he therefore resolved, in virtue of God's gift called *free-will*, to run the gauntlet six and thirty times. He underwent this discipline twice. The regiment being composed of two thousand men, he received four thousand lashes, which laid open all his muscles and nerves, from the nape of the neck to the back. As they were proceeding to a third course, Candide, being quite spent, begged as a favor that they would be so kind as to shoot him; he obtained his request; they hoodwinked him, and made him kneel; the King of the Bulgarians, passing by, inquired into the crime of the delinquent; and as this prince was a person of great penetration, he discovered from what he heard of Candide, that he was a young metaphysician, entirely ignorant of the things of this world; and he granted him his pardon, with a clemency which will be extolled in all histories, and throughout all ages. An experienced surgeon cured Candide in three weeks, with e-mollients prescribed by no less master than Dioscorides. His skin had already begun to grow again, and he was able to walk, when the King of the Bulgarians gave battle to the King of the Abares.

III

How Candide Made His Escape from the Bulgarians, and What Afterwards Befell Him

Nothing could be so fine, so neat, so brilliant, so well ordered, as the two armies. The trumpets, fifes, hautboys, drums, and cannon, formed an harmony superior to what hell itself could invent. The cannon swept off at first about six thousand men on each side; afterwards, the musketry carried away from the best of worlds, about nine or ten thousand rascals that infected its surface. The bayonet was likewise the sufficient reason of the death of some thousands of men. The whole number might amount to about thirty thousand souls. Candide, who trembled like a philosopher, hid himself as well as he could, during this heroic butchery.

At last, while each of the two kings were causing *Te Deum*—glory to God —to be sung in their respective camps, he resolved to go somewhere else, to reason upon the effects and causes. He walked over heaps of the dead and dying; he came at first to a neighboring village belonging to the Abares, but found it in ashes; for it had been burnt by the Bulgarians, according to the law of nations. Here were to be seen old men full of wounds, casting their eyes on their murdered wives, who were holding their infants to their bloody breasts. You might see in another place virgins outraged after they had satisfied the natural desires of some of those heroes, whilst breathing out their last sighs. Others, half-burnt, praying earnestly for instant death. The whole field was covered with brains, and with legs and arms lopped off.

Candide betook himself with all speed to another village. It belonged to the Bulgarians, and had met with the same treatment from the Abarian heroes. Candide, walking still forward over quivering limbs, or through rubbish of houses, got at last out of the theatre of war, having some small quantity of provisions in his knapsack, and never forgetting Miss Cunegonde. His provisions failed him when he arrived in Holland; but having heard that every one was rich in that country, and that they were Christians, he did not doubt but he should be as well treated there as he had been in my Lord the Baron's castle, before he had been expelled thence on account of Miss Cunegonde's sparkling eyes.

He asked alms from several grave looking persons, who all replied, that if he continued that trade, they would confine him in a house of correction, where he should learn to earn his bread.

He replied afterwards to a man, who for a whole hour had been discoursing on the subject of charity, before a large assembly. This orator, looking at him askance, said to him:

"What are you doing here? Are you for the good cause?"

"There is no effect without a cause," replied Candide, modestly; "all is necessarily linked, and ordered for the best. A necessity banished me from Miss Cunegonde; a necessity forced me to run the gauntlet; another necessity makes me beg my bread, till I can get into some business by which to earn it. All this could not be otherwise."

"My friend," said the orator to him, "do you believe that the Anti-Christ is alive?"

"I never heard whether he is or not," replied Candide; "but whether he is, or is not, I want bread!"

"You do not deserve to eat any," said the other; "get you gone, you rogue; get you gone, you wretch; never in thy life come near me again!"

The orator's wife, having popped her head out of the chamber window, and seeing a man who doubted whether Anti-Christ was alive, poured on his head a full vessel of dirty water. Oh heavens! to what excess does religious zeal transport the fair sex!

A man who had not been baptized, a good Anabaptist, named *James*, saw the barbarous and ignominious manner with which they treated one of his brethren, a being with two feet, without feathers, and endowed with a rational soul. He took him home with him, cleaned him, gave him bread and beer, made him a present of two florins, and offered to teach him the method of working in his manufactories of Persian stuffs, which are fabricated in Holland. Candide, prostrating himself almost to the ground, cried out, "Master Pangloss argued well when he said that everything is for the best in this world; for I am infinitely more affected with your very great generosity, than by the hard-heartedness of that gentleman with the cloak, and the lady his wife."

Next day, as he was taking a walk, he met a beggar, all covered over with sores, his eyes half dead, the tip of his nose eaten off, his mouth turned to one side of his face, his teeth black, speaking through his throat, tormented with a violent cough, with gums so rotten, that his teeth came near falling out every time he spit.

IV

How Candide Met His Old Master of Philosophy, Dr. Pangloss, and What Happened to Them

Candide moved still more with campassion than with horror, gave this frightful mendicant the two florins which he had received of his honest Anabaptist James. The spectre fixed his eyes attentively upon him, dropt some tears, and was going to fall upon his neck. Candide, affrighted, drew back.

"Alas!" said the one wretch to the other, "don't you know your dear Pangloss?"

"What do I hear! Is it you, my dear master! you in this dreadful condition! What misfortune has befallen you? Why are you no longer in the most magnificent of castles? What has become of Miss Cunegonde, the nonpareil of the fair sex, the master-piece of nature?"

"I have no more strength," said Pangloss.

Candide immediately carried him to the Anabaptist's stable, where he gave him a little bread to eat. When Pangloss was refreshed a little, "Well," said Candide, "what has become of Cunegonde?"

"She is dead," replied the other.

Candide fainted away at this word; but his friend recovered his senses, with a little bad vinegar which he found by chance in the stable.

Candide, opening his eyes, cried out, "Cunegonde is dead! Ah, best of worlds, where art thou now? But of what distemper did she die? Was not the cause her seeing me driven out of the castle by my Lord, her father, with such hard kicks on the breech?"

"No," said Pangloss, "she was gutted by some Bulgarian soldiers, after having been barbarously ravished. They knocked my Lord the Baron on the head for attempting to protect her; my Lady the Baroness was cut in pieces; my poor pupil was treated like his sister; and as for the castle, there is not one stone left upon another, nor a barn, nor a sheep, nor a duck, nor a tree. But we have been sufficiently revenged; for the Abarians have done the very same thing to a neighboring barony, which belonged to a Bulgarian Lord."

At this discourse, Candide fainted away a second time, but coming to himself, and having said all that he ought to say, he enquired into the cause and the effect, and into the sufficient reason that had reduced Pangloss to so deplorable a condition. "Alas," said the other, "it was love; love, the comforter of the human race, the preserver of the universe, the soul of all sensible beings, tender love." "Alas!" said Candide, "I know this love, the sovereign of hearts, the soul of our soul; yet it never cost me more than a kiss, and twenty kicks. But how could this charming cause produce in you so abominable an effect?"

Pangloss made answer as follows: "Oh my dear Candide, you knew Paquetta, the pretty attendant on our noble Baroness; I tasted in her arms the delights of Paradise, which produced those torments of hell with which you see me devoured. She was infected, and perhaps she is dead. Paquetta received this present from a very learned cavalier, who had it from an old countess, who received it from a captain of horse, who was indebted for it to a marchioness, who got it from a Spaniard. For my part, I shall give it to nobody, for I am dying."

"Oh Pangloss!" cried Candide, "what a strange genealogy! Was not the devil at the head of it?" "Not at all," replied the great man; "it was a thing indispensable; a necessary ingredient in the best of worlds; for if the Spaniard had not catched, in an island of America, this distemper, we should have had neither chocolate nor cochineal. It may also be observed, that to this day, upon our continent, this malady is as peculiar to us, as is religious controversy. The Turks, the Indians, the Persians, the Chinese, the Siamese, and the Japanese know nothing of it yet. But there is sufficient reason why they, in their turn, should become acquainted with it, a few centuries hence. In the mean time, it has made marvellous progress among us, and especially in those great armies composed of honest hirelings, well disciplined, who decide the fate of states; for we may rest assured, that when thirty thousand men in a pitched battle fight against troops equal to them in number, there are about twenty thousand of them on each side who have the pox."

"That is admirable," said Candide; "but you must be cured." "Ah! how can I?" said Pangloss; "I have not a penny, my friend; and throughout the whole extent of this globe, we cannot get any one to bleed us, or give us a glister, without paying for it, or getting some other person to pay for us."

This last speech determined Candide. He went and threw himself at the feet of his charitable Anabaptist James, and gave him so touching a description of the state his friend was reduced to, that the good man did not hesitate to entertain Dr. Pangloss, and he had him cured at his own expense. During the cure, Pangloss lost only an eye and an ear. As he wrote well, and understood arithmetic perfectly, the Anabaptist made him his bookkeeper. At the end of two months, being obliged to go to Lisbon on account of his business, he took the two philosophers along with him, in his ship. Pangloss explained to him how every thing was such as it could not be better; but James was not of this opinion. "Mankind," said he, "must have somewhat corrupted their nature, for they were not born wolves, and yet they have become wolves; God has given them neither cannon of twenty-four pounds, nor bayonets; and yet they have made cannon and bayonets to destroy one another, I might throw into the account bankrupts; and the law which seizes on the effects of bankrupts only to bilk the creditors." "All this was indispensable," replied the one-eyed doctor, "and private misfortunes constitute the general good; so that the more private misfortunes there are, the whole is better." While he was thus reasoning, the air grew dark, the winds blew from the four quarters of the world, and the ship was attacked by a dreadful storm, within sight of the harbor of Lisbon.

V

TEMPEST, SHIPWRECK, EARTHQUAKE AND WHAT BECAME OF DR. PANGLOSS, CANDIDE AND JAMES THE ANABAPTIST

ONE half of the passengers being weakened, and ready to breathe their last, with the inconceivable anguish which the rolling of the ship conveyed through the nerves and all the humors of the body, which were quite disordered, were not capable of being alarmed at the danger they were in. The other half uttered cries and made prayers; the sails were rent, the masts broken, and the ship became leaky. Every one worked that was able, nobody cared for any thing, and no order was kept. The Anabapist contributed his assistance to work the ship. As he was upon deck, a furious sailor rudely struck him, and laid him sprawling on the planks; but with the blow he gave him, he himself was so violently jolted, that he tumbled overboard with his head foremost, and remained suspended by a piece of a broken mast. Honest James ran to his assistance, and helped him on deck again; but in the attempt, he fell into the sea, in the sight of the sailor, who suffered him to perish, without deigning to look upon him. Candide drew near and saw his benefactor, one moment emerging, and the next swallowed up for ever. He was just going to throw himself into the sea after him, when the philosopher Pangloss hindered him, by demonstrating to him, that the road to Lisbon had been made on purpose for this Anabaptist to be drowned in. While he was proving this, *a priori*, the vessel foundered, and all perished except Pangloss, Candide, and the brutal sailor, who drowned the virtuous Anabaptist. The villain luckily swam ashore, whither Pangloss and Candide were carried on a plank.

When they had recovered themselves a little, they walked towards Lisbon. They had some money left, with which they hoped to save themselves from hunger, after having escaped from the storm.

Scarce had they set foot in the city, bewailing the death of their benefactor, when they perceived the earth to tremble under their feet, and saw the sea swell in the harbor, and dash to pieces the ships that were at anchor. The whirling flames and ashes covered the streets and public places, the houses tottered, and their roofs fell to the foundations, and the foundations were scattered; thirty thousand inhabitants of all ages and sexes were crushed to death in the ruins. The sailor, whistling and swearing, said: "There is some booty to be got here." "What can be the sufficient reason of this phenomenon?" said Pangloss. "This is certainly the last day of the world," cried Candide. The sailor ran quickly into the midst of the ruins, encountered death to find money, found it, laid hold of it, got drunk, and having slept himself sober, purchased the favors of the first willing girl he met with, among the ruins of the demolished houses, and in the midst of the dying and the dead. While he was thus engaged, Pangloss pulled him by the sleeve. "My friend," said he, "this is not right; you trespass against universal reason, you choose your time badly." "Brains and blood!" answered the other; "I am a sailor, and was born at Batavia; you have mistaken your man, this time, with your universal reason."

Some pieces of stone having wounded Candide, he lay sprawling in the street, and covered with rubbish. "Alas!" said he to Pangloss, "get me a little wine and oil; I am dying." "This trembling of the earth is no new thing," answered Pangloss. The City of Lima, in America, experienced the same concussions last year; the same cause has the same effects; there is certainly a train of sulphur under the earth, from Lima to Lisbon." "Nothing is more probable," said Candide; "but, for God's sake, a little oil and wine." "How probable?" replied the philosopher; "I maintain that the thing is demonstrable." Candide lost all sense, and Pangloss brought him a little water from a neighboring fountain.

The day following, having found some provisions, in rummaging through the rubbish, they recruited their strength a little. Afterwards, they employed themselves like others, in administering relief to the inhabitants that had escaped from death. Some citizens that had been relieved by them gave them as good a dinner as could be expected amidst such a disaster. It is true that the repast was mournful, and the guests watered their bread with their tears. But Pangloss consoled them by the assurance that things could not be otherwise; "For," said he, "all this must necessarily be for the best. As this volcano is at Lisbon, it could not be elsewhere; as it is impossible that things should not be what they are, as all is good."

A little man clad in black, who belonged to the inquisition, and sat at his side, took him up very politely, and said: "It seems, sir, you do not believe in original sin; for if all is for the best, then there has been neither fall nor punishment."

"I most humbly ask your excellency's pardon," answered Pangloss, still more politely; "for the fall of man and the curse necessarily entered into the best of worlds possible." "Then, sir, you do not believe there is liberty," said the inquisitor. "Your excellency will excuse me," said Pangloss; "liberty can consist with absolute necessity; for it was necessary we should be free; because, in short, the determinate will——"

Pangloss was in the middle of his proposition, when the inquisitor made a signal with his head to the tall armed footman in a cloak, who waited upon him, to bring him a glass of port wine.

VI

How a Fine Inquisition Was Celebrated to Prevent Earthquakes, and How Candide Was Whipped

AFTER the earthquake, which had destroyed three-fourths of Lisbon, the sages of the country could not find any means more effectual to prevent a total destruction, than to give the people a splendid inquisition. It had been decided by the university of Coimbra, that the spectacle of some persons burnt to death by a slow fire, with great ceremony, was an infallible antidote for earthquakes.

In consequence of this resolution, they had seized a Biscayan, convicted of having married his god-mother, and two Portuguese, who, in eating a pullet, had stripped off the lard. After dinner, they came and secured Dr. Pangloss, and his disciple Candide; the one for having spoken too freely, and the other for having heard with an air of approbation. They were both conducted to separate apartments, extremely damp, and never incommoded with the sun. Eight days after, they were both clothed with a gown and had their heads—adorned with paper crowns. Candide's crown and gown were painted with inverted flames, and with devils that had neither tails nor claws; but Pangloss' devils had claws and tails, and the flames were pointed upwards. Being thus dressed, they marched in procession, and heard a very pathetic speech followed by fine music on a squeaking organ. Candide was whipped on the back in cadence, while they were singing; the Biscayan, and the two men who would not eat lard, were burnt; and Pangloss, though it was contrary to custom, was hanged. The same day, the earth shook anew, with a most dreadful noise.

Candide, affrighted, interdicted, astonished, all bloody, all panting, said to himself: "If this is the best of possible worlds, what then are the rest? Supposing I had not been whipped now, I have been so, among the Bulgarians; but, oh, my dear Pangloss, thou greatest of philosophers, that it should be my fate to see thee hanged without knowing for what! Oh! my dear Anabaptist! thou best of men, that it should be thy fate to be drowned in the harbor! Oh! Miss Cunegonde! the jewel of ladies, that it should be thy fate to have been outraged and slain!"

He returned, with difficulty, supporting himself, after being lectured, whipped, absolved, and blessed, when an old woman accosted him, and said: "Child, take courage, and follow me."

VII

How an Old Woman Took Care of Candide, and How He Found the Object He Loved

CANDIDE did not take courage, but he followed the old woman to a ruinated house. She gave him a pot of pomatum to anoint himself, left him something to eat and drink, and showed him a very neat little bed, near which was a complete suit of clothes. "Eat, drink, and sleep," said she to him, "and may God take care of you. I will be back to-morrow." Candide, astonished at all he had seen, at all he had suffered, and still more at the charity of the old woman, offered to kiss her hand. "You must not kiss my hand," said the old woman, "I will be back to-morrow. Rub yourself with the pomatum, eat and take rest."

Candide, notwithstanding so many misfortunes, ate, and went to sleep. Next morning, the old woman brought him his breakfast, looked at his back, and rubbed it herself with another ointment; she afterwards brought him his dinner; and she returned at night, and brought him his supper. The day following she performed the same ceremonies. "Who are you?" would Candide always say to her. "Who has inspired you with so much goodness? What thanks can I render you?" The good woman made no answer; she returned in the evening, but brought him no supper. "Come along with me," said she, "and say not a word." She took him by the arm, and walked with him into the country about a quarter of a mile; they arrived at a house that stood by itself; surrounded with gardens and canals. The old woman knocked at a little door, which being opened, she conducted Candide by a private stair-case into a gilded closet, and leaving him on a brocade couch, shut the door and went her way. Candide thought he was in a revery, and looked upon all his life as an unlucky dream, but at the present moment, a very agreeable vision.

The old woman returned very soon, supporting with difficulty a woman trembling, of a majestic port, glittering with jewels, and covered with a veil. "Take off that veil," said the old woman to Candide. The young man approached and took off the veil with a trembling hand. What joy! what surprise! he thought he saw Miss Cunegonde; he saw her indeed! It was she herself. His strength failed him, he could not utter a word, but fell down at her feet. Cunegonde fell upon the carpet. The old woman applied aromatic waters; they recovered their senses, and spoke to one another. At first, their words were broken, their questions and answers crossed each other, amidst sighs, tears and cries. The old woman recommended them to make less noise, and then left them to themselves. "How! is it you?" said Candide; "are you still alive? do I find you again in Portugal? You were not ravished then, as the philosopher Pangloss assured me?" "Yes, all this was so," said the lovely Cunegonde; "but death does not always follow from these two accidents." "But your father and mother! were they not killed?" "It is but too true," answered Cunegonde, weeping. "And your brother?" "My brother was killed too." "And why are you in Portugal? And how did you know that I was here? and by what strange adventure did you contrive to bring me to this house?" "I will tell you all that, presently," replied the lady; "but first you must inform me of all that has happened to you, since the harmless kiss you gave me, and the rude kicking which you received for it."

Candide obeyed her with the most profound respect; and though he was forbidden to speak, though his voice was weak and faltering, and though his back still pained him, yet he related to her, in the most artless manner, every thing that had befallen him since the moment of their separation. Cunegonde lifted up her eyes to heaven; she shed tears at the death of the good Anabaptist, and of Pangloss; after which she thus related her adventures to Candide, who lost not a word, but looked on her, as if he would devour her with his eyes.

VIII

THE HISTORY OF CUNEGONDE

"I WAS in my bed and fast asleep, when it pleased heaven to send the Bulgarians to our fine castle of Thunder-ten-tronckh; they murdered my father and my brother, and cut my mother to pieces. A huge Bulgarian, six feet high, perceiving the horrible sight had deprived me of my senses, set himself to ravish me. This abuse made me come to myself; I recovered my senses, I cried, I struggled, I bit, I scratched, I wanted to tear out the huge Bulgarian's eyes, not considering that what had happened in my father's castle was a common thing in war. The brute gave me a cut with his hanger, the mark of which I still bear about me." "Ah! I anxiously wish to see it," said the simple Candide. "You shall," answered Cunegonde; "but let me finish my story." "Do so," replied Candide.

She then resumed the thread of her story, as follows: "A Bulgarian captain

came in, and saw me bleeding; but the soldier was not at all disconcerted. The
Captain flew into a passion at the little respect the brute showed him, and
killed him upon my body. He then caused me to be dressed, and carried me as
a prisoner of war to his own quarters. I washed the scanty linen he had, and
cooked his victuals. He found me very pretty, I must say it; and I cannot deny
but he was well shaped, and that he had a white, soft skin; but for the rest, he
had little sense or philosophy; one could plainly see that he was not bred under
Dr. Pangloss. At the end of three months, having lost all his money, and being
grown out of conceit with me, he sold me to a Jew, named *Don Issachar,* who
traded to Holland and Portugal, and had a most violent passion for women.
This Jew laid close siege to my person, but could not triumph over me; I
have resisted him better than I did the Bulgarian soldier. A woman of honor
may be ravished once, but her virtue gathers strength from such rudeness.
The Jew, in order to render me more tractable, brought me to this country-
house that you see. I always imagined hitherto that no place on earth was
so fine as the castle of Thunder-ten-tronckh; but I am now undeceived.

"The grand inquisitor, observing me one day, ogled me very strongly, and
sent me a note, saying he wanted to speak with me upon private business.
Being conducted to his palace, I informed him of my birth; upon which he
represented to me how much it was below my family to belong to an Israelite.
A proposal was then made by him to Don Issachar, to yield me up to my
Lord. But Don Issachar, who is the court-banker, and a man of credit, would
not come into his measures. The inquisitor threatened him. At last, my Jew,
being affrighted, concluded a bargain, by which the house and myself should
belong to them both in common; the Jew to have possession Monday, Friday,
and Saturday, and the inquisitor, the other days of the week. This agreement
has now continued six months. It has not, however, been without quarrels; for
it has been often disputed whether Saturday night or Sunday belonged to the
old, or to the new law. For my part, I have hitherto disagreed with them both:
and I believe that this is the reason I am still beloved by them.

"At length, to avert the scourge of earthquakes and to intimidate Don
Issachar, it pleased his Lordship the Inquisitor to celebrate. He did me the
honor to invite me to it. I got a very fine seat, and the ladies were served
with refreshments between the ceremonies. I was seized with horror at seeing
them burn the two Jews, and the honest Biscayan who married his godmother;
but how great was my surprise, my consternation, my anguish, when I saw in
a sanbenito and mitre, a person that somewhat resembled Pangloss! I rubbed
my eyes, I looked upon him very attentively and I saw him hanged. I fell into
a swoon, and scarce had I recovered my senses, when I saw you stripped stark
naked; this was the height of horror, consternation, grief, and despair. I will
frankly own to you that your skin is still whiter, and of a better complexion
than that of my Bulgarian captain. This sight increased all the sensation that
oppressed and distracted my soul. I cried out, I was going to say stop,
barbarians; but my voice failed me, and all my cries would have been to no
purpose. When you had been severely whipped: How is it possible, said I, that

the amiable Candide, and the sage Pangloss, should both be at Lisbon—the one to receive a hundred lashes and the other to be hanged by order of my Lord the Inquisitor, by whom I am so greatly beloved? Pangloss certainly deceived me most cruelly, when he said that everything was for the best in this world.

"Agitated, astonished, sometimes beside myself, and sometimes ready to die with weakness; my head filled with the massacre of my father, my mother, and my brother, the insolence of the vile Bulgarian soldier, the stab he gave me with his hanger, my abject servitude, and my acting as cook to the Bulgarian captain; the rascal Don Issachar, my abominable inquisitor, the execution of Dr. Pangloss, the grand music on the organ while you were whipped, and especially the kiss I gave you behind the screen, the last day I saw you. I praised the Lord for having restored you to me after so many trials. I charged my old woman to take care of you, and to bring you hither as soon as she could. She has executed her commission very well; I have tasted the inexpressible pleasure of seeing you, hearing you, and speaking to you. You must have a ravenous appetite, by this time; I am hungry myself, too; let us therefore, sit down to supper."

On this, they both sat down to table; and after supper, they seated themselves on the fine couch before mentioned. They were there, when Signor Don Issachar, one of the masters of the house, came in. It was his Sabbath day, and he came to enjoy his right, and to express his tender love.

IX

What Happened to Cunegonde, Candide, the Grand Inquisitor and the Jew

This Issachar was the most choleric Hebrew that had been seen in Israel since the captivity in Babylon. "What," said he, "you dog of a Galilean, is it not enough to share with Monsieur the Inquisitor? but must this varlet also share with me?" When he had thus spoke, he drew out a long poniard, which he always carried about him, and not suspecting that his antagonist had any weapons, he fell upon Candide; but our honest Westphalian had received a fine sword from the old woman, along with his full suit. He drew his rapier, and in spite of his amiable temper, he laid the Israelite dead upon the spot, at the feet of Cunegonde.

"My God," cried she; "what will become of us? a man murdered in my apartment! If the peace-officer comes in, we are ruined." "If Pangloss had not been hanged," said Candide, "he would have given us excellent advice in this emergency; for he was a great philosopher. In this extremity, let us consult the old woman"—she was a very prudent woman, and began to give her advice, when another little door opened. It was now about one o'clock in the morning, and consequently the beginning of Sunday. This day was allotted to my Lord the Inquisitor. Entering, he saw the kicked Candide with a sword in his hand, a dead body stretched on the floor, Cunegonde in a dreadful fright, and the old woman giving advice.

See now what passed in Candide's mind at this instant, and how he reasoned: "If this holy man calls in assistance, he will infallibly have me roasted alive; he may treat Cunegonde in the same manner; he has caused me to be whipped without mercy; he is my rival; I am already in for manslaughter; there is no time to hesitate." This reasoning was clear and rapid; and without giving time to the inquisitor to recover from his surprise, he ran through the body, and laid him by the side of the Jew. "Behold, a second kill!" said Cunegonde; "there is no pardon for us; we are damned, our last hour is come. How could you, who are so very gentle, kill a Jew and a lord in two minutes' time?" "My fair Lady," answered Candide, "when a man is in love, jealous, and has been whipped by the inquisition, he does not know what he does."

The old woman then put in her word, and said, "There are three Andalusian horses in the stable, with their saddles and bridles; which the gallant Candide may get ready; Madam has some money and jewels; let us get on horseback without delay, and let us go to Cadiz; the weather is delightful, and very pleasant it is to travel in the cool of night."

Candide immediately saddled the three horses. Cunegonde, the old woman, and he travelled thirty miles on a stretch. While they were making the best of their way, the citizenry came to the house; they buried my Lord in a magnificent church and threw Issachar into a common sewer.

Candide, Cunegonde, and the old woman had now got to the little town of Avacena, in the middle of the mountains of Sierra Morena; having put up at an inn, they talked on affairs as follows.

X

In What Distress Candide, Cunegonde, and the Old Woman Arrived at Cadiz and of Their Embarkation

"Who could have robbed me of my pistoles and my diamonds?" said Cunegonde, with tears in her eyes; "what shall we live on? What shall we do? Where shall I find inquisitors and Jews to give me more money and jewels?" "Alas," said the old woman, "I strongly suspect a cavalier who slept yesterday in the same inn with us at Badajos. God preserve me from judging rashly, but he came twice into our chamber, and went away a long time before us." "Ah!" said Candide, "the good Pangloss has often demonstrated to me, that the goods of this world are common to all men, and that every one has an equal right to them. According to these principles, the cavalier ought to have left us enough to carry us to our journey's end. Have you nothing at all left then, my pretty Cunegonde?" "Not a farthing," said she. "What course shall we take?" said

Candide. "Let us sell one of the horses," said the old woman; "I can ride behind Miss, and we shall thus manage to reach Cadiz."

In the same inn was a Benedictine prior, who bought the horse very cheap. Candide, Cunegonde, and the old woman passed through Lucena, Chillas and Lebrixa and arrived at length at Cadiz, where they were fitting out a fleet, and assembling troops for bringing to reason the reverend fathers, the Jesuits of Parragua, who were accused of having excited one of their hordes, near the city of St. Sacrament, to revolt from their allegiance to the Kings of Spain and Portugal. Candide having served among the Bulgarians, performed the military exercise of that nation before the commander of this little army, with so much grace, celerity, address, dexterity and agility, that he gave him command of a company of infantry. Being now made a captain, he embarked with Miss Cunegonde, the old woman, two valets, and the two Andalusian horses, which had belonged to his Lordship, the grand Inquisitor of Portugal.

During the whole voyage, they argued a great deal on the philosophy of poor Pangloss. "We are going to another world," said Candide; "it is there, without doubt, that every thing is for the best. For it must be confessed that one has reason to be a little uneasy at what passes in this world, with respect to both physics and morals." "I love you with all my heart," said Cunegonde, "by my mind is still terrified at what I have seen and experienced." "All will be well," replied Candide; "the seas of the new world are preferable to those of Europe; they are more calm and the winds are more constant. Certainly, the new world is the best of all possible worlds."

"God grant it," said Cunegonde; "but I have been so terribly unfortunate here, that my heart is almost shut up against hope." "You complain, indeed," said the old woman; "alas! you have not met with such misfortunes as I have."

Cunegonde was almost ready to fall a laughing, and thought the old woman very comical, for pretending to be more unfortunate than herself.

"Alas, my good dame," said Cunegonde; "unless you have been ravished by two Bulgarians, and received two cuts with a hanger and had two castles demolished, and had two fathers and two mothers murdered, and have seen two lovers whipped, I cannot see how you can have the advantage of me. Add to this, that I was born a baroness, with seventy-two armorial quarterings, and that I have, nevertheless, been a cook-maid." "My Lady," answered the old woman, "you know nothing of my ancestry, and were I to show you my back, you would not talk as you do, but would suspend your judgment." This discourse having raised an insatiable curiosity in the minds of Cunegonde and Candide, the old woman related her story as follows.

XI

The History of the Old Woman

My eyes have not always been bleared, and bordered with scarlet; my nose has not always touched my chin; nor have I been always a servant. I am the daughter of a king, and the Princess of Palestrina. I was brought up, till I was fourteen, in a palace, to which all the castles of your German barons would not have served for stables, and one of my robes cost more than all the magnificence in Westphalia. I increased in beauty, in charms, and in fine accomplishments, amidst pleasures, homages, and high expectations. I began to captivate every heart. My neck was formed—oh, what a neck! white, firm and shaped like that of the Venus de Medici. And what eyes; what eyelids! what fine black eyebrows! what flames sparkled from my eyeballs; the poets of my country told me they eclipsed the twinkling of the stars! The maids who dressed and undressed me fell into an ecstasy when they viewed me, and all the men would gladly have been in their places.

I was betrothed to a prince, the sovereign of Massa Carara. What a prince! as handsome as myself, all sweetness and charms, of a witty mind, and burning with love. I loved him, as one always loves for the first time, with idolatry, with transport. Preparations were made for our nuptials. The pomp and magnificence were inconceivable; nothing but continual feasts, carousals, and operas; and all Italy made sonnets upon me, of which there was scarce one tolerable. I was just on the point of reaching the summit of happiness, when an old marchioness, who had been mistress to my prince, invited him to drink chocolate at her house. He died there in less than two hours' time in terrible convulsions. But this is only a mere trifle. My mother, in despair, and yet less afflicted than I was, resolved to retreat for some time from so mournful a place. She had a very fine country-seat near Gaeta. We embarked on board a galley of the country, gilt equal to the altar of St. Peter at Rome. We were scarcely at sea, when a corsair of Sallee fell upon and boarded us. Our soldiers defended themselves like true soldiers; they all fell upon their knees, after throwing away their arms, and asked pardon, *in articulo mortis,* of the corsair.

We were instantly stripped naked as monkeys; my mother, our maids of honor, and myself too, meeting with no better usage. It is a very surprising thing with what expedition these pirate gentry undress people. But what surprised me most was that they should touch us where we women do not ordinarily allow. This ceremony appeared very strange to me; but so we judge of everything that is not done in our own country. I soon learned that the search was to find out whether we had not concealed some of our jewels there. It is a custom established time out of mind among civilized nations that scour the sea. I know that those gentlemen, the pious knights of Malta, never omit to practice it, when they capture Turks of either sex. It is one of the laws of nations, from which they never deviate.

I need not tell you how great a hardship it is for a young princess and her mother to be carried slaves to Morocco. You may easily form a notion of what we underwent on board the vessel of the corsair. My mother was still very handsome, our maids of honor, nay, our plain chambermaids, had more charms than are to be found throughout all Africa. As for myself, I was all attraction, I was all beauty, and all charms; nay, more, I was a virgin. However, I was not one long; for this flower, which had been reserved for the accomplished Prince of Massa Carara, was taken from me by the captain of the corsair. He was an ugly negro, but fancied he did me a great deal of honor. Indeed Her Highness, the Princess of Palestrina, and myself must have been very strong to resist all the violence we met with till our arrival at Morocco. But let me pass over that; these things are so very common that they are hardly worth the mentioning.

Morocco overflowed with blood when we arrived there. Fifty sons of the Emperor Muley Ismael had each their adherents; this produced, in effect, fifty civil wars, of blacks against blacks, of blacks against tawnies, of tawnies against tawnies, and of mulattoes against mulattoes. In a word, there was one continued carnage all over the empire.

No sooner were we landed than the blacks of a party adverse to that of my corsair made an attempt to rob him of his booty. Next to the jewels and the gold, we were the most valuable things he had. I was here witness to such a battle as you never saw in your European climates. The people of the north have not so much fire in their blood, nor have they that raging passion for women that is so common in Africa. One would think that you Europeans had nothing but milk in your veins; but it is vitriol and fire that runs in those of the inhabitants of Mount Atlas and the neighboring countries. They fought with the fury of lions, tigers, and serpents of the country, to determine who should have us. A Moor seized my mother by the right arm, while my captain's lieutenant held her by the left; a Moorish soldier took hold of her by one leg, and our pirates held her by the other. All our women found themselves almost in a moment seized thus by four soldiers. My captain kept me concealed at his back. He had a scimitar in his hand, and killed every one that opposed his fury. In short, I saw all our Italian women and my mother torn to pieces, hacked and mangled by the brutes that fought for them. My fellow-prisoners, those who had taken them, soldiers, sailors, blacks, whites, mulattoes, and lastly my captain himself, were all killed; and I remained expiring upon a heap of dead bodies. These barbarous scenes extended, as every one knows, over more than three hundred leagues, without the perpetrators ever omitting the five prayers a day ordained by Mahomet.

I disengaged myself with great difficulty from the weight of so many dead, bloody carcasses heaped upon me, and made shift to crawl to a large orange-tree on the bank of a neighboring rivulet, where I sank down oppressed with fear, fatigue, horror, despair, and hunger. Soon after, my senses being overpowered, I fell into a sleep, which resembled a fainting fit rather than sleep. I was in this state of weakness and insensibility, between death and life, when I felt myself pressed by something that moved near my body. I opened my eyes, and saw a white man of a very good mien, who sighed, and muttered between his teeth in my own speech.

XII

The Sequel of the Old Woman's Adventures

Astonished, and transported with joy, to hear my own country language, I roused myself and determined to relate the great misfortunes that had befallen me. I then gave him a short account of the horrid scenes I had undergone, and relapsed again into a swoon. He carried me to a neighboring house, caused me to be put to bed, gave me something to eat, waited upon me, comforted and flattered me, and said that he had never seen any one so handsome as I was. "I was born at Naples," said he, "where they castrate two or three thousand children every year; some die of the operation, others acquire a finer voice than that of any woman, and others become governors of states. This operation was performed on me with great success, and I became a singer in the chapel of her Highness, the Princess of Palestrina." "Of my mother!" cried I. "Of your mother?" cried he again, shedding tears. "What! are you that young princess, whom I had the care of bringing up till she was six years old, and who bid fair, even then, to be as handsome as you are now?" "It is myself; my mother lies about four hundred paces from hence, cut into four quarters, under a heap of dead bodies."

I related to him all that had befallen me; he likewise told me his adventures, and informed me that he was sent to the King of Morocco, by a Christian prince, to conclude a treaty with that monarch, by which he was to furnish him with ammunition, artillery, and ships, to enable him entirely to destroy the commerce of other Christians. "My commission is fulfilled," said the honest eunuch to me; "I am going to embark at Ceuta, and will carry you to Italy."

I thanked him with tears of gratitude; but instead of conducting me to Italy, he carried me to Algiers, and sold me to the Dey of that province. Scarce was I sold, when the plague, which had made the tour of Africa, Asia, and Europe, broke out at Algiers with great fury. You have seen earthquakes; but pray, Miss, have you ever had the plague!" "Never," answered the Baroness.

"Had you had it," replied the old woman, "you would confess that it is far more terrible than an earthquake." It is very common in Africa; I was seized with it. Figure to yourself the situation of a king's daughter, about fifteen years of age, who, in the space of three months, had undergone poverty and slavery, had been ravished almost every day, had seen her mother cut into four quarters, had experienced both famine and war, and was dying of the plague at Algiers. I did not die for all that. But my eunuch, and the Dey, and almost all the seraglio at Algiers perished.

When the first ravages of this dreadful pestilence were over, they sold the slaves belonging to the Dey. A merchant purchased me, and carried me to Tunis. There he sold me to another merchant, who sold me again at Tripoli; from Tripoli, I was sold again at Alexandria; from Alexandria, I was sold again at Smyrna; and from Smyrna at Constantinople. At last, I became the property of an Aga of the Janissaries, who was soon after ordered to go to the defence of Asoph, then besieged by the Russians.

The Aga, who was a man of great gallantry, took all his seraglio along with him, and lodged us in a small fort on the Palus Mæotis, under the guard of two black eunuchs and twenty soldiers. We killed a great number of the Russians, who returned the compliment with interest. Asoph was put to fire and sword, and no regard was paid to age or sex. There remained only our little fort, which the enemy resolved to reduce by famine. The twenty Janissaries had sworn that they would never surrender. The extremities of famine to which they were reduced, obliged them to eat our two eunuchs, for fear of violating their oath; and a few days after, they resolved to devour the women.

We had an Iman, a very religious and humane man. He preached an excellent sermon to them, in which he dissuaded them from killing us all at once. "Cut only one of the backs of these ladies," said he, "and you will fare excellently well; if you must come to it again, you will have the same entertainment a few days hence. Heaven will bless you for so charitable an action, and you will find relief."

As he had an eloquent tongue, he easily persuaded them. This horrible operation was performed upon us, and the Iman applied the same balsam to us that is applied to children. We were all ready to die.

The Janissaries had scarce finished the feast with which we had supplied them, when the Russians came in their flat bottomed boats, and not a single Janissary escaped. The Russians showed no concern about the condition we were in. As there are French surgeons in every country, one of them who was a person of very great skill took us under his care and cured us; and I shall remember as long as I live that when my wounds were pretty well healed, he made me amorous proposals. To be short, he told us all to cheer up, and assured us that the like misfortune had happened in several sieges; and that it was the law of war.

As soon as my companions were able to walk, they were obliged to go to Moscow. I fell to the lot of a Boyard, who made me his gardener, and gave me twenty lashes with his whip every day. But my lord having been broke on the wheel, within two years after, along with thirty more Boyards, on account of some quarrel at court, I availed myself of this event, and made my escape. After traversing over all Russia, I was a long time servant to an innkeeper at Riga, afterwards at Rostock, Wismar, Leipsic, Cassel, Utrecht, Leyden, the Hague, and Rotterdam. I grew old in misery and disgrace, having only one half of my back, but still remembering that I was a king's daughter. A hundred

times have I had thoughts of killing myself; but still I was fond of life. This
ridiculous weakness is perhaps one of our most melancholy foibles. For can
anything be more stupid than to be desirous of continually carrying a burden,
which one has a good mind to throw down on the ground? to dread existence,
and yet preserve it? in a word, to caress the serpent that devours us, till he has
gnawed our very heart out?

In the countries through which it has been my fate to travel, and in the inns
where I have been a servant, I have seen a prodigious number of people who
looked upon their own existence as a curse; but I never knew of more than
eight who voluntarily put an end to their misery, viz., three negroes, four
Englishmen, and a German professor named *Robeck*. My last service was with
Don Issachar the Jew, who placed me near your person, my fair lady. I am
resolved to share your fate; and I have been more affected with your misfortunes than with my own. I should never have spoken of my sufferings, if
you had not vexed me a little, and if it had not been customary, on board a ship,
to tell stories, by way of amusement. In short, Miss, I have a good deal of experience, and I have known the world. Divert yourself, and prevail upon each
passenger to tell you his story; and if there is one found who has not frequently cursed his life, and has not as often said to himself, that he was the
unhappiest of mortals, I will give you leave to throw me into the sea, head
foremost.

XIII

How Candide Was Obliged to Part from the Fair Cunegonde and the Old Woman

The beautiful Cunegonde having heard the old woman's story, paid her all the
civilities that were due to a person of her rank and merit. She approved of her
proposal, and engaged all the passengers, one after another, to relate their adventures, and then both Candide and she confessed that the old woman was in
the right. "It is a great pity," said Candide, "that the sage Pangloss was hanged,
contrary to custom, for he would tell us most surprising things concerning the
physical and moral evils which cover both land and sea; and I should be bold
enough, with due respect, to propose some objections."

While each passenger was relating his story, the ship advanced in her voyage.
They landed at Buenos-Ayres. Cunegonde, Capt. Candide, and the old woman,
waited on the governor, Don Fernandes d'Ibaraa, y Figueora, y Mascarenes, y
Lampourdos, y Souza. This nobleman was possessed of pride suitable to a person dignified with so many titles. He spoke to other people with so noble a
disdain, turned up his nose, carried his head so high, raised his voice so intoler-
ably, assumed so imperious an air, and affected so lofty a gait, that all those who
saluted him were tempted to beat him. He was an excessive lover of the fair sex.
Cunegonde appeared to him the prettiest woman he had ever seen. The first

thing he did, was to ask whether she was not the Captain's wife? The manner in which he put the question alarmed Candide. He durst not say that she was his wife, because, in reality she was not. He durst not tell him that she was his sister, because she was not that either, and though this officious lie might have been of service to him, yet his soul was too refined to betray the truth. "Miss Cunegonde," said he, "intends me the honor of marrying me, and we beseech your Excellency to grace our nuptials with your presence."

Don Fernandes d'Ibaraa, y Figueora, y Mascarenes, y Lampourdos, y Souza, turning up his mustaches, forced a grim smile, and ordered Capt. Candide to go and review his company. Candide obeyed, and the Governor remained alone with Miss Cunegonde. He declared his passion, protested that he would marry her the next day in the face of the church, or otherwise, as it should be agreeable to a person of her charms. Cunegonde desired a quarter of an hour to consider the proposal, to consult with the old woman, and to make up her mind.

Said the old woman, to Cunegonde, "Miss, you can reckon up seventy-two descents in your family, and not one farthing in your pocket. It is now in your power to be the wife of the greatest lord in South America, who has very pretty whiskers; and what occasion have you to pique yourself upon inviolable fidelity? You have been ravished by the Bulgarians; a Jew and an inquisitor have been in your good graces. Misfortunes have no law on their side. I confess, that were I in your place, I should have no scruples to marry the governor, and make the fortune of Capt. Candide."

While the old woman was thus speaking, with all the prudence which age and experience dictated, they descried a small vessel entering the port, which had on board an alcald and alguazils. The occasion of their voyage was this.

The old woman had shrewdly guessed, that it was a cavalier with a big sleeve that stole the money and jewels from Cunegonde in the city of Badajos, when she and Candide were making their escape. The man having offered to sell some of the diamonds to a jeweller, the latter recognized them as the inquisitor's. The cavalier, before he was hanged, confessed he had stolen them. He described the persons he had stolen them from, and told the route they had taken. The flight of Cunegonde and Candide being by this means discovered, they were traced to Cadiz, where a vessel was immediately sent in pursuit of them; and now the vessel was in the port of Buenos-Ayres. A report was spread, that an Alcald was going to land, and that he was in pursuit of the murderers of my lord the grand inquisitor. The old woman saw in a moment what was to be done. "You cannot run away," said she to Cunegonde, "and you have nothing to fear; it was not you that killed my lord; and besides, the governor, who is in love with you, will not suffer you to be ill treated. Therefore stay here." She then ran to Candide: "Fly," said she, "or in an hour you will be burnt alive." He had not a moment to lose; but how could he part from Cunegonde, and where could he fly to for shelter?

XIV

How Candide and Cacambo Were Received by the Clerics of Paraguay

Candide had brought such a valet with him from Cadiz, as one often meets with on the coasts of Spain, and in the colonies. He was a quarter-blooded Spaniard, born of a mongrel in Tucuman, and had been a singing-boy, a sexton, a sailor, a factor, a soldier, and a lacquey. His name was *Cacambo*, and he had a strong love for his master, because his master was a very good sort of man. Having saddled the two Andalusian horses with all expedition: "Let us go, Master, let us follow the old woman's advice, let us set off, and run without looking behind us." Candide dropped some tears: "Oh, my dear Cunegonde," said he, "must I leave you just at the time when the governor was going to have us married! Cunegonde, what will become of you in this strange country?" "She will do as well as she can," said Cacambo; "women are never at a loss; God will provide for her; let us run." "Whither art thou carrying me?" said Candide; "where are we going? what shall I do without Cunegonde?" "By St. James of Compostella," said Cacambo, "you were going to fight against the clerics; now let us go and fight *for* them. I know the road perfectly well; I will conduct you to their kingdom; they will be charmed to have a captain that knows the Bulgarian exercise; you will make a prodigious fortune; though one cannot find his account in one world, he may in another. It is a great pleasure to see new sights and perform new exploits."

"Have you been in Paraguay?" said Candide.

"Yes, in truth, I have," said Cacambo. "I was usher to the college and am acquainted with the government of the good clerics as well as I am with the streets of Cadiz. It is an admirable sort of government. The kingdom is upwards of three hundred leagues in diameter, and divided into thirty provinces. The rulers there are masters of everything, and the people have nothing. It is the masterpiece of reason and justice. For my part I see nothing so divine as the clerics who wage war here against the Kings of Spain and Portugal, and in Europe are their advisers, who in this country, kill Spaniards, and at Madrid, send them counsel. This transports me; let us therefore push forward; you are going to be the happiest of mortals. What pleasure will it be to those rulers when they know that a captain who understands the Bulgarian exercise comes to offer them his service!"

As soon as they reached the first barrier, Cacambo told the advanced guard, that a captain desired to speak with my lord the commandant. They went to inform the chief guard of it. A Paraguayan officer ran on foot to the commandant, to impart the news to him. Candide and Cacambo were at first disarmed, and their two Andalusian horses were seized. The two strangers were introduced between two files of musketeers; the commandant was at the further end, with a cap on his head, his gown tucked up, a sword by his side, and a staff in his hand. He made a signal, and straightway four and twenty soldiers surrounded the newcomers. A serjeant told them they must wait; that the commandant could not speak to them; that the lord ruler does not permit any Spaniard to open his mouth but in his presence, or to stay above three hours in the province. "And where is the lord ruler?" said Cacambo. "He is upon the parade," answered the serjeant: "and you cannot kiss his spurs in less than three hours." "But," said Cacambo, "my master, the Captain, who is ready to die for hunger as well as myself, is not a Spaniard, but a German; cannot we have something for breakfast, while we wait for his lordship?"

The serjeant went to give an account of this discourse to the commandant. "God be praised," said the commandant; "since he is a German, I may speak with him; bring him into my arbor." Candide was immediately conducted into a green pavilion, decorated with a very handsome balustrade of green and gilt marble, with intertextures of vines, containing parrots, humming-birds, fly-birds, Guinea-hens, and all other sorts of rare birds. An excellent breakfast was provided in vessels of gold, and while the Paraguayans were eating Indian corn mush out of wooden dishes, in the open fields, exposed to the sultry heat of the sun, the commandant retired to his arbor.

He was a very handsome young man, with a full face, tolerably fair, fresh colored, his eyebrows were arched, his eyes full of fire, his ears red, his lips like vermillion; his hair was somewhat fierce, but of a fierceness which differed both from that of a Spaniard and Cleric. They now returned to Candide and Cacambo the arms, which had been taken from them, together with the two Andalusian horses, which Cacambo took the liberty to feed near the arbor, keeping his eye upon them, for fear of a surprise.

Candide immediately kissed the hem of the commandant's garment; after which, they both sat down to table. "You are a German, then?" said the Cleric to him, in that language. "Yes," said Candide. In pronouncing these words, they looked at each other with extreme surprise, which they were not able to account for. "And what part of Germany do you belong to?" said the Cleric. "To the lower part of Westphalia," said Candide; "I was born in the Castle of Thunder-ten-tronckh." "Heavens! is it possible!" cried the commandant. "What a miracle is this!" cried Candide. "Is it You?" said the commandant, " 'Tis impossible!" said Candide. On this they both fell backwards; but getting up again, they embraced each other, and shed tears of joy. "What! is it you, you! the brother of the fair Cunegonde! you that was slain by the Bulgarians! you, the Baron's son! are you a ruler at Paraguay? I must confess, that this is a strange world indeed! Ah! Pangloss! Pangloss! how pleased you would now be, if you had not been hanged."

The commandant ordered the negro slaves, and the Paraguayans, that poured out the liquor in cups of rock crystal, to retire. He thanked God, a thousand times; folded Candide in his arms: their faces being all the while bathed in tears. "You will be more astonished, more affected, more out of your wits," said Candide, "when I tell you that Miss Cunegonde, your sister, who you thought was dead is as well as I am." "Where?" "In your neighborhood; at the house of the governor of Buenos-Ayres; and I came here to fight against you." Every word they spoke in this long conversation heaped surprise upon surprise. Their souls dwelt upon their tongues, listened in their ears, and sparkled in their eyes. As they were Germans, they made a long meal (according to custom), waiting for the lord ruler, when the commandant thus addressed their dear Candide.

XV

How Candide Killed the Brother of His Dear Cunegonde

"I shall ever have present to my memory," said the baron, "that horrible day, wherein I saw my father and mother killed, and my sister ravished. When the Bulgarians were gone, my sweet sister was nowhere to be found; and I, together with my father and mother, two maids, and three little lads that were murdered, were flung into a cart, in order to be buried in a chapel, which belonged to the clerics, about two leagues distant from our family-castle. A cleric sprinkled us with holy water, which being very salt, and some drops falling into my eyes, he could perceive my eye-balls move; on which he put his hand on my side, and felt my heart beat; I was taken care of, and, in about three weeks time, no one would have thought that any thing had ailed me. You know very well my dear Candide, I was very handsome, but I grew more so; on which account, the superior of the house conceived a very great affection for me, and some time after sent me to training. The superior was then looking out for a recruit of young men from Germany. For the rulers of Paraguay take as few Spanish as they can; but choose foreigners, because they think they can tyrannize over them as they please. I was therefore made choice of, as a proper person to go to work in this vineyard. I set sail in company with a Polander and a Tirolesian. On my arrival, I was honored with a lieutenancy. At present I am a colonel. We shall give the King of Spain's army a warm reception; I can assure you that they will be beaten. Providence has sent you hither to assist us. But is it true, that my dear sister Cunegonde is in our neighborhood, at the governor of Buenos-Ayres's house?" Candide swore that it was as true as the gospel. On this their tears gushed out afresh.

The Baron could not refrain from embracing Candide, whom he called his brother, and his protector. "Ah, perhaps," said he, "we two may enter the city in triumph, and recover my sister Cunegonde." "There is nothing I could wish for more," said Candide, "for I expected to be married to her, and I have some hopes I shall yet." "The insolence of the fellow!" replied the Baron. "Can you dare to think of marrying my sister, who can show seventy-two quarterings in her coat of arms? How dare you have the effrontery to speak to me thus!" Candide being quite thunderstruck at this, replied, "my revered father, all the quarterings in the world do not signify a farthing. I have delivered your sister from the hands of a Jew, and an inquisitor; she lies under a great many obligations to me, and is willing to marry me. Master Pangloss always told me that all men are equal. I am determined to marry her." "We will see whether you will, you villain!" said the cleric Baron of Thunder-ten-tronckh, at the same time giving him a blow on the face with the flat part of his sword. Candide drew his weapon immediately, and plunged it up to the hilt in the Baron's body; but drawing it out again, and looking upon it as it reeked, he cried out, "O God! I have killed my old master, my friend, my brother-in-law. I am one of the best-natured men in the world, yet I have killed three men."

Cacambo, who stood sentry at the door of the arbor, and who heard the noise, ran in. "We have nothing now to do but to sell our lives as dearly as we can," said his master to him; "and if they should force their way into the arbor, let us at least die with our arms in our hands."

Cacambo, who had been in circumstances of a similar nature, did not stand long to rack his brains for an expedient, but took the dress which the Baron wore, put it upon Candide, gave him the dead man's cap, and made him mount his horse. All this was done in the twinkling of an eye. "Let us gallop away, master," says he; "everybody will take you for some cleric that is going express, and we shall get to the frontiers before they can overtake us."

They fled like lightning, before these words were quite out of his mouth, crying out in Spanish, "Make way, make way for the Colonel."

XVI

What Passed Between Our Two Travellers and Two Girls, Two Monkeys, and the Savages Called Oreillons

Candide and his valet had got beyond the pass, before any person in the camp got the least intimation of the death of the German. The provident Cacambo had taken care to fill his wallet with bread, chocolate, ham, and some bottles of wine. They pushed with their Andalusian horses into a strange country, where they could not discover any path or road. At last, a pleasant meadow, which was divided by a river, presented itself to their eyes. Our two travellers turned their horses out to graze, and Cacambo proposed to his master to eat a bit, at the same time setting him the example. "Do you think," said Candide, "that I can feast upon ham, when I have killed the Baron's son, and find myself under a necessity never to see Cunegonde again as long as I live? What signifies it to prolong my days in misery, since I must spend them far away from her, a prey to remorse and despair? and what will the Journal of Trevoux say of me?"

Having thus spoke, he refused to eat a morsel. The sun was now set, when our two wanderers, to their very great surprise, heard faint cries, which seemed to come from women. It was not easy to determine these cries; they rose immediately, with all the anxiety and apprehension to which people are subject in a strange place, and immediately discovered that the noise was made by two girls, who ran, unclothed, on the banks of the meadow, pursued by two large monkeys. Candide was moved with pity, and as he had learned to shoot, among the Bulgarians, and was so good a marksman that he could hit a nut in a bush without touching the leaves, he took up his Spanish fuzee, which was double-charged, and killed the two monkeys. "God be praised, my dear Cacambo," said he; "I have delivered the two poor girls from this great danger. If I have been guilty of a sin in killing the inquisitor, I have now made ample amends for it by saving the lives of two innocent girls. They may chance to prove a couple of ladies of rank; and who knows but this adventure may do us great service, in this country?"

He was going on at this rate, thinking that he had done a great feat, but how great was his surprise, when he saw the two girls, instead of rejoicing, embrace the monkeys with marks of the most tender affection! they bathed their bodies with tears, and filled the air with shrieks that testified the deepest distress. "I never expected to have seen such a sight as this," said he to Cacambo; who replied, "You have done a fine piece of work, indeed, Sir, you have killed the ladies' sweethearts." "Their sweethearts! is it possible? Surely you are in jest, Cacambo; who the deuce could believe you to be in earnest?" "My dear Sir," replied Cacambo, "you are always for making mountains of mole-hills; why should you think it incredible that in some countries monkeys enjoy the favors of the ladies?" "Ay," replied Candide, "now I recollect, Mr. Pangloss has told me, that there may be many an instance of this kind, and that these mixtures gave birth to the Ægipans, Fauns, and Satyrs; that a great many of the ancients had seen them with their own eyes; but I always looked upon it as a mere romance." "You ought, at present, to see your mistake," said Cacambo, "and own that the doctor was in the right for once. And you may see what those people do, who have not received a particular education. All I am afraid of is, that these ladies will play us some spiteful trick." These wise reflections induced Candide to quit the meadow, and take to a wood; where he and Cacambo supped together; and, after heartily cursing the Portuguese inquisitor, the governor of Buenos-Ayres, and the Baron, they fell asleep.

On waking, they found that they could not stir, for the Oreillons, the inhabitants of the country, whom the two lasses had informed of their adventure, had bound them in the nighttime with cords made of the bark of a tree. They were surrounded by a body of fifty Oreillons, stark naked, armed with arrows, clubs, and hatchets made of flint. Some of them were making a great cauldron boil, others preparing spits, and all of them crying out, "He's a cleric, he's a cleric; we will make him pay sauce for it; we will pick his bones for him; let us eat the cleric, let us eat the cleric."

"You may remember I told you my dear master," cried Cacambo, in a lamentable tone, "that those two lasses would play us some spiteful trick."

Candide perceiving the cauldron and the spits, cried out, "O Lord! we are certainly going to be roasted or boiled. Ah! if Mr. Pangloss had seen nature without disguise, would he have said whatever is, is right? It may be so; but I must confess it is a sad thing to have lost Miss Cunegonde, and to be roasted or boiled for food by the Oreillons."

Cacambo was never at a loss for an invention; "Never despair," said he to the disconsolate Candide. "I understand the jargon of these people a little, and am going to speak to them." "Don't fail," said Candide, "to represent to them the inhumanity of cooking men, and what an unchristian practice it is."

"Gentlemen," says Cacambo, "you fancy that you are going to feast on a cleric to-day; a very good dish, I make no doubt, nor is there any thing more just than to serve one's enemies so. In effect, the law of nature teaches us to kill our fellow creatures, and it is a principle which is put in practice all over the globe. If we do not make use of the right of eating him, it is because we have plenty of victuals without it; but as you have not that advantage, it must certainly be better for you to eat your enemies than to fling away the fruit of your victories a feast to crows and ravens. But, Gentlemen, I suppose you would not relish to eat your friends. You fancy you are going to spit or boil a cleric, but, believe me, I assure you, it is your defender, it is the enemy of your enemies, that you are preparing to treat thus. As to myself, I was born among you. The gentleman you see here is my master, and so far from being a cleric, he has just now killed a cleric, and he is only dressed in his spoils, which is the cause of your mistake. In order to confirm my assertion, let one of you take his gown off, carry it to the first pass of the government of the fathers, and inform himself whether my master has not killed a cleric officer. It is an affair that won't take up much time, and you may always have it in your power to eat us, if you catch me in a lie. But if I have told you the truth, and nothing but the truth, you are too well acquainted with the principles of natural right, morality and law, not to show us some favor."

The Oreillons were so fully convinced of the reasonableness of this proposal, that they deputed two of their chiefs to go and inform themselves of the truth of what he had told them. The two deputies acquitted themselves of their charge like men of sense, and returned soon with a favorable account. The Oreillons then unbound the prisoners, showed them a thousand civilities, offered them women, gave them refreshments, and conducted them back again to the confines of their state, crying all the while, like madmen, "He is no cleric, he is no cleric."

Candide could not help admiring the subject of his deliverance. "What a people!" said he; "what men! what manners! If I had not had the good luck to run Miss Cunegonde's brother through the body, I should inevitably have been eaten up. But, after all, the dictates of pure nature are always best, since this people, instead of eating me, showed me a thousand civilities as soon as they knew that I was not a cleric."

XVII

The Arrival of Candide and His Man at the Country of Eldorado

When they had reached the frontiers of the Oreillons, "You see now," said Cacambo to Candide, "that this part of the world is not one pin better than the other. Take a fool's advice for once, and let us return to Europe as fast as ever we can." "How is that possible?" said Candide; "and pray what part of it would you have us go to? If I go to my own country, the Bulgarians and Arabians kill all they meet with there; if I return to Portugal, I am sure I shall be burnt alive; if we stay in this country, we run the hazard of being roasted every moment. And again, how can I think of leaving that part of the globe where Miss Cunegonde lives?"

"Why, then, let us take our course towards Cayenne," said Cacambo; "we shall meet with some Frenchmen there, for you know they are to be met with all over the globe; perhaps they will give us some relief, and God may have pity upon us."

It was no easy matter for them to go to Cayenne, as they did not know whereabouts it lay; besides, mountains, rivers, precipices, banditti, and savages, were difficulties they were sure to encounter in their journey. Their horses died with fatigue, and their provisions were soon consumed. After having lived a whole month on the wild fruits, they found themselves on the banks of a small river, which was bordered by cocoa trees, which both preserved their lives and kept up their hopes.

Cacambo, who was on all occasions as good a counsellor as the old woman, said to Candide, "We can hold out no longer; we have walked enough already, and here's an empty canoe upon the shore, let's fill it with cocoa, then get on board, and let it drift with the stream. A river always runs to some inhabited place. If we don't meet with what we like, we are sure to meet with something new." "Why, what you say is very right, e'en let us go," said Candide, "and recommend ourselves to the care of Providence."

They rowed some leagues between the two banks, which were enamelled with flowers in some places, in others barren, in some parts level, and in others very steep. The river grew broader as they proceeded, and at last, lost itself in a vault of frightful rocks, which reached as high as the clouds. Our two travellers still had the courage to trust themselves to the stream. The river now growing narrower drove them along with such rapidity and noise as filled them with the utmost horror. In about four and twenty hours they got sight of daylight again, but their canoe was dashed in pieces against the breakers. They were obliged to crawl from one rock to another for a whole league; after which. they came in sight of a spacious plain, bounded with inaccessible mountains. The country was highly cultivated, both for pleasure and profit; the useful and the ornamental were most agreeably blended. The roads were covered, or, more properly speaking, were adorned, with carriages, whose figures and materials were very brilliant, they were full of men and women, of an extraordinary beauty, and were drawn with great swiftness, by large red sheep, which, for fleetness. surpassed the finest horses of Andalusia, Tetuan, or Mequinez.

"This certainly," said Candide, "is a better country than Westphalia." He and Cacambo got on shore near the first village they came to. The very children of the village were dressed in gold brocades, all tattered, playing at quoits, at the entrance of the town. Our two travellers from the other world amused themselves with looking at them. The quoits were made of large round pieces, yellow, red, and green, and cast a surprising light. Our travellers' hands itched prodigiously to be fingering some of them; for they were almost certain that they were either gold, emeralds, or rubies; the least of which, would have been no small ornament to the throne of the Great Mogul. "To be sure," said Cacambo, "these must be the children of the king of the country, diverting themselves at quoits." The master of the village, coming at that instant to call them to school; "That's the preceptor to the royal family," cried Candide.

The little brats immediately quitted their play, leaving their quoits and other playthings behind them. Candide picked them up, ran to the schoolmaster, and presented them to him with a great deal of humility, acquainting him, by signs, that their Royal Highnesses had forgot their gold and jewels. The master of the village smiled, and flung them upon the ground; and having stared at Candide with some degree of surprise, walked off.

Our travellers did not fail immediately to pick up the gold, rubies, and emeralds. "Where have we got to now?" cried Candide. "The princes of the blood must certainly be well educated here, since they are taught to despise both gold and jewels." Cacambo was as much surprised as Candide. At length they drew near to the first house in the village, which was built like one of our European palaces. There was a vast crowd of people at the door, and still a greater within. They heard very good music, and their nostrils were saluted by a most refreshing smell from the kitchen.

Cacambo went up to the door, and heard them speaking the Peruvian language, which was his mother-tongue; for every one of my readers knows that Cacambo was born at Tucuman, a village where they make use of no other language. "I'll be your interpreter, master," cried Cacambo, in the greatest rapture, "this is a tavern, in with you, in with you."

Immediately, two waiters and two maids that belonged to the house, dressed in cloths of gold tissue, and having their hair tied back with ribbands, invited them to sit down to table with the landlord. They served up four soups, each garnished with two parroquets, a boiled vulture that weighed about two hundred pounds, two apes roasted, of an excellent taste, three hundred humming birds in one plate, and six hundred flybirds in another; together with exquisite ragouts, and the most delicious tarts, all in plates of a species of rock-crystal. After which, the lads and lasses served them with a great variety of liquors made from the sugar cane.

The guests were mostly tradesmen and carriers, all extremely polite, who asked some questions of Cacambo, with the greatest discretion and circumspection, and received satisfactory answers.

When the repast was ended, Cacambo and Candide thought to discharge their reckoning, by putting down two of the large pieces of gold which they had picked up. But the landlord and landlady burst into a loud fit of laughing, and could not restrain it for some time. Recovering themselves at last; "Gentlemen," says the landlord, "we can see pretty well that you are strangers, we are not much used to such guests here. Pardon us for laughing, when you offered us the stones of our highways in discharge of your reckoning. It is plain, you have got none of the money of this kingdom; but there is no occasion for it, in order to dine here. All the inns, which are established for the conveniency of trade, are maintained by the government. You have had but a sorry entertainment here, because this is but a poor village; but anywhere else, you will be sure to be received in a manner suitable to your merit."

Cacambo explained the host's speech to Candide, who heard it with as much astonishment and wonder as his friend Cacambo interpreted it. "What country can this be," said they to each other, "which is unknown to the rest of world, and of so different a nature from ours? it is probably that country where everything really is for the best; for it is absolutely necessary that there should be one of that sort. And in spite of all Doctor Pangloss' arguments, I could not help thinking that things were very bad in Westphalia."

XVIII

What They Saw in the Country of Eldorado

CACAMBO could not conceal his curiosity from his landlord. "For my part," said the latter to him, "I am very ignorant, and I am well aware of it; but we have an old man here, who has retired from court, and is reckoned both the wisest and most communicative person in the kingdom." So saying, without any more ado, he conducted Cacambo to the old man's house. Candide acted now only the second personage, and followed his servant. They entered into a very plain house, for the door was nothing but silver, and the ceilings nothing but gold, but finished with so much taste, that the handsomest ceilings of Europe did not surpass them. The ante-chamber was indeed only covered with rubies and emeralds, but the order in which every thing was arranged made amends for this great simplicity.

The old gentleman received the two strangers on a sofa stuffed with the feathers of humming birds, and ordered them to be served with liquors in vessels of diamond; after which he satisfied their curiosity in the following manner.

"I am now in my hundred and seventy-second year, and I have heard my deceased father, who was groom to his Majesty, mention the surprising revolutions of Peru, of which he was an eye-witness. The kingdom we are in at present is the ancient country of the Incas, who left it very indiscreetly, in order to conquer one part of the world; instead of doing which, they themselves were all destroyed by the Spaniards.

"The princes of their family who remained in their native country were more wise; they made a law, by the unanimous consent of their whole nation, that none of our inhabitants should ever go out of our little kingdom; and it is owing to this that we have preserved both our innocence and our happiness. The Spaniards have had some confused idea of this country, and have called it *Eldorado;* and an Englishman, named Sir *Walter Raleigh*, has been on our coasts, above a hundred years ago; but as we are surrounded by inaccessible rocks and precipices, we have hitherto been sheltered from the rapacity of the European nations, who are inspired with an insensate rage for the stones and dirt of our land; to possess these, I verily believe they would not hesitate a moment to murder us all."

The conference between Candide and the old man was pretty long, and turned upon the form of government, the manners, the women, the public amusements, and the arts of Eldorado. At last, Candide, who had always a taste for Metaphysics, bid Cacambo ask if there was any religion in that country?

The old gentleman, reddening a little, "How is it possible," said he, "that you should question it? Do you take us for ungrateful wretches?" Cacambo then humbly asked him, what the religion of Eldorado was? This made the old gentleman redden again. "Can there be more religions than one?" said he; "we profess, I believe, the religion of the whole world; we worship the deity from evening to morning." "Do you worship one God?" said Cacambo, who still acted as interpreter in explaining Candide's doubts. "You may be sure we do," said the old man, "since it is evident there can be neither two, nor three, nor four. I must say, that the people of your world propose very odd questions." Candide was not yet wearied in interrogating the good old man; he wanted to know how they prayed to God in Eldorado. "We never pray at all," said the respectable sage; "we have nothing to ask of him; he has given us all we need, and we incessantly return him thanks."

Candide had a curiosity to see their priests, and bid Cacambo ask, where they were. This made the old gentleman smile. "My friends," said he, "we are all of us priests; the king, and the heads of each family, sing their songs of thanksgiving every morning, accompanied by five or six thousand musicians." "What!" said Cacambo, "have you no clerics to preach, to dispute, to tyrannize, to set people together by the ears, and to get those burnt who are not of the same opinions as themselves?" "We must be very great fools indeed if we had," said the old gentleman; "we are all of us of the same opinion, here, and we don't understand what you mean by clerics."

Candide was in an ecstasy during all this discourse, and said to himself, "This place is vastly different from Westphalia, and my lord the Baron's castle. If our friend Pangloss had seen Eldorado, he would never have maintained, that nothing upon earth could surpass the castle of Thunder-ten-tronckh. It is plain that everybody should travel."

After this long conversation was finished, the good old man ordered a coach and six sheep to be got ready, and twelve of his domestics to conduct the travellers to the court. "Excuse me," says he to them, "if my age deprives me of the honor of attending you. The king will receive you in a manner that you will not be displeased with, and you will, I doubt not, make allowance for the customs of the country, if you should meet with anything that you disapprove of."

Candide and Cacambo got into the coach, and the six sheep were so fleet, that in less than four hours they reached the King's palace, which was situated at one end of the metropolis. The gate was two hundred and twenty feet high, and one hundred broad; it is impossible to describe the materials it was composed of. But one may easily guess, that it must have prodigiously surpassed those stones, and the sand which we call gold and jewels.

Candide and Cacambo, on their alighting from the coach, were received by twenty maids of honor, of an exquisite beauty, who conducted them to the baths, and presented them with robes made of the down of humming-birds; after which, the great officers and their ladies introduced them into his Majesty's apartment, between two rows of musicians, consisting of a thousand in each, according to the custom of the country.

When they approached the foot of the throne, Cacambo asked one of the great officers in what manner they were to behave when they went to pay their respects tc his Majesty; whether they were to fall down on their knees, or their bellies; whether they were to put their hands upon their heads or upon their backs; whether they were to lick up the dust of the room; and, in a word, what the ceremony was? "The custom is," said the great officer, "to embrace the King, and kiss him on both cheeks." Candide and Cacambo accordingly clasped his Majesty round the neck, who received them in the most polite manner imaginable, and very genteelly invited them to sup with him.

In the interim, they showed them the city, the public edifices, that seemed almost to touch the clouds; the market places, embellished with a thousand columns; fountains of pure water, besides others of rose-water, and the liquors that are extracted from the sugar canes, which played continually in the squares, which were paved with a kind of precious stones, that diffused a fragrance like that of cloves or cinnamon. Candide asking them to show them their courts of justice, and their parliament house, they told him they had none, and that they were strangers to law-suits. He then inquired if they had any prisons, and was told they had not. What surprised him most, and gave him the greatest pleasure, was the palace of sciences, in which he saw a gallery two thousand paces in length, full of mathematical instruments and scientific apparatus.

After having spent the afternoon in going over about a thousandth part of the city, they were re-conducted to the palace. Candide seated himself at table with his Majesty, his valet Cacambo, and a great many ladies. Never was there a better entertainment; and never was more wit shown at table than what his Majesty displayed. Cacambo interpreted the King's repartees to Candide, and though they were translated, they appeared excellent repartees still; a thing which surprised Candide about as much as anything else.

They spent a whole month in this hospitable manner; Candide continually remarking to Cacambo, "I must say it again and again, my friend, that the castle where I was born was nothing in comparison to the country where we are now; but yet Miss Cunegonde is not here, and without doubt you have left a sweetheart behind you in Europe. If we stay where we are, we shall be looked upon only as other folks; whereas, if we return to our own world, only with twelve sheep loaded with pebbles of Eldorado, we shall be richer than all the kings put together; we shall have no need to be afraid of the inquisitors, and we may easily recover Miss Cunegonde."

This proposal was extremely agreeable to Cacambo; so fond are we of running about, of making a figure among our countrymen, of telling our exploits, and what we have seen in our travels, that these two really happy men resolved to be no longer so, and accordingly asked his Majesty's leave to depart.

"You are very foolish," said his Majesty to them. "I am not ignorant that my country is a small affair, but when one is well off it's best to keep so. I certainly have no right to detain strangers; it is a degree of tyranny inconsistent with our customs and laws; all men are free; you may depart when you please; but you cannot get away without the greatest difficulty. It is impossible to go against the current up the rapid river which runs under the rocks; your passage hither was a kind of miracle. The mountains which surround my kingdom are a thousand feet high, and as steep as a wall; they are at least ten leagues over, and their descent is a succession of precipices. However, since you seem determined to leave us, I will immediately give orders to the constructors of my machines, to make one to transport you comfortably. When they have conveyed you to the other side of the mountains, no one must attend you; because my subjects have made a vow never to pass beyond them, and they are too wise to break it. There is nothing else you can ask of me which shall not be granted."

"We ask your Majesty," said Cacambo, very eagerly, "only a few sheep loaded with provisions, together with some of the common stones and dirt of your country."

The King laughed heartily; "I cannot," said he, "conceive what pleasure you Europeans find in our yellow clay; but you are welcome to take as much of it as you please, and much good may it do you."

He gave immediate orders to his engineers to construct a machine to hoist up and transport these two extraordinary persons out of his kingdom. Three thousand able mechanics set to work, and in a fortnight's time the machine was completed, which cost no more than twenty millions sterling of their currency.

Candide and Cacambo were both placed on the machine, together with two large red sheep bridled and saddled for them to ride on, when they were over the mountains, twenty sheep of burden, loaded with provisions, thirty with the greatest curiosities of the country, by way of present, and fifty with gold, precious stones, and diamonds. The King, after tenderly embracing the two vagabonds, took his leave of them.

It was a very fine spectacle to see them depart, and the ingenious manner in which they and the sheep were hoisted over the mountains. The contrivers of the machine took their leave of them, after having got them safe over, and now Candide had no other desire and no other aim, than to go to present his sheep to Miss Cunegonde. "We have now got enough," said he, "to pay for the ransom of Miss Cunegonde, no matter what price the governor of Buenos-Ayres puts upon her. Let us march towards Cayenne, there take shipping, and then we will determine what kingdom to make a purchase of."

XIX

What Happened to Them at Surinam, and How Candide Became Acquainted with Martin

THE first day's journey of our two travellers was very agreeable, they being elated with the idea of finding themselves masters of more treasure than Asia, Europe or Africa could scrape together. Candide was so transported, that he carved the name of Cunegonde upon almost every tree that he came to. The second day, two of their sheep sank in a morass, and were lost, with all that they carried; two others died of fatigue a few days after; seven or eight died at once of want, in a desert; and some few days after, some others fell down a precipice. In short, after a march of one hundred days, their whole flock amounted to no more than two sheep.

"My friend," said Candide to Cacambo, "you see how perishable the riches of this world are; there is nothing durable, nothing to be depended on but virtue, and the happiness of once more seeing Miss Cunegonde." "I grant it," said Cacambo; "but we have still two sheep left, besides more treasure than ever the King of Spain was master of; and I see a town a good way off, that I take to be Surinam, belonging to the Dutch. We are at the end of our troubles, and at the beginning of our happiness."

As they drew nigh to the city, they saw a negro stretched on the ground, more than half naked, having only a pair of drawers of blue cloth; the poor fellow had lost his left leg and his right hand. "Good God!" said Candide to him, in Dutch, "what do you here, in this terrible condition?" "I am waiting for my master, Mynheer Vanderdendur, the great merchant," replied the negro. "And was it Mynheer Vanderdendur that used you in this manner?" said Candide. "Yes sir," said the negro, "it is the custom of the country. They give us a pair of linen drawers for our whole clothing twice a year. If we should chance to have one of our fingers caught in the mill, as we are working in the sugarhouses, they cut off our hand; if we offer to run away, they cut off one of our legs; and I have had the misfortune to be found guilty of both these offences. Such are the conditions on which you eat sugar in Europe! Yet when my mother sold me for ten crowns at Patagonia on the coast of Guinea, she said to me, My dear boy, bless our fetiches, adore them always, they will make you live happily. You have the honor to be a slave to our lords, the whites, and will by that means be in a way of making the fortunes both of your father and your mother. Alas! I do not know whether I have made their fortunes, but I am sure they have not made mine. The dogs, monkeys, and parrots are a thousand times less wretched than we. The Dutch missionaries who converted me, told me every Sunday, that we all are sons of Adam, both blacks and whites. I am not a genealogist, myself; but if these preachers speak the truth, we are all cousins-german; and you must own that it is a shocking thing to use one's relations in this barbarous manner."

"Ah! Pangloss," cried Candide, "you never dreamed of such an abominable piece of cruelty and villainy! there is an end of the matter; I see I must at last renounce your optimism." "What do you mean by optimism?" said Cacambo. "Why," said Candide, "it is the folly of maintaining that everything is right, when it is wrong." He then looked upon the negro with tears in his eyes, and entered Surinam weeping.

Their first business was to inquire whether there was any vessel in the harbor wherein they could hire a passage for Buenos-Ayres. The person they applied to was no other than a Spanish commander, who offered to make an honorable bargain with them. He appointed to meet them at an inn, whither Candide and the faithful Cacambo went to wait for him with their two sheep.

Candide whose heart was always on his lips, told the Spaniard his adventures, and confessed that he was determined to run away with Miss Cunegonde. "I shall take care how I carry you to Buenos-Ayres, if that is the case," said the captain; "for I should be hanged, and so would you. The fair Cunegonde is my Lord's favorite mistress."

This was a thunder-clap to Candide; he wept a long time, but at last, drawing Cacambo aside, "I will tell you, my dear friend," said he, "what I would have you do. We have each of us about five or six millions of diamonds in our pocket; and as you are smarter at a bargain than I am, go you and fetch Miss Cunegonde from Buenos-Ayres. If the governor should make any objection, give him a million diamonds; if that does not succeed, give him two millions. As you did not murder the inquisitor, they will have no complaint against you; in the mean time, I will fit out another vessel, and go and wait for you at Venice; that is a safe place, and I need not be afraid there of Bulgarians, Abares, Jews, or Inquisitors." Cacambo applauded this sage resolution. He was, indeed, under great concern at leaving so good a master, who used him like a familiar friend; but the pleasure of being serviceable to him soon got the better of the sorrow he felt in parting with him.

They took leave of each other with tears; Candide recommending to him at the same time not to forget their good old woman. The same day Cacambo set sail. This Cacambo was a very honest fellow.

Candide stayed some time at Surinam, waiting for another vessel to carry him and the two remaining sheep to Italy. He hired servants, and purchased everything necessary for so long a voyage; at last, Mynheer Vanderdendur, the master of a large vessel, came and offered his service. "What will you charge?" said he to the Dutchman, "for carrying me, my servants, goods, and the two sheep you see here, directly to Venice?" The master of the vessel asked ten thousand piastres; Candide made no objection.

"Oh, oh," said the crafty Vanderdendur to himself, after he had left him, "if this stranger can give ten thousand piastres, without any words about it, he must be immensely rich." Returning a few minutes after, he let him know that he could not go for less than twenty thousand. "Well, you shall have twenty thousand then," said Candide.

"Odso," said the captain with a low voice, "this man makes no more of twenty thousand piastres than he did of ten!" He then returned a second time, and said that he could not carry him to Venice for less than thirty thousand piastres. "You shall have thirty thousand then," replied Candide.

"Oh, oh," said the Dutch trader again to himself, "this man makes nothing of thirty thousand piastres; no doubt but the two sheep are loaded with immense treasures; let us stand out no longer; let us, however, finger the thirty thousand piastres first, and then we shall see."

Candide sold two small diamonds, the least of which was worth more than what the captain had asked. He advanced him the money. The two sheep were put aboard the vessel. Candide followed in a small wherry, intending to join the vessel in the road. But the captain improved his opportunity, unfurled sails, and unmoored. The wind being favorable, Candide, distracted and out of his wits, soon lost sight of him. "Ah!" cried he, "this is a trick worthy of the old world." He returned on shore, overwhelmed with sorrow; for he had lost more than would have made the fortunes of twenty princes.

He ran immediately to the Dutch judge, and as he hardly knew what he was about, knocked very loud at the door; he went in, told his case, and raised his voice a little higher than became him. The judge began by making him pay ten thousand piastres for the noise he had made; after which he heard him very patiently, and promised to examine into the affair, as soon as ever the trader should return; at the same time, making him pay ten thousand piastres more for the expense of hearing his case.

This proceeding made Candide stark mad. He had indeed experienced misfortunes a thousand times more affecting, but the coolness of the judge, and the knavish trick of the master of the vessel who had robbed him, fired his spirits, and plunged him into a profound melancholy. The villainy of mankind presented itself to his mind in all its deformity, and he dwelt upon nothing but the most dismal ideas. At last, a French vessel being ready to sail for Bordeaux, as he had no sheep loaded with diamonds to carry with him, he paid the common price as a cabin passenger, and ordered the crier to give notice all over the city, that he would pay the passage and board of any honest man that would go the voyage with him, and give him two thousand piastres besides, on condition that he would make it appear, that he was the most disgusted with his condition, and the most wretched person in that province.

A vast multitude of candidates presented themselves, enough to have manned a fleet. Candide selected twenty from among them, who seemed to have the best pretensions, and to be the most sociable. But as every one of them thought the preference due to himself, he invited them all to his inn, and gave them a supper, on condition that each one of them should take an oath, that he would relate his adventures faithfully, promising to choose that person who seemed to be the greatest object of pity, and had the greatest reason to be dissatisfied with his lot, and to give a small present to the rest, as a recompense for their trouble.

The assembly continued till four o'clock the next morning. As Candide was employed in hearing their adventures, he could not help recollecting what the old woman had told him during their voyage to Buenos-Ayres, and the bet she had made, that there was not a single person in the ship that had not experienced some terrible misfortune. He thought of Pangloss at every adventure that was related. "That Pangloss," said he, "would be hard put to it to defend his system now. I wish he was but here. Indeed, if everything is ordered for the best, it must be at Eldorado, but nowhere else on earth." At last, he decided in favor of a poor scholar, who had written ten years for the booksellers at Amsterdam. For he thought there could not be a more disagreeable employment in the world.

This scholar, though in other respects a good sort of a man, had been robbed by his wife, beat by his son, abandoned by his daughter, who got a Portuguese to run away with her; had been stripped of a small employment, which was all he had to subsist on, and was persecuted by the clerics at Surinam, because they took him for a Socinian.

It must indeed be confessed, that most of the other candidates were as unhappy as he; but he met with a preference, because Candide thought that a scholar was best calculated to amuse him during the voyage. All his competitors thought that Candide did them a great piece of injustice; but he appeased them by giving each of them a hundred piastres.

XX

What Happened to Candide and Martin at Sea

The old scholar, who was named *Martin*, embarked for Bordeaux along with Candide. They had both of them seen and suffered a great deal; and if the vessel had been going to sail from Surinam to Japan, by the way of the Cape of Good Hope, they would have found enough wherewith to entertain themselves on the subject of physical and moral evil, during the whole voyage.

Candide, however, had one great advantage over Martin, which was, that he still hoped to see Miss Cunegonde again; but as for Martin, he had nothing to hope for; to which we may add, that Candide had both gold and diamonds; and though he had lost a hundred large red sheep, loaded with the greatest treasure that the earth could produce, though the knavery of the Dutch captain was always uppermost in his thoughts, yet when he reflected upon what he had still left in his pockets, and when he talked about Cunegonde, especially toward the latter end of a hearty meal, he inclined to Pangloss' hypothesis.

"But you, Mr. Martin," said he to the scholar, "what is your opinion? what is your notion of physical and moral evil?" "Sir," replied Martin, "the clerics have accused me of being a Socinian; but the truth is I am a Manichean."

"You are in jest, sure," said Candide; "there are no longer any Manicheans in the world!" "I am one, though," said Martin; "I cannot well account for it, but yet I am not able to think otherwise." "The devil must be in you, then," said Candide. "He concerns himself so much in the affairs of this world," said Martin, "that he may possibly be in me as well as anywhere else; but I must confess that when I cast my eyes over this globe, or rather over this globule, I cannot help thinking that God has abandoned it to some malignant being: I always except Eldorado. I never met with a city that did not wish the destruction of its neighbor city, nor one family that did not desire to exterminate another family. All over the world, the poor curse the rich, to whom they are obliged to cringe; and the rich treat the poor like so many sheep, whose wool and flesh is sold to the highest bidder. A million assassins, formed into regiments, scour Europe from one extremity to another, committing murder and rapine systematically and according to discipline, for their bread, because they cannot find a more honest or honorable profession; and in those cities which seem to enjoy the blessings of peace, and where the arts are cultivated, mankind are devouured with greater envy, care and disquietude, than a city meets with when it is besieged. Private torments are still more insupportable than public calamities. In a word, I have seen and experienced so much that I have become a Manichean."

"There's some good in the world, for all that," replied Candide. "That may be," said Martin, "but I do not know where to find it."

In the midst of this dispute, they heard the report of cannon. The noise increasing every moment, each person took out his spy-glass, and soon clearly discovered two vessels about three miles distant, engaged in battle. The wind brought the combatants so near the French vessel that they had the pleasure of seeing the fight very clearly. At length one of the vessels gave the other a broadside between wind and water, which sunk it to the bottom. Candide and Martin plainly perceived about a hundred men on the deck of the ship which was sinking, lifting up their hands towards heaven, and making the most dismal lamentations; and in an instant they were all swallowed up by the sea.

"Well," said Martin, "see how mankind treat one another." "It is true," said Candide, "there's something diabolical in this affair." As he was saying this, he perceived something red and glittering swimming near his ship. They immediately sent the longboat to see what it could be, when it proved to be one of those red sheep. Candide felt more of joy at the recovery of this sheep, than he had of trouble at the loss of a hundred such, loaded with the large diamonds of Eldorado.

The French captain soon found that the captain of the conquering vessel was a Spaniard, and that the commander of the vessel which was sunk was a Dutch pirate, and the very same who had robbed Candide. The immense riches which the villain had amassed were buried in the sea along with him, and there was only a single sheep saved.

"You see," said Candide to Martin, "that wickedness sometimes meets with condign punishment; that rascal, the Dutch commander, has met with the fate he merited." "Yes," said Martin; "but why should the passengers on board of his ship also perish together with him? God indeed has punished the villain, but he has permitted the devil to drown the rest."

In the mean time, the Frenchman and the Spaniard continued their course, and Candide pursued his debates with Martin. They disputed fifteen days without intermission; and, at the end of the fifteen days, both were as far from being convinced as when they began. But they chatted, intercommunicated their ideas, and amused each other reciprocally. Candide caressing his sheep, "Since I have found you," said he, "I have some hopes of recovering Cunegonde."

XXI

Candide and Martin Draw Near to the Coast of France and Continue to Discuss

At length they descried the coast of France. "Have you ever been in France, Mr. Martin?" said Candide. "Yes," said Martin, "I have travelled over several of its provinces. In some, half the inhabitants are mere fools; in others, they are too cunning; in others, either very polite and good natured, or very brutish; in others, they affect to be wits; and in all of them the chief occupation is love, the next lying, and the third to talk nonsense." "But, Mr. Martin, have you ever been in Paris?" "Yes, I have; the people are just the same there; it is a mere chaos; a crowd in which every one is in search after pleasure, but no one finds it, as far as I have been able to discover. I spent a few days there on my arrival, and I was robbed of all I had, by some sharpers, at the fair of St. Germain. Nay, I myself was taken up for a robber, and was eight days in prison; after which I turned corrector of the press, to get a small matter to carry me on foot to Holland. I know the whole tribe of scribblers, with malcontents and fanatics. They say the people are very polite in that city; I wish I could believe them."

"For my part, I have no curiosity to see France," said Candide; "you may easily fancy that when a person has once spent a month at Eldorado, he is very indifferent whether he sees anything else on earth, except Miss Cunegonde. I am going to wait for her at Venice; we will go through France, in our way towards Italy. Won't you bear me company?" "With all my heart," said Martin; "they say that Venice is not fit for any but the noble Venetians; but, for all that, they receive strangers very well, provided they have a good deal of money. I have none; you have; therefore, I'll follow you all the world over." "Now I think of it," said Candide, "do you imagine that the earth was originally nothing but water, as is asserted in the great book belonging to the Captain?" "I don't believe a word of it," said Martin, "no more than I do of all the reveries that have been published for some time." "But for what end was the world created, then?" said Candide. "To make people mad," replied Martin. "Were not you greatly surprised," continued Candide, "at the story I told you of the passion which the two girls in the country of the Oreillons had for those two apes?" "Not at all," said Martin; "I see nothing strange in that passion; for I have seen so many strange things already, that I can look upon nothing as extraordinary." "Do you believe," said Candide, "that mankind have always been cutting one another's throats; that they were always liars, knaves, treacherous and ungrateful; always thieves, sharpers, highwaymen, lazy, envious and gluttons; always drunkards, misers, ambitious and blood-thirsty; always backbiters, debauchees, fanatics, hypocrites and fools?" "Do you not believe," said Martin, "that hawks have always preyed upon pigeons, when they could light upon them?" "Certainly," said Candide. "Well, then," said Martin, "if the hawks have always had the same nature, what reason can you give why mankind should have changed theirs?" "Oh!" said Candide, "there is a great deal of difference, because free-will * * *."

In the midst of this dispute, they arrived at Bordeaux.

XXII

What Happened in France to Candide and Martin

Candide stayed no longer at Bordeaux than till he could dispose of some of the pebbles of Eldorado, and furnish himself with a post-chaise large enough to hold two persons; for he could not part with his philosopher Martin. He was indeed very sorry to part with his sheep, which he left at the Academy of Sciences at Bordeaux, which proposed for the subject of this year's prize, the reason why this sheep's wool was red; and the prize was adjudged to a learned man in the North, who demonstrated. by A *plus* B *minus* C divided by Z, that the sheep must be red, and die of the rot.

In the meantime, all the travellers whom Candide met in the inns on the road, telling him they were going to Paris, this general eagerness to see the capital inspired him, at length, with the same desire, as it was not much out of the way in his journey towards Venice.

He entered Paris by the suburb of St. Marçeau, and fancied himself to be in the dirtiest village in Westphalia.

Candide had scarce got to his inn, when he was seized by a slight indisposition, caused by his fatigues. As he had a very large diamond on his finger, and the people had taken notice of a pretty heavy box among his baggage, in a moment's time he had no less than two physicians to attend him, who did not wait to be sent for; a few intimate friends, that never left him, sat up with him together with a couple of female friends that took care to have his broths warmed. "I remember," said Martin, "that when I was sick at Paris, in my first journey, I was very poor, and could meet neither with friends, nurses, nor physicians; but I recovered."

Meanwhile, by medicines and bleedings, Candide's disorder grew more serious, and the clerk of the town came, with great modesty to ask a bill for the other world, payable to the bearer. Candide refused to accord it: the nurses assured him that it was a new fashion. Candide replied, that he was resolved not to follow the fashion. Martin was going to throw the clerk out of the window. The clerk swore that Candide should not be buried. Martin swore he would bury the clerk, if he continued to be troublesome. The quarrel grew high, and Martin took the clerk by the shoulders, and pushed him out of doors. This occasioned a great deal of scandal, and an action was commenced against him.

Candide recovered, and while he was convalescent, had the best company to sup with him. They gamed high and Candide was very much surprised that he never could throw an ace; but Martin was not surprised at all.

Among those who did him the honors of the city was a little cleric of Perigord, one of those people that are always busy, always alert, always ready to do one service, forward, fawning, and accommodating themselves to every one's humor; who watch for strangers on their journey, tell them the scandalous history of the town, and offer them help at all prices. This man took Candide and Martin to the playhouse, where a new tragedy was to be acted. Candide found himself seated near the critics, but this did not prevent him from weeping at some scenes that were well acted. One of these critics, who stood at his elbow, said to him, in the midst of one of the acts, "You were in the wrong to shed tears; that's a shocking actress, the actor who plays with her is worse than she is, and the piece is still worse than the actors. The author does not understand a single word of Arabic, and yet the scene lies in Arabia; but besides, he is a man who does not believe that our ideas are innate. I'll bring you twenty pamphlets against him to-morrow."

"Pray sir," said Candide, to the cleric, "how many theatrical pieces have you in France?" "Five or six thousand," replied the other. "Indeed! that is a great many," said Candide; "but how many good ones are there among them?" "Some fifteen or sixteen," was the reply. "Oh, that is a great many," said Martin.

Candide was greatly taken with an actress who played Queen Elizabeth in a dull kind of tragedy, that was occasionally put on the stage. "That actress," said he to Martin, "pleases me greatly. She has some sort of resemblance to Miss Cunegonde. I should be very glad to pay my respects to her." The cleric of Perigord offered his services to introduce him to her at her own house. Candide, who was brought up in Germany, desired to be informed as to the ceremony used on these occasions, and how a queen of England was treated in France. "There is a distinction to be observed in these matters," said the cleric. "In the country towns, we take them to a tavern; here, in Paris, they are treated with great respect during their lifetime, provided they are handsome; and when they die, we throw their bodies on a dunghill." "How!" said Candide, "throw a queen's body on a dunghill?" "The gentleman is quite correct," said Martin; "he tells you nothing but the truth. I happened to be in Paris when Miss Mevina made her exit, as they say, from this world to the other. She was refused what they here call the rights of sepulture: that is, to say, she was denied the privilege of rotting in a church-yard with all the beggars in the parish. They buried her at the corner of Burgundy Street, which most cer-

tainly would have shocked her extremely, for she was very high spirited."
"This was a very unfeeling act," said Candide. "What would you do?" said
Martin. "It is the way of these people. Figure to yourself all the contradictions, and all the absurdities possible, and you will find them in the church, in
the government, in the tribunals, and in the theatres, of this droll nation." "Is
it true that the Parisians are always laughing?" said Candide. "Yes," said the
cleric, "but it is with hearts full of anger. They complain amidst bursts of
laughter; they even commit the most detestable actions, laughing all the while."

"Who," said Candide, "was that ill-mannered hog, who spoke so disparag-
ingly of the scene in the play that made me weep, and of the actors who gave
me so much pleasure?" "It is a miserable creature," replied the cleric, "who
gets his living by running down all the new plays and all the new books. He
hates those who meet with success, as eunuchs hate all who enjoy themselves.
He is one of those literary serpents who nourish themselves on venom. He is
a pamphleteer." "What do you call a pamphleteer?" said Candide. "It is," said
the cleric, "a maker of pamphlets; a Freron."

Thus Candide, Martin and the Perigordin conversed together, on the stair-
way, whilst seeing the spectators go out of the theatre. "Although I am very
anxious to see Miss Cunegonde, I would like to sup with Mademoiselle Clairon,
she appears so amiable," said Candide.

The cleric was not the man to approach Mademoiselle Clairon, who received only the best company. "She is engaged this evening," said he; "but
permit me the honor to introduce you to a lady of quality, who will make you
as well acquainted with Paris as though you had lived there four years."

Candide who was naturally curious, allowed himself to be taken to the house
of the lady, situated in the faubourg Saint Honore; the company was playing
at faro; twelve melancholy looking punters held each in their hands a small
pack of cards, with the corners turned down, as if to register their losses. Profound silence reigned. The faces of all the punters were very pale, he who held
the bank was the very picture of anxiety, and the lady of the house, seated
near this pitiless man, observed with the eyes of a lynx every word, every
sept-et-le-va with which each player of the company bent the corners of his
cards; she made them straighten them out again; and was very strict in that respect, yet very polite, for fear of losing their custom. The lady assumed the
title of Marchioness of Parolignac. Her daughter, about fifteen years of age, was
one of the punters, and notified her mother by a wink of her eye of the little
tricks the poor people they were victimizing resorted to in trying to repair
their losses.

Candide and Martin enter. No one rises, no one salutes them, nobody even
looks at them; all are intensely occupied with their cards. "Madame the Baroness of Thunder-ten-tronckh was more polite," thought Candide.

Meanwhile, the cleric whispered in the ear of the marchioness, who, partly
rising, honored Candide with a gracious smile, and Martin with a majestic nod.
She ordered a seat and a hand of cards to be given to Candide, who lost fifty
thousand francs in two deals. After which, they supped very merrily, and all

the company were astonished that Candide was not in the least cast down by his losses. The waiters came to the conclusion among themselves that he must be some English lord.

The supper was, like most suppers at Paris, begun in silence; afterwards, there was a noise of words that no one could distinguish. Then came insipid jokes, false news, and bad arguments; a little politics, and a great deal of scandal. They even conversed about new books. "Have you seen the romance of Mr. Gauchet, professor of philosophy?" said the cleric of Perigord. "Yes," replied one of the company, "but I couldn't finish reading it. We have a crowd of impertinent writers, but all of them together don't come up to the impertinence of Gauchet, professor of philosophy. I am so disgusted with this immensity of detestable books with which we are inundated, that I have taken to playing faro."

"And the Miscellanies of Troublet, what do you think of them?" said the cleric. "Ah!" said Madame de Parolignac; "the tiresome creature! How curiously he tells you what all the world knows. How weightily he discusses what is not worth being ever so lightly remarked. How he appropriates the genius of others without having the least genius himself. How he spoils what he steals; how he disgusts me; but he will disgust me no more; it is enough to have read a few pages."

There was at table a man of learning and taste, who inclined to what the marchioness had said. The conversation turning on tragedies, the lady asked how it happened that there were tragedies which were sometimes played, that nobody cared to read. The man of taste explained how a play could be somewhat interesting, yet have scarcely any merit. He proved, in a few words, that "it is not enough to introduce one or two of those scenes which are found in all the romances, and which always seduce the spectators. It is necessary to be new without being fickle, often sublime, and always natural; to understand the human heart, and make it speak; to be a good poet, without letting any character in the play appear like one; to be perfectly acquainted with language, to speak it with purity and continuous harmony, and never sacrifice sense to rhyme. Whoever," added he, "does not observe all these rules, may write one or two tragedies that will be applauded at the theatre, but he will never rank among good writers. There are very few good tragedies. Some are idyls in dialogue, well written and well rhymed; others are political reasonings which put us to sleep, or amplifications which repel us; others are dreams of demoniacs in barbarous style, desultory talk, long apostrophes to the gods because the author does not understand how to talk to men, false maxims and bombast."

Candide listened to all this with attention, and conceived a high opinion of the discourser; and as the marchioness had taken care to place him at her side, he took the liberty of asking, in a whisper, who this man was, who spoke so well. "It is a scholar," said the lady, "who never puntes, and whom the cleric sometimes brings along with him to supper. He is perfectly acquainted with tragedies and books, he has written a hissed tragedy, and a book which he ·dedicated to me; but the only copy that has ever seen the outside of the publisher's store is the one he presented to me." "The great man!" said Candide, "he is another Pangloss."

Then turning to him, he said: "Sir, you believe, no doubt, that all is for the best in the physical and moral world, and that nothing can be otherwise?" "Me," replied the scholar, "I don't think anything of the kind. I find that all goes contrary with us, that no one knows what is his rank, or what is his employment, or what he does, or what he ought to do; and except entertainments which are very gay, and over which there appears to be considerable union, all the rest of the time passes in impertinent quarrels, Jansenists against Molinists, members of parliament against dignitaries of the church, men of letters against men of letters, courtezans against courtezans, financiers against the people, wives against husbands, relations against relations; it is a continual warfare."

"I have seen the worst," replied Candide, "but a very great philosopher, who had the misfortune to be hanged, has taught me that all this is wonderfully well; a mere shadow on a very fine picture." "Your philosopher who has been hanged made a great fool of himself," said Martin; "your shadows are horrible blemishes." "It is men who make the blemishes," said Candide, "and they can't help it." "Then it is not their fault," said Martin. Most of the punters, who understood nothing of this language employed their time in drinking. Martin kept on reasoning with the scholar, and Candide related a part of his adventures to the lady of the house.

After supper, the marchioness conducted Candide into her private room, and seated him on a sofa. "Ah, well, you love Miss Cunegonde, of Thunder-ten-tronckh, to distraction." "Yes, Madam," said Candide. To this the marchioness replied with a tender smile, "You answer me just like a young Westphalian; a Frenchman would have said:—'It is true that I did love Mademoiselle Cunegonde, but having seen you, Madam, I fear I shall never love her any more.'" "Well, Madam," said Candide, "I will answer thus if you wish." "Your passion for her," said the marchioness, "commenced in picking up her handkerchief; will you please to pick up my garter?" "With all my heart," said Candide, and he picked it up. "Now I want you to tie it on," said the lady; and Candide tied it on. "Look you," said the lady, "you are a stranger; I sometimes make my Parisian lovers languish a fortnight, but I surrender to you the first night, *parce qu'il faut faire les honneurs de son pays* to a young man from Westphalia. The lady perceiving two enormous diamonds worn by her young stranger, praised them so much that they immediately passed from the fingers of Candide to those of the marchioness.

Candide, in returning with the cleric of Perigord, expressed remorse for having been guilty of infidelity towards Miss Cunegonde; the cleric consoled him; he had only a small part of the fifty thousand francs which Candide lost at play, and of the value of the two brilliants, half given, half extorted. His design was to profit as much as he could from the advantages Candide's acquaintanceship might procure him. He talked continually of Cunegonde, and Candide assured him that he would ask pardon of this beauty when he should meet her at Venice.

The cleric redoubled his politeness and attentions, and took a very tender interest in all Candide said, in all he did, and in all he wished to do.

"You have then, sir," said he, "a *rendez vous* at Venice?" "Yes, Mr. Cleric," said Candide, "I must certainly go there, to find Miss Cunegonde." Then, led away by the pleasure of speaking of one he so loved, he related, as was his custom, a part of his adventures with this illustrious Westphalian.

"I fancy," said the cleric, "that Miss Cunegonde is a lady of very great accomplishments, that she writes charming letters?" "I never received any letters from her," said Candide, "for, being driven out of the castle on account of my passion for her, I could not write to her; soon after, I heard she was dead; afterwards, I found her, and lost her; and I have now sent an express to her about two thousand five hundred leagues from hence, and wait for an answer."

The cleric heard him with great attention, and appeared to be a little thoughtful. He soon took leave of the two strangers, after a most affectionate embrace. The next day, as soon as Candide awoke, he received a letter couched in the following terms:

"My dearest love, I have been ill these eight days in this town, and have learned that you are here. I would fly to your arms, if I were able to stir. I knew of your passage to Bordeaux, where I have left the faithful Cacambo and the old woman, who are to follow me very soon. The governor of Buenos-Ayres has taken all from me, but your heart is still left me. Come; your presence will restore me to life, unless it kills me with pleasure."

This charming and unexpected letter transported Candide with inexpressible joy, whilst the sickness of his dear Cunegonde overwhelmed him with sorrow. Distracted between these two passions, he took his gold and diamonds, and got somebody to conduct him and Martin to the house where Miss Cunegonde was lodged.

On his entrance, he trembled in every limb, his heart beat quick, and his voice was choked-up with sighs; he asked them to bring a light, and was going to open the curtains of the bed. "Take care, sir," said the nurse, "she can't bear light, it would kill her"; and immediately she drew the curtains close again. "My dear Cunegonde," said Candide, weeping, "how do you find yourself? though you can't see me, you may speak to me, at least." "She cannot speak," said the maid. The sick lady then put a plump little hand out of the bed, which Candide for some time bathed with his tears, and afterwards filled with diamonds, leaving a bag full of gold upon the easy chair.

In the midst of his transports, a lifeguardman came in, followed by the Perigordin cleric and a file of soldiers. "There," said he, "are the two suspected foreigners." He caused them to be immediately seized, and ordered his men to drag them to prison. "It is not thus they treat travellers at Eldorado," said Candide. "I am more a Manichean than ever," said Martin. "But pray, sir, where are you going to carry us?" said Candide. "To a hole in the lowest dungeon," said the lifeguardman.

Martin having recovered his usual coolness, saw at once that the lass who pretended to be Cunegonde was a cheat; that the Perigordin cleric was an impostor, who had taken advantage of Candide's simplicity; and that the life-guardman was another sharper, whom they might easily get clear of.

Rather than expose himself before a court of justice, Candide, by his counsellor's advice, and besides, being very impatient to see the real Cunegonde, offered the lifeguardman three small diamonds, worth about 3,000 pistoles each. "Ah, sir," said the man with the ivory baton, "though you had committed all the crimes that can be imagined, this would make me think you the most honest gentleman in the world! Three diamonds! worth 3,000 pistoles apiece! Sir, instead of putting you in a dungeon, I would lose my life for you; all strangers are arrested here, but let me alone for that; I have a brother at Dieppe in Normandy; I'll conduct you thither, and if you have any diamonds to give him, he will take as good care of you as I would myself."

"And why do they put all strangers under arrest?" said Candide. The cleric of Perigord then put in his word: "Because," said he, "a knave of Atrebatia listened to some foolish stories, which made him commit a parricide, not like that in May, 1610, but like that in December, 1594; and just like those that a great many other knaves have been guilty of, in other months and other years, after listening to foolish stories.

The lifeguardman then gave him a more particular account of their crimes. "Oh! the monsters," cried Candide; "are there then such terrible crimes among people who dance and sing? Can I not immediately get out of this country, where monkeys provoke tigers? I have seen bears in my own country, but I never met with men except at Eldorado. In the name of God, Mr. Officer, conduct me to Venice, where I am to wait for Miss Cunegonde." "I can conduct you no where except to Lower Normandy," said the mock officer. Immediately he ordered his irons to be struck off, said he was under a mistake, discharged his men, conducted Candide and Martin to Dieppe, and left them in the hands of his brother.

There was then a small Holland trader in the harbor. The Norman, by means of three more diamonds, became the most serviceable man in the world, put Candide and his attendants safe on board the vessel, which was ready to sail for Portsmouth, in England.

This was not the way to Venice; but Candide thought he had escaped from hell, and resolved to resume his voyage towards Venice the first opportunity that offered.

XXIII

CANDIDE AND MARTIN GO TO THE ENGLISH COAST, AND WHAT THEY SAW THERE

"AH! PANGLOSS! Pangloss! Ah! Martin! Martin! ah! my dear Cunegonde! what a world is this!" said Candide on board the Dutch ship. "A very foolish and abominable one indeed," replied Martin. "You are acquainted with England, then," said Candide; "are they as great fools there as in France?" "They have a different kind of folly," said Martin. "You know that these two nations are at war about a few acres of snow in Canada, and that they have spent a great deal more upon this war than all Canada is worth. To tell you precisely whether there are more people who ought to be confined in a madhouse in one country than in the other, is more than my weak capacity is able to perform. I only know in general that the people we are going to see are very melancholic."

As they were talking in this manner, they arrived at Portsmouth. The shore was covered with a multitude of people, who were looking very attentively at a pretty stout man who was kneeling, with his eyes bandaged, on the deck of a ship of war; four soldiers, that were placed opposite to him, shot three balls apiece through his head, with the greatest coolness imaginable, and the whole assembly went away very well satisfied. "What is the meaning of this?" said Candide; "and what demon is it that exercises his dominion all over the globe?"

He inquired who the stout gentleman was that was killed with so much ceremony. "He is an admiral," replied some of them. "And why was this admiral killed?" "Because," said they, "he did not kill men enough himself. He attacked the French admiral, and was found guilty of not being near enough to him." "But then," said Candide, "was not the French admiral as far off from the English admiral, as he was from him?" "That is what cannot be doubted," replied they. "But in this country it is of very great service to kill an admiral now and then, in order to make the rest fight better."

Candide was so astonished and shocked at what he had seen and heard, that he would not set foot on shore, but agreed with the master of the Dutch vessel (though he was sure to be robbed by him, as he had been by his countryman at Surinam) to carry him directly to Venice.

The master was ready in two days. They coasted all along France. Passing within sight of Lisbon, Candide gave a very deep groan.

They passed the Straits, entered the Mediterranean, and at last arrived at Venice.

"The Lord be praised," said Candide, embracing Martin, "it is here that I shall see the fair Cunegonde again! I have as good an opinion of Cacambo, as of myself. Everything is right, everything goes well; everything is the best that it can possibly be."

XXIV

CONCERNING PAQUETTA AND GIROFFLEE

As soon as they arrived at Venice, he caused search for Cacambo in all the inns, in all the coffeehouses, and among all the girls of the town, but could not find him. He sent every day to all the ships and barks that arrived; but no news of Cacambo. "Well," said he to Martin, "I have had time enough to go from Surinam to Bordeaux, from Bordeaux to Paris, from Paris to Dieppe, from Dieppe to Portsmouth; after that I have coasted along Portugal and Spain, and traversed the Mediterranean, and have now been some months at Venice, and yet, for all that, the lovely Cunegonde is not come. Instead of her, I have only met with a cheating hussy, and a treacherous man of Perigord. Cunegonde is certainly dead, and I have nothing to do but to die also. Ah! it would have been far better for me to have stayed in that paradise, Dorado, than to have returned again to this cursed Europe. You are certainly right, my dear Martin, all is illusion and misery here."

He fell into a deep melancholy, and never frequented the opera, or the other diversions of the carnival; nay, he was proof against all the charms of the fair sex. Martin said to him, "You are very simple indeed, to fancy that a mongrel valet, with five or six millions in his pocket, would go to the end of the world in quest of your mistress, and bring her to Venice. If he meets with her, he'll keep her for himself; if he cannot find her, he'll get somebody else. Let me advise you to forget both your valet Cacambo and your mistress Cunegonde." Martin was a most wretched comforter. The melancholy of Candide increased; and Martin never ceased preaching that there was but very little virtue, and as little happiness, to be found on earth, excepting, perhaps, at Eldorado, where it was almost impossible for any one to go.

Whilst they were disputing on this important subject, and waiting for Cunegonde, Candide perceived a young guard in the Place St. Mark, with his arm around a young girl. He looked fresh, plump, and full of vigor; his eyes were sparkling, his air bold, his mien lofty, and his gait firm. This girl was tolerably handsome, and was singing a song; she ogled her companion with a great deal of passion, and now and then would give his fat cheeks a pinch.

"At least, you will grant me," said Candide to Martin, "that these two folks are happy. I have never found any but unhappy wretches till now, all over this habitable globe, excepting at Eldorado; but as for the girl and the guard, I will lay any wager that they are as happy as happy can be." "I will lay a wager that they are not," said Martin. "Let us invite them to dinner," said Candide, "then we shall see whether I am mistaken or not."

He immediately accosted them, made them a bow, and invited them to his inn to eat macaroni, partridges of Lombardy, and caviare, and to drink montepulciano, Cyprus and Samos wine. The girl blushed; the guard accepted the invitation, and the girl followed him, looking at Candide with surprise and confusion, whilst the tears trickled down her cheeks. Scarce had she entered into Candide's room, when she said to him, "What! does not Mr. Candide know his old friend Paquetta again?" At these words, Candide, who had not yet looked at her with any degree of attention, because Cunegonde engrossed all his thoughts, said to her, "Ah! my poor girl, is it you? you, who reduced Dr. Pangloss to the dreadful plight in which I saw him?"

"Ah, Sir! 'tis I myself," said Paquetta; "I find you know the whole story; and I have been informed of all the terrible disasters which have happened to the family of my Lady the Baroness, and the fair Cunegonde. My fate, I assure you, has not been less melancholy. I was very innocent when you knew me. A cavalier easily seduced me. The effects of it were terrible. I was obliged to leave the castle some time after the Baron kicked and thrust you out of the door. If a celebrated quack had not taken pity on me, I should have perished. I was the quack's mistress for some time by way of recompense. His wife, who was as jealous as the devil, beat me every day, most unmercifully; she was a very fiend of hell. The doctor was one of the ugliest fellows I ever saw in my life, and I one of the most wretched creatures that ever existed, to be beat every day for the sake of a man whom I hated. You know how dangerous it is for a jealous woman to be married to a doctor. Being quite exasperated with his wife's behavior, he gave her one day so efficacious a remedy to cure her of a slight cold she had, that she died two hours after in the most horrid convulsions. My mistress's relations entered a criminal action against my master; he took to his heels and I was carried to jail. My innocence would never have saved me, if I had not been so handsome. The Judge acquitted me, on condition of his succeeding the doctor. I was soon afterwards supplanted by a rival, driven out of doors without any recompense, and obliged to continue this abominable occupation, which appears so pleasant to you men, while it is to us women the very abyss of misery. I am come to practice my profession at Venice. Ah, Sir, if you could imagine what it is to be obliged to caress indifferently, an old merchant, a counsellor, a gondolier; to be exposed to all sorts of insults and outrages; to be often reduced to borrow a petticoat, to have it rudely pulled up by a disagreeable rascal; to be robbed by one gallant of what one has got from another; to be fleeced by the officers of justice, and to have nothing in prospect but a frightful old age, a hospital, and a dunghill for a sepulchre, you would confess that I am one of the most unfortunate creatures in the world."

Paquetta opened her mind in this manner to the good Candide, in his closet, in the presence of Martin; who said to Candide, "You see I have won half the wager already."

Girofflee waited in the dining-room, and drank a glass or two while he was waiting for dinner. "But," said Candide, to Paquetta, "you had an air so gay, so content, when I first met you, you sung, and caressed the guard with so much warmth, that you seemed to be as happy then as you pretend to be miserable now." "Ah, Sir," replied Paquetta, "this is one of the miseries of the trade. Yesterday, I was robbed and beaten by an officer, and to-day I am obliged to appear in good humor to please a guard." Candide wanted no more, to be satisfied, and he owned that Martin was in the right. They sat down to table with Paquetta and the soldier; the repast was very entertaining, and towards the end they began to speak to each other with some degree of confidence. "My man," said Candide to the guard, "you seem to enjoy a state that all the world might look on with envy. The flower of health blossoms on your countenance, and your physiognomy speaks nothing but happiness; you have a very pretty girl to divert you, and you seem to be well satisfied with your station as a guard."

"Faith, Sir," said Girofflee, "I wish that all the guards were at the bottom of the sea. I have been tempted an hundred times to set fire to the camp, and go and turn Turk. My parents forced me, at the age of fifteen, to put on this cursed uniform, to increase the fortune of an elder brother of mine, whom God confound. Jealousy, discord, and fury reside there. It is true, indeed, I have brought me in a little money; one part of which the commander robbed me of, and the rest serves me to spend with the girls; but every evening, when I enter the camp, I am ready to dash out my brains against the walls; and all the rest are in the same case."

Martin turned towards Candide, with his usual coolness, "Well," said he to him, "have not I won the whole wager now?" Candide gave two thousand piastres to Paquetta, and one thousand to Girofflee. "I'll answer for it," said he, "this will make them happy." "I don't believe a word of it," said Martin; "you may perhaps make them a great deal more miserable by your piastres." "Be that as it may," said Candide; "but one thing comforts me, I see that one oftens finds those persons whom one never expected to find any more; and as I have found my red sheep and Paquetta again, it may be I may find Cunegonde again too." "I wish," said Martin, "that she may one day make you happy; but it is what I very much question." "You are very incredulous," said Candide. "That is what I always was," said Martin.

"But only look on these gondoliers," said Candide; "are they not perpetually singing?" "You don't see them at home with their wives, and their monkeys of children," said Martin. "The Doge has his inquietudes, and the gondoliers have theirs. Indeed, generally speaking, the condition of a gondolier is preferable to that of a doge; but I believe that the difference is so small, that it is not worth the trouble of examining into."

"People speak," said Candide, "of Seignior Pococurante, who lives in that fine palace upon the Brenta, and who entertains strangers in the most polite manner. They pretend that this man never felt any uneasiness." "I should be glad to see so extraordinary a phenomenon," said Martin. On which Candide instantly sent to Seignior Pococurante, to get permission to pay him a visit the next day.

XXV

The Visit to Seignior Pococurante, the Noble Venetian

Candide and Martin went in a gondola on the Brenta, and arrived at the palace of the noble Pococurante. His gardens were very spacious and ornamented with fine statues of marble, and the palace itself was a piece of excellent architecture. The master of the house, a very rich man, of about threescore, received our two inquisitives very politely, but with very little heartiness; which, though it confused Candide, did not give the least uneasiness to Martin.

At first, two young girls, handsome, and very neatly dressed, served them with chocolate, which was frothed extremely well. Candide could not help dropping them a compliment on their beauty, their politeness, and their address. "The creatures are well enough," said the senator Pococurante: "I sometimes make them sleep with me; for I am quite disgusted with the ladies of the town; their coquetry, their jealousies, quarrels, humors, monkey-tricks, pride, follies, and the sonnets one is obliged to make, or hire others to make for them; but, after all, these two girls begin to grow tiresome to me."

After breakfast, Candide, taking a walk in a long gallery, was charmed with the beauty of the pictures. He asked by what master were the two first. "They are by Raphael," said the senator; "I bought them at a very high price, merely out of vanity, some years ago. They are said to be the finest paintings in Italy: but they do not please me at all; the colors are dead, the figures not finished, and do not appear with *relief* enough; the drapery is very bad. In short, let people say what they will, I do not find there a true imitation of nature. I do not like a piece, unless it makes me think I see nature itself; but there are no such pieces to be met with. I have, indeed, a great many pictures, but I do not value them at all."

While they were waiting for dinner, Pococurante entertained them with a concert; Candide was quite charmed with the music. "This *noise*," said Pococurante, "might divert one for half an hour, or so; but if it were to last any longer, it would grow tiresome to everybody, though no soul durst own it. Music is, now-a-days, nothing else but the art of executing difficulties; and what has nothing but difficulty to recommend it, does not please in the long run.

"I might, perhaps, take more pleasure in the opera, if they had not found out the secret of making such a monster of it as shocks me. Let those go that will to see wretched tragedies set to music, where the scenes are composed for no other end than to lug in by the head and ears two or three ridiculous songs, in order to show off the throat of an actress to advantage. Let who will, or can, swoon away with pleasure, at hearing a eunuch trill out the part of Cæsar and Cato, while strutting upon the stage with a ridiculous and affected air. For my part, I have long ago bid adieu to those paltry entertainments, which constitute the glory of Italy, and are purchased so extravagantly dear." Candide disputed the point a little, but with great discretion. Martin was entirely of the same sentiments with the senator. They sat down to table, and after an excellent dinner, went into the library. Candide, casting his eyes upon a Homer very handsomely bound, praised his High Mightiness for the goodness of his taste. "There," said he, "is a book that was the delight of the good Pangloss, the greatest philosopher in Germany." "It doesn't delight me," said Pococurante, with utter indifference; "I was made to believe formerly that I took a pleasure in reading Homer. But his continued repetition of battles that resemble each other; his gods, who are always very busy without bringing anything to a decision; his Helen, who is the subject of the war, and has scarce anything to do in the whole piece; I say all these defects give me the greatest disgust. I have asked some learned men, if they perused him with as little pleasure as I did? Those who were candid confessed to me that they could not bear to touch the book, but that they were obliged to give it a place in their libraries, as a monument of antiquity, as they do old rusty medals, which are of no use in commerce."

"Your Excellence does not entertain the same opinion of Virgil?" said Candide. "I confess," replied Pococurante, "that the second, the fourth, and the sixth book of his Æneid are excellent; but as for his pious Æneas, his brave Cloanthus, his friend Achates, the little Ascanius, the infirm King Latinus, the burgess Amata, and the insipid Lavinia, I do not think any thing can be more frigid or more disagreeable. I prefer Tasso, and Ariosto's soporiferous tales far before him."

"Shall I presume to ask you, sir," said Candide, "whether you do not enjoy a great deal of pleasure in perusing Horace?" "He has some maxims," said Pococurante, "which may be of a little service to a man who knows the world, and being delivered in expressive numbers, are imprinted more easily on the memory. But I set little value on his voyage to Brundusium, his description of his bad dinner, and the Billingsgate squabble between one Pupillus, whose speech he said was full of filthy stuff, and another whose words were as sharp as vinegar. I never could read without great disgust his indelicate lines against old women and witches; and I cannot see any merit in his telling his friend Mæcenas, that if he should be ranked by him amongst the lyric poets, he would strike the stars with his sublime brow. Some fools admire everything in an author of reputation; for my part, I read only for myself; I approve nothing but what suits my own taste." Candide, having been taught to judge of nothing for himself, was very much surprised at what he heard; but Martin looked upon the sentiment of Pococurante as very rational.

"Oh, there's Cicero," said Candide; "this great man, I fancy, you are never tired of reading." "I never read him at all," replied the Venetian. "What is it to me, whether he pleads for Rabirius or Cluentius? I have trials enough of my own. I might, indeed, have been a greater friend to his philosophical works, but when I found he doubted of everything, I concluded I knew as much as he did, and that I had no need of a tutor to learn ignorance."

"Well! here are four and twenty volumes of the Academy of Sciences," cried Martin; "it is possible there may be something valuable in them." "There might be," said Pococurante, "if a single one of the authors of this hodgepodge had been even the inventor of the art of making pins; but there is nothing in all those volumes but chimerical systems, and scarce a single article of real use."

"What a prodigious number of theatrical pieces you have got here," said Candide, "in Italian, Spanish, and French!" "Yes," said the Senator, "there are about three thousand, and not three dozen good ones among them all. As for that collection of sermons, which all together are not worth one page of Seneca, and all those huge volumes of divinity, you may be sure they are never opened either by me or anybody else."

Martin perceiving some of the shelves filled with English books; "I fancy."

said he, "a republican, as you are, must certainly be pleased with compositions that are writ with so great a degree of freedom." "Yes," said Pococurante, "it is commendable to write what one thinks; it is the privilege of man. But all over our Italy they write nothing but what they don't think. Those who now inhabit the country of the Cæsars and Antonines, dare not have a single idea, without taking out a license from a Jacobin. I should be very well satisfied with the freedom that breathes in the English writers, if passion and the spirit of party did not corrupt all that was valuable in it."

Candide discovering a Milton, asked him if he did not look upon that author as a great genius? "What!" said Pococurante, "that blockhead, that has made a long commentary in ten books of rough verse, on the first chapter of Genesis? that gross imitator of the Greeks, who has disfigured the creation, and who, when Moses has represented the Eternal producing the world by a word, makes the Messiah take a large pair of compasses from the armory of God, to mark out his work? How can I have any esteem for one who has spoiled the hell and devils of Tasso; who turns Lucifer sometimes into a toad, and sometimes into a pigmy; makes him deliver the same speech a hundred times over; represents him disputing on divinity; and who, by a serious imitation of Ariosto's comic invention of firearms, represents the devils letting off their cannon in heaven? Neither myself, nor any one else in Italy, can be pleased at these outrages against common sense; but the marriage of Sin and Death, and the adders of which Sin was brought to bed, are enough to make every person of the least delicacy or taste vomit. This obscure, fantastical, and disgusting poem was despised at its first publication; and I only treat the author now in the same manner as he was treated in his own country by his contemporaries. By the by, I speak what I think; and I give myself no uneasiness whether other people think as I do, or not."

Candide was vexed at this discourse; for he respected Homer, and was fond of Milton. "Ah!" said he, whispering to Martin, "I am very much afraid that this strange man has a sovereign contempt for our German poets." "There would be no great harm in that," said Martin. "Oh, what an extraordinary man!" said Candide, muttering to himself. "What a great genius is this Pococurante! nothing can please him."

After having thus reviewed all the books, they went down into the garden. Candide expatiated upon its beauties. "I never knew anything laid out in such bad taste," said the master; "we have nothing but trifles here; but a day or two hence, I shall have one laid out upon a more noble plan."

When our two inquisitives had taken their leave of his Excellency, "Now, surely," said Candide to Martin, "you will confess that he is one of the happiest men upon earth, for he is above everything that he has." "Do not you see," said Martin, "that he is disgusted with everything that he has? Plato has said a long time ago, that the best stomachs are not those which cast up all sorts of victuals." "But," said Candide, "is not there pleasure in criticising everything? in perceiving defects where other people fancy they see beauties?" "That is to say," replied Martin, "that there is pleasure in having no pleasure."

"Ah, well," said Candide, "no person will be so happy as myself, when I see Miss Cunegonde again." "It is always best to hope," said Martin.

In the mean time, days and weeks passed away, but no Cacambo was to be found. And Candide was so immersed in grief, that he did not recollect that Paquetta and Girofflee never so much as once came to return him thanks.

XXVI

Of Candide and Martin Supping with Six Strangers, and Who They Were

ONE night as Candide, followed by Martin, was going to seat himself at table with some strangers who lodged in the same hotel, a man with a face black as soot came behind him, and taking him by the arm, said, "Get ready to start with us immediately; don't fail!" He turned his head and saw Cacambo. Nothing but the sight of Cunegonde could have surprised or pleased him more. He was ready to run mad for joy. Embracing his dear friend, "Cunegonde is here," said he, "without doubt; where is she? Carry me to her, that I may die with joy in her company!" "Cunegonde is not here," said Cacambo, "she is at Constantinople." "Oh, Heavens! at Constantinople? But, if she was in China, I would fly thither; let us begone." "We will go after supper," replied Cacambo; I can tell you no more; I am a slave; my master expects me, and I must go and wait at table; say not a word; go to supper and hold yourself in readiness."

Candide, distracted between joy and grief, charmed at having seen his trusty agent, astonished at beholding him a slave, full of the idea of finding his mistress again, his heart palpitating, and his understanding confused, set himself down at the table with Martin (who looked on all these adventures without the least emotion), and with six strangers that were come to spend the carnival at Venice.

Cacambo, who poured out wine for one of the six strangers, drew near to his master, towards the end of the repast, and whispered him in the ear, "Sire, your Majesty may set out when you think proper, the ship is ready." On saying these words, he went out. The guests looked at each other in surprise, without speaking a word; when another servant approaching his master, said to him, "Sire, your Majesty's chaise is at Padua, and the yacht is ready." The master gave a nod, and the domestic retired. All the guests stared at one another again, and their mutual surprise was increased. A third servant approaching the third stranger, said to him, "Sire, believe me, your Majesty must not stay here any longer; I am going to get everything ready"; and immediately he disappeared.

Candide and Martin had by this time concluded that this was a masquerade of the carnival. A fourth domestic said to the fourth master: "Your Majesty may depart whenever you please"; and went out as the others had done. The fifth servant said the same to the fifth master; but the sixth servant spoke in a different manner to the sixth stranger, who sat near Candide: " 'Faith, Sire," said he, "no one will trust your Majesty any longer, nor myself neither; and we may both be sent to jail this very night; I shall, however, take care of myself. Adieu."

All the domestics having disappeared, the six strangers, with Candide and Martin, remained in a profound silence. At last Candide broke the silence; "Gentlemen," said he, "this is something very droll; but why should you be all Kings? For my part, I own to you, that I am not, neither is Martin."

Cacambo's master answered very gravely in Italian, "I assure you that I am not in jest; I am Achmet III. I was Grand Sultan for several years; I dethroned my brother; my nephew dethroned me; my viziers were beheaded; I pass my life in the old seraglio. But my nephew, the Grand Sultan Mahmoud, permits me to take a voyage sometimes for the benefit of my health, and I have come to pass the carnival at Venice."

A young man who sat near Achmet spoke next; "My name is *Ivan;* I was Emperor of all the Russians; I was dethroned in my cradle; my father and mother were imprisoned; I was brought up in prison. I have sometimes permission to travel, accompanied by two persons as guards; I am also come to pass the carnival at Venice."

The third said, "I am Charles Edward, King of England; my father ceded his rights to the throne to me. I have sought to defend them; eight hundred of my adherents had their hearts torn out alive, and their heads struck off. I myself have been in prison; I am going to Rome, to pay a visit to my father, who has been dethroned, as well as myself and my grandfather, and am come to Venice to celebrate the carnival."

The fourth then said, "I was King of Poland; the fortune of war has deprived me of my hereditary dominion; my father experienced the same reverse; I resign myself to providence, like the Sultan Achmet, the Emperor Ivan, and Charles Edward, whom God long preserve; and I am come to pass the carnival at Venice."

The fifth said, "I was King of Poland; I lost my kingdom twice; but providence has given me another government, in which I have done more good than all the kings of the Sarmatians put together have been able to do on the banks of the Vistula. I resign myself to providence, and am come to pass the carnival at Venice."

It was now the sixth monarch's turn to speak. "Gentlemen," said he, "I am not so great a prince as any of you; but for all that, I have been a King, as well as the best of you. I am Theodore; I was elected King of Corsica; I was once called *Your Majesty,* but at present am scarce allowed the title of *Sir.* I have caused money to be coined, but am not master at present of a farthing. I have had two secretaries of state, but now have scarce a single servant. I have been myself on a throne, and have for some time lain upon straw in a common jail in London. I am afraid I shall meet with the same treatment here, although i came hither, like your Majesties, to pass the carnival at Venice."

The five other kings heard this speech with a noble compassion. Each of them gave King Theodore twenty sequins to buy him some clothes and shirts, and Candide made him a present of a diamond worth two thousand sequins. "Who," said the five kings, "can this person be, who is able to give, and really has given an hundred times as much as either of us?" "Sir, are you also a King?" "No, gentlemen," said Candide, "nor have I any desire to be one."

At the instant they rose from the table there arrived at the same inn four Serene Highnesses, who had also lost their dominions by the fortune of war, and were come to pass the carnival at Venice. But Candide took no notice of these new comers, his thoughts being wholly taken up with going to Constantinople in search of his dear Cunegonde.

XXVII

CANDIDE'S VOYAGE TO CONSTANTINOPLE

THE faithful Cacambo had already prevailed on the Turkish captain who was going to carry Sultan Achmet back again to Constantinople, to receive Candide and Martin on board. They both of them embarked, after they had prostrated themselves before his miserable Highness. As Candide was on his way, he said to Martin, "There were six dethroned kings that we supped with; and what is still more, among these six kings there was one that I gave alms to. Perhaps there may be a great many other princes more unfortunate still. For my own part, I have lost only one hundred sheep, and am flying to the arms of Cunegonde. My dear Martin, I must still say, Pangloss was in the right; all things are for the best." "I wish they were," said Martin. "But," said Candide, "the adventure we met with at Venice is something romantic. Such a thing was never before either seen or heard of, that six dethroned kings should sup together at a common inn." "This is not more extraordinary," replied Martin, "than most of the things that have happened to us. It is a common thing for kings to be dethroned; and with respect to the honor that we had of supping with them, it is a trifle that does not merit our attention."

Scarce had Candide got on board, when he fell on the neck of his old servant and friend Cacambo. "Well," said he, "what news of Cunegonde? is she still a miracle of beauty? does she love me still? how does she do? No doubt but you have bought a palace for her at Constantinople?"

"My dear master," replied Cacambo, "Cunegonde washes dishes on the banks of the Propontis, for a prince who has very few to wash; she is a slave in the house of an ancient sovereign named *Ragotsky*, to whom the Grand Turk allows three crowns a day to support him in his asylum; but, what is worse than all, she has lost her beauty, and is become shockingly ugly." "Well, handsome or ugly," replied Candide, "I am a man of honor, and it is my duty to love her still. But how came she to be reduced to so abject a condition, with the five or six millions that you carried her?" "Well," said Cacambo, "was I

not to give two millions to Signor Don Fernandes d'Ibaraa, y Figueora, y
Mascarenes, y Lampourdos, y Souza, the governor of Buenos-Ayres, for permission to take Miss Cunegonde back again? and did not a pirate rob us of
all the rest? Did not this pirate carry us to Cape Matapan, to Milo, to Nicaria,
to Samos, to Dardanelles, to Marmora, to Scutari? Cunegonde and the old
woman are servants to the prince I told you of, and I am a slave of the
dethroned sultan." "What a chain of shocking calamities!" said Candide. "But,
after all, I have some diamonds, I shall easily purchase Cunegonde's liberty.
It is a pity that she is grown so ugly."

Then, turning himself to Martin, "Who do you think," says he, "is most
to be pitied; the Sultan Achmet, the Emperor Ivan, King Charles Edward, or
myself?" "I cannot tell," said Martin, "I must look into your hearts to be able
to tell." "Ah!" said Candide, "if Pangloss were here, he would know and tell
us." "I know not," replied Martin, "in what sort of scales your Pangloss would
weigh the misfortunes of mankind, and how he would appraise their sorrows.
All that I can venture to say is, that there are millions of men upon earth a
hundred times more to be pitied than King Charles Edward, the Emperor
Ivan, or Sultan Achmet."

"That may be so," said Candide.

In a few days they reached the Black Sea. Candide began with ransoming
Cacambo at an extravagant price; and, without loss of time, he got into a
galley with his companions, to go to the banks of the Propontis, in search of
Cunegonde, however ugly she might have become.

Among the crew, there were two slaves that rowed very badly, to whose
bare shoulders the Levant trader would now and then apply severe strokes
with a bull's pizzle. Candide, by a natural sympathy, looked at them more
attentively than at the rest of the galley-slaves, and went up to them with a
heart full of pity. The features of two of their faces, though very much disfigured, seemed to bear some resemblance to those of Pangloss, and the unfortunate Baron, the brother of Miss Cunegonde. This fancy made him feel very
sad. He looked at them again more attentively. "Really," said he to Cacambo,
"if I had not seen the good Pangloss hanged, and had not had the misfortune
to kill the Baron myself, I should think it was they who are rowing in this
galley."

At the names of the Baron and Pangloss, the two galley-slaves gave a loud
shriek, became as if petrified in their seats, and let their oars drop. The master
of the Levanter ran up to them, and redoubled the lashes of the bull's pizzle
upon them. "Hold! Hold! Seignior," cried Candide, "I will give you what money
you please." "What! it is Candide!" said one of the galley-slaves. "Oh! it is
Candide!" said the other. "Do I dream?" said Candide; "am I awake? am I in
this galley? is that Master Baron whom I killed? is that Master Pangloss whom
I saw hanged?"

"It is ourselves! It is our very selves!" they exclaimed. "What! is that the
great philosopher?" said Martin. "Harkee, Master Levant Captain," said Candide, "what will you take for the ransom of Monsieur Thunder-ten-tronckh,

one of the first Barons of the empire, together with Master Pangloss, the most profound metaphysician of Germany?" "You Christian dog," said the Levant captain, "since these two dogs of Christian slaves are a baron and a metaphysician, which, without doubt, are high dignities in their own country, you shall give me fifty thousand sequins." "You shall have the money, sir; carry me back again, like lightning, to Constantinople, and you shall be paid directly. But stop, carry me to Miss Cunegonde first." The Levant captain, on the first offer of Candide, had turned the head of the vessel towards the city, and made the other slaves row faster than a bird cleaves the air.

Candide embraced the Baron and Pangloss a hundred times. "How happened it that I did not kill you, my dear Baron? and, my dear Pangloss, how came you to life again, after being hanged? and how came both of you to be galley-slaves in Turkey?" "Is it true that my dear sister is in this country?" said the Baron. "Yes," replied Cacambo. "Then I see my dear Candide once more," said Pangloss.

Candide presented Martin and Cacambo to them; the whole party mutually embraced, and all spoke at the same time. The galley flew like lightning, and they were already in the port. A Jew was sent for, to whom Candide sold a diamond for fifty thousand sequins, which was worth a hundred thousand, the Israelite swearing by Abraham that he could not give any more. He immediately paid the ransom of the Baron and Pangloss. The latter threw himself at the feet of his deliverer, and bathed them with his tears; as for the other, he thanked him with a nod, and promised to repay him the money the first opportunity. "But is it possible that my sister is in Turkey?" said he. "Nothing is more possible," replied Cacambo; "for she scours dishes in the house of a prince of Transylvania!" Two more Jews were instantly sent for, to whom Candide sold some more diamonds; and he and his party all set out again, in another galley, to go and deliver Cunegonde.

XXVIII

What Happened to Candide, Cunegonde, Pangloss, Martin, Etc.

"I ask your pardon once more," said Candide to the Baron. "I ask pardon for having thrust my sword through your body." "Don't let us say any more about it," said the Baron; "I was a little too hasty, I must confess. But since you desire to know by what fatality I came to be a galley-slave, I will inform you. After I was cured of my wound, by a brother who was apothecary, I was attacked and carried off by a party of Spaniards, who confined me in prison at Buenos-Ayres, at the very time my sister was setting out from thence. I demanded leave to return to Europe. I was nominated to go as almoner to Constantinople, with the French ambassador. I had not been eight days engaged in this employment, when one day I met with a young, well-made Icoglan. It was then very hot; the young man went to bathe himself, and I took the opportunity to bathe myself too. I did not know that it was a capital crime for a Christian to be found naked with a young Mussulman. A cadi ordered me to receive a hundred strokes of the bastinado on the soles of my feet, and condemned me to the galleys. I do not think there ever was a greater act of injustice. But I should be glad to know how it comes about, that my sister is dish-washer in the kitchen of a Transylvania prince, who is a refugee among the Turks."

"But you, my dear Pangloss," said Candide, "how came I ever to set eyes on you again!" "It is true, indeed," said Pangloss, "that you saw me hanged; I ought naturally to have been burnt; but you may remember, that it rained prodigiously when they were going to roast me; the storm was so violent that they despaired of lighting the fire. I was therefore hanged because they could do no better. A surgeon bought my body, carried it home with him, and began to dissect me. He first made a crucial incision. No one could have been more slovenly hanged than I was. The executioner of the inquisition burnt people marvellously well, but he was not used to the art of hanging them. The cord being wet did not slip properly, and the noose was badly tied: in short, I still drew my breath. The crucial incision made me give such a dreadful shriek, that my surgeon fell down backwards, and fancying he was dissecting the devil, he ran away, ready to die with the fright, and fell down a second time on the stair-case, as he was making off. His wife ran out of an adjacent closet, on hearing the noise, saw me extended on the table with my crucial incision, and being more frightened than her husband, fled also, and tumbled over him. When they were come to themselves a little, I heard the surgeon's wife say to him, "My dear, how came you to be so foolish as to venture to dissect a heretic? Don't you know that the devil always takes possession of the bodies of such people? I will go immediately and fetch a priest to exorcise him." I shuddered at this proposal, and mustered up what little strength I had left to cry out, Oh! have pity upon me! At length the Portuguese barber took courage, sewed up my skin, and his wife nursed me so well, that I was upon my feet again in about fifteen days. The barber got me a place, to be footman to a knight of Malta, who was going to Venice; but my master not being able to pay me my wages, I engaged in the service of a Venetian merchant, and went along with him to Constantinople.

"One day I took a fancy to go into a mosque. There was nobody there but an old iman, and a very handsome young devotee saying her prayers. Her breast was uncovered; she had in her bosom a beautiful nosegay of tulips, anemones, ranunculuses, hyacinths, and auriculas; she let her nosegay fall; I took it up, and presented it to her with the most profound reverence. However, I was so long in handing it to her, that the iman fell into a passion, and seeing I was a Christian, called out for help. They carried me before the cadi, who ordered me a hundred bastinadoes, and to be sent to the galleys. I was chained to the same galley and the same bench with the Baron. There were on board this galley four young men from Marseilles, five Neapolitan priests, and two monks of Corfu, who told us that the like adventures happened every day. The Baron pretended that he had suffered more injustice than I; and I insisted that it was far more innocent to put a nosegay into a young woman's bosom, than to be found stark naked with an Icoglan. We were perpetually disputing, and we received twenty lashes every day with a bull's pizzle, when the concatenation of events in this universe brought you to our galley, and you ransomed us."

"Well, my dear Pangloss," said Candide, "when you were hanged, dissected, severely beaten, and tugging at the oar in the galley, did you always think that things in this world were all for the best?" "I am still as I always have been, of my first opinion," answered Pangloss; "for as I am a philosopher, it would be inconsistent with my character to contradict myself; especially as Liebnitz could not be in the wrong; and his pre-established harmony is certainly the finest system in the world, as well as his gross and subtle matter."

XXIX

How Candide Found Cunegonde and the Old Woman Again

While Candide, the Baron, Pangloss, Martin, and Cacambo, were relating their adventures to each other, and disputing about the contingent and non-contingent events of this world, and while they were arguing upon effects and causes, on moral and physical evil, on liberty and necessity, and on the consolations a person may experience in the galleys in Turkey, they arrive on the banks of the Propontis, at the house of the Prince of Transylvania. The first objects which presented themselves were Cunegonde and the old woman, hanging out some table-linen on the line to dry.

The Baron grew pale at this sight. Even Candide, the affectionate lover, on seeing his fair Cunegonde awfully tanned, with her eye-lids reversed, her neck withered, her cheeks wrinkled, her arms red and rough, was seized with horror, jumped near three yards backwards, but afterwards advanced to her, but with more politeness than passion. She embraced Candide and her brother, who, each of them, embraced the old woman, and Candide ransomed them both.

There was a little farm in the neighborhood, which the old woman advised Candide to hire, till they could meet with better accommodations for their whole company. As Cunegonde did not know that she had grown ugly, nobody having told her of it, she put Candide in mind of his promise to marry her, in so peremptory a manner, that he durst not refuse her. But when this thing was intimated to the Baron: "I will never suffer," said he, "such meanness on her part, nor such insolence on yours. With this infamy I will never be reproached. The children of my sister shall never be enrolled in the chapters of Germany. No; my sister shall never marry any but a Baron of the empire." Cunegonde threw herself at her brother's feet, and bathed them with her tears, but he remained inflexible. "You ungrateful puppy, you," said Candide to him. "I have

delivered you from the galleys; I have paid your ransom; I have also paid
that of your sister, who was a scullion here, and is very homely; I have the
goodness, however, to make her my wife, and you are fool enough to oppose
it; I have a good mind to kill you again, you make me so angry." "You may
indeed kill me again," said the Baron; "but you shall never marry my sister,
while I have breath."

XXX

Conclusion

CANDIDE had no great desire, at the bottom of his heart, to marry Cunegonde.
But the extreme impertinence of the Baron determined him to conclude the
match, and Cunegonde pressed it so earnestly, that he could not retract. He
advised with Pangloss, Martin, and the trusty Cacambo. Pangloss drew up an
excellent memoir, in which he proved, that the Baron had no right over his
sister, and that she might, according to all the laws of the empire, espouse
Candide with her left hand. Martin was for throwing the Baron into the
sea: Cacambo was of opinion that it would be best to send him back again
to the Levant captain, and make him work at the galleys. This advice was
thought good; the old woman approved it, and nothing was said to his sister
about it. The scheme was put in execution for a little money, and so they
had the pleasure of punishing the pride of a German Baron.

It is natural to imagine that Candide, after so many disasters, married to his
sweetheart, living with the philosopher Pangloss, the philosopher Martin, the
discreet Cacambo, and the old woman, and especially as he had brought so
many diamonds from the country of the ancient Incas, must live the most
agreeable life of any man in the whole world. But he had been so cheated by
the Jews, that he had nothing left but the small farm; and his wife, growing
still more ugly, turned peevish and insupportable. The old woman was very
infirm, and worse humored than Cunegonde herself. Cacambo, who worked
in the garden, and went to Constantinople to sell its productions, was worn
out with labor, and cursed his fate. Pangloss was ready to despair, because
he did not shine at the head of some university in Germany. As for Martin,
as, he was firmly persuaded that all was equally bad throughout, he bore
things with patience. Candide, Martin, and Pangloss, disputed sometimes
about metaphysics and ethics. They often saw passing under the windows of
the farm-house boats full of effendis, bashaws, and cadis, who were going into
banishment to Lemnos, Mitylene, and Erzerum. They observed that other
cadis, other bashaws, and other effendis, succeeded in the posts of those who
were exiled, only to be banished themselves in turn. They saw heads nicely
impaled, to be presented to the Sublime Porte. These spectacles increased
the number of their disputations; and when they were not disputing, their
ennui was so tiresome that the old woman would often say to them, "I want
to know which is the worst;—to be ravished an hundred times by negro pirates,

to run the gauntlet among the Bulgarians, to be whipped and hanged, to be dissected, to row in the galleys; in a word, to have suffered all the miseries we have undergone, or to stay here, without doing anything?" "That is a great question," said Candide.

This discourse gave rise to new reflections, and Martin concluded, upon the whole, that mankind were born to live either in the distractions of inquietude, or in the lethargy of disgust. Candide did not agree with that opinion, but remained in a state of suspense. Pangloss confessed, that he had always suffered dreadfully; but having once maintained that all things went wonderfully well, he still kept firm to his hypothesis, though it was quite opposed to his real feelings.

What contributed to confirm Martin in his shocking principles, to make Candide stagger more than ever, and to embarrass Pangloss, was, that one day they saw Paquetta and Giroflee, who were in the greatest distress, at their farm. They had quickly squandered away their three thousand piastres, had parted, were reconciled, quarrelled again, had been confined in prison, had made their escape, and Giroflee had at length turned Turk. Paquetta continued her trade wherever she went, but made nothing by it, "I could easily foresee," said Martin to Candide, "that your presents would soon be squandered away, and would render them more miserable. You and Cacambo have spent millions of piastres, and are not a bit happier than Giroflee and Paquetta." "Ha! ha!" said Pangloss to Paquetta, "has Providence then brought you amongst us again, my poor child? Know, then, that you have cost me the tip of my nose, one eye, and one of my ears, as you see. What a world this is!" This new adventure set them a philosophizing more than ever.

There lived in the neighborhood a very famous dervise, who passed for the greatest philosopher in Turkey. They went to consult him. Pangloss was chosen speaker, and said to him, "Master, we are come to desire you would tell us, why so strange an animal as man was created."

"What's that to you?" said the dervise; "is it any business of thine?" "But, my reverend father," said Candide, "there is a horrible amount of evil in the world." "What signifies," said the dervise, "whether there be good or evil? When his Sublime Highness send a vessel to Egypt, does it trouble him, whether the mice on board are at their ease or not?" "What would you have one do then?" said Pangloss. "Hold your tongue," said the dervise. "I promised myself the pleasure," said Pangloss, "of reasoning with you upon effects and causes, the best of possible worlds, the origin of evil, the nature of the soul, and the pre-established harmony."—The dervise, at these words, shut the door in their faces.

During this conference, news was brought that two viziers and a mufti were strangled at Constantinople, and a great many of their friends impaled. This catastrophe made a great noise for several hours. Pangloss, Candide, and Martin, on their way back to the little farm, met a good-looking old man, taking the air at his door, under an arbor of orange trees. Pangloss, who had as much curiosity as philosophy, asked him the name of the mufti who was lately strangled. "I know nothing at all about it," said the good man; "and what's more, I never knew the name of a single mufti, or a single vizier, in my life. I am an entire stranger to the story you mention; and presume that, generally speaking, they who trouble their heads with state affairs, sometimes die shocking deaths, not without deserving it. But I never trouble my head about what is doing at Constantinople; I content myself with sending my fruits thither, the produce of my garden, which I cultivate with my own hands!" Having said these words, he introduced the strangers into his house. His two daughters and two sons served them with several kinds of sherbet, which they made themselves, besides caymac, enriched with the peels of candied citrons, oranges, lemons, bananas, pistachio nuts, and Mocoa coffee, unadulterated with the bad coffee of Batavia and the isles. After which, the two daughters of this good Mussulman perfumed the beards of Candide, Pangloss, and Martin.

"You must certainly," said Candide to the Turk, "have a very large and very opulent estate!" "I have only twenty acres," said the Turk; "which I, with my children, cultivate. Labor keeps us free from three of the greatest evils: tiresomeness, vice, and want."

As Candide returned to his farm, he made deep reflections on the discourse of the Turk. Said he to Pangloss and Martin, "The condition of this good old man seems to me preferable to that of the six kings with whom we had the honor to sup." "The grandeurs of royalty," said Pangloss, "are very precarious, in the opinion of all philosophers. For, in short, Eglon, king of the Moabites, was assassinated by Ehud; Absalom was hung by the hair of his head, and pierced through with three darts; King Nadab, the son of Jeroboam, was killed by Baasha; King Elah by Zimri; Ahaziah by Jehu; Athaliah by Jehoiadah; the kings Joachim, Jechonias, and Zedekias, were carried into captivity. You know the fates of Crœsus, Astyages, Darius, Dionysius of Syracuse, Pyrrhus, Perseus, Hannibal, Jugurtha, Ariovistus, Cæsar, Pompey, Nero, Otho, Vitellius, Domitian, Richard II., Edward II., Henry VI., Richard III., Mary Stuart, Charles I. of England, the three Henrys of France, and the Emperor Henry IV. You know——" "I know very well," said Candide, "that we ought to look after our garden." "You are in the right," said Pangloss, "for when man was placed in the garden of Eden, he was placed there, *ut operatur cum*, to cultivate it; which proves that mankind are not created to be idle." "Let us work," said Martin, "without disputing; it is the only way to render life supportable."

All their little society entered into this laudable design, according to their different abilities. Their little piece of ground produced a plentiful crop. Cunegonde was indeed very homely, but she became an excellent pastry cook. Paquetta worked at embroidery, and the old woman took care of the linen. There was no idle person in the company, not excepting even Girofflee; he made a very good carpenter, and became a very honest man.

As to Pangloss, he evidently had a lurking consciousness that his theory required unceasing exertions, and all his ingenuity, to sustain it. Yet he stuck to it to the last; his thinking and talking faculties could hardly be diverted from it for a moment. He seized every occasion to say to Candide, "All the events in this best of possible worlds are admirably connected. If a single link in the great chain were omitted, the harmony of the entire universe would be destroyed. If you had not been expelled from that beautiful castle, with those cruel kicks, for your love to Miss Cunegonde; if you had not been imprisoned by the inquisition; if you had not travelled over a great portion of America on foot; if you had not plunged your sword through the baron; if you had not lost all the sheep you brought from that fine country, Eldorado, together with the riches with which they were laden, you would not be here to-day, eating preserved citrons, and pistachio nuts."

"That's very well said, and may all be true," said Candide; "but let's cultivate our garden."

THE HURON, OR PUPIL OF NATURE

I

THE HURON ARRIVES IN FRANCE

ONE DAY, Saint Dunstan, an Irishman by nation, left Ireland and took his route toward the coast of France, and set his saintship down in the bay of St. Malo.

Here St. Dunstan laid the foundation of a small priory, and gave it the name of the Priory Mountain, which it still keeps, as everybody knows.

In the year 1689, the fifteenth day of July, in the evening, the abbot Kerkabon, prior of the Mountain, happened to take the air along the shore with Miss Kerkabon, his sister. The prior, who was becoming aged, was a very good clergyman, beloved by his neighbors.

Miss Kerkabon, who had never been married, notwithstanding her hearty wishes so to be, had preserved a freshness of complexion in her forty-fifth year. Her character was that of a good and sensible woman. She was fond of pleasure, and was a devotee.

As they were walking, the prior, looking on the sea, said to his sister:

"It was here, alas! that our poor brother embarked with our dear sister-in-law, Madam Kerkabon, his wife, on board the frigate 'Swallow,' in 1669, to serve the king in Canada. Had he not been killed, probably he would have written to us."

"Do you believe," says Miss Kerkabon, "that our sister-in-law has been eaten by the Cherokees, as we have been told?"

"Certain it is, had she not been killed, she would have come back. I shall weep for her all my lifetime. She was a charming woman; and our brother, who had a great deal of wit, would no doubt have made a fortune."

Thus were they going on with mutual tenderness, when they beheld a small vessel enter the bay of Rence with the tide. It was from England, and came to sell provisions. The crew leaped on shore without looking at the prior or Miss, his sister, who were shocked at the little attention shown them.

That was not the behavior of a well-made youth, who, darting himself over the heads of his companions, stood on a sudden before Miss Kerkabon. Being unaccustomed to bowing, he made her a sign with his head. His figure and his dress attracted the notice of brother and sister. His head was uncovered, and his legs bare. Instead of shoes, he wore a kind of sandals. From his head his long hair flowed in tresses. A small close doublet displayed the beauty of his shape. He had a sweet and martial air. In one hand he held a small bottle of Barbadoes water, and in the other a bag, in which he had a goblet, and some sea biscuit. He spoke French very intelligibly. He offered some of his Barbadoes to Miss Kerkabon and her brother. He drank with them, he made them drink a second time, and all this with an air of such native simplicity, that quite charmed brother and sister. They offered him their service, and asked him who he was, and whither going? The young man answered: That he knew not where he should go; that he had some curiosity; that he had a desire to see the coast of France; that he had seen it, and should return.

The prior, judging by his accent that he was not an Englishman, took the liberty of asking of what country he was.

"I am a Huron," answered the youth.

Miss Kerkabon, amazed and enchanted to see a Huron who had behaved so politely to her, begged the young man's company to supper. He complied immediately, and all three went together to the priory of our Lady of the Mountain. This short and round Miss devoured him with her little eyes, and said from time to time to her brother:

"This tall lad has a complexion of lilies and roses. What a fine skin he has for a Huron!"

"Very true, sister," says the prior.

She put a hundred questions, one after another, and the traveler answered always pertinently.

The report was soon spread that there was a Huron at the priory. All the genteel company of the country came to supper. The abbot of St. Yves came with Miss, his sister, a fine, handsome, well-educated girl. The bailiff, the tax-gatherer, and their wives, came all together. The foreigner was seated between Miss Kerkabon and Miss St. Yves. The company eyed him with admiration. They all questioned him together. This did not confound the Huron. He seemed to have taken Lord Bolingbroke's motto, *Nil admirari*. But at last tired out with so much noise, he told them in a sweet but serious tone:

"Gentlemen, in my country one talks after another. How can I answer you, if you will not allow me to hear you?"

Reasoning always brings people to a momentary reflection. They were all silent.

Mr. Baliff, who always made a property of a foreigner wherever he found him, and who was the first man for asking questions in the province, opening a mouth of large size, began:

"Sir, what is your name?"

"I have always been called the *Ingenu*," answered the Huron; "and the English have confirmed that name, because I always speak as I think, and act as I like."

"But, being born a Huron, how could you come to England?"

"I have been carried thither. I was made prisoner by the English after some resistance, and the English, who love brave people, because they are as brave and honest as we, proposed to me, either to return to my family, or go with them to England. I accepted the latter, having naturally a relish for traveling."

"But, sir," says the bailiff, with his usual gravity, "how could you think of abandoning father and mother?"

"Because I never knew either father or mother," says the foreigner.

This moved the company; they all repeated:

"Neither father nor mother!"

"We will be in their stead," says the mistress of the house, to her brother, the prior: "How interesting this Huron gentleman is!"

The *Ingenu* thanked her with a noble and proud cordiality, and gave her to understand that he wanted the assistance of nobody.

"I perceive, Mr. Huron," said the huge bailiff, "that you talk better French than can be expected from an Indian."

"A Frenchman," answered he, "whom they had made prisoner when I was a boy, and with whom I contracted a great friendship, taught it me. I rapidly learn what I like to learn. When I came to Plymouth, I met with one of your French refugees, whom you, I know not why, call Huguenots. He improved my knowledge of your language; and as soon as I could express myself intelligibly, I came to see your country, because I like the French well enough, if they do not put too many questions."

Notwithstanding this candid remark, the abbe of St. Yves asked him which of the three languages pleased him best, the Huron, English, or French?

"The Huron, to be sure," answered the *Ingenu*.

"Is it possible?" cried Miss Kerkabon. "I always thought the French was the first of all languages, after that of Low Brittainy."

Then all were eager to know how, in Huron, they asked for snuff? He replied:

"*Taya.*"

"What signifies to eat?"

"*Essenten.*"

Miss Kerkabon was impatient to know how they called, to make love?

He informed her, *Trovander;* and insisted on it, not without reason, that these words were well worth their synonyms in French and English. *Trovander,* especially, seemed very pretty to all the company. The prior, who had in his library a Huron grammar, which had been given him, rose from the table to consult it. He returned quite panting with tenderness and joy. He acknowledged the foreigner for a true Huron. The company speculated a little on the multiplicity of languages; and all agreed that had it not been for the unfortunate affair of the Tower of Babel, all the world would have spoken French.

The inquisitive bailiff, who till then had some suspicions of the foreigner, conceived the deepest respect for him. He spoke to him with more civility than before, and the Huron took no notice of it.

Miss St. Yves was very curious to know how people made love among the Hurons.

"In performing great actions to please such as resemble you."

All the company admired and applauded. Miss St. Yves blushed, and was extremely well pleased. Miss Kerkabon blushed likewise, but was not so well pleased. She was a little piqued that this gallantry was not addressed to her; but she was so good-natured, that her affection for the Huron was not diminished at all. She asked him, with great complacency, how many mistresses he had at home.

"Only one," answered the foreigner; "Miss Abacaba, the good friend of my dear nurse. The reed is not straighter, nor is ermine whiter,—no lamb meeker, no eagle fiercer, nor a stag swifter, than was my Abacaba. One day she pursued a hare not above fifty leagues from my habitation: a base Algonquin, who dwells an hundred leagues further, took her hare from her. I was told of it; I ran thither, and with one stroke of my club leveled him with the ground. I brought him to the feet of my mistress, bound hand and foot. Abacaba's parents were for burning him, but I always had a disrelish for such scenes. I set him at liberty. I made him my friend. Abacaba was so pleased with my conduct, that she preferred me to all her lovers. And she would have continued to love me, had she not been devoured by a bear! I slew the bear, and wore his skin a long while; but that has not comforted me."

Miss St. Yves felt a secret pleasure at hearing that Abacaba had been his only mistress, and that she was no more; yet she understood not the cause of her own pleasure. All eyes were riveted on the Huron, and he was much applauded for delivering an Algonquin from the cruelty of his countrymen.

The merciless bailiff had now grown so furious, that he even asked the Huron what religion he was of; whether he had chosen the English, the French, or that of the Huguenots?

"I am of my own religion," said he, "just as you are of yours."

"Lord!" cried Miss Kerkabon, "I see already that those wretched English have not once thought of baptizing him!"

"Good heavens," said Miss Yves, "how is it possible?"

The Huron assured her that no true American had ever changed his opinion, and that there was not in their language a word to express inconstancy.

These last words extremely pleased Miss St. Yves.

"Oh! we'll baptize him, we'll baptize him," said Miss Kerkabon to the prior. "You shall have that honor, my dear brother, and I will be his godmother. The Abbot St. Yves shall present him to the font. It will make a fine appearance: it will be talked of all over Brittany, and do us the greatest honor."

The company were all of the same mind with the mistress of the house; they all cried:

"We'll baptize him."

The Huron interrupted them by saying, that in England every one was allowed to live as he pleased. He rather showed some aversion to the proposal which was made, and could not help telling them, that the laws of the Hurons were to the full as good as those of Low Brittany. He finished with saying that he should return the next day. The bottles grew empty, and the company went to bed.

After the Huron had been conducted to his room, they saw that he spread the blankets on the floor, and laid himself down upon them in the finest attitude in the world.

II

THE HURON, CALLED THE INGENU, ACKNOWLEDGED BY HIS RELATIONS

THE *Ingenu,* according to custom, awoke with the sun, at the crowing of the cock, which is called in England and Huronia "the trumpet of the day." He did not imitate what is styled good company, who languish in the bed of indolence till the sun has performed half its daily journey, unable to sleep, but not disposed to rise, and lose so many precious hours in that doubtful state between life and death, and who nevertheless complain that life is too short.

He had already traversed two or three leagues, and killed fifteen brace of game with his rifle, when, upon his return, he found the prior of the Lady of the Mountain, with his discreet sister, walking in their little garden. He presented them with the spoils of his morning labor, and taking from his bosom a kind of little talisman, which he constantly wore about his neck, he entreated them to accept of it as an acknowledgment for the kind reception they had given him.

"It is," said he, "the most valuable thing I am possessed of. I have been assured that I shall always be happy whilst I carry this little toy about me; and I give it you that you may be always happy."

The prior and Miss smiled with pity at the frankness of the *Ingenu.* This present consisted of two little portraits, poorly executed, and tied together with a greasy string.

Miss Kerkabon asked him if there were any painters in Huronia?

"No," replied the *Ingenu,* "I had this curiosity from my nurse. Her husband had obtained it by conquest, in stripping some of the French of Canada, who had made war upon us. This is all I know of the matter."

The prior looked attentively upon these pictures, whilst he changed color; his hands trembled, and he seemed much affected.

"By our Lady of the Mountain," he cried out, "I believe these to be the faces of my brother, the captain, and his lady."

Miss, after having consulted them with the like emotion, thought the same. They were both struck with astonishment and joy blended with grief. They both melted, they both wept, their hearts throbbed, and during their disorder, the pictures were interchanged between them at least twenty times in a second. They seemed to devour the Huron's pictures with their eyes. They asked one after another, and even both at once, at what time, in what place, and how these miniatures fell into the hands of the nurse? They reckoned and computed the time from the captain's departure: they recollected having received notice that he had penetrated as far as the country of the Hurons; and from that time they had never heard anything more of him.

The Huron had told them, that he had never known either father or mother. The prior, who was a man of sense, observed that he had a little beard, and he knew very well that the Hurons never had any. His chin was somewhat hairy; he was therefore the son of an European. My brother and sister-in-law were never seen after the expedition against the Hurons, in 1669. My nephew must then have been nursing at the breast. The Huron nurse has preserved his life, and been a mother to him. At length, after an hundred questions and answers, the prior and his sister concluded that the Huron was their own nephew. They embraced him, whilst tears streamed from their eyes: and the Huron laughed to think that an Indian should be nephew to a prior of Lower Brittany.

All the company went down stairs. Mr. de St. Yves, who was a great physiognomist, compared the two pictures with the Huron's countenance. They observed, very skillfully, that he had the mother's eyes, the forehead and nose of the late Captain Kerkabon, and the cheeks common to both.

Miss St. Yves, who had never seen either father or mother, was strenuously of opinion that the young man had a perfect resemblance of them. They all admired Providence, and wondered at the strange events of this world. In a word, they were so persuaded, so convinced of the birth of the Huron, that he himself consented to be the prior's nephew, saying that he would as soon have him for his uncle as another.

The prior went to return thanks in the church of our Lady of the Mountain; whilst the Huron, with an air of indifference, amused himself with drinking in the house.

The English who had brought him over, and who were ready to set sail, came to tell him that it was time to depart.

"Probably," said he to them, "you have not met with any of your uncles and aunts. I shall stay here. Go you back to Plymouth. I give you all my clothes, as I have no longer occasion for anything in this world, since I am the nephew of a prior."

The English set sail, without being at all concerned whether the Huron had any relations or not in Lower Brittany.

After the uncle, the aunt, and the company had rejoiced; after the bailiff had once more overwhelmed the Huron with questions; after they had exhausted all their astonishment, joy, and tenderness, the prior of the Mountain and the Abbe of St. Yves concluded that the Huron should be baptized with all possible expedition. But the case was very different with a tall robust Indian of twenty-two, and an infant who is regenerated without his knowing anything of the matter. It was necessary to instruct him, and this appeared difficult; for the Abbe of St. Yves supposed that a man who was not born in France could not be endowed with common sense.

The prior, indeed, observed to the company, that though, in fact, the ingenious gentleman, his nephew, was not so fortunate as to be born in Lower Brittany, he was not, upon that account, any way deficient in sense; which might be concluded from all his answers; and that, doubtless, nature had greatly favored him, as well on his father's as on his mother's side.

He then was asked if he had ever read any books? He said, he had read Rabelais translated into English, and some passages in Shakespeare, which he knew by heart; that these books belonged to the captain, on board of whose ship he came from America to Plymouth; and that he was very well pleased with them. The bailiff failed not to put many questions to him concerning these books.

"I acknowledge," said the Huron, "I thought, in reading them, I understood some things, but not the whole."

The Abbe of St. Yves reflected upon this discourse, that it was in this manner he had always read, and that most men read no other way.

"You have," said he to the Huron, "doubtless read the Bible?"

"Never, Mr. Abbe: it was not among the captain's books. I never heard it mentioned."

"This is the way with those cursed English," said Miss Kerkabon; "they think more of a play of Shakespeare's, a plum pudding, or a bottle of rum, than they do of the Pentateuch. For this reason they have never converted any Indians in America. They are certainly cursed by God; and we shall conquer Jamaica and Virginia from them in a very short time."

Be this as it may, the most skillful tailor in all St. Malo was sent for to dress the Huron from head to foot. The company separated, and the bailiff went elsewhere to display his inquisitiveness. Miss St. Yves, in parting, returned several times to observe the young stranger, and made him lower courtesies than ever she did any one in her life.

The bailiff, before he took his leave, presented to Miss St. Yves a stupid dolt of a son, just come from college; but she scarce looked at him, so mucn was she taken up with the politeness of the Huron.

III

THE HURON CONVERTED

THE prior finding that he was somewhat advanced in years, and that God had sent him a nephew for his consolation, took it into his head that he would resign his benefice in his favor, if he succeeded in baptizing him and of making him enter into orders.

The Huron had an excellent memory. A good constitution, inherited from his ancestors of Lower Brittany, strengthened by the climate of Canada, had made his head so vigorous that when he was struck upon it he scarce felt it; and when any thing was graven in it, nothing could efface it. Nothing had ever escaped his memory. His conception was the more sure and lively, because his infancy had not been loaded with useless fooleries, which overwhelm ours. Things entered into his head without being clouded. The prior at length resolved to make him read the New Testament. The Huron devoured it with great pleasure; but not knowing at what time, or in what country all the adventures related in this book had happened, he did not in the least doubt that the scene of action had been in Lower Brittany; and he swore, that he would cut off Caiaphas and Pontius Pilate's ears, if ever he met those scoundrels.

His uncle, charmed with this good disposition, soon brought him to the point. He applauded his zeal, but at the same time acquainted him that it was needless, as these people had been dead upwards of 1690 years. The Huron soon got the whole book by heart. He sometimes proposed difficulties that greatly embarrassed the prior. He was often obliged to consult the Abbe St. Yves, who, not knowing what to answer, brought a cleric of Lower Brittany to perfect the conversion of the Huron.

Grace, at length, operated; and the Huron promised to become a Christian. He did not doubt but that the first step toward it was circumcision.

"For," said he, "I do not find in the book that was put into my hands a single person who was not circumcised. It is therefore evident that I must make a sacrifice to the Hebrew custom, and the sooner the better."

He sent for the surgeon of the village, and desired him to perform the operation. The surgeon, who had never performed such an operation, acquainted the family, who screamed out. The good Miss Kerkabon trembled lest her nephew, whom she knew to be resolute and expeditious, should perform the operation unskillfully himself; and that fatal consequences might ensue.

The prior rectified the Huron's mistake, representing to him that circumcision was no longer in fashion; that baptism was much more gentle and salutary; that the law of grace was not like the law of rigor. The Huron, who had much good sense, and was well disposed, disputed, but soon acknowledged his error, which seldom happens in Europe among disputants. In a word, he promised to let himself be baptized whenever they pleased.

The Bishop of St. Malo was chosen for the ceremony, who flattered, as may be believed, at baptizing a Huron, arrived in a pompous equipage, followed by his clergy. Miss St. Yves put on her best gown to bless God, and sent for a hair dresser from St. Malo's, to shine at the ceremony. The inquisitive bailiff brought the whole country with him. The church was magnificently ornamented. But when the Huron was summoned to attend the baptismal font, he was not to be found.

His uncle and aunt sought for him everywhere. It was imagined that he had gone a hunting, according to his usual custom. Every one present at the festival searched the neighboring woods and villages; but no intelligence could be obtained of the Huron. They began to fear he had returned to England. Some remembered that he had said he was very fond of that country. The prior and his sister were persuaded that nobody was baptized there, and were troubled for their nephew's soul. The bishop was confounded, and ready to return home. The prior and the Abbe St. Yves were in despair. The bailiff interrogated all passengers with his usual gravity. Miss Kerkabon melted into tears. Miss St. Yves did not weep, but she vented such deep sighs, as seemed to testify her sacramental disposition. They were walking in this melancholy mood, among the willows and reeds upon the banks of the little river Rence, when they perceived, in the middle of the stream, a large figure, tolerably white, with its two arms across its breast. They screamed out, and ran away. But curiosity being stronger than any other consideration, they advanced softly amongst the reeds; and when they were pretty certain they could not be seen, they were willing to descry what it was.

IV

THE HURON BAPTIZED

THE prior and the abbe having run to the river side, they asked the Huron what he was doing?

"In faith," said he, "gentlemen, I am waiting to be baptized. I have been an hour in the water, up to my neck, and I do not think it is civil to let me be quite exhausted."

"My dear nephew," said the prior to him, tenderly, "this is not the way of being baptized in Lower Brittany. Put on your clothes, and come with us."

Miss St. Yves, listening to the discourse, said in a whisper to her companion: "Miss, do you think he will put his clothes on in such a hurry?"

The Huron, however, replied to the prior:

"You will not make me believe now as you did before. I have studied very well since, and I am very certain there is no other kind of baptism. The eunuch of Queen Candace was baptized in a rivulet. I defy you to show me, in the book you gave me, that people were ever baptized in any other way. I either will not be baptized at all, or the ceremony shall be performed in the river."

It was in vain to remonstrate to him that customs were altered. He always recurred to the eunuch of Queen Candace. And though Miss and his aunt, who had observed him through the willows, were authorized to tell him, that he had no right to quote such a man; they, nevertheless, said nothing;—so great was their discretion. The bishop came himself to speak to him, which was a great thing; but he could not prevail. The Huron disputed with the bishop.

"Show me," said he, "in the book my uncle gave me, one single man that was not baptized in a river, and I will do whatever you please."

His aunt, in despair, had observed, that the first time her nephew bowed, he made a much lower bow to Miss St. Yves than to any one in the company—that he had not even saluted the bishop with so much respect, blended with cordiality, as he did that agreeable young lady. She thought it advisable to apply to her in this great embarrassment. She earnestly entreated her to use her influence to engage the Huron to be baptized according to the custom of Brittany, thinking that her nephew could never be a Christian if he persisted in being christened in the stream.

Miss St. Yves blushed at the secret joy she felt in being appointed to execute

so important a commission. She modestly approached the Huron, and squeez-
ing his hand in quite a noble manner, she said to him:

"What, will you do nothing to please me?"

And in uttering these words, she raised her eyes from a downcast look into
a graceful tenderness.

"O! yes, Miss, every thing you require, all that you command, whether it
is to be baptized in water, fire, or blood;—there is nothing I can refuse you."

Miss St. Yves had the glory of effecting, in two words, what neither the
importunities of the prior, the repeated interrogations of the bailiff, nor the
reasoning of the bishop, could effect. She was sensible of her triumph; but
she was not yet sensible of its utmost latitude.

Baptism was administered, and received with all the decency, magnificence,
and propriety possible. His uncle and aunt yielded to the Abbe St. Yves and
his sister the favor of supporting the Huron upon the font. Miss St. Yves's
eyes sparkled with joy at being a god-mother. She was ignorant how much
this high title compromised her. She accepted the honor, without being acquainted with its fatal consequences.

As there never was any ceremony that was not followed by a good dinner,
the company took their seats at table after the christening. The humorists of
Lower Brittany said, "they did not choose to have their wine baptized." The
prior said, that "wine, according to Solomon, cherished the heart of man."
The bishop added, "that the Patriarch Judah ought to have tied his ass-colt to
the vine, and steeped his cloak in the blood of the grape; and that he was sorry
the same could not be done in Lower Brittany, to which God had not allotted
vines." Every one endeavored to say a good thing upon the Huron's christening, and strokes of gallantry to the godmother. The bailiff, ever interrogating,
asked the Huron, if he was faithful in keeping his promises?

"How," said he, "can I fail keeping them, since I have deposited them in
the hands of Miss St. Yves?"

The Huron grew warm; he had drunk repeatedly his godmother's health.

"If," said he, "I had been baptized with your hand, I feel that the water
which was poured on the nape of my neck would have burnt me."

The bailiff thought that this was too poetical, being ignorant that allegory
is a familiar figure in Canada. But his godmother was very well pleased.

The Huron had, at his baptism, received the name of Hercules.

V

THE HURON IN LOVE

IT MUST be acknowledged, that from the time of this christening and this
dinner, Miss St. Yves passionately wished that the bishop would again make
her an assistant with Mr. Hercules in some other fine ceremony—that is,
the marriage ceremony. However, as she was well brought up, and very

modest,—she did not entirely agree with herself in regard to these tender sentiments; but if a look, a word, a gesture, a thought, escaped from her, she concealed it admirably under the veil of modesty. She was tender, lively, and sagacious.

As soon as the bishop was gone, the Huron and Miss St. Yves met together, without thinking they were in search of one another. They spoke together, without premeditating what they said. The sincere youth immediately declared, "that he loved her with all his heart; and that the beauteous Abacaba, with whom he had been desperately in love in his own country, was far inferior to her." Miss replied, with her usual modesty, "that the prior, her uncle, and the lady, her aunt, should be spoken to immediately; and that, on her side, she would say a few words to her dear brother, the Abbe of St. Yves, and that she flattered herself it would meet with no opposition."

The youth replied: "that the consent of any one was entirely superfluous, that it appeared to him extremely ridiculous to go and ask others what they were to do; that when two parties were agreed, there was no occasion for a third, to accomplish their union."

"I never consult any one," said he, "when I have a mind to breakfast, to hunt, or to sleep. I am sensible, that in love it is not amiss to have the consent of the person whom we wish for; but as I am neither in love with my uncle nor my aunt, I have no occasion to address myself to them in this affair; and if you will believe me, you may equally dispense with the advice of the Abbe of St. Yves."

It may be supposed that the young lady exerted all the delicacy of her wit, to bring her Huron to the terms of good breeding. She was very angry, but soon softened. In a word, it cannot be said how this conversation would have ended, if the declining day had not brought the Abbe to conduct his sister home. The Huron left his uncle and aunt to rest, they being somewhat fatigued with the ceremony, and long dinner. He passed part of the night in writing verses in the Huron language, upon his well-beloved; for it should be known, that there is no country where love has not rendered lovers poets.

The next day his uncle spoke to him in the following manner: "I am somewhat advanced in years. My brother has left only a little bit of ground, which is a very small matter. I have a good priory. If you will only make yourself a sub-deacon, as I hope you will, I will resign my priory in your favor; and you will live quite at your ease, after having been the consolation of my old age."

The Huron replied:

"Uncle, much good may it do you; live as long as you can. I do not know what it is to be a sub-deacon, or what it is to resign; but every thing will be agreeable to me, provided I have Miss St. Yves at my disposal."

"Good heavens, nephew! What is it you say? Do you love that beautiful young lady so earnestly?"

"Yes, uncle."

"Alas! nephew, it is impossible you should ever marry her."

"It is very possible, uncle; for she did not only squeeze my hand when she left me, but she promised she would ask me in marriage. I certainly shall wed her."

"It is impossible, I tell you, she is your godmother. It is a dreadful sin for a godmother to give her hand to her god-son. It is contrary to all laws, human and divine."

"Why the deuce, uncle, should it be forbidden to marry one's godmother. when she is young and handsome? I did not find, in the book you gave me, that it was wrong to marry young women who assisted at christenings. I perceive, every day, that an infinite number of things are done here which are not in your book, and nothing is done that is said in it. I must acknowledge to you, that this astonishes and displeases me. If I am deprived of the charming Miss St. Yves on account of my baptism, I give you notice, that I will run away with her and unbaptize myself."

The prior was confounded; his sister wept.

Whilst he was yet speaking, the bailiff entered, and, according to his usual custom, asked him where he was going?

"I am going to get married," replied the ingenuous Hercules, running along; and in less than a quarter of an hour he was with his charming dear mistress, who was still asleep.

"Ah! my dear brother," said Miss Kerkabon to the prior, "you will never make a sub-deacon of our nephew."

The bailiff was very much displeased at this journey; for he laid claim to Miss St. Yves in favor of his son, who was a still greater and more insupportable fool than his father.

VI

The Huron Flies to His Mistress, and Becomes Quite Furious

No sooner had the ingenuous Hercules reached the house, than having asked the old servant, which was his mistress's apartment, he forced open the door. which was badly fastened, and flew toward the bed. Miss St. Yves, startled out of her sleep, cried:

"Ah! what, is it you! Stop, what are you about?" He answered.

"I am going to marry."

She opposed him with all the decency of a young lady so well educated; but the Huron did not understand raillery, and found all evasions extremely disagreeable.

"Miss Abacaba, my first mistress," said he, "did not behave in this manner; you have no honesty; you promised me marriage, and you will not marry; this is being deficient in the first laws of honor."

The outcries of the lady brought the sagacious Abbe de St. Yves with his housekeeper, an old devoted servant, and the parish priest. The sight of these moderated the courage of the assailant.

"Good heavens!" cried the Abbe, "my dear neighbor, what are you about?"

"My duty," replied the young man. "I am fulfilling my promises, which are sacred."

Miss St. Yves adjusted herself, not without blushing. The lover was conducted into another apartment. The Abbe remonstrated to him on the enormity of his conduct. The Huron defended himself upon the privileges of the law of nature, which he understood perfectly well. The Abbe maintained that the law positive should be allowed all its advantages; and that without conventions agreed on between men, the law of nature must almost constantly be nothing more than natural felony.

The ingenuous Hercules made answer with the observation constantly adopted by savages:

"You are then very great rogues, since so many precautions are necessary." This remark somewhat disconcerted the Abbe.

"There are, I acknowledge, libertines and cheats among us, and there would be as many among the Hurons if they were united in a great city: but, at the same time, we have discreet, honest, enlightened people; and these are the men who have framed the laws. The more upright we are, the more readily we should submit to them, as we thereby set an example to the vicious, who respect those bounds which virtue has given herself."

This answer struck the Huron. It has already been observed, that his mind was well disposed. He was softened by flattering speeches, which promised him hopes; all the world is caught in these snares; and Miss St. Yves herself appeared, after having been at her toilet. Every thing was now conducted with the utmost good breeding.

It was with much difficulty that Hercules was sent back to his relations. It was again necessary for the charming Miss St. Yves to interfere; the more she perceived the influence she had upon him, the more she loved him. She made him depart, and was much affected at it. At length, when he was gone, the Abbe, who was not only Miss St. Yves's elder brother by many years, but was also her guardian, endeavored to wean his ward from the importunities of this dreadful lover. He went to consult the bailiff, who had always intended his son for the Abbe's sister, and who advised him to place the poor girl in a convent. This was a terrible stroke. Such a measure would, to a young lady unaffected with any particular passion, have been inexpressible punishment; but to a lovesick maid, equally sagacious and tender, it was despair itself.

When the ingenuous Hercules returned to the Prior's, he related all that had happened with his usual frankness. He met with the same remonstrances, which had some effect upon his mind, though none upon his senses; but the next day, when he wanted to return to his mistress, in order to reason with her upon the law of nature and the law of convention, the bailiff acquainted him, with insulting joy, that she was in a convent.

"Very well," said he, "I'll go and reason with her in this convent."

"That cannot be," said the bailiff; and then entered into a long explanation of the nature of a convent, telling him that this word was derived from *con-*

ventus, in the Latin, which signifies "an assembly;" and the Huron could not comprehend why he might not be admitted into this assembly; he became as furious as was his patron Hercules, when Euritus, king of Oechalia, no less cruel than the Abbe of St. Yves, refused him the beauteous Iola, his daughter, not inferior in beauty to the Abbe's sister. He was upon the point of going to set fire to the convent to carry off his mistress, or be burnt with her. Miss Kerkabon, terrified at such a declaration, gave up all hopes of ever seeing her nephew a sub-deacon; and, sadly weeping, she exclaimed: "The devil has certainly been in him since he has been christened."

VII

THE HURON REPULSES THE ENGLISH

THE ingenuous Hercules walked toward the sea-coast, wrapped in deep and gloomy melancholy, with his double-charged fusee upon his shoulder, and his cutlass by his side, shooting now and then a bird, and often tempted to shoot himself; but he had still some affection for life, for the sake of his dear mistress; by turns execrating his uncle and aunt, all Lower Brittany, and his christening; then blessing them, as they had introduced him to the knowledge of her he loved. He resolved upon going to burn the convent, and he stopped short for fear of burning his mistress. The waves of the Channel are not more agitated by the easterly and westerly winds, than was his heart by so many contrary emotions.

He was walking along very fast, without knowing whither he was going, when he heard the beat of a drum. He saw, at a great distance, a vast multitude, part of whom ran toward the coast, and the other part in the opposite direction.

A thousand shrieks re-echoed on every side. Curiosity and courage hurried him, that instant, toward the spot where the greatest clamor arose, which he attained in a few leaps. The commander of the militia, who had supped with him at the Prior's, knew him immediately, and he ran to the Huron with open arms:

"Ah! it is the sincere American: he will fight for us."

Upon which the militia, who were almost dead with fear, recovered themselves, crying with one voice:

"It is the Huron, the ingenuous Huron."

"Gentlemen," said he, "what is the matter? Why are you frightened? Have they shut your mistresses up in convents?"

Instantly a thousand confused voices cried out:

"Do you not see the English, who are landing?"

"Very well," replied the Huron, "they are a brave people; they never proposed making me a sub-deacon; they never carried off my mistress."

The commander made him understand that they were coming to pillage the Abbe of the Mountain, drink his uncle's wine, and perhaps carry off Miss St.

Yves; that the little vessel which set him on shore in Brittany had come only to reconnoitre the coast; that they were committing acts of hostility, without having declared war against France; and that the province was entirely exposed to them.

"If this be the case," said he, "they violate the law of nature: let me alone; I lived a long time among them; I am acquainted with their language, and I will speak to them. I cannot think they can have so wicked a design."

During this conversation the English fleet had approached; the Huron ran toward it, and having jumped into a little boat, soon rowed to the Admiral's ship, and having gone on board, asked "whether it was true, that they were come to ravage the coast, without having honestly declared war?"

The Admiral and his crew burst out into laughter, made him drink some punch, and sent him back.

The ingenuous Hercules, piqued at this reception, thought of nothing else but beating his old friends for his countrymen and the Prior. The gentlemen of the neighborhood ran from all quarters, and joined them: they had some cannon, and he discharged them one after the other. The English landed, and he flew toward them, when he killed three of them with his own hand. He even wounded the Admiral, who had made a joke of him. The entire militia were animated with his prowess. The English returned to their ships, and went on board; and the whole coast re-echoed with the shouts of victory, "Live the king! live the ingenuous Hercules!"

Every one ran to embrace him; every one strove to stop the bleeding of some slight wounds he had received.

"Ah!" said he, "if Miss St. Yves were here, she would put on a plaster for me."

The bailiff who had hid himself in his cellar during the battle came to pay his compliments like the rest. But he was greatly surprised, when he heard the ingenuous Hercules say to a dozen young men, well disposed for his service, who surrounded him:

"My friends, having delivered the Abbe of the Mountain is nothing; we must rescue a nymph."

The warm blood of these youths was fired at the expression. He was already followed by crowds, who repaired to the convent. If the bailiff had not immediately acquainted the commandant with their design, and he had not sent a detachment after the joyous troop, the thing would have been done. The Huron was conducted back to his uncle and aunt, who overwhelmed him with tears and tenderness.

"I see very well," said his uncle, "that you will never be either a sub-deacon or a prior; you will be an officer, and one still braver than my brother the Captain, and probably as poor."

Miss Kerkabon could not stop an incessant flow of tears, whilst she embraced him, saying, "he will be killed too, like my brother; it were much better he were a sub-deacon."

The Huron had, during the battle, picked up a purse full of guineas, which the Admiral had probably lost. He did not doubt but that this purse would buy all Lower Brittany, and, above all, make Miss St. Yves a great lady. Every one persuaded him to repair to Versailles, to receive the recompense due to his services. The commandant, and the principal officers, furnished him with certificates in abundance. The uncle and aunt also approved of this journey. He was to be presented to the king without any difficulty. This alone would give him great weight in the province. These two good folks added to the English purse a considerable present out of their savings. The Huron said to himself, "When I see the king, I will ask Miss St. Yves of him in marriage, and certainly he will not refuse me." He set out accordingly, amidst the acclamations of the whole district, stifled with embraces, bathed in tears by his aunt, blessed by his uncle, and recommending himself to the charming Miss St. Yves.

VIII

The Huron Goes to Court, Sups upon the Road with Some Huguenots

The ingenuous Hercules took the Saumur road in the coach, because there was at that time no other convenience. When he came to Saumur, he was astonished to find the city almost deserted, and to see several families going away. He was told that half a dozen years before, Saumur contained upwards of fifty thousand inhabitants, and that at present there were not six thousand. He mentioned this at the inn, whilst at supper. Several Protestants were at table; some complained bitterly, others trembled with rage, others, weeping, said, *Nos dulcia linquimus arva, nos patriam fugimus.* The Huron, who did not understand Latin, had these words explained to him, which signified, "We abandon our sweet fields;—We fly from our country."

"And why do you fly from your country, gentlemen?"

"Because we must otherwise acknowledge the Pope."

"And why not acknowledge him? You have no godmothers, then, that you want to marry; for I am told it is he that grants this permission."

"Ah! sir, this Pope says, that he is master of the domains of kings."

"But, gentlemen, what religion are you of?"

"Why, sir, we are for the most part drapers and manufacturers."

"If the Pope, then, is not the master of your clothes and manufactures, you do very well not to acknowledge him; but as to kings, it is their business, and why do you trouble yourselves about it?"

Here a little black man took up the argument, and very learnedly set forth the grievances of the company. He talked of the revocation of the edict of Nantes with so much energy; he deplored, in so pathetic a manner, the fate of fifty thousand fugitive families, and of fifty thousand others converted by dragoons; that the ingenuous Hercules could not refrain from shedding tears. "Whence arises it," said he, "that so great a king, whose renown expands itself even to the Hurons, should thus deprive himself of so many hearts that would have loved him, and so many arms that would have served him?"

"Because he has been imposed upon, like other great kings," replied the little orator, "he has been made to believe, that as soon as he utters a word, all people think as he does; and that he can make us change our religion, just as his musician Lulli, in a moment, changes the decorations of his opera. He has not only already lost five or six hundred thousand very useful subjects, but he has turned many of them into enemies; and King William, who is at this time master of England, has formed several regiments of these identical Frenchmen, who would otherwise have fought for their monarch."

"Such a disaster is more astonishing, as the present Pope, to whom Louis XIV. sacrifices a part of his people, is his declared enemy. A violent quarrel has subsisted between them for nearly nine years. It has been carried so far, that France was in hopes of at length casting off the yoke, by which it has been kept in subjection for so many ages to this foreigner, and, more particularly, of not giving him any more money, which is the *primum mobile* of the affairs of this world. It, therefore, appears evident that this great king has been imposed on, as well with respect to his interest, as the extent of his power, and that even the magnanimity of his heart has been struck at."

The Huron, becoming more and more interested, asked: "Who were the Frenchmen who thus deceived a monarch so dear to the Hurons?"

"They are the clerics," he was answered, "and, particularly, the king's adviser. It is to be hoped that God will one day punish them for it, and that they will be driven out, as they now drive us. Can any misfortune equal ours? Mons. de Louvois besets us on all sides with clerics and dragoons."

"Well, gentlemen," replied the Huron, "I am going to Versailles to receive the recompense due to my services; I will speak to Mons. de Louvois. I am told it is he who makes war from his closet. I shall see the king, and I will acquaint him with the truth. It is impossible not to yield to this truth, when it is felt. I shall return very soon to marry Miss St. Yves, and I beg you will be present at our nuptials."

These good people now took him for some great Lord, who traveled *incognito* in the coach. Some took him for the king's fool.

There was at table a disguised cleric, who acted as a spy to the king's adviser. He gave him an account of everything that passed, and he reported it to M. de Louvois. The spy wrote. The Huron and the letter arrived almost at the same time at Versailles.

IX

THE ARRIVAL OF THE HURON AT VERSAILLES. HIS RECEPTION AT COURT

THE ingenuous Hercules was set down from a public carriage, in the court of the kitchens. He asks the chairmen, what hour the king can be seen? The chairmen laugh in his face, just as the English Admiral had done: and he treated them in the same manner—he beat them. They were for retaliation, and the scene had like to have proved bloody, if a soldier, who was a gentleman of Brittany, had not passed by, and who dispersed the mob.

"Sir," said the traveler to him, "you appear to me to be a brave man. I am nephew to the Prior of our Lady of the Mountain. I have killed Englishmen, and I am come to speak to the king: I beg you will conduct me to his chamber."

The soldier, delighted to find a man of courage from his province, who did not seem acquainted with the customs of the court, told him it was necessary to be presented to M. de Louvois.

"Very well, then, conduct me to M. de Louvois, who will doubtless conduct me to the king."

"It is more difficult to speak to M. de Louvois than the king. But I will conduct you to Mr. Alexander, first commissioner of war, and this will be just the same as if you spoke to the minister."

They accordingly repair to Mr. Alexander's, who is first clerk; but they cannot be introduced, he being closely engaged in business with a lady of the court, and no person is allowed admittance.

"Well," said the soldier, "there is no harm done, let us go to Mr. Alexander's first clerk. This will be just the same as if you spoke to Mr. Alexander himself."

The Huron, quite astonished, followed him. They remained together half an hour in a little ante-chamber.

"What is all this?" said the ingenuous Hercules. "Is all the world invisible in this country? It is much easier to fight in Lower Brittany against Englishmen, than to meet with people at Versailles, with whom one hath business."

He amused himself for some time with relating his amours to his country-man; but the clock striking recalled the soldier to his post, when a mutual promise was given of meeting on the morrow.

The Huron remained another half hour in the ante-chamber, meditating upon Miss St. Yves and the difficulty of speaking to kings and first clerks.

At length the patron appeared.

"Sir," said the ingenuous Hercules, "if I had waited to repulse the English as long as you have made me wait for my audience, they would certainly have ravaged all Lower Brittany without opposition."

These words impressed the clerk. He at length said to the inhabitant of Brittany, "What is your request?"

"A recompense," said the other: "these are my titles;" showing his certificates.

The clerk read, and told him, "that probably he might obtain leave to purchase a lieutenancy."

"Me? what, must I pay money for having repulsed the English? Must I pay a tax to be killed for you, whilst you are peaceably giving your audience here? You are certainly jesting. I require a company of cavalry for nothing. I require that the king shall set Miss St. Yves at liberty from the convent, and give her to me in marriage. I want to speak to the king in favor of fifty thousand families, whom I propose restoring to him. In a word, I want to be useful. Let me be employed and advanced."

"What is your name, sir, who talk in such a high style?"

"Oh! oh!" answered the Huron; "you have not then read my certificates? This is the way they are treated. My name is *Hercules de Kerkabon.* I am christened, and I lodge at the Blue Dial." The clerk concluded, like the people at Saumur, that his head was turned, and did not pay him any further attention.

The same day, the king's adviser received his spy's letter, which accused the Breton Kerkabon of favoring in his heart the Huguenots, and condemning the conduct of the clerics. M. de Louvois had, on his side, received a letter from the inquisitive bailiff, which depicted the Huron as a wicked, lewd fellow, inclined to burn convents.

Hercules, after having walked in the gardens of Versailles, which had become irksome to him; after having supped like a native of Huronia and Lower Brittany, had gone to rest, in the pleasant hope of seeing the king the next day; of obtaining Miss St. Yves in marriage; of having, at least, a company of cavalry; and of setting aside the persecution against the Huguenots. He was rocking himself asleep with these flattering ideas, when the *Marechaussée* entered his chamber, and seized upon his double-charged fusee and his great saber.

They took an inventory of his ready money, and then conducted him to the castle erected by King Charles V., son to John II., near the street of St. Antoine, at the gates des Tournelles.

What was the Huron's astonishment on his way thither the reader is left to imagine. He at first fancied it was all a dream; and remained for some time in a state of stupefaction. Presently, transported with rage, that gave him more than common strength, he collared two of his conductors who were with him in the coach, flung them out of the door, cast himself after them, and then dragged the third, who wanted to hold him. He fell in the attempt, when they tied him, and replaced him in the carriage.

"This, then," said he, "is what one gets for driving the English out of Lower Brittany! What wouldst thou say, charming Miss St. Yves, if thou didst see me in this situation?"

They at length arrived at the place of their destination. He was carried without any noise into the chamber in which he was to be locked up, like a dead corpse going to the grave. This room was already occupied by an old solitary student of Port Royal, named Gordon, who had been languishing here for two years.

"See," said the chief of the *Marechaussée*, "here is company I bring you;" and immediately the enormous bolts of this strong door, secured with large iron bars, were fastened upon them. These two captives were thus separated from all the universe besides.

X

The Huron Is Shut up in the Bastile with a Jansenist

Mr. Gordon was a healthy old man, of a serene disposition, who was acquainted with two great things; the one was, to bear adversity; the other, to console the afflicted. He approached his companion with an open sympathizing air, and said to him, whilst he embraced him:

"Whoever thou art that is come to partake of my grave, be assured, that I shall constantly forget myself to soften thy torments in the infernal abyss where we are plunged. Let us adore Providence that has conducted us here. Let us suffer in peace, and trust in hope."

These words had the same effect upon the youth as cordial drops, which recall a dying person to life, and show to his astonished eyes a glimpse of light.

After the first compliments were over, Gordon, without urging him to relate the cause of his misfortune, inspired him by the sweetness of his discourse and by that interest which two unfortunate persons share with each other, with a desire of opening his heart and of disburdening himself of the weight which oppressed him; but he could not guess the cause of his misfortune, and the good man Gordon was as much astonished as himself.

"God must, doubtless," said the Jansenist to the Huron, "have great designs upon you, since he conducted you from Lake Ontario into England, from thence to France; caused you to be baptized in Lower Brittany, and has now lodged you here for your salvation."

"I' faith," replied Hercules, "I believe the devil alone has interfered in my destiny. My countrymen in America would never have treated me with the barbarity that I have here experienced; they have not the least idea of it. They are called savages;—they are good people, but rustic; and the men of this country are refined villains. I am indeed, greatly surprised to have come from another world, to be shut up in this, under four bolts with a cleric; but I consider what an infinite number of men set out from one hemisphere to go and get killed in the other, or are cast away in the voyage, and are eaten by the fishes. I cannot discover the gracious designs of God over all these people."

Their dinner was brought them through a wicket. The conversation turned upon Providence, *lettres de cachet*, and upon the art of not sinking under disgrace, to which all men in this world are exposed.

"It is now two years since I have been here," said the old man, "without any other consolation than myself and books; and yet I have never been a single moment out of temper."

"Ah! Mr. Gordon," cried Hercules, "you are not then in love with your godmother. If you were as well acquainted with Miss St. Yves as I am, you would be in a state of desperation."

At these words he could not refrain from tears, which greatly relieved him from his oppression.

"How is it then that tears solace us?" said the Huron. "It seems to me that they should have quite an opposite effect."

"My son," said the good old man, "every thing is physical about us; all secretions are useful to the body, and all that comforts it, comforts the soul. We are the machines of Providence."

The ingenuous Huron, who, as we have already observed more than once, had a great share of understanding, entered deeply into the consideration of this idea, the seeds whereof appeared to be in himself. After which he asked his companion:

"Why his machine had for two years been confined by four bolts?"

"By effectual grace," answered Gordon; "I pass for a Jansenist; I know Arnaud and Nicole; the clerics have persecuted us."

"This is very strange," said the Huron, "all the unhappy people I have met with have been made so solely by persecution. With respect to your effectual grace, I acknowledge I do not understand what you mean. But I consider it as a very great favor, that God has let me, in my misfortunes, meet with a man, who pours into my heart such consolation as I thought myself incapable of receiving."

The conversation became each day more interesting and instructive. The souls of the two captives seemed to unite in one body. The old man had acquired knowledge, and the young man was willing to receive instruction. At the end of the first month, he eagerly applied himself to the study of geometry. Gordon made him read *Rohault's Physics*, which book was still in fashion; and he had good sense enough to find in it nothing but doubts and uncertainties.

He afterward read the first volume of the *Enquiry After Truth*. This instructive work gave him new light.

"What!" said he, "do our imagination and our senses deceive us to that degree? What, are not our ideas formed by objects, and can we not acquire them by ourselves?"

When he had gone through the second volume, he was not so well satisfied; and he concluded it was much easier to destroy than to build.

His colleague, astonished that a young ignoramus should make such a remark, conceived a very high opinion of his understanding, and was more strongly attached to him.

"Your Malebranche," said he to Gordon one day, "seems to have written half his book whilst he was in possession of his reason, and the other half with the assistance only of imagination and prejudice."

Some days after, Gordon asked him what he thought of the soul, and the manner in which we receive our ideas of volition, grace, and free agency.

"Nothing," replied the Huron. "If I think sometimes, it is that we are under the power of the Eternal Being, like the stars and the elements—that he operates everything in us—that we are small wheels of the immense machine, of which he is the soul—that he acts according to general laws, and not from particular views. This is all that appears to me intelligible; all the rest is to me a dark abyss."

"But this, my son, would be making God the author of sin!"

"But, father, your effectual grace would equally make him the author of sin; for certainly all those to whom this grace was refused, would sin; and is not an all-powerful being who permits evil, virtually the author of evil?"

This sincerity greatly embarrassed the good man; he found that all his endeavors to extricate himself from this quagmire were ineffectual; and he heaped such quantities of words upon one another, which seemed to have meaning, but which in fact had none, that the Huron could not help pitying him. This question evidently determined the origin of good and evil; and poor Gordon was reduced to the necessity of recurring to Pandora's box—Oromasdes's egg pierced by Arimanes—the enmity between Typhon and Osiris —and, at last, original sin; and these he huddled together in profound darkness, without their throwing the least glimmering light upon one another. However, this romance of the soul diverted their thoughts from the contemplation of their own misery; and, by a strange magic, the multitude of calamities dispersed throughout the world diminished the sensation of their own miseries. They did not dare complain when all mankind was in a state of sufferance.

But in the repose of night, the image of the charming Miss St. Yves effaced from the mind of her lover every metaphysical and moral idea. He awoke with his eyes bathed in tears; and the old Jansenist forgot his effectual grace, and the Abbe of St. Cyran, and even Jansenius himself, to afford consolation to a youth whom he had judged guilty of a mortal sin.

After these lectures and their reasonings were over, their adventures furnished them with subjects of conversation; after this store was exhausted, they read together, or separately. The Huron's understanding daily increased; and he would certainly have made great progress in mathematics, if the thought of Miss St. Yves had not frequently distracted him.

He read histories, which made him melancholy. The world appeared to him too wicked and too miserable. In fact, history is nothing more than a picture of crimes and misfortunes. The crowd of innocent and peaceable men are always invisible upon this vast theatre. The *dramatis personæ* are composed of ambitious, perverse men. The pleasure which history affords is derived from the same source as tragedy, which would languish and become insipid, were it not inspired with strong passions, great events, and piteous misfortunes. Clio must be armed with a poniard as well as Melpomene.

Though the history of France is not less filled with horror than those of other nations, it nevertheless appeared to him so disgusting in the beginning, so dry in the continuation, and so trifling in the end (even in the time of Henry IV.); ever destitute of grand monuments, or foreign to those fine discoveries which have illustrated other nations; that he was obliged to resolve upon not being tired, in order to go through all the particulars of obscure calamities confined to a little corner of the world.

Gordon thought like him. They both laughed with pity when they read of the sovereigns of Fezensacs, Fesansaguer, and Astrac: such a study could be relished only by their heirs, if they had any. The brilliant ages of the Roman Republic made him sometimes quite indifferent as to any other part of the globe. The spectacle of victorious Rome, the lawgiver of nations, engrossed his whole soul. He glowed in contemplating a people who were governed for seven hundred years by the enthusiasm of liberty and glory.

Thus rolled days, weeks, and months; and he would have thought himself happy in the sanctuary of despair, if he had not loved.

The natural goodness of his heart was softened still more when he reflected upon the Prior of our Lady of the Mountain, and the sensible Kerkabon.

"What must they think," he would often repeat, "when they can get no tidings of me? They must think me an ungrateful wretch." This idea rendered him inconsolable. He pitied those who loved him much more than he pitied himself.

XI

How the Huron Discloses His Genius

READING aggrandizes the soul, and an enlightened friend affords consolation. Our captive had these two advantages in his favor which he had never expected.

"I shall begin to believe in the Metamorphoses," said he, "for I have been transformed from a brute into a man."

He formed a chosen library with part of the money which he was allowed to dispose of. His friend encouraged him to commit to writing such observations as occurred to him. These are his notes upon ancient history:

"I imagine that nations were for a long time like myself; that they did not become enlightened till very late; that for many ages they were occupied with nothing but the present moment which elapsed: that they thought very little of what was past, and never of the future. I have traversed five or six hundred leagues in Canada, and I did not meet with a single monument: no one is the least acquainted with the actions of his predecessors. Is not this the natural state of man? The human species of this continent appears to me superior to that of the other. They have extended their being for many ages by arts and knowledge. Is this because they have beards upon their chins and God has refused this ornament to the Americans? I do not believe it; for I find the Chinese have very little beard, and that they have cultivated arts for upwards of five thousand years. In effect, if their annals go back upwards of four thousand years, the nation must necessarily have been united and in a flourishing state more than five hundred centuries.

"One thing particularly strikes me in this ancient history of China, which is, that almost every thing is probable and natural. I admire it because it is not tinctured with anything of the marvelous.

"Why have all other nations adopted fabulous origins? The ancient chronicles of the history of France, which, by the by, are not very ancient, make the French descend from one Francus, the son of Hector. The Romans said they were the issue of a Phrygian, though there was not in their whole language a single word that had the least connection with the language of Phrygia. The gods had inhabited Egypt for ten thousand years, and the devils Scythia, where they had engendered the Huns. I meet with nothing before Thucydides but romances similar to the Amadis, and far less amusing. Apparitions, oracles, prodigies, sorcery, metamorphoses, are interspersed throughout with the explanation of dreams, which are the bases of the destiny of the greatest empires and the smallest states. Here are speaking beasts, there brutes that are adored, gods transformed into men, and men into gods. If we must have fables, let us, at least, have such as appear the emblem of truth. I admire the fables of philosophers, but I laugh at those of children, and hate those of impostors."

He one day hit upon a history of the Emperor Justinian. It was there related, that some Appedeutes of Constantinople had delivered, in very bad Greek, an edict against the greatest captain of the age, because this hero had uttered the following words in the warmth of conversation: "Truth shines forth with its proper light, and people's minds are not illumined with flaming piles." The Appedeutes declared that this proposition was heretical, bordering upon heresy; and that the contrary action was catholic, universal, and Grecian: "The minds of the people are enlightened but with flaming piles, and truth cannot shine forth with its own light." These Limostolians thus condemned several discourses of the captain, and published an edict.

"What!" said the Huron, with much emotion, "shall such people publish edicts?"

"They are not edicts," replied Gordon: "they are contradictions, which all the world laughed at in Constantinople, and the Emperor the first. He was a wise prince, who knew how to reduce the Linostolian Appedeutes to a state incapable of doing anything but good. He knew that these gentlemen, and several other Pastophores, had tried the patience of the Emperors, his predecessors, with contradictions in more serious matters."

"He did quite right," said the Huron, "the Pastophores should not be supported, but constrained."

He committed several other observations to paper, which astonished old Gordon. "What," said he to himself, "have I consumed fifty years in instruction and not attained to the degree of natural good sense of this child, who is almost a savage? I tremble to think I have so arduously strengthened prejudices, and he listens to simple nature only."

The good man had some little books of criticism, some of those periodical pamphlets wherein men, incapable of producing anything themselves, blacken the productions of others; where a Vise insults a Racine, and a Faidit a Fenelon. The Huron ran over some of them. "I compare them," said he, "to certain gnats that lodge their eggs in the nostrils of the finest horses, which do not, however, retard their speed."

The two philosophers scarce deigned to cast their eyes upon these dregs of literature.

They soon after went through the elements of astronomy. The Huron sent for some globes: he was ravished at this great spectacle.

"How hard it is," said he, "that I should only begin to be acquainted with heaven, when the power of contemplating it is ravished from me! Jupiter and Saturn revolve in these immense spaces,—millions of suns illumine myriads of worlds; and, in this corner of the earth on which I am cast, there are beings that deprive me of seeing and studying those worlds to which my eye might reach, and even that in which God has placed me. The light created for the whole universe is lost to me. It was not hidden from me in the northern horizon, where I passed my infancy and youth. Without you, my dear Gordon, I should be annihilated."

XII

The Huron's Sentiments upon Theatrical Pieces

The young Huron resembled one of those vigorous trees, which, languishing in an ungrateful soil, extend in a little time their roots and branches when transplanted to a more favorable spot; and it was very extraordinary that this favorable spot should be a prison.

Among the books which employed the leisure of the two captives were some poems and also translations of Greek tragedies, and some dramatic pieces in French. Those passages that dwelt on love communicated at once pleasure and pain to the soul of the Huron. They were but so many images of his dear Miss St. Yves. The fable of the two pigeons rent his heart: for he was far estranged from his tender dove.

Molière enchanted him. He taught him the manners of Paris and of human nature.

"To which of his comedies do you give the preference?"

"Doubtless to his *Tartuffe*."

"I am of your opinion," said Gordon; "it was a Tartuffe that flung me into this dungeon, and perhaps they were Tartuffes who have been the cause of your misfortunes."

"What do you think of these Greek tragedies?"

"They are very good for Grecians."

But when he read the modern *Iphigenia, Phædrus, Andromache,* and *Athalia,* he was in ecstasy, he sighed, he wept,—and he learned them by heart, without having any such intention.

"Read *Rodogune*," said Gordon; "that is said to be a capital production; the other pieces which have given you so much pleasure are trifles compared to this."

The young man had scarce got through the first page, before he said, "This is not written by the same author."

"How do you know it?"

"I know nothing yet: but these lines neither touch my ear nor my heart."

"O!" said Gordon, "the versification does not signify." The Huron asked, "What must I judge by then?"

After having read the piece very attentively without any other design than being pleased, he looked steadfastly at his friend with much astonishment, not knowing what to say. At length, being urged to give his opinion with respect to what he felt, this was the answer he made: "I understood very little of the beginning; the middle disgusted me; but the last scene greatly moved me, though there appears to me but little probability in it. I have no prejudices for or against any one, but I do not remember twenty lines, I, who recollect them all when they please me."

"This piece, nevertheless, passes for the best upon our stage."

"If that be the case," said he, "it is perhaps like many people who are not worthy of the places they hold. After all, this is a matter of taste, and mine cannot yet be formed. I may be mistaken; but you know I am accustomed to say what I think or rather what I feel. I suspect that illusion, fashion, caprice, often warp the judgments of men."

Here he repeated some lines from *Iphigenia*, which he was full of; and though he declaimed but indifferently, he uttered them with such truth and emotion that he made the old Jansenist weep. He then read *Cinna*, which did not excite his tears, but his admiration.

XIII

The Beautiful Miss St. Yves Goes to Versailles

Whilst the unfortunate Hercules was more enlightened than consoled, whilst his genius, so long stifled, unfolded itself with so much rapidity and strength; whilst nature, which was attaining a degree of perfection in him, avenged herself of the outrages of fortune; what became of the Prior, his good sister, and the beautiful recluse, Miss St. Yves? The first month they were uneasy, and the third they were immersed in sorrow. False conjectures, ill-grounded reports, alarmed them. At the end of six months, it was concluded he was dead. At length, Mr. and Miss Kerkabon learned, by a letter of ancient date, which one of the king's guards had written to Brittany, that a young man resembling the Huron arrived one night at Versailles, but that since that time no one had heard him spoken of.

"Alas," said Miss Kerkabon, "our nephew had done some ridiculous thing, which has brought on some terrible consequences. He is young, a *Low Breton*, and cannot know how to behave at court. My dear brother, I never saw Versailles nor Paris; here is a fine opportunity, and we shall perhaps find our poor nephew. He is our brother's son, and it is our duty to assist him. Who knows? we may perhaps at length prevail upon him to become a sub-deacon when the fire of youth is somewhat abated. He was much inclined to the sciences. Do you recollect how he reasoned upon the Old and New Testament? We are answerable for his soul. He was baptized at our instigation. His dear mistress Miss St. Yves does nothing but weep incessantly. Indeed, we must go to Paris. If he is concealed in any of those infamous houses of pleasure, which I have often heard of, we will get him out."

The Prior was affected at his sister's discourse. He went in search of the Bishop of St. Malo's, who had baptized the Huron, and requested his protection and advice. The Prelate approved of the journey. He gave the Prior letters of recommendation to the king's adviser, who was invested with the first dignity in the kingdom.

At length, the brother and sister set out; but when they came to Paris, they found themselves bewildered in a great labyrinth without clue or end. Their fortune was but middling, and they had occasion every day for carriages to pursue their discovery, which they could not accomplish.

He at length saw the minister, who received him with open arms, protesting he had always entertained the greatest private esteem for him, though he had never known him. He swore that his society had always been attached to the inhabitants of Lower Brittany.

"But," said he, "has not your nephew the misfortune of being a Huguenot?"

"No, certainly."

"May he not be a Jansenist?"

"I can assure you that he is scarce a Christian. It is about eleven months since he was christened."

"This is very well;—we will take care of him. Is your benefice considerable?"

"No, a very trifle, and our nephew costs us a great deal."

"Are there any Jansenists in your neighborhood? Take great care, my dear Mr. Prior, they are more dangerous than Huguenots, or even Atheists."

"We have none; it is not even known at our Lady of the Mountain what Jansenism is."

"So much the better; go, there is nothing I will not do for you."

He dismissed the Prior in this affectionate manner, but thought no more about him.

Time slipped away, and the Prior and his good sister were almost in despair.

In the meanwhile, the cursed bailiff urged very strenuously the marriage of his great booby son with the beautiful Miss St. Yves, who was taken purposely out of the convent. She always entertained a passion for her god-son in proportion as she detested the husband who was designed for her. The insult that had been offered her, by shutting her up in a convent, increased her affection; and the mandate for wedding the bailiff's son completed her antipathy for him. Chagrin, tenderness, and terror, racked her soul. Love, we know, is much more inventive and more daring in a young woman than friendship in an aged Prior and an aunt upwards of forty-five. Besides, she had received good instructions in her convent with the assistance of romances, which she read by stealth.

The beautiful Miss St. Yves remembered the letter that had been sent by one of the king's guards to Lower Brittany, which had been spoken of in the province. She resolved to go herself and gain information at Versailles; to throw herself at the minister's feet, if her husband should be in prison as it was said, and obtain justice for him. I know not what secret intelligence she had gained that at court nothing is refused to a pretty woman; but she knew not the price of these boons.

Having taken this resolution, it afforded her some consolation; and she enjoyed some tranquillity without upbraiding Providence with the severity of her lot. She receives her detested intended father-in-law, caresses her brother, and spreads happiness throughout the house. On the day appointed for the ceremony, she secretly departs at four o'clock in the morning, with the little nuptial presents she has received, and all she could gather. Her plan was so well laid, that she was about ten leagues upon her journey, when, about noon, her absence was discovered, and when every one's consternation and surprise was inexpressible. The inquisitive bailiff asked more questions that day than he had done for a week before; the intended bridegroom was more stupefied than ever. The Abbe St. Yves resolved in his rage to pursue his sister. The bailiff and his son were disposed to accompany him. Thus fate led almost the whole canton of Lower Brittany to Paris.

The beautiful Miss St. Yves was not without apprehensions that she should be pursued. She rode on horseback, and she got all the intelligence she could from the couriers, without being suspected. She asked if they had not met an abbe, an enormous bailiff, and a young booby, galloping as fast as they could to Paris. Having learned, on the third day, that they were not far behind, she took quite a different road, and was skillful and lucky enough to arrive at Versailles, whilst they were in a fruitless pursuit after her, at Paris. But how was she to behave at Versailles? Young, handsome, untutored, unsupported, unknown, exposed to every danger, how could she dare go in search of one of the king's guards? She had some thoughts of applying to a cleric of low rank, for there were some for every station of life; as God, they say, has given different ailments to every species of animals. The beautiful Miss St. Yves addressed herself to one of these last, who was called *Tout-à-tous* (all to every one). She set forth her adventure, her situation, her danger, and conjured him to get her a lodging with some good devotee, who might shelter her from temptation.

Tout-à-tous introduced her to the wife of the cup-bearer, one of his most trusty friends. From the moment Miss St. Yves became her lodger, she did her utmost to obtain the confidence and friendship of this person. She gained intelligence of the Breton-Guard, and invited him to visit her. Having learned from him that her lover had been carried off after having had a conference with one of the clerks, she flew to this clerk. The sight of a fine woman softened him, for it must be allowed God created woman only to tame mankind.

The scribe, thus mollified, acknowledged to her every thing.

"Your lover has been in the bastile almost a year, and without your intercession he would, perhaps, have ended his days there."

The tender Miss St. Yves swooned at this intelligence. When she had recovered herself, her informer told her:

"I have no power to do good; all my influence extends to doing harm. Take my advice, wait upon M. de St. Pouange, who has the power of doing both good and ill; he is Mons. de Louvois's cousin and favorite. This minister has two souls: the one is M. de St. Pouange, and Mademoiselle de Belle is the other, but she is at present absent from Versailles; so that you have nothing to do but captivate the protector I have pointed out to you."

The beautiful Miss St. Yves, divided between some trifling joy and excessive grief, between a glimmering of hope and dreadful apprehensions;—pursued by her brother, idolizing her lover, wiping her tears, which flowed in torrents; trembling and feeble, yet summoning all her courage;—in this situation, she flew on the wings of love to M. de St. Pouange's.

XIV

RAPID PROGRESS OF THE HURON'S INTELLECT

THE ingenuous youth was making a rapid progress in the sciences, and particularly in the science of man. The cause of this sudden disclosure of his understanding was as much owing to his savage education as to the disposition of his soul; for, having learned nothing in his infancy, he had not imbibed any prejudices. His mind, not having been warped by error, had retained all its primitive rectitude. He saw things as they were; whereas the ideas that are communicated to us in our infancy make us see them all our life in a false light.

"Your persecutors are very abominable wretches," said he to his friend Gordon. "I pity you for being oppressed, but I condemn you for being a Jansenist. All sects appear to me to be founded in error. Tell me if there be any sectaries in geometry?"

"No, my child," said the good old Gordon, heaving a deep sigh; "all men are agreed concerning truth when demonstrated, but they are too much divided about latent truths."

"If there were but one single hidden truth in your load of arguments, which have been so often sifted for such a number of ages, it would doubtless have been discovered, and the universe would certainly have been unanimous, at least, in that respect. If this truth had been as necessary as the sun is to the earth, it would have been as brilliant as that planet. It is an absurdity, an insult to human nature—it is an attack upon the Infinite and Supreme Being to say there is a truth essential to the happiness of man which God conceals."

All that this ignorant youth, instructed only by nature, said, made a very deep impression upon the mind of the old unhappy scholiast.

"Is it really certain," he cried, "that I should have made myself truly miserable for mere chimeras? I am much more certain of my misery than of effectual grace. I have spent my time in reasoning about the liberty of God and human nature, but I have lost my own. Neither St. Augustine nor St. Prosner will extricate me from my present misfortunes."

The ingenuous Huron, who gave way to his natural instincts, at length said:

"Will you give me leave to speak to you boldly and frankly? Those who bring upon themselves persecution for such idle disputes seem to me to have very little sense; those who persecute, appear to me very monsters."

The two captives entirely coincided with respect to the injustice of their captivity.

"I am a hundred times more to be pitied than you," said the Huron; "I am born free as the air: I had two lives, liberty and the object of my love; and I am deprived of both. We are both in fetters, without knowing who put them on us, or without being able to enquire. It is said that the Hurons are barbarians, because they avenge themselves on their enemies; but they never oppress their friends. I had scarce set foot in France, before I shed my blood for this country. I have, perhaps, preserved a whole province, and my recompense is imprisonment. In this country men are condemned without being heard. This is not the case in England. Alas! it was not against the English that I should have fought."

Thus his growing philosophy could not brook nature being insulted in the first of her rights, and he gave vent to his just indignation.

His companion did not contradict him. Absence ever increases ungratified love, and philosophy does not diminish it. He as frequently spoke of his dear Miss St. Yves, as he did of morality or metaphysics. The more he purified his sentiments, the more he loved. He read some new romances; but he met with few that depicted to him the real state of his soul. He felt that his heart stretched beyond the bounds of his author.

"Alas!" said he, "almost all these writers have nothing but wit and art."

At length, the good Jansenist became, insensibly, the confidant of his tenderness. He was already acquainted with love as a sin with which a penitent accuses himself at confession. He now learned to know it as a sentiment equally noble and tender; which can elevate the soul as well as soften it, and can at times produce virtues. In fine, for the last miracle, a Huron converted a Jansenist.

XV

THE BEAUTIFUL MISS ST. YVES VISITS M. DE ST. POUANGE

THE charming Miss St. Yves, still more afflicted than her lover, waited accordingly upon M. de St. Pouange, accompanied by her friend with whom she lodged, each having their faces covered with their hoods. The first thing she saw at the door was the Abbe St. Yves, her brother coming out. She was terrified, but her friend supported her spirits.

"For the very reason," said she, "that people have been speaking against you, speak to him for yourself. You may be assured, that the accusers in this part of the world are always in the right, unless they are immediately detected. Besides, your presence will have greater effect, or else I am much mistaken, than the words of your brother."

Ever so little encouragement to a passionate lover makes her intrepid. Miss St. Yves appears at the audience. Her youth, her charms, her languishing eyes, moistened with some involuntary tears, attract every one's attention. Every sycophant to the deputy minister forgot for an instant the idol of power to contemplate that of beauty. St. Pouange conducted her into a closet. She spoke with an affecting grace. St. Pouange felt some emotion. She trembled, but he told her not to be afraid.

"Return to-night," said he; "your business requires some reflection, and it must be discussed at leisure. There are too many people here at present. Audiences are rapidly dispatched. I must get to the bottom of all that concerns you."

He then paid her some compliments upon her beauty and address, and advised her to come at seven in the evening.

She did not fail attending at the hour appointed, and her pious friend again accompanied her; but she remained in the hall, where she read whilst St. Pouange and the beauteous Miss St. Yves were in the back closet. He began by saying:

"Would you believe it, Miss, that your brother has been to request me to grant him a *lettre de cachet* against you; but, indeed, I would sooner grant one to send him back to Lower Brittany."

"Alas! sir," said she, "*lettres de cachet* are granted very liberally in your offices, since people come from the extremity of the kingdom to solicit them like pensions. I am very far from requesting one against my brother, yet I have much reason to complain of him. But I respect the liberty of mankind; and, therefore, supplicate for that of a man whom I want to make my husband; of a man to whom the king is indebted for the preservation of a province; who can beneficially serve him; and who is the son of an officer killed in his service. Of what is he accused? How could he be treated so cruelly without being heard?"

The deputy minister then showed her the letter of the spy, and that of the perfidious bailiff.

"What!" said she with astonishment, "are there such monsters upon earth? and would they force me to marry the stupid son of a ridiculous, wicked man? and is it upon such evidence that the fate of citizens is determined?"

She threw herself upon her knees, and with a flood of tears solicited the freedom of a brave man who adored her. Her charms appeared to the greatest advantage in such a situation. She was so beautiful, that St. Pouange, bereft of all shame, used words with some reserve, which brought on others less delicate, which were succeeded by those still more expressive. The revocation of the *lettre de cachet* was proposed, and he at length went so far as to state the only means of obtaining the liberty of the man whose interest she had so violently and affectionately at heart.

This uncommon conversation continued for a long time. The devotee in the ante-chamber said to herself:

"My lord St. Pouange never before gave so long an audience. Perhaps he has refused every thing to this poor girl, and she is still entreating him."

At length her companion came out of the closet in the greatest confusion, without being able to speak. She was lost in deep meditation upon the character of the great and the half great, who so slightly sacrifice the liberty of men and the honor of women.

She did not utter a syllable all the way back. But having returned to her friend's she burst out, and told all that had happened. Her pious friend made frequent signs of the cross.

"My dear friend," said she, "you must consult to-morrow *Tout-à-tous*, our director. He has much influence over M. de St. Pouange. Yield to him; this is my way; and I always found myself right. We weak women stand in need of a man to lead us: and so, my dear friend, I'll go to-morrow in search of *Tout-à-tous*."

XVI

Miss St. Yves Consults a Cleric

No sooner was the beautiful and disconsolate Miss St. Yves with her director than she told him, "that a powerful, voluptuous man, had proposed to her to set at liberty the man whom she intended making her lawful husband, and that he required a great price for his service; that she held such infidelity in the highest detestation; and that if her life only had been required, she would much sooner have sacrificed it than to have submitted."

"This is a most abominable sinner," said *Tout-à-tous*. "You should tell me the name of this vile man. He must certainly be some Jansenist. I will inform against him to the king's adviser, who will place him in the situation of your dear beloved intended bridegroom."

The poor girl, after much hesitation and embarrassment, at length mentioned St. Pouange.

"My Lord St. Pouange!" cried the cleric. "Ah! my child, the case is quite different. He is cousin to the greatest minister we have ever had; a man of worth, a protector of the good cause, a good Christian. He could not entertain such a thought. You certainly must have misunderstood him."

"Oh! I did but understand him too well. I am lost on which ever side I turn. The only alternative I have to choose is misery or shame; either my lover must be buried alive, or I must make myself unworthy of living. I cannot let him perish, nor can I save him."

Tout-à-tous endeavored to console her with these gentle expressions:

"In the *first place*, my child, never use the word lover. It intimates something worldly, which may offend God. Say my husband. You consider him as such, and nothing can be more decent.

"*Secondly:* Though he be ideally your husband, and you are in hopes he will be such eventually, yet he is not so in reality.

"*Thirdly:* Actions are not maliciously culpable, when the intention is virtuous; and nothing can be more virtuous than to procure your husband his liberty."

The beautiful Miss St. Yves, who was no less terrified with the cleric's discourse than with the proposals of the deputy minister, returned in despair to her friend. She was tempted to deliver herself by death from the horror of her situation.

XVII

THE CLERIC TRIUMPHS

THE unfortunate Miss St. Yves entreated her friend to kill her; but this lady, who was fully as indulgent as the cleric, spoke to her still more clearly.

"Alas!" said she, "at this agreeable, gallant, and famous court, business is always thus transacted. The most considerable, as well as the most indifferent places are seldom given away without a consideration. The dignities of war are solicited by the queen of love, and, without regard to merit, a place is often given to him who has the handsomest advocate.

"You are in a situation that is extremely critical. The object is to restore your lover to liberty, and to marry him. It is a sacred duty that you are to fulfill. The world will applaud you. It will be said, that you only allowed yourself to be guilty of a weakness, through an excess of virtue."

"Heavens!" cried Miss St. Yves. "What kind of virtue is this? What a labyrinth of distress! What a world! What men to become acquainted with! A king's adviser and a ridiculous bailiff imprison my lover; I am persecuted by my family; assistance is offered me, only that I may be dishonored! A cleric has ruined a brave man, another wants to ruin me. On every side snares are laid for me, and I am upon the very brink of destruction! I must even speak to the king; I will throw myself at his feet as he goes to mass or to the theatre."

"His attendants will not let you approach," said her good friend; "and if you should be so unfortunate as to speak to him, M. de Louvois, or the king's adviser might bury you in a convent for the rest of your days."

Whilst this generous friend thus increased the perplexities of Miss St. Yves's tortured soul, and plunged the dagger deeper in her heart, a messenger arrived from M. de St. Pouange with a letter, and two fine pendant earrings. Miss St. Yves, with tears, refused to accept of any part of the contents of the packet; but her friend took the charge of them upon herself.

As soon as the messenger had gone, the *confidante* read the letter, in which a *petit-souper* (a little supper) was proposed to the two friends for that night. Miss St. Yves protested she would not go, whilst her pious friend endeavored to make her try on the diamond earrings; but Miss St. Yves could not endure them, and opposed it all the day long; being entirely wrapped up in the contemplation of her lover's imprisonment. At length, after a long resistance—after sighs, moans, and torrents of tears—driven by excitement almost to the verge of insanity—weakened with the conflict, overwhelmed and irresolute, the innocent victim, not knowing whither she was going, was dragged by this artful woman to the fatal supper of the "good Christian and protector of the good cause," M. de St. Pouange.

XVIII

Miss St. Yves Delivers Her Lover and a Jansenist

At day-break she fled to Paris with the minister's mandate. It would be difficult to depict the agitation of her mind in this journey. Imagine a virtuous and noble soul, humbled by its own reproaches, intoxicated with tenderness, distracted with the remorse of having betrayed her lover, and elated with the pleasure of releasing the object of her adoration. Her torments and conflicts by turns engaged her reflections. She was no longer that innocent girl whose ideas were confined to a provincial education. Love and misfortunes had united to remould her. Sentiment had made as rapid a progress in her mind, as reason had in that of her lover.

Her dress was dictated by the greatest simplicity. She viewed with horror the trappings with which she had appeared before her fatal benefactor. Her companion had taken the earrings without her having looked at them. Anxious and confused, idolizing the Huron and detesting herself, she at length arrived at the gate of that dreadful castle—the palace of vengeance—where crimes and innocence are alike immured.

When she was upon the point of getting out of the coach her strength failed her. Some people came to her assistance. She entered, whilst her heart was in the greatest palpitation, her eyes streaming, and her whole frame bespoke the greatest consternation. She was presented to the governor. He was going to speak to her, but she had lost all power of expression: she showed her order, whilst, with great difficulty, she articulated some accents. The governor entertained a great esteem for his prisoner, and he was greatly pleased at his being released. His heart was not callous, like those of most of his brethren, who think of nothing but the fees their captives are to pay them; extort their revenues from their victims; and living by the misery of others, conceive a horrid joy at the lamentations of the unfortunate.

He sent for the prisoner into his apartment. The two lovers swooned at the sight of each other. The beautiful Miss St. Yves remained for a long time motionless, without any symptoms of life; the other soon recalled his fortitude.

"This lady," said the governor, "is probably your wife. You did not tell me you were married. I am informed that it is through her generous solicitude that you have obtained your liberty."

"Alas!" said the beautiful Miss St. Yves, in a faltering voice, "I am not worthy of being his wife"; and swooned again.

When she recovered her senses, she presented, with a trembling hand and averted eyes, the grant and written promise of a company.

The Huron, equally astonished and affected, awoke from one dream to fall into another.

"Why was I shut up here? How could you deliver me? Where are the monsters that immured me? You are a divinity sent from heaven to succor me."

The beautiful Miss St. Yves, with a dejected air, looked at her lover, blushed, and instantly turned away her streaming eyes. In a word, they told him all she knew, and all she had undergone, except what she was willing to conceal forever, but which any other than the Huron, more accustomed to the world and better acquainted with the customs of courts, would easily have guessed.

"Is it possible," said he, "that a wretch like the bailiff can have deprived me of my liberty?

"Alas! I find that men, like the vilest of animals, can all injure.

"But is it possible that a cleric, the king's adviser, should have contributed to my misfortunes as much as the bailiff, without my being able to imagine under what pretence this detestable knave has persecuted me? Did he make me pass for a Jansenist? In fine, how came you to remember me? I did not deserve it; I was then only a savage.

"What! could you, without advice, without assistance, undertake a journey to Versailles?

"You there appeared, and my fetters were broken!

"There must then be in beauty and virtue an invincible charm, that opens gates of adamant and softens hearts of steel."

At the word virtue, a flood of tears issued from the eyes of the beautiful Miss St. Yves. She did not know how far she had been virtuous in the crime with which she reproached herself.

Her lover thus continued:

"Thou angel, who hast broken my chains, if thou hast had sufficient influence (which I cannot yet comprehend) to obtain justice for me, obtain it likewise for an old man who first taught me to think, as thou didst to love. Misfortunes have united us; I love him as a father; I can neither live without thee nor him."

"I solicit?"

"The same man."

"Who!"

"Yes, I will be beholden to you for everything, and I will owe nothing to any one but yourself. Write to this man in power. Overwhelm me with kindness—complete what you have begun—perfect your miracle."

She was sensible she ought to do everything her lover desired. She wanted to write, but her hand refused its office. She began her letter three times and tore it as often. At length she got to the end, and the two lovers left the prison, after having embraced the old martyr to efficacious grace.

The happy yet disconsolate Miss St. Yves knew where her brother lodged; thither she repaired; and her lover took an apartment at the same house.

They had scarce reached their lodging, before her protector sent the order for releasing the good old Gordon, at the same time making an appointment with her for the next day.

She gave the order of release to her lover, and refused the appointment of a benefactor whom she could no more see without expiring with shame and grief.

Her lover would not have left her upon any other errand than to release his friend. He flew to the place of his confinement and fulfilled this duty, reflecting, meanwhile, upon the strange vicissitudes of this world, and admiring the courageous virtue of a young lady, to whom two unfortunate men owed more than life.

XIX

The Huron, the Beautiful Miss St. Yves, and Their Relations Are Convened

The generous and respectable, but injured girl, was with her brother the Abbe de St. Yves, the good Prior of the Mountain, and Lady de Kerkabon. They were equally astonished, but their situations and sentiments were very different. The Abbe de St. Yves was expiating the wrongs he had done his sister at her feet, and she pardoned him. The prior and his sympathizing sister likewise wept, but it was for joy. The filthy bailiff and his insupportable son did not trouble this affecting scene. They had set out upon the first report that their antagonist had been released. They flew to bury in their own province their folly and fear.

The four *dramatis personæ*, variously agitated, were waiting for the return of the young man who had gone to deliver his friend. The Abbe de St. Yves did not dare to raise his eyes to meet those of his sister. The good Kerkabon said:

"I shall then see once more my dear nephew."

"You will see him again," said the charming Miss St. Yves, "but he is no longer the same man. His behavior, his manners, his ideas, his sense, have all undergone a complete mutation. He has become as respectable as he was before ignorant and strange to everything. He will be the honor and consolation of your family; would to heaven that I might also be the honor of mine!"

"What, are you not the same as you were?" said the prior. "What then has happened to work so great a change?"

During this conversation the Huron returned in company with the Jansenist. The scene was now changed, and became more interesting. It began by the uncle and aunt's tender embraces. The Abbe de St. Yves almost kissed the knees of the ingenuous Huron, who, by the by, was no longer ingenuous. The language of the eyes formed all the discourse of the two lovers, who, nevertheless, expressed every sentiment with which they were penetrated. Satisfaction and acknowledgment sparkled in the countenance of the one, whilst embarrassment was depicted in Miss St. Yves's melting but half-averted eyes. Every one was astonished that she should mingle grief with so much joy.

The venerable Gordon soon endeared himself to the whole family. He had been unhappy with the young prisoner, and this was a sufficient title to their esteem. He owed his deliverance to the two lovers, and this alone reconciled him to love. The acrimony of his former sentiments was dismissed from his heart—he was converted by gratitude, as well as the Huron. Every one related his adventures before supper. The two Abbes and the aunt listened like children to the relation of stories of ghosts, and both were deeply interested.

"Alas!" said Gordon, "there are perhaps upwards of five hundred virtuous people in the same fetters as Miss St. Yves has broken. Their misfortunes are unheeded. Many hands are found to strike the unhappy multitude,—how seldom one to succor them."

This very just reflection increased his sensibility and gratitude. Everything heightened the triumph of the beautiful Miss St. Yves. The grandeur and intrepidity of her soul were the subject of each one's admiration. This admiration was blended with that respect which we feel in spite of ourselves for a person who we think has some influence at court. But the Abbe de St. Yves enquired:

"What could my sister do to obtain this influence so soon?"

Supper being ready, every one was already seated, when, lo! the worthy *confidante* of Versailles arrived, without being acquainted with anything that had passed. She was in a coach and six, and it was easily seen to whom the equipage belonged. She entered with that air of authority assumed by people in power who have a great deal of business—saluted the company with much indifference, and, pulling the beautiful Miss St. Yves on one side, said:

"Why do you make people wait so long? Follow me. There are the diamonds you forgot."

However softly she uttered these expressions, the Huron, nevertheless, over-heard them. He saw the diamonds. The brother was speechless. The uncle and aunt exhibited the surprise of good people, who had never before beheld such magnificence. The young man, whose mind was now formed by an experience of twelve months, could not help making some reflections against his will, and was for a moment in anxiety. His mistress perceived it, and a mortal paleness spread itself over her countenance; a tremor seized her, and it was with difficulty she could support herself.

"Ah! madam," said she to her fatal friend, "you have ruined me—you have given me the mortal blow."

These words pierced the heart of the Huron: but he had already learned to possess himself. He did not dwell upon them, lest he should make his mistress uneasy before her brother, but turned pale as well as she.

Miss St. Yves, distracted with the change she perceived in her lover's countenance, pulled the woman out of the room into the passage, and there threw the jewels at her feet, saying:

"Alas! these were not my seducer's, as you well know: but he that gave them shall never set eyes on me again."

Her friend took them up, whilst Miss St. Yves added:

"He may either take them again, or give them to you. Begone, and do not make me still more odious to myself."

The ambassadress at length departed, not being able to comprehend the remorse to which she had been witness.

The beautiful Miss St. Yves, greatly oppressed and feeling a revolution in her body that almost suffocated her, was compelled to go to bed; but that she might not alarm any one she kept her pains and sufferings to herself: and under pretence of only being weary, she asked leave to take a little rest. This, however, she did not do till she had reanimated the company with consolatory and flattering expressions, and cast such a kind look upon her lover as darted fire into his soul.

The supper, of which she did not partake, was in the beginning gloomy; but this gloominess was of that interesting kind which inspires reflection and useful conversation, so superior to that frivolous excitement commonly exhibited, and which is usually nothing more than a troublesome noise.

Gordon, in a few words, gave the history of Jansenism and Molinism; of those persecutions with which one party hampered the other; and of the obstinacy of both. The Huron entered into a criticism thereupon, pitying those men who, not satisfied with all the confusion occasioned by these opposite interests, create evils by imaginary interests and unintelligible absurdities. Gordon related—the other judged. The guests listened with emotion, and gained new lights. The duration of misfortunes, and the shortness of life, then became the topics. It was remarked that all professions have peculiar vices and dangers annexed to them; and that from the prince down to the lowest beggar, all seemed alike to accuse providence. How happens it that so many men, for so little, perform the office of persecutors, sergeants, and executioners, to others? With what inhuman indifference does a man in authority sign papers for the destruction of a family; and with what joy, still more barbarous, do mercenaries execute them.

"I saw in my youth," said the good old Gordon, "a relation of the Marshal de Marillic, who, being prosecuted in his own province on account of that illustrious but unfortunate man, concealed himself under a borrowed name in Paris. He was an old man near seventy-two years of age. His wife, who accompanied him, was nearly of the same age. They had a libertine son, who at fourteen years of age absconded from his father's house, turned soldier, and deserted. He had gone through every gradation of debauchery and misery: at length having changed his name, he was in the guards of the king and had obtained an exempt's staff in their company of sergeants.

"This adventurer was appointed to arrest the old man and his wife, and acquitted himself with all the obduracy of a man who was willing to please his master. As he was conducting them, he heard these two victims deplore the long succession of miseries which had befallen them from their cradle. This aged couple reckoned as one of their greatest misfortunes the wildness and loss of their son. He recollected them, but he nevertheless led them to prison; assuring them that the king was to be served in preference to everybody else. His Highness rewarded his zeal.

"I have seen a spy of the king's adviser betray his own brother, in hopes of a little benefice, which he did not obtain; and I saw him die, not of remorse, but of grief at having been cheated by the man.

"The vocation of an adviser, which I for a long while exercised, made me acquainted with the secrets of families. I have known very few, who, though immersed in the greatest distress, did not externally wear the mask of felicity and every appearance of joy; and I have always observed that great grief was the fruit of our unconstrained desires."

"For my part," said the Huron, "I imagine, that a noble, grateful, sensible man, may always be happy; and I hope to enjoy an uncheckered felicity with the charming, generous Miss St. Yves. For I flatter myself," added he, in addressing himself to her brother with a friendly smile, "that you will not now refuse me as you did last year: besides, I shall pursue a more decent method."

The Abbe was confounded in apologies for the past, and in protesting an eternal attachment.

Uncle Kerkabon said this would be the most glorious day of his whole life. His good aunt Kerkabon, in ecstasies of joy, cried out:

"I always said you would never be a sub-deacon."

And now all vied with each other in applauding the gentle Miss St. Yves.

Her lover's heart was too full of what she had done for him, and he loved her too much, for the affair of the jewels to make any permanent impression on him. But those words, which he too well heard, "*you have given me the mortal blow*," still secretly terrified him, and interrupted all his joy; whilst the eulogiums paid his beautiful mistress still increased his love. In a word, nothing was thought of but her,—nothing was mentioned but the happiness those two lovers deserved. A plan was agitated to live altogether at Paris, and schemes of grandeur and fortune were formed. These hopes, which the smallest ray of happiness engenders, were predominant. But the Huron felt, in the secret recesses of his heart, a sentiment that exploded the illusion. He read over the promises signed by St. Pouange, and the commission signed by Louvois. These men were painted to him such as they were, or such as they were thought to be. Every one spoke of the ministers and administration with the freedom of convivial conversation, which is considered in France as the most precious liberty to be obtained on earth.

"If I were king of France," said the Huron, "this is the kind of minister that I would choose for the war department. I would have a man of the highest birth, as he is to give orders to the nobility. I would require that he should himself have been an officer, and have passed through the various gradations; or, at least, that he had attained the rank of Lieutenant General, and was worthy of being a Marshal of France. For, to be acquainted with the details of the service, is it not necessary that he himself should have served? and will not officers obey, with a hundred times more alacrity, a military man, who like themselves has been signalized by his courage, rather than a mere man of the cabinet, who, whatever natural ability he may possess, can, at most, only guess at the operations of a campaign? I should not be displeased at my minister's generosity, even though it might sometimes embarrass a little the keeper of the royal treasure. I should desire him to have a facility in business, and that he should distinguish himself by that kind of gaiety of mind, which is the lot of men superior to business, which is so agreeable to the nation, and which renders the performance of every duty less irksome."

This is the character he would have chosen for a minister, as he had constantly observed that such an amiable disposition is incompatible with cruelty.

Monsieur de Louvois would not, perhaps, have been satisfied with the Huron's wishes. His merit lay in a different walk. But whilst they were still at table, the disorder of the unhappy Miss St. Yves took a fatal turn. Her blood was on fire,—the symptoms of a malignant fever had appeared. She suffered, but did not complain, being unwilling to disturb the pleasure of the guests.

Her brother, thinking that she was not asleep, went to the foot of her bed. He was astonished at the condition he found her in. Everybody flew to her. Her lover appeared next to her brother. He was certainly the most alarmed, and the most affected of any one; but he had learned to unite discretion to all the happy gifts nature had bestowed upon him, and a quick sensibility of decorum began to prevail over him.

A neighboring physician was immediately sent for. He was one of those itinerant doctors who confound the last disorder they were consulted upon with the present;—who follow a blind practice in a science from which the most mature investigations and careful observations do not preclude uncertainty and danger. He greatly increased the disorder by prescribing a fashionable nostrum. Can fashion extend to medicine? This frenzy was then too prevalent in Paris.

The grief of Miss St. Yves contributed still more than her physician to render her disorder fatal. Her body suffered martyrdom in the torments of her mind. The crowd of thoughts which agitated her breast communicated to her veins a more dangerous poison than that of the most burning fever.

XX

The Death of the Beautiful Miss St. Yves and Its Consequences

ANOTHER physician was called in. But, instead of assisting nature and leaving it to act in a young person whose organs recalled the vital stream, he applied himself solely to counteract the effects of his brother's prescription. The disorder, in two days, became mortal. The brain, which is thought to be the seat of the mind, was as violently affected as the heart, which, we are told, is the seat of the passions. By what incomprehensible mechanism are our organs held in subjection to sentiment and thought? How is it that a single melancholy idea shall disturb the whole course of the blood; and that the blood should in turn communicate irregularities to the human understanding? What is that unknown fluid which certainly exists and which, quicker and more active than light, flies in less than the twinkling of an eye into all the channels of life,— produces sensations, memory, joy or grief, reason or frenzy,—recalls with horror what we would choose to forget; and renders a thinking animal, either a subject of admiration, or an object of pity and compassion?

These were the reflections of the good old Gordon; and these observations, so natural, which men seldom make, did not prevent his feeling upon this occasion; for he was not of the number of those gloomy philosophers who pique themselves upon being insensible.

He was affected at the fate of this young woman, like a father who sees his dear child yielding to a slow death. The Abbe de St. Yves was desperate; the prior and his sister shed floods of tears; but who could describe the situation of her lover? All expression falls far short of the intensity of his affliction.

His aunt, almost lifeless, supported the head of the departing fair in her feeble arms; her brother was upon his knees at the foot of the bed; her lover squeezed her hand, which he bathed in tears; his groans rent the air, whilst he called her his guardian angel, his life, his hope, his better half, his mistress, his wife. At the word wife, a sigh escaped her, whilst she looked upon him with inexpressible tenderness, and then abruptly gave a horrid scream. Presently in one of those intervals when brief, the oppression of the senses, and pain subside and leave the soul its liberty and powers, she cried out:

"I your wife? Ah! dear lover, this name, this happiness, this felicity, were not destined for me! I die, and I deserve it. O idol of my heart! O you, whom I sacrificed to infernal demons—it is done—I am punished—live and be happy!"

These tender but dreadful expressions were incomprehensible; yet they melted and terrified every heart. She had the courage to explain herself, and her auditors quaked with astonishment, grief and pity. They with one voice destested the man in power, who repaired a shocking act of injustice only by his crimes, and who had forced the most amiable innocence to be his accomplice.

"Who? you guilty?" said her lover, "no, you are not. Guilt can only be in the heart;—yours is devoted solely to virtue and to me."

This opinion he corroborated by such expressions as seemed to recall the beautiful Miss St. Yves back to life. She felt some consolation from them and was astonished at being still beloved. The aged Gordon would have condemned her at the time he was only a Jansenist; but having attained wisdom, he esteemed her, and wept.

In the midst of these lamentations and fears, whilst the dangerous situation of this worthy girl engrossed every breast, and all were in the greatest consternation, a courier arrived from court.

"A courier? from whom, and upon what account?"

He was sent by the king's adviser to the Prior of the Mountain.

He wrote to the Abbe of the Mountain, "that had been informed of his nephew's exploits· that his being sent to prison was through mistake; that such little accidents frequently happened, and should therefore not be attended to; and, in fine, it behoved him, the prior, to come and present his nephew the next day: that he was to bring with him that good man Gordon; and that he should introduce them to M. de Louvois, who would say a word to them in his ante-chamber."

To which he added, "that the history of the Huron, and his combat against the English, had been related to the king; that doubtless the king would deign to take notice of him in passing through the gallery, and perhaps he might even nod his head to him."

The letter concluded by flattering him with hopes that all the ladies of the court would show their eagerness to recognize his nephew; and that several among them would say to him, "Good day, Mr. Huron;" and that he would certainly be talked of at the king's supper.

The prior having read the letter aloud, his furious nephew for an instant suppressed his rage, and said nothing to the bearer: but turning toward the companion of his misfortunes, asked him, what he thought of that communication? Gordon replied:

"This, then, is the way that men are treated! They are first beaten and then, like monkeys, they dance."

The Huron resuming his character, which always returned in the great emotions of his soul, tore the letter to bits, and threw them in the courier's face:

"There is my answer," said he.

His uncle was in terror, and fancied he saw thunderbolts, and twenty *lettres de cachet* at once fall upon him. He immediately wrote the best excuse he could for these transports of passion in a young man, which he considered as the ebullition of a great soul.

But a solicitude of a more melancholy stamp now seized every heart. The beautiful and unfortunate Miss St. Yves was already sensible of her approaching end; she was serene, but it was that kind of shocking serenity, the result of exhausted nature being no longer able to withstand the conflict.

"Oh, my dear lover!" said she, in a faltering voice, "death punishes me for my weakness; but I expire with the consolation of knowing you are free. I adored you whilst I betrayed you, and I adore you in bidding you an eternal adieu."

She did not make a parade of a ridiculous fortitude; she did not understand that miserable glory of having some of her neighbors say, "she died with courage." Who, at twenty, can be at once torn from her lover, from life, and what is called honor, without regret, without some pangs? She felt all the horror of her situation, and made it felt by those expiring looks and accents which speak with so much energy. In a word, she shed tears like other people at those intervals that she was capable of giving vent to them.

Let others strive to celebrate the pompous deaths of those who insensibly rush into destruction. This is the lot of all animals. We die like them only when age or disorders make us resemble them by the paralysis of our organs.

Whoever suffers a great loss must feel great regrets. If they are stifled, it is nothing but vanity that is pursued, even in the arms of death.

When the fatal moment came, all around her most feelingly expressed their grief by incessant tears and lamentations. The Huron was senseless. Great souls feel more violent sensations than those of less tender dispositions. The good old Gordon knew enough of his companion to dread that when he came to himself he would be guilty of suicide. All kinds of arms were put out of his way, which the unfortunate young man perceived. He said to his relations and Gordon, without shedding any tears, without a groan, or the least emotion:

"Do you then think that any one upon earth hath the right and power to prevent my putting an end to my life?"

Gordon took care to avoid making a parade of those common-place declamations and arguments which are relied on to prove that we are not allowed to exercise our liberty in ceasing to be when we are in a wretched situation; that we should not leave the house when we can no longer remain in it; that a man is like a soldier at his post; as if it signified to the Being of beings whether the conjunction of the particles of matter were in one spot or another. Impotent reasons, to which a firm and concentrated despair disdains to listen, and to which Cato replied only with the use of a poniard.

The Huron's sullen and dreadful silence, his doleful aspect, his trembling lips, and the shivering of his whole frame, communicated to every spectator's soul that mixture of compassion and terror, which fetters all our powers, precludes discourse, or compels us to speak only in faltering accents. The hostess and her family were excited. They trembled to behold the state of his desperation, yet all kept their eyes upon him, and attended to all his motions. The ice-cold corpse of the beautiful Miss St. Yves had already been carried into a lower hall out of the sight of her lover, who seemed still in search of it, though incapable of observing any object.

In the midst of this spectacle of death, whilst the dead body was exposed at the door of the house; whilst her relations were drowned in tears, and every one thought the lover would not survive his loss;—in this situation St. Pouange arrived with his female Versailles friend.

He alighted from his coach; and the first object that presented itself was a bier: he turned away his eyes with that simple distaste of a man bred up in pleasures, and who thinks he should avoid a spectacle which might recall him to the contemplation of human misery. He is inclined to go up stairs, whilst his female friend enquires through curiosity whose funeral it is. The name of Miss St. Yves is pronounced. At this name she turned, and gave a piercing shriek. St. Pouange now returns, whilst surprise and grief possess his soul. The good old Gordon stood with streaming eyes. He for a moment ceased his lamentations, to acquaint the courier with all the circumstances of this melancholy catastrophe. He spoke with that authority which is the companion to sorrow and virtue. St. Pouange was not naturally wicked. The torrent of business and amusements had hurried away his soul, which was not yet acquainted with itself. He did not border upon that grey age which usually hardens the hearts of ministers. He listened to Gordon with a downcast look, and some tears escaped him, which he was surprised to shed. In a word, he repented.

"I will," said he, "absolutely see this extraordinary man you have mentioned to me. He affects me almost as much as this innocent victim, whose death I have occasioned."

Gordon followed him as far as the chamber in which the Prior Kerkabon, the Abbe St. Yves, and some neighbors, were striving to recall to life the young man, who had again fainted.

"I have been the cause of your misfortunes," said the deputy minister, when the Huron had regained consciousness, "and my whole life shall be employed in making reparation for my error."

The first idea that struck the Huron was to kill him and then destroy himself. But he was without arms, and closely watched. St. Pouange was not repulsed with refusals accompanied with reproach, contempt, and the insults he deserved, which were lavished upon him. Time softens everything. Mons. de Louvois at length succeeded in making an excellent officer of the Huron, who has appeared under another name at Paris and in the army, respected by all honest men, being at once a warrior and an intrepid philosopher.

He never mentioned this adventure without being greatly affected, and yet his greatest consolation was to speak of it. He cherished the memory of his beloved Miss St. Yves to the last moment of his life.

The Abbe St. Yves and the Prior were each provided with good livings. The good Kerkabon rather chose to see his nephew invested with military honors than in the sub-deaconry. The devotee of Versailles kept the diamond earrings, and received besides a handsome present. *Tout-à-tous* had presents of chocolate, coffee, and confectionery. Good old Gordon lived with the Huron till his death, in the most friendly intimacy: he had also a benefice, and forgot, forever, essential grace, and the concomitant concourse. He took for his motto, "Misfortunes are of some use." How many worthy people are there in the world who may justly say, "Misfortunes are good for nothing?"

MICROMEGAS

I

A Voyage to the Planet Saturn by a Native of Sirius

In one of the planets that revolve round the star known by the name of Sirius, was a certain young gentleman of promising parts, whom I had the honor to be acquainted with in his last voyage to this our little ant-hill. His name was Micromegas, an appellation admirably suited to all great men, and his stature amounted to eight leagues in height, that is, twenty-four thousand geometrical paces of five feet each.

Some of your mathematicians, a set of people always useful to the public, will, perhaps, instantly seize the pen, and calculate that Mr. Micromegas, inhabitant of the country of Sirius, being from head to foot four and twenty thousand paces in length, making one hundred and twenty thousand royal feet, that we, denizens of this earth, being at a medium little more than five feet high, and our globe nine thousand leagues in circumference: these things being premised, they will then conclude that the periphery of the globe which produced him must be exactly one and twenty millions six hundred thousand times greater than that of this our tiny ball. Nothing in nature is more simple and common. The dominions of some sovereigns of Germany or Italy, which may be compassed in half an hour, when compared with the empires of Ottoman, Russia, or China, are no other than faint instances of the prodigious difference that nature hath made in the scale of beings. The stature of his excellency being of these extraordinary dimensions, all our artists will agree that the measure around his body might amount to fifty thousand royal feet,—a very agreeable and just proportion.

His nose being equal in length to one-third of his face, and his jolly countenance engrossing one-seventh part of his height, it must be owned that the nose of this same Sirian was six thousand three hundred and thirty-three royal feet to a hair, which was to be demonstrated. With regard to his understanding, it is one of the best cultivated I have known. He is perfectly well acquainted with abundance of things, some of which are of his own invention; for, when his age did not exceed two hundred and fifty years, he studied, according to the custom of the country, at the most celebrated university of the whole planet, and by the force of his genius discovered upwards of fifty propositions of Euclid, having the advantage by more than eighteen of Blaise Pascal, who, (as we are told by his own sister,) demonstrated two and thirty for his amusement and then left off, choosing rather to be an indifferent philosopher than a great mathematician.

About the four hundred and fiftieth year of his age, or latter end of his childhood, he dissected a great number of small insects not more than one hundred feet in diameter, which are not perceivable by ordinary microscopes, of which he composed a very curious treatise, which involved him in some trouble. The mufti of the nation, though very old and very ignorant, made shift to discover in his book certain lemmas that were suspicious, unseemly, rash, heretic, and unsound, and prosecuted him with great animosity; for the subject of the author's inquiry was whether, in the world of Sirius, there was any difference between the substantial forms of a flea and a snail.

Micromegas defended his pholosophy with such spirit as made all the female sex his proselytes; and the process lasted two hundred and twenty years; at the end of which time, in consequence of the mufti's interest, the book was condemned by judges who had never read it, and the author expelled from court for the term of eight hundred years.

Not much affected at his banishment from a court that teemed with nothing but turmoils and trifles, he made a very humorous song upon the mufti, who gave himself no trouble about the matter, and set out on his travels from planet to planet, in order (as the saying is) to improve his mind and finish his education. Those who never travel but in a postchaise or berlin, will, doubtless, be astonished at the equipages used above; for we that strut upon this little mole hill are at a loss to conceive anything that surpasses our own customs. But our traveler was a wonderful adept in the laws of gravitation, together with the whole force of attraction and repulsion, and made such seasonable use of his knowledge, that sometimes by the help of a sunbeam, and sometimes by the convenience of a comet, he and his retinue glided from sphere to sphere, as the bird hops from one bough to another. He in a very little time posted through the milky way, and I am obliged to own he saw not a twinkle of those stars supposed to adorn that fair empyrean, which the illustrious Dr. Derham brags to have observed through his telescope. Not that I pretend to say the doctor was mistaken. God forbid! But Micromegas was upon the spot, an exceeding good observer, and I have no mind to contradict any man. Be that as it may, after many windings and turnings, he arrived at the planet Saturn; and, accustomed as he was to the sight of novelties, he could not for his life repress a supercilious and conceited smile, which often escapes the wisest philosopher, when he perceived the smallness of that globe, and the diminutive size of its inhabitants; for really Saturn is but about nine hundred times larger than this our earth, and the people of that country mere dwarfs, about a thousand fathoms high. In short, he at first derided those poor pigmies, just as an Indian fiddler laughs at the music of Lully, at his first arrival in Paris: but as this Sirian was a person of good sense, he soon perceived that a thinking being may not be altogether ridiculous, even though he is not quite six thousand feet high; and therefore he became familiar with them, after they had ceased to wonder at his extraordinary appearance. In particular, he contracted an intimate friendship with the secretary of the Academy of Saturn, a man of good understanding, who, though in truth he had invented nothing of his own, gave a very good account of the inventions of others, and enjoyed in peace the reputation of a little poet and great calculator. And here, for the edification of the reader, I will repeat a very singular conversation that one day passed between Mr. Secretary and Micromegas.

II

The Conversation Between Micromegas and the Inhabitant of Saturn

His excellency having laid himself down, and the secretary approached his nose:

"It must be confessed," said Micromegas, "that nature is full of variety."

"Yes," replied the Saturnian, "nature is like a parterre, whose flowers—"

"Pshaw!" cried the other, "a truce with your parterres."

"It is," resumed the secretary, "like an assembly of fair and brown women, whose dresses—"

"What a plague have I to do with your brunettes?" said our traveler.

"Then it is like a gallery of pictures, the strokes of which—"

"Not at all," answered Micromegas, "I tell you once for all, nature is like nature, and comparisons are odious."

"Well, to please you," said the secretary—

"I won't be pleased," replied the Sirian, "I want to be instructed; begin, therefore, without further preamble, and tell me how many senses the people of this world enjoy."

"We have seventy and two," said the academician, "but we are daily complaining of the small number, as our imagination transcends our wants, for, with the seventy-two senses, our five moons and ring, we find ourselves very much restricted; and notwithstanding our curiosity, and the no small number of those passions that result from these few senses, we have still time enough to be tired of idleness."

"I sincerely believe what you say," cried Micromegas, "for, though we Sirians have near a thousand different senses, there still remains a certain vague desire, an unaccountable inquietude incessantly admonishing us of our own unimportance, and giving us to understand that there are other beings who are much our superiors in point of perfection. I have traveled a little, and seen mortals both above and below myself in the scale of being, but I have met with none who had not more desire than necessity, and more want than gratification. Perhaps I shall one day arrive in some country where nought is wanting, but hitherto I have had no certain information of such a happy land."

The Saturnian and his guest exhausted themselves in conjectures upon this subject, and after abundance of argumentation equally ingenious and uncertain, were fain to return to matter of fact.

"To what age do you commonly live?" said the Sirian.

"Lack-a-day! a mere trifle," replied the little gentleman.

"It is the very same case with us," resumed the other, "the shortness of life is our daily complaint, so that this must be an universal law in nature."

"Alas!" cried the Saturnian, "few, very few on this globe outlive five hundred great revolutions of the sun (these, according to our way of reckoning, amount to about fifteen thousand years). So, you see, we in a manner begin to die the very moment we are born: our existence is no more than a point, our duration an instant, and our globe an atom. Scarce do we begin to learn a little, when death intervenes before we can profit by experience. For my own part, I am deterred from laying schemes when I consider myself as a single drop in the midst of an immense ocean. I am particularly ashamed, in your presence, of the ridiculous figure I make among my fellow-creatures."

To this declaration, Micromegas replied:

"If you were not a philosopher, I should be afraid of mortifying your pride by telling you that the term of our lives is seven hundred times longer than the date of your existence: but you are very sensible that when the texture of the body is resolved, in order to reanimate nature in another form, which is the consequence of what we call death—when that moment of change arrives, there is not the least difference betwixt having lived a whole eternity, or a single day. I have been in some countries where the people live a thousand times longer than with us, and yet they murmured at the shortness of their time. But one will find everywhere some few persons of good sense, who know how to make the best of their portion, and thank the author of nature for his bounty. There is a profusion of variety scattered through the universe, and yet there is an admirable vein of uniformity that runs through the whole: for example, all thinking beings are different among themselves, though at bottom they resemble one another in the powers and passions of the soul. Matter, though interminable, hath different properties in every sphere. How many principal attributes do you reckon in the matter of this world?"

"If you mean those properties," said the Saturnian, "without which we believe this our globe could not subsist, we reckon in all three hundred, such as extent, impenetrability, motion, gravitation, divisibility, et cætera."

"That small number," replied the traveler, "probably answers the views of the creator on this your narrow sphere. I adore his wisdom in all his works. I see infinite variety, but everywhere proportion. Your globe is small: so are the inhabitants. You have few sensations; because your matter is endued with few properties. These are the works of unerring providence. Of what color does your sun appear when accurately examined?"

"Of a yellowish white," answered the Saturnian, "and in separating one of his rays we find it contains seven colors."

"Our sun," said the Sirian, "is of a reddish hue, and we have no less than thirty-nine original colors. Among all the suns I have seen there is no sort of resemblance, and in this sphere of yours there is not one face like another."

After divers questions of this nature, he asked how many substances, essentially different, they counted in the world of Saturn; and understood that they numbered but thirty: such as God; space; matter; beings endowed with sense and extension; beings that have extension, sense, and reflection; thinking beings who have no extension; those that are penetrable; those that are impenetrable, and also all others. But this Saturnian philosopher was prodigiously

astonished when the Sirian told him they had no less than three hundred, and
that he himself had discovered three thousand more in the course of his
travels. In short, after having communicated to each other what they knew, and
even what they did not know, and argued during a complete revolution of the
sun, they resolved to set out together on a small philosophical tour.

III

The Voyage of These Inhabitants of Other Worlds

Our two philosophers were just ready to embark for the atmosphere of Saturn,
with a large provision of mathematical instruments, when the Saturnian's mistress, having got an inkling of their design, came all in tears to make her pro-
tests. She was a handsome brunette, though not above six hundred and threescore fathoms high; but her agreeable attractions made amends for the smallness
of her stature.

"Ah! cruel man," cried she, "after a courtship of fifteen hundred years, when
at length I surrendered, and became your wife, and scarce have passed two
hundred more in thy embraces, to leave me thus, before the honeymoon is
over, and go a rambling with a giant of another world! Go, go, thou art a mere
virtuoso, devoid of tenderness and love! If thou wert a true Saturnian, thou
wouldst be faithful and invariable. Ah! whither art thou going? what is thy
design? Our five moons are not so inconstant, nor our ring so changeable as
thee! But take this along with thee, henceforth I ne'er shall love another man."

The little gentleman embraced and wept over her, notwithstanding his
philosophy; and the lady, after having swooned with great decency, went to
console herself with more agreeable company.

Meanwhile our two virtuosi set out, and at one jump leaped upon the ring,
which they found pretty flat, according to the ingenious guess of an illustrious
inhabitant of this our little earth. From thence they easily slipped from moon
to moon; and a comet changing to pass, they sprang upon it with all their
servants and apparatus. Thus carried about one hundred and fifty million of
leagues, they met with the satellites of Jupiter, and arrived upon the body of the
planet itself, where they continued a whole year; during which they learned
some very curious secrets, which would actually be sent to the press, were it
not for fear of the gentlemen inquisitors, who have found among them some
corollaries very hard of digestion.

But to return to our travelers. When they took leave of Jupiter, they
traversed a space of about one hundred millions of leagues, and coasting along
the planet Mars, which is well known to be five times smaller than our little
earth, they descried two moons subservient to that orb, which have escaped the
observation of all our astronomers. I know Castel will write, and that pleasantly
enough, against the existence of these two moons; but I entirely refer myself

to those who reason by analogy. Those worthy philosophers are very sensible that Mars, which is at such a distance from the sun, must be in a very uncomfortable situation, without the benefit of a couple of moons. Be that as it may, our gentlemen found the planet so small, that they were afraid they should not find room to take a little repose; so that they pursued their journey like two travelers who despise the paltry accommodation of a village, and push forward to the next market town. But the Sirian and his companion soon repented of their delicacy; for they journeyed a long time without finding a resting place, till at length they discerned a small speck, which was the Earth. Coming from Jupiter, they could not but be moved with compassion at the sight of this miserable spot, upon which, however, they resolved to land, lest they should be a second time disappointed. They accordingly moved toward the tail of the comet, where, finding an Aurora Borealis ready to set sail, they embarked, and arrived on the northern coast of the Baltic on the fifth day of July, new style, in the year 1737.

IV

What Befell Them upon This Our Globe

Having taken some repose, and being desirous of reconnoitering the narrow field in which they were, they traversed it at once from north to south. Every step of the Sirian and his attendants measured about thirty thousand royal feet: whereas, the dwarf of Saturn, whose stature did not exceed a thousand fathoms, followed at a distance quite out of breath; because, for every single stride of his companion, he was obliged to make twelve good steps at least. The reader may figure to himself (if we are allowed to make such comparisons) a very little rough spaniel dodging after a captain of the Prussian grenadiers.

As those strangers walked at a good pace, they compassed the globe in six and thirty hours; the sun, it is true, or rather the earth, describes the same space in the course of one day; but it must be observed that it is much easier to turn upon an axis than to walk a-foot. Behold them then returned to the spot from whence they had set out, after having discovered that almost imperceptible sea, which is called the Mediterranean; and the other narrow pond that surrounds this mole-hill, under the denomination of the great ocean; in wading through which the dwarf had never wet his mid-leg, while the other scarce moistened his heel. In going and coming through both hemispheres, they did all that lay in their power to discover whether or not the globe was inhabited. They stooped, they lay down, they groped in every corner; but their eyes and hands were not at all proportioned to the small beings that crawl upon this earth; and, therefore, they could not find the smallest reason to suspect that we and our fellow-citizens of this globe had the honor to exist.

The dwarf, who sometimes judged too hastily, concluded at once that there were no living creatures upon earth; and his chief reason was, that he had seen nobody. But Micromegas, in a polite manner, made him sensible of the unjust conclusion:

"For," said he, "with your diminutive eyes you cannot see certain stars of the fiftieth magnitude, which I easily perceive; and do you take it for granted that no such stars exist?"

"But I have groped with great care," replied the dwarf.

"Then your sense of feeling must be bad," said the other.

"But this globe," said the dwarf, "is ill contrived; and so irregular in its form as to be quite ridiculous. The whole together looks like a chaos. Do but observe these little rivulets; not one of them runs in a straight line: and these ponds which are neither round, square, nor oval, nor indeed of any regular figure; together with these little sharp pebbles (meaning the mountains) that roughen the whole surface of the globe, and have torn all the skin from my feet. Besides, pray take notice of the shape of the whole, how it flattens at the poles, and turns round the sun in an awkward oblique manner, so as that the polar circles cannot possibly be cultivated. Truly, what makes me believe there is no inhabitant on this sphere, is a full persuasion that no sensible being would live in such a disagreeable place."

"What then?" said Micromegas, "perhaps the beings that inhabit it come not under that denomination; but, to all appearance, it was not made for nothing. Everything here seems to you irregular; because you fetch all your comparisons from Jupiter or Saturn. Perhaps this is the very reason of the seeming confusion which you condemn; have I not told you, that in the course of my travels I have always met with variety?"

The Saturnian replied to all these arguments; and perhaps the dispute would have known no end, if Micromegas, in the heat of the contest, had not luckily broken the string of his diamond necklace, so that the jewels fell to the ground; they consisted of pretty small unequal karats, the largest of which weighed four hundred pounds, and the smallest fifty. The dwarf, in helping to pick them up, perceived, as they approached his eye, that every single diamond was cut in such a manner as to answer the purpose of an excellent microscope. He therefore took up a small one, about one hundred and sixty feet in diameter, and applied it to his eye, while Micromegas chose another of two thousand five hundred feet. Though they were of excellent powers, the observers could perceive nothing by their assistance, so they were altered and adjusted. At length, the inhabitant of Saturn discerned something almost imperceptible moving between two waves in the Baltic. This was no other than a whale, which, in a dexterous manner, he caught with his little finger, and, placing it on the nail of his thumb, showed it to the Syrian, who laughed heartily at the excessive smallness peculiar to the inhabitants of this our globe. The Saturnian, by this time convinced that our world was inhabited, began to imagine we had no other animals than whales; and being a mighty debater, he forthwith set about investigating the origin and motion of this small atom, curious to know whether or not it was furnished with ideas, judgment, and free will. Micromegas was very much perplexed upon this subject. He examined the animal with the most patient attention, and the result of his inquiry was, that he could see no reason to believe a soul was lodged in such a body. The two travelers were actually inclined to think there was no such thing as mind in this our habitation, when, by the help of their microscope, they perceived something as large as a whale floating upon the surface of the sea. It is well known that, at this period, a flight of philosophers were upon their return from the polar circle, where they had been making observations, for which nobody has hitherto been the wiser. The gazettes record that their vessel ran ashore on the coast of Bothnia and that they with great difficulty saved their lives; but in this world one can never dive to the bottom of things. For my own part, I will ingenuously recount the transaction just as it happened, without any addition of my own; and this is no small effort in a modern historian.

V

The Travelers Capture a Vessel

Micromegas stretched out his hand gently toward the place where the object appeared, and advanced two fingers, which he instantly pulled back, for fear of being disappointed, then opening softly and shutting them all at once, he very dexterously seized the ship that contained those gentlemen, and placed it on his nail, avoiding too much pressure, which might have crushed the whole in pieces.

"This," said the Saturnian dwarf, "is a creature very different from the former."

Upon which the Sirian placing the supposed animal in the hollow of his hand, the passengers and crew, who believed themselves thrown by a hurricane upon some rock, began to put themselves in motion. The sailors having hoisted out some casks of wine, jumped after them into the hand of Micromegas: the mathematicians having secured their quadrants, sectors, and Lapland servants, went overboard at a different place, and made such a bustle in their descent, that the Sirian at length felt his fingers tickled by something that seemed to move. An iron bar chanced to penetrate about a foot deep into his forefinger; and from this prick he concluded that something had issued from the little animal he held in his hand; but at first he suspected nothing more: for the microscope, that scarce rendered a whale and a ship visible, had no effect upon an object so imperceptible as man.

I do not intend to shock the vanity of any person whatever; but here I am obliged to beg your people of importance to consider that, supposing the stature of a man to be about five feet, we mortals make just such a figure upon the earth, as an animal the sixty thousandth part of a foot in height would exhibit upon a bowl ten feet in circumference. When you reflect upon a being who could hold this whole earth in the palm of his hand, and is provided with organs proportioned to those we possess, you will easily conceive that there must be a great variety of created substances;—and pray, what must such beings think of those battles by which a conqueror gains a small village, to lose it again in the sequel?

I do not at all doubt, but if some captain of grenadiers should chance to read this work, he would add two large feet at least to the caps of his company; but I assure him his labor will be in vain; for, do what he will, he and his soldiers will never be other than infinitely diminutive and inconsiderable.

What wonderful address must have been inherent in our Sirian philosopher that enabled him to perceive those atoms of which we have been speaking. When Leuwenhoek and Hartsoecker observed the first rudiments of which we are formed, they did not make such an astonishing discovery. What pleasure, therefore, was the portion of Micromegas, in observing the motion of those little machines, in examining all their pranks, and following them in all their operations! With what joy did he put his microscope into his companion's hand; and with what transport did they both at once exclaim:

"I see them distinctly,—don't you see them carrying burdens, lying down and rising up again?"

So saying, their hands shook with eagerness to see, and apprehension to lose such uncommon objects. The Saturnian, making a sudden transition from the most cautious distrust to the most excessive credulity, imagined he saw them engaged in their devotions and cried aloud in astonishment.

Nevertheless, he was deceived by appearances: a case too common, whether we do or do not make use of microscopes.

VI

What Happened in Their Intercourse with Men

Micromegas being a much better observer than the dwarf, perceived distinctly that those atoms spoke; and made the remark to his companion, who was so much ashamed of being mistaken in his first suggestion, that he would not believe such a puny species could possibly communicate their ideas: for, though he had the gift of tongues, as well as his companion, he could not hear those particles speak; and therefore supposed they had no language.

"Besides, how should such imperceptible beings have the organs of speech? and what in the name of Jove can they say to one another? In order to speak, they must have something like thought, and if they think, they must surely have something equivalent to a soul. Now, to attribute anything like a soul to such an insect species appears a mere absurdity."

"But just now," replied the Sirian, "you believed they were engaged in devotional exercises; and do you think this could be done without thinking, without using some sort of language, or at least some way of making themselves understood? Or do you suppose it is more difficult to advance an argument than to engage in physical exercise? For my own part, I look upon all faculties as alike mysterious."

"I will no longer venture to believe or deny," answered the dwarf: "in short I have no opinion at all. Let us endeavor to examine these insects, and we will reason upon them afterward."

"With all my heart," said Micromegas, who, taking out a pair of scissors which he kept for paring his nails, cut off a paring from his thumb nail, of which he immediately formed a large kind of speaking trumpet, like a vast tunnel, and clapped the pipe to his ear: as the circumference of this machine included the ship and all the crew, the most feeble voice was conveyed along the circular fibres of the nail; so that, thanks to his industry, the philosopher could distinctly hear the buzzing of our insects that were below. In a few hours he distinguished articulate sounds, and at last plainly understood the French language. The dwarf heard the same, though with more difficulty.

The astonishment of our travelers increased every instant. They heard a nest of mites talk in a very sensible strain: and that *Lusus Naturæ* seemed to them inexplicable. You need not doubt but the Sirian and his dwarf glowed with impatience to enter into conversation with such atoms. Micromegas being afraid that his voice, like thunder, would deafen and confound the mites, without being understood by them, saw the necessity of diminishing the sound; each, therefore, put into his mouth a sort of small toothpick, the slender end of which reached to the vessel. The Sirian setting the dwarf upon his knees, and the ship and crew upon his nail, held down his head and spoke softly. In fine, having taken these and a great many more precautions, he addressed himself to them in these words:

"O ye invisible insects, whom the hand of the Creator hath deigned to produce in the abyss of infinite littleness! I give praise to his goodness, in that he hath been pleased to disclose unto me those secrets that seemed to be impenetrable."

If ever there was such a thing as astonishment, it seized upon the people who heard this address, and who could not conceive from whence it proceeded. The chaplain of the ship repeated exorcisms, the sailors swore, and the philosophers formed a system: but, notwithstanding all their systems, they could not divine who the person was that spoke to them. Then the dwarf of Saturn, whose voice was softer than that of Micromegas, gave them briefly to understand what species of beings they had to do with. He related the particulars of their voyage from Saturn, made them acquainted with the rank and quality of Monsieur Micromegas; and, after having pitied their smallness, asked if they had always been in that miserable state so near akin to annihilation; and what their business was upon that globe which seemed to be the property of whales. He also desired to know if they were happy in their situation? if they were inspired with souls? and put a hundred questions of the like nature.

A certain mathematician on board, braver than the rest, and shocked to hear his soul called in question, planted his quadrant, and having taken two observations of this interlocutor, said: "You believe then, Mr. what's your name, that because you measure from head to foot a thousand fathoms——"

"A thousand fathoms!" cried the dwarf, "good heavens! How should he know the height of my stature? A thousand fathoms! My very dimensions to a hair. What, measured by a mite! This atom, forsooth, is a geometrician, and knows exactly how tall I am: while I, who can scarce perceive him through a microscope, am utterly ignorant of his extent!"

"Yes, I have taken your measure," answered the philosopher, "and I will now do the same by your tall companion."

The proposal was embraced: his excellency reclined upon his side; for, had he stood upright, his head would have reached too far above the clouds. Our mathematicians planted a tall tree near him, and then, by a series of triangles joined together, they discovered that the object of their observation was a strapping youth, exactly one hundred and twenty thousand royal feet in length. In consequence of this calculation, Micromegas uttered these words:

"I am now more than ever convinced that we ought to judge of nothing by its external magnitude. O God! who hast bestowed understanding upon such seemingly contemptible substances, thou canst with equal ease produce that which is infinitely small, as that which is incredibly great: and if it be possible, that among thy works there are beings still more diminutive than these, they may nevertheless, be endued with understanding superior to the intelligence of those stupendous animals I have seen in heaven, a single foot of whom is larger than this whole globe on which I have alighted."

One of the philosophers assured him that there were intelligent beings much smaller than men, and recounted not only Virgil's whole fable of the bees; but also described all that Swammerdam hath discovered, and Reaumur dissected. In a word, he informed him that there are animals which bear the same proportion to bees, that bees bear to man; the same as the Sirian himself compared to those vast beings whom he had mentioned; and as those huge animals as to other substances, before whom they would appear like so many particles of dust. Here the conversation became very interesting, and Micromegas proceeded in these words:

"O ye intelligent atoms, in whom the Supreme Being hath been pleased to manifest his omniscience and power, without all doubt your joys on this earth must be pure and exquisite: for, being unincumbered with matter, and, to all appearance, little else than soul, you must spend your lives in the delights of pleasure and reflection, which are the true enjoyments of a perfect spirit. True happiness I have no where found; but certainly here it dwells."

At this harangue all the philosophers shook their heads, and one among them, more candid than his brethren, frankly owned, that excepting a very small number of inhabitants who were very little esteemed by their fellows, all the rest were a parcel of knaves, fools, and miserable wretches.

"We have matter enough," said he, "to do abundance of mischief, if mischief comes from matter; and too much understanding, if evil flows from understanding. You must know, for example, that at this very moment, while I am speaking, there are one hundred thousand animals of our own species, covered with hats, slaying an equal number of their fellow-creatures, who wear turbans; at least they are either slaying or being slain; and this hath usually been the case all over the earth from time immemorial."

The Sirian, shuddering at this information, begged to know the cause of those horrible quarrels among such a puny race; and was given to understand that the subject of the dispute was a pitiful mole-hill [called Palestine,] no larger than his heel. Not that any one of those millions who cut one another's throats pretends to have the least claim to the smallest particle of that clod. The question is, whether it shall belong to a certain person who is known by the name of Sultan, or to another whom (for what reason I know not) they dignify with the appellation of King. Neither the one nor the other has seen or ever will see the pitiful corner in question; and probably none of these wretches, who so madly destroy each other, ever beheld the ruler on whose account they are so mercilessly sacrificed!

"Ah, miscreants!" cried the indignant Sirian, "such excess of desperate rage is beyond conception. I have a good mind to take two or three steps, and trample the whole nest of such ridiculous assassins under my feet."

"Don't give yourself the trouble," replied the philosopher, "they are industrious enough in procuring their own destruction. At the end of ten years the hundredth part of those wretches will not survive; for you must know that, though they should not draw a sword in the cause they have espoused, famine, fatigue, and intemperance, would sweep almost all of them from the face of the earth. Besides, the punishment should not be inflicted upon them, but upon those sedentary and slothful barbarians, who, from their palaces, give orders for murdering a million of men and then solemnly thank God for their success."

Our traveler was moved with compassion for the entire human race, in which he discovered such astonishing contrast. "Since you are of the small number of the wise," said he, "and in all likelihood do not engage yourselves in the trade of murder for hire, be so good as to tell me your occupation."

"We anatomize flies," replied the philosopher, "we measure lines, we make calculations, we agree upon two or three points which we understand, and dispute upon two or three thousand that are beyond our comprehension."

"How far," said the Sirian, "do you reckon the distance between the great star of the constellation Gemini and that called Caniculæ?"

To this question all of them answered with one voice: "Thirty-two degrees and a half."

"And what is the distance from hence to the moon?"

"Sixty semi-diameters of the earth."

He then thought to puzzle them by asking the weight of the air; but they answered distinctly, that common air is about nine hundred times specifically lighter than an equal column of the lightest water, and nineteen hundred times lighter than current gold. The little dwarf of Saturn, astonished at their answers, was now tempted to believe those people sorcerers, who, but a quarter of an hour before, he would not allow were inspired with souls.

"Well," said Micromegas, "since you know so well what is without you, doubtless you are still more perfectly acquainted with that which is within. Tell me what is the soul, and how do your ideas originate?"

Here the philosophers spoke altogether as before; but each was of a different opinion. The eldest quoted Aristotle; another pronounced the name of Descartes; a third mentioned Mallebranche; a fourth Leignitz; and a fifth Locke. An old peripatecian, lifting up his voice, exclaimed with an air of confidence: "The soul is perfection and reason, having power to be such as it is, as Aristotle expressly declares, page 633, of the Louvre edition:

"Εντελεχεια τις εςι, και λογος τ8 δυναμιν εχοντθς τοι8δι ειται."

"I am not very well versed in Greek," said the giant.

"Nor I either," replied the philosophical mite.

"Why then do you quote that same Aristotle in Greek?" resumed the Sirian.

"Because," answered the other, "it is but reasonable we should quote what we do not comprehend in a language we do not understand."

Here the Cartesian interposing: "The soul," said he, "is a pure spirit or intelligence, which hath received before birth all the metaphysical ideas; but after that event it is obliged to go to school and learn anew the knowledge which it hath lost."

"So it was necessary," replied the animal of eight leagues, "that thy soul should be learned before birth, in order to be so ignorant when thou hast got a beard upon thy chin. But what dost thou understand by spirit?"

"I have no idea of it," said the philosopher, "indeed it is supposed to be immaterial."

"At least, thou knowest what matter is?" resumed the Sirian.

"Perfectly well," answered the other. "For example: that stone is gray, is of a certain figure, has three dimensions, specific weight, and divisibility."

"I want to know," said the giant, "what that object is, which, according to thy observation, hath a gray color, weight, and divisibility. Thou seest a few qualities, but dost thou know the nature of the thing itself?"

"Not I, truly," answered the Cartesian.

Upon which the Sirian admitted that he also was ignorant in regard to this subject. Then addressing himself to another sage, who stood upon his thumb, he asked "what is the soul? and what are her functions?"

"Nothing at all," replied this disciple of Mallebranche; "God hath made everything for my convenience. In him I see everything, by him I act; he is the universal agent, and I never meddle in his work."

"That is being a nonentity indeed," said the Sirian sage; and then, turning to a follower of Leibnitz, he exclaimed: "Hark ye, friend, what is thy opinion of the soul?"

"In my opinion," answered this metaphysician, "the soul is the hand that points at the hour, while my body does the office of the clock; or, if you please, the soul is the clock, and the body is the pointer; or again, my soul is the mirror of the universe, and my body the frame. All this is clear and uncontrovertible."

A little partisan of Locke who chanced to be present, being asked his opinion on the same subject, said: "I do not know by what power I think; but well I know that I should never have thought without the assistance of my senses. That there are immaterial and intelligent substances I do not at all doubt; but that it is impossible for God to communicate the faculty of thinking to matter, I doubt very much. I revere the eternal power, to which it would ill become me to prescribe bounds. I affirm nothing, and am contented to believe that many more things are possible than are usually thought so."

The Sirian smiled at this declaration, and did not look upon the author as the least sagacious of the company: and as for the dwarf of Saturn, he would have embraced this adherent of Locke, had it not been for the extreme disproportion in their respective sizes. But unluckily there was another animalcule in a square cap, who, taking the word from all his philosophical brethren, affirmed that he knew the whole secret. He surveyed the two celestial strangers from top to toe, and maintained to their faces that their persons, their fashions, their suns and their stars, were created solely for the use of man. At this wild assertion our two travelers were seized with a fit of that uncontrollable laughter, which (according to Homer) is the portion of the immortal gods: their bellies quivered, their shoulders rose and fell, and, during these convulsions, the vessel fell from the Sirian's nail into the Saturnian's pocket, where these worthy people searched for it a long time with great diligence. At length, having found the ship and set everything to rights again, the Sirian resumed the discourse with those diminutive mites, and promised to compose for them a choice book of philosophy which would demonstrate the very essence of things. Accordingly, before his departure, he made them a present of the book, which was brought to the Academy of Sciences at Paris, but when the old secretary came ʼo open it he saw nothing but blank paper.

"Ay, ay," said he, "this is just what I suspected."

THE WORLD AS IT GOES

AMONG the genii who preside over the empires of the earth, Ithuriel held one of the first ranks, and had the department of Upper Asia. He one morning descended into the abode of Babouc, the Scythian, who dwelt on the banks of the Oxus, and said to him:

"Babouc, the follies and vices of the Persians have drawn upon them our indignation. Yesterday an assembly of the genii of Upper Asia was held, to consider whether we would chastise Persepolis or destroy it entirely. Go to that city; examine everything; return and give me a faithful account; and, according to thy report, I will then determine whether to correct or extirpate the inhabitants."

"But, my lord," said Babouc with great humility, "I have never been ir Persia, nor do I know a single person in that country."

"So much the better," said the angel, "thou wilt be the more impartial: thou hast received from heaven the spirit of discernment, to which I now add the power of inspiring confidence. Go, see, hear, observe, and fear nothing. Thou shalt everywhere meet with a favorable reception."

Babouc mounted his camel, and set out with his servants. After having traveled some days, he met, near the plains of Senaar, the Persian army, which was going to attack the forces of India. He first addressed himself to a soldier, whom he found at a distance from the main army, and asked him what was the occasion of the war?

"By all the gods," said the soldier, "I know nothing of the matter. It is none of my business. My trade is to kill and to be killed, to get a livelihood. It is of no consequence to me whom I serve. To-morrow, perhaps, I may go over to the Indian camp; for it is said that they give their soldiers nearly half a copper drachma a day more than we have in this cursed service of Persia. If thou desires to know why we fight, speak to my captain."

Babouc, having given the soldier a small present, entered the camp. He soon became acquainted with the captain, and asked him the cause of the war.

"How canst thou imagine that I should know it?" said the captain, "or of what importance is it to me? I live about two hundred leagues from Persepolis: I hear that war is declared: I instantly leave my family, and, having nothing else to do, go, according to our custom, to make my fortune, or to fall by a glorious death."

"But are not thy companions," said Babouc, "a little better informed than thee?"

"No," said the officer, "there are none but our principal satraps that know the true cause of our cutting one another's throats."

Babouc, struck with astonishment, introduced himself to the generals, and soon became familiarly acquainted with them. At last one of them said:

"The cause of this war, which for twenty years past hath desolated Asia, sprang originally from a quarrel between a eunuch belonging to one of the concubines of the great king of Persia, and the clerk of a factory belonging to the great king of India. The dispute was about a claim which amounted nearly to the thirtieth part of a daric. Our first minister, and the representative of India, maintained the rights of their respective masters with becoming dignity. The dispute grew warm. Both parties sent into the field an army of a million of soldiers. This army must be recruited every year with upwards of four hundred thousand men. Massacres, burning of houses, ruin and devastation, are daily multiplied; the universe suffers; and their mutual animosity still continues. The first ministers of the two nations frequently protest that they have nothing in view but the happiness of mankind; and every protestation is attended with the destruction of a town, or the desolation of a province."

Next day, on a report being spread that peace was going to be concluded, the Persian and Indian generals made haste to come to an engagement. The battle was long and bloody. Babouc beheld every crime, and every abomination. He was witness to the arts and stratagems of the principal satraps, who did all that lay in their power to expose their general to the disgrace of a defeat. He saw officers killed by their own troops, and soldiers stabbing their already expiring comrades in order to strip them of a few bloody garments torn and covered with dirt. He entered the hospitals to which they were conveying the wounded, most of whom died through the inhuman negligence of those who were well paid by the king of Persia to assist these unhappy men.

"Are these men," cried Babouc, "or are they wild beasts? Ah! I plainly see that Persepolis will be destroyed."

Full of this thought, he went over to the camp of the Indians, where, according to the prediction of the genii, he was as well received as in that of the Persians; but he saw there the same crimes which had already filled him with horror.

"Oh!" said he to himself, "if the angel Ithuriel should exterminate the Persians, the angel of India must certainly destroy the Indians."

But being afterward more particularly informed of all that passed in both armies, he heard of such acts of generosity, humanity, and greatness of soul, as at once surprised and charmed him:

"Unaccountable mortals! as ye are," cried he, "how can you thus unite so much baseness and so much grandeur, so many virtues and so many vices?"

Meanwhile the peace was proclaimed; and the generals of the two armies, neither of whom had gained a complete victory, but who, for their own private interest, had shed the blood of so many of their fellow-creatures, went to solicit their courts for rewards. The peace was celebrated in public writings which announced the return of virtue and happiness to the earth.

"God be praised," said Babouc, "Persepolis will now be the abode of spotless innocence, and will not be destroyed, as the cruel genii intended. Let us haste without delay to this capital of Asia."

He entered that immense city by the ancient gate, which was entirely barbarous, and offended the eye by its disagreeable rusticity. All that part of the town savored of the time when it was built; for, notwithstanding the obstinacy of men in praising ancient at the expense of modern times, it must be owned that the first essays in every art are rude and unfinished.

Babouc mingled in a crowd of people composed of the most ignorant, dirty and deformed of both sexes, who were thronging with a stupid air into a large and gloomy inclosure. By the constant hum; by the gestures of the people; by the money which some persons gave to others for the liberty of sitting down, he imagined that he was in a market, where chairs were sold; but observing several women fall down on their knees with an appearance of looking directly before them, while in reality they were leering at the men by their sides, he was soon convinced that he was in a temple. Shrill, hoarse, savage and discordant voices made the vault re-echo with ill articulated sounds, that produced the same effect as the braying of asses, when, in the plans of Pictavia, they answer the cornet that calls them together. He stopped his ears; but he was ready to shut his mouth and hold his nose, when he saw several laborers enter into the temple with picks and spades, who removed a large stone, and threw up the earth on both sides, from whence exhaled a pestilential vapor. At last some others approached, deposited a dead body in the opening, and replaced the stone upon it.

"What!" cried Babouc, "do these people bury their dead in the place where they adore the deity? What! are their temples paved with carcasses? I am no longer surprised at those pestilential diseases that frequently depopulate Persepolis. The putrefaction of the dead, and the infected breath of such numbers of the living, assembled and crowded together in the same place, are sufficient to poison the whole terrestrial globe. Oh! what an abominable city is Persepolis! The angels probably intend to destroy it in order to build a more beautiful one in its place, and to people it with inhabitants who are more virtuous and better singers. Providence may have its reasons for so doing; to its disposal let us leave all future events."

Meanwhile the sun approached his meridian height. Babouc was to dine at the other end of the city with a lady for whom her husband, an officer in the army, had given him some letters: but he first took several turns in Persepolis, where he saw other temples, better built and more richly adorned, filled with a polite audience, and resounding with harmonious music. He beheld public fountains, which, though ill-placed, struck the eye by their beauty; squares where the best kings that had governed Persia seemed to breathe in bronze, and others where he heard the people crying out:

"When shall we see our beloved master?"

He admired the magnificent bridges built over the river; the superb and commodious quay; the palaces raised on both sides; and an immense house, where thousands of old soldiers, covered with scars and crowned with victory, offered their daily praises to the god of armies. At last he entered the house of the lady, who, with a set of fashionable people, waited his company to dinner. The house was neat and elegant; the repast delicious; the lady, young, beautiful, witty, and engaging; and the company worthy of her; and Babouc every moment said to himself:

"The angel Ithuriel has little regard for the world, or he would never think of destroying such a charming city."

In the meantime he observed that the lady, who had begun by tenderly asking news about her husband, spoke more tenderly to a young magi, toward the conclusion of the repast. He saw a magistrate, who, in presence of his wife, paid his court with great vivacity to a widow, while the indulgent widow held out her hand to a young citizen, remarkable for his modesty and graceful appearance.

Babouc then began to fear that the genius Ithuriel had but too much reason for destroying Persepolis. The talent he possessed of gaining confidence let him that same day into all the secrets of the lady. She confessed to him her affection for the young magi, and assured him that in all the houses in Persepolis he would meet with similar examples of attachment. Babouc concluded that such a society could not possibly survive: that jealousy, discord, and vengeance must desolate every house; that tears and blood must be daily shed; and, in fine, that Ithuriel would do well to destroy immediately a city abandoned to continual disasters.

Such were the gloomy ideas that possessed his mind, when a grave man in a black gown appeared at the gate and humbly begged to speak to the young magistrate. This stripling, without rising or taking the least notice of the old gentleman, gave him some papers with a haughty and careless air, and then dismissed him. Babouc asked who this man was. The mistress of the house said to him in a low voice:

"He is one of the best advocates in the city, and hath studied the law these fifty years. The other, who is but twenty-five years of age, and has only been a satrap of the law for two days, hath ordered him to make an extract of a process he is going to determine, though he has not as yet examined it."

"This giddy youth acts wisely," said Babouc, "in asking counsel of an old man. But why is not the old man himself the judge?"

"Thou art surely in jest," said they; "those who have grown old in laborious and inferior posts are never raised to places of dignity. This young man has a great post, because his father is rich; and the right of dispensing justice is purchased here like a farm."

"O unhappy city!" cried Babouc, "this is surely the height of anarchy and confusion. Those who have thus purchased the right of judging will doubtless sell their judgments; nothing do I see here but an abyss of iniquity!"

While he was thus expressing his grief and surprise, a young warrior, who that very day had returned from the army, said to him:

"Why wouldst thou not have seats in the courts of justice offered for sale? I myself purchased the right of braving death at the head of two thousand men who are under my command. It has this year cost me forty darics of gold to lie on the earth thirty nights successively in a red dress, and at last to receive two wounds with an arrow, of which I still feel the smart. If I ruin myself to serve the emperor of Persia, whom I never saw, the satrap of the law may well pay something for enjoying the pleasure of giving audience to pleaders."

Babouc was filled with indignation, and could not help condemning a country, where the highest posts in the army and the law were exposed for sale.

He at once concluded that the inhabitants must be entirely ignorant of the art of war, and the laws of equity; and that, though Ithuriel should not destroy them, they must soon be ruined by their detestable administration.

He was still further confirmed in his bad opinion by the arrival of a fat man, who, after saluting all the company with great familiarity, went up to the young officer and said:

"I can only lend thee fifty thousand darics of gold; for indeed the taxes of the empire have this year brought me in but three hundred thousand."

Babouc inquired into the character of this man who complained of having gained so little, and was informed that in Persepolis there were forty plebeian kings who held the empire of Persia by lease, and paid a small tribute to the monarch.

After dinner he went into one of the most superb temples in the city, and seated himself amidst a crowd of men and women, who had come thither to pass away the time. A magi appeared in a machine elevated above the heads of the people, and talked a long time of vice and virtue. He divided into several parts what needed no division at all: he proved methodically what was sufficiently clear, and he taught what everybody knew. He threw himself into a passion with great composure, and went away perspiring and out of breath. The assembly then awoke and imagined they had been present at a very instructive discourse. Babouc said:

"This man had done his best to tire two or three hundred of his fellow-citizens; but his intention was good, and there is nothing in this that should occasion the destruction of Persepolis."

Upon leaving the assembly he was conducted to a public entertainment, which was exhibited every day in the year. It was in a kind of great hall, at the end of which appeared a palace. The most beautiful women of Persepolis and the most considerable satraps were ranged in order, and formed so fine a spectacle that Babouc at first believed that this was all the entertainment. Two or three persons, who seemed to be kings and queens, soon appeared in the vestibule of their palace. Their language was very different from that of their people; it was measured, harmonious, and sublime. Nobody slept. The audience kept a profound silence which was only interrupted by expressions of sensibility and admiration. The duty of kings, the love of virtue, and the dangers arising from unbridled passions, were all described by such lively and affecting strokes, that Babouc shed tears. He doubted not but that these heroes and heroines, these kings and queens whom he had just heard, were the preachers of the empire; he even purposed to engage Ithuriel to come and hear them, being confident that such a spectacle would forever reconcile him to the city.

As soon as the entertainment was finished, he resolved to visit the principal queen, who had recommended such pure and noble morals in the palace. He desired to be introduced to her majesty, and was led up a narrow staircase to an ill-furnished apartment in the second story, where he found a woman in a mean dress, who said to him with a noble and pathetic air:

"This employment does not afford me a sufficient maintenance. I want money, and without money there is no comfort."

Babouc gave her an hundred darics of gold, saying:

"Had there been no other evil in the city but this, Ithuriel would have been to blame for being so much offended."

From thence he went to spend the evening at the house of a tradesman who dealt in magnificent trifles. He was conducted thither by a man of sense, with whom he had contracted an acquaintance. He bought whatever pleased his fancy; and the toy man with great politeness sold him everything for more than it was worth. On his return home his friends showed him how much he had been cheated. Babouc set down the name of the tradesman in his pocketbook, in order to point him out to Ithuriel as an object of peculiar vengeance on the day when the city should be punished. As he was writing, he heard somebody knock at the door: this was the toy man himself, who came to restore him his purse, which he had left by mistake on the counter.

"How canst thou," cried Babouc, "be so generous and faithful, when thou hast had the assurance to sell me these trifles for four times their value?"

"There is not a tradesman," replied the merchant, "of ever so little note in the city, that would not have returned thee thy purse; but whoever said that I sold thee these trifles for four times their value is greatly mistaken: I sold them for ten times their value; and this is so true, that wert thou to sell them again in a month hence, thou wouldst not get even this tenth part. But nothing is more just. It is the variable fancies of men that set a value on these baubles; it is this fancy that maintains an hundred workmen whom I employ; it is this that gives me a fine house and a handsome chariot and horses; it is this, in fine, that excites industry, encourages taste, promotes circulation, and produces abundance.

"I sell the same trifles to the neighboring nation at a much higher rate than I have sold them to thee, and by these means I am useful to the empire."

Babouc, after having reflected a moment, erased the tradesman's name from his tablets.

Babouc, not knowing as yet what to think of Persepolis, resolved to visit the magi and the men of letters; for, as the one studied wisdom and the other religion, he hoped that they in conjunction would obtain mercy for the rest of the people. Accordingly, he went next morning into a college of magi. The archimandrite confessed to him, that he had an hundred thousand crowns a year for having taken the vow of poverty, and that he enjoyed a very extensive empire in virtue of his vow of humility; after which he left him with an inferior brother, who did him the honors of the place.

While the brother was showing him the magnificence of this house of penitence, a report was spread abroad that Babouc was come to reform all these houses. He immediately received petitions from each of them, the substance of which was, "Preserve us and destroy all the rest." On hearing their apologies, all these societies were absolutely necessary: on hearing their mutual accusations, they all deserved to be abolished. He was surprised to find that all the members of these societies were so extremely desirous of edifying the world, that they wished to have it entirely under their dominion.

Soon after a little man appeared, who was a demi-magi, and who said to him: "I plainly see that the work is going to be accomplished: for Zerdust is returned to earth; and the little girls prophesy, pinching and whipping themselves. We therefore implore thy protection against the great lama."

"What!" said Babouc, "against the royal pontiff, who resides at Tibet?"

"Yes, against him, himself."

"What! you are then making war upon him, and raising armies!"

"No, but he says that man is a free agent, and we deny it. We have written several pamphlets against him, which he never read. Hardly has he heard our name mentioned. He has only condemned us in the same manner as a man orders the trees in his garden to be cleared from caterpillars."

Babouc was incensed at the folly of these men who made profession of wisdom; and at the intrigues of those who had renounced the world; and at the ambition, pride and avarice of such as taught humility and a disinterested spirit: from all which he concluded that Ithuriel had good reason to destroy the whole race.

On his return home, he sent for some new books to alleviate his grief, and in order to exhilarate his spirits, invited some men of letters to dine with him; when, like wasps attracted by a pot of honey, there came twice as many as he desired. These parasites were equally eager to eat and to speak; they praised two sorts of persons, the dead and themselves; but none of their contemporaries, except the master of the house. If any of them happened to drop a smart and witty expression, the rest cast down their eyes and bit their lips out of mere vexation that it had not been said by themselves. They had less dissimulation than the magi, because they had not such grand objects of ambition. Each of them behaved at once with all the meanness of a valet and all the dignity of a great man. They said to each other's face the most insulting things, which they took for strokes of wit. They had some knowledge of the design of Babouc's commission; one of them entreated him in a low voice to extirpate an author who had not praised him sufficiently about five years before; another requested the ruin of a citizen who had never laughed at his comedies; and the third demanded the destruction of the academy because he had not been able to get admitted into it. The repast being ended, each of them departed by himself; for in the whole crowd there were not two men that could endure the company or conversation of each other, except at the houses of the rich, who invited them to their tables. Babouc thought that it would be no great loss to the public if all these vermin were destroyed in the general catastrophe.

Having now got rid of these men of letters, he began to read some new books, where he discovered the true spirit by which his guests had been actuated. He observed with particular indignation those slanderous gazettes, those archives of bad taste, dictated by envy, baseness, and hunger; those ungenerous satires, where the vulture is treated with lenity, and the dove torn in pieces; and those dry and insipid romances, filled with characters of women to whom the author was an utter stranger.

All these detestable writings he committed to the flames, and went to pass the evening in walking. In this excursion he was introduced to an old man possessed of great learning, who had not come to increase the number of his parasites. This man of letters always fled from crowds; he understood human nature, availed himself of his knowledge, and imparted it to others with great discretion. Babouc told him how much he was grieved at what he had seen and read.

"Thou hast read very despicable performances," said the man of letters; "but in all times, in all countries, and in all kinds of literature, the bad swarm and the good are rare. Thou hast received into thy house the very dregs of pedantry. In all professions, those who are least worthy of appearing are always sure to present themselves with the greatest impudence. The truly wise live among themselves in retirement and tranquillity; and we have still some men and some books worthy of thy attention."

While he was thus speaking, they were joined by another man of letters; and the conversation became so entertaining and instructive, so elevated above vulgar prejudices, and so conformable to virtue, that Babouc acknowledged he had never heard the like.

"These are men," said he to himself, "whom the angel Ithuriel will not presume to touch, or he must be a merciless being indeed."

Though reconciled to men of letters, he was still enraged against the rest of the nation.

"Thou art a stranger," said the judicious person who was talking to him; "abuses present themselves to thy eyes in crowds, while the good, which lies concealed, and which is even sometimes the result of these very abuses, escapes thy observation."

He then learned that among men of letters there were some who were free from envy; and that even among the magi themselves there were some men of virtue. In fine, he concluded that these great bodies, which by their mutual shocks seemed to threaten their common ruin, were at bottom very salutary institutions; that each society of magi was a check upon its rivals; and that though these rivals might differ in some speculative points, they all taught the same morals, instructed the people, and lived in subjection to the laws; not unlike to those preceptors who watch over the heir of a family while the master of the house watches over them. He conversed with several of these magi, and found them possessed of exalted souls. He likewise learned that even among the fools who pretended to make war on the great lama there had been some men of distinguished merit; and from all these particulars he conjectured that it might be with the manners of Persepolis as it was with the buildings; some of which moved his pity, while others filled him with admiration.

He said to the man of letters:

"I plainly see that these magi, whom I at first imagined to be so dangerous, are in reality extremely useful; especially when a wise government hinders them from rendering themselves too necessary; but thou wilt at least acknowledge that your young magistrates, who purchase the office of a judge as soon as they can mount a horse, must display in their tribunals the most ridiculous impertinence and the most iniquitous perverseness. It would doubtless be better to give these places gratuitously to those old civilians who have spent their lives in the study of the law."

The man of letters replied:

"Thou hast seen our army before thy arrival at Persepolis; thou knowest that our young officers fight with great bravery, though they buy their posts; perhaps thou wilt find that our young magistrates do not give wrong decisions, though they purchase the right of dispensing justice."

He led him next day to the grand tribunal, where an affair of great importance was to be decided. The cause was known to all the world. All the old advocates that spoke on the subject were wavering and unsettled in their opinions. They quoted an hundred laws, none of which were applicable to the question. They considered the matter in a hundred different lights, but never in its true point of view. The judges were more quick in their decisions than the advocates in raising doubts. They were unanimous in their sentiments. They decided justly, because they followed the light of reason. The others reasoned falsely because they only consulted their books.

Babouc concluded that the best things frequently arose from abuses. He saw the same day that the riches of the receivers of the public revenue, at which he had been so much offended, were capable of producing an excellent effect; for the emperor having occasion for money, he found in an hour by their means what he could not have procured in six months by the ordinary methods. He saw that those great clouds, swelled with the dews of the earth, restored in plentiful showers what they had thence derived. Besides, the children of these new gentlemen, who were frequently better educated than those of the most ancient families, were sometimes more useful members of society; for he whose father hath been a good accountant may easily become a good judge, a brave warrior, and an able statesman.

Babouc was insensibly brought to excuse the avarice of the farmer of the revenues, who in reality was not more avaricious than other men, and besides was extremely necessary. He overlooked the folly of those who ruined themselves in order to obtain a post in the law or army; a folly that produces great magistrates and heroes. He forgave the envy of men of letters, among whom there were some that enlightened the world; and he was reconciled to the ambitious and intriguing magi, who were possessed of more great virtues than little vices. But he had still many causes of complaint. The gallantries of the ladies especially, and the fatal effects which these must necessarily produce, filled him with fear and terror.

As he was desirous of prying into the characters of men of every condition, he went to wait on a minister of state; but trembled all the way, lest some wife should be assassinated by her husband in his presence. Having arrived at the statesman's, he was obliged to remain two hours in the ante-chamber before his name was sent in, and two hours more after that was done. In this interval, he resolved to recommend to the angel Ithuriel both the minister and his insolent porters. The ante-chamber was filled with ladies of every rank, magi of all colors, judges, merchants, officers, and pedants; and all of them complained of the minister. The miser and the usurer said:

"Doubtless this man plunders the provinces."

The capricious reproached him with fickleness; the voluptuary said:

"He thinks of nothing but his pleasure."

The factious hoped to see him soon ruined by a cabal; and the women flattered themselves that they should soon have a younger minister.

Babouc heard their conversation, and could not help saying:

"This is surely a happy man; he hath all his enemies in his ante-chamber; he crushes with his power those that envy his grandeur; he beholds those who detest him groveling at his feet."

At length he was admitted into the presence-chamber, where he saw a little old man bending under the weight of years and business, but still lively and full of spirits.

The minister was pleased with Babouc, and to Babouc he appeared a man of great merit. The conversation became interesting. The minister confessed that he was very unhappy; that he passed for rich, while in reality he was poor; that he was believed to be all-powerful, and yet was constantly contradicted; that he had obliged none but a parcel of ungrateful wretches; and that, in the course of forty years labor, he had hardly enjoyed a moment's rest. Babouc was moved with his misfortunes; and thought that if this man had been guilty of some faults, and Ithuriel had a mind to banish him, he ought not to cut him off, but to leave him in possession of his place.

While Babouc was talking to the minister, the beautiful lady with whom he had dined entered hastily, her eyes and countenance showing all the symptoms of grief and indignation. She burst into reproaches against the statesman; she shed tears; she complained bitterly that her husband had been refused a place to which his birth allowed him to aspire, and which he had fully merited by his wounds and his service. She expressed herself with such force; she uttered her complaints with such a graceful air; she overthrew objections with so much address, and enforced her arguments with so much eloquence, that she did not leave the chamber till she had made her husband's fortune.

Babouc gave her his hand, and said: "Is it possible, madam, that thou canst take so much pains to serve a man whom thou dost not love, and from whom thou hast everything to fear?"

"A man whom I do not love!" cried she; "know, sir, that my husband is the best friend I have in the world; and there is nothing I would not sacrifice for him, except my own inclinations."

The lady conducted Babouc to her own house. The husband, who had at last arrived overwhelmed with grief, received his wife with transports of joy and gratitude. He embraced by turns his wife, the little magi, and Babouc. Wit, harmony, cheerfulness, and all the graces, embellished the repast.

Babouc, though a Scythian, and sent by a geni, found that should he continue much longer in Persepolis, he would forget even the angel Ithuriel. He began to grow fond of a city, the inhabitants of which were polite, affable, and beneficent, though fickle, slanderous, and vain. He was much afraid that Persepolis would be condemned. He was even afraid to give in his account.

This, however, he did in the following manner. He caused a little statue, composed of different metals, of earth, and stones, the most precious and the most vile, to be cast by one of the best founders in the city, and carried it to Ithuriel.

"Wilt thou break," said he, "this pretty statue, because it is not wholly composed of gold and diamonds?"

Ithuriel immediately understood his meaning, and resolved to think no more of punishing Persepolis, but to leave "The world as it goes."

"For," said he, "if all is not well, all is passable."

Thus Persepolis was suffered to remain; nor did Babouc complain like Jonas, who, [according to the scriptures], was highly incensed at the preservation of Nineveh.

THE BLACK AND THE WHITE

THE adventure of the youthful Rustan is generally known throughout the whole province of Candahar. He was the only son of a Mirza of that country. The title of Mirza there is much the same as that of Marquis among us, or that of Baron among the Germans. The mirza, his father, had a handsome fortune. Young Rustan was to be married to a mirzasse, or young lady of his own rank. The two families earnestly desired their union. Rustan was to become the comfort of his parents, to make his wife happy, and to live blest in her possession.

But he had unfortunately seen the princess of Cachemire at the fair of Kaboul, which is the most considerable fair in the world, and much more frequented than those of Bassora and Astracan. The occasion that brought the old prince of Cachemire to the fair with his daughter was as follows:

He had lost the two most precious curiosities of his treasury, one of them was a diamond as thick as a man's thumb, upon which the figure of his daughter was engraved by an art which was then possessed by the Indians, and has since been lost; the other was a javelin, which went of itself wherever its owner thought proper to send it. This is nothing very extraordinary among us, but it was thought so at Cachemire.

A fakir belonging to his highness stole these two curiosities; he carried them to the princess:

"Keep these two curiosities with the utmost care; your destiny depends upon them;" said he, and then departed.

The Duke of Cachemire, in despair, resolved to visit the fair of Kaboul, in order to see whether there might not, among the merchants who go thither from all quarters of the world, be some one possessed of his diamond and his weapon. The princess carried his diamond well fastened to her girdle; but the javelin, which she could not so easily hide, she had carefully locked up at Cachemire, in a large chest.

Rustan and she saw each other at Kaboul. They loved one another with all the sincerity of persons of their age, and all the tenderness of affection natural to those of their country. The princess gave Rustan her diamond as a pledge of her love, and he promised at his departure to go incognito to Cachemire, in order to pay her a visit.

The young mirza had two favorites, who served him as secretaries, grooms, stewards, and valets de chambre. The name of one was Topaz; he was handsome, well-shaped, fair as a Circassian beauty, as mild and ready to serve as an Armenian, and as wise as a Gueber. The name of the other was Ebene; he was a very beautiful negro, more active and industrious than Topaz, and one that thought nothing difficult. The young mirza communicated his intention of traveling to these. Topaz endeavored to dissuade him from it, with the circumspect zeal of a servant who was unwilling to offend him. He represented to him the great danger to which he exposed himself. He asked him how he could leave two families in despair? how he could pierce the hearts of his parents? He shook the resolution of Rustan; but Ebene confirmed it anew, and obviated all his objections.

The young man was not furnished with money to defray the charge of so long a voyage. The prudent Topaz would not have lent him any; Ebene supplied him. He with great address stole his master's diamond, made a false one exactly like it which he put in its place, and pledged the true one to an Armenian for several thousand rupees.

As soon as the marquis possessed these rupees, all things were in readiness for his departure. An elephant was loaded with his baggage. His attendants mounted on horseback.

Topaz said to his master: "I have taken the liberty to expostulate with you upon your enterprise, but after expostulating it is my duty to obey. I am devoted to you, I love you, I will follow you to the extremity of the earth; but let us by the way consult the oracle that is but two parasongs distant from here."

Rustan consented. The answer returned by the oracle, was:

"If you go to the east you will be at the west."

Rustan could not guess the meaning of this answer. Topaz maintained that it boded no good. Ebene, always complaisant to his master, persuaded him that it was highly favorable.

There was another oracle at Kaboul; they went to it. The oracle of Kaboul made answer in these words:

"If you possess, you will cease to possess; if you are conqueror, you will not conquer; if you are Rustan, you will cease to be so."

This oracle seemed still more unintelligible than the former.

"Take care of yourself," said Topaz.

"Fear nothing," said Ebene; and this minister, as may well be imagined, was always thought in the right by his master, whose passions and hopes he encouraged. Having left Kaboul, they passed through a vast forest. They seated themselves upon the grass in order to take a repast, and left their horses grazing. The attendants were preparing to unload the elephant which carried the dinner, the table, cloth, plates, &c., when, all on a sudden, Topaz and Ebene were perceived by the little caravan to be missing. They were called, the forest resounded with the names of Topaz and Ebene; the lackeys seek them on every side, and fill the forest with their cries; they return without having seen anything, and without having received any answer.

"We have," said they to Rustan, "found nothing but a vulture that fought with an eagle, and stripped it of all its feathers."

The mention of this combat excited the curiosity of Rustan; he went on foot to the place; he perceived neither vulture nor eagle; but he saw his elephant, which was still loaded with baggage, attacked by a huge rhinoceros: one struck with his horn, the other with its proboscis. The rhinoceros desisted upon seeing Rustan; his elephant was brought back, but his horses were not to be found.

"Strange things happen in forests to travelers," cried Rustan.

The servants were in great consternation, and the master in despair from having at once lost his horse, his dear negro, and the wise Topaz, for whom he still entertained a friendship, though always differing from him in opinion.

The hope of being soon at the feet of the beautiful princess still consoled the mirza, who, journeying on, now met with a huge streaked ass, which a vigorous two-handed country clown beat with an oaken cudgel. The asses of this sort are extremely beautiful, very scarce, and beyond comparison swift in running. The ass resented the repeated blows of the clown by kicks which might have rooted up an oak. The young mirza, as was reasonable, took upon him the defence of the ass, which was a charming creature. The clown betook himself to flight, crying to the ass, "You shall pay for this."

The ass thanked her deliverer in her own language, and approaching him, permitted his caresses and caressed him in her turn. After dinner, Rustan mounted her, and took the road to Cachemire with his servants, who followed him, some on foot and some upon the elephant. Scarce had he mounted his ass, when that animal turned toward Kaboul, instead of proceeding to Cachemire. It was to no purpose for her master to turn the bridle, to kick, to press the sides of the beast with his knees, to spur, to slacken the bridle, to pull toward him, to whip both on the right and the left. The obstinate animal persisted in running toward Kaboul.

Rustan in despair fretted and raved, when he met with a dealer in camels, who said to him:

"Master, you have there a very malicious beast, that carries you where you do not choose to go. If you will give it to me, I will give you the choice of four of my camels."

Rustan thanked providence for having thrown so good a bargain in the way.

"Topaz was very much in the wrong," said he, "to tell me that my journey would prove unprosperous."

He mounts the handsome camel, the others follow; he rejoins his caravan and fancies himself on the road to happiness.

Scarce had he journeyed four parasongs, when he was stopped by a deep, broad, and impetuous torrent, which rolled over huge rocks white with foam. The two banks were frightful precipices which dazzled the sight and made the blood run cold. To pass was impracticable; to go to the right or to the left was impossible.

"I am beginning to be afraid," said Rustan, "that Topaz was in the right in blaming my journey, and that I was in the wrong in undertaking it. If he were still here he might give me good advice. If I had Ebene with me, he would comfort me and find expedients; but everything fails me." This perplexity was increased by the consternation of his attendants. The night was dark, and they passed it in lamentations. At last fatigue and dejection made the amorous traveler fall asleep. He awoke at day-break, and saw, spanning the torrent, a beautiful marble bridge which reached from shore to shore.

Nothing was heard but exclamations, cries of astonishment and joy. Is it possible? Is this a dream? What a prodigy is this! What an enchantment! Shall we venture to pass? The whole company kneeled, rose up, went to the bridge, kissed the ground, looked up to heaven, stretched out their hands, set their feet on it with trembling, went to and fro, fell into ecstasies; and Rustan said:

"At last heaven favors me. Topaz did not know what he was saying. The oracles were favorable to me. Ebene was in the right, but why is he not here?"

Scarce had the company got beyond the torrent, when the bridge sank into the water with a prodigious noise.

"So much the better, so much the better," cried Rustan. "Praised be God, blessed be heaven; it would not have me return to my country, where I should be nothing more than a gentleman. The intention of heaven is, that I should wed her I love. I shall become prince of Cachemire; thus in possessing my mistress I shall cease to possess my little marquisate at Candahar. 'I shall be Rustan, and I shall not be Rustan,' because I shall have become a great prince: thus is a great part of the oracle clearly explained in my favor. The rest will be explained in the same manner. I am very happy. But why is not Ebene with me? I regret him a thousand times more than Topaz."

He proceeded a few parasongs farther with the greatest alacrity imaginable; but, at the close of day, a chain of mountains more rugged than a counterscarp, and higher than the tower of Babel would have been had it been finished, stopped the passage of the caravan, which was again seized with dread.

All the company cried out: "It is the will of God that we perish here! he broke the bridge merely to take from us all hopes of returning; he raised the mountain for no other reason than to deprive us of all means of advancing. Oh, Rustan! oh, unhappy marquis! we shall never see Cachemire; we shall never return to the land of Candahar."

The most poignant anguish, the most insupportable dejection, succeeded in the soul of Rustan, to the immoderate joy which he had felt, to the hopes with which he had intoxicated himself. He was no longer disposed to interpret the prophecies in his favor.

"Oh, heavens! oh, God of my fathers!" said he, "must I then lose my friend Topaz!"

As he pronounced these words, fetching deep sighs and shedding tears in the midst of his disconsolate followers, the base of the mountain opened, a long gallery appeared to the dazzled eyes in a vault lighted with a hundred thousand torches. Rustan immediately begins to exult, and his people to throw themselves upon their knees and to fall upon their backs in astonishment, and cry out, "A miracle! a miracle! Rustan is the favorite of Witsnow, the well-beloved of Brahma. He will become the master of mankind."

Rustan believed it; he was quite beside himself; he was raised above himself.

"Alas, Ebene," said he, "my dear Ebene, where are you? Why are you not witness of all these wonders? How did I lose you? Beauteous princess of Cachemire, when shall I again behold your charms!"

He advances with his attendants, his elephants, and his camels, under the hollow of the mountain; at the end of which he enters into a meadow enameled with flowers and encompassed with rivulets. At the extremity of the meadows are walks of trees to the end of which the eye cannot reach, and at the end

of these alleys is a river, on the sides of which are a thousand pleasure houses
with delicious gardens. He everywhere hears concerts of vocal and instru-
mental music; he sees dances; he makes haste to go upon one of the bridges
of the river; he asks the first man he meets what fine country that is?

He whom he addressed himself to answered:

"You are in the province of Cachemire; you see the inhabitants immersed in
joy and pleasure. We celebrate the marriage of our beauteous princess, who is
going to be married to the lord Barbabou, to whom her father promised her.
May God perpetuate their felicity!"

At these words Rustan fainted away, and the Cachemirian lord thought he
was troubled with the falling sickness. He caused him to be carried to his house,
where he remained a long time insensible. He sent in search of the two most
able physicians in that part of the country. They felt the patient's pulse, who
having somewhat recovered his spirits, sobbed, rolled his eyes, and cried from
time to time, "Topaz, Topaz, you were entirely in the right!"

One of the two physicians said to the Cachemirian lord:

"I perceive, by this young man's accent, that he is from Candahar, and that
the air of this country is hurtful to him. He must be sent home. I perceive by
his eyes that he has lost his senses. Entrust me with him, I will carry him
back to his own country, and cure him."

The other physician maintained that grief was his only disorder; and that
it was proper to carry him to the wedding of the princess, and make him
dance. Whilst they were in consultation, the patient recovered his health. The
two physicians were dismissed, and Rustan remained along with his host.

"My lord," said he, "I ask your pardon for having been so free as to faint
in your presence. I know it to be a breach of politeness. I entreat you to accept
of my elephant, as an acknowledgment of the kindness you have shown me."

He then related to him all his adventure, taking particular care to conceal
from him the occasion of his journey.

"But, in the name of Witsnow and Brahma," said he to him, "tell me who is
this happy Barbabou, who is to marry the princess of Cachemire? Why has her
father chosen him for his son-in-law, and why has the princess accepted of
him for an husband?"

"Sir," answered the Cachemirian, "the princess has by no means accepted
of Barbadou. She is, on the contrary, in tears, whilst the whole province joyfully celebrates her marriage. She has shut herself up in the tower of her palace.
She does not choose to see any of the rejoicings made upon the occasion."

Rustan, at hearing this, perceived himself revived. The bloom of his complexion, which grief had caused to fade, appeared again upon his countenance.

"Tell me, I entreat you," continued he, "why the prince of Cachemire is
obstinately bent upon giving his daughter to lord Barbabou whom she does
not love?"

"This is the fact," answered the Cachemirian. "Do you know that our august
prince lost a large diamond and a javelin which he considered as of great
value?"

"Ah! I very well know that," said Rustan.

"Know then," said his host, "that our prince, being in despair at not having heard of his two precious curiosities after having caused them to be sought for all over the world, promised his daughter to whoever should bring him either the one or the other. A lord Barbabou came who had the diamond, and he is to marry the princess to-morrow."

Rustan turned pale, stammered out a compliment, took leave of his host, and galloped upon his dromedary to the capital city, where the ceremony was to be performed. He arrives at the palace of the prince, he tells him he has something of importance to communicate to him, he demands an audience. He is told that the prince is taken up with the preparations for the wedding.

"It is for that very reason," said he, "that I am desirous of speaking to him." Such is his importunity, that he is at last admitted.

"Prince," said he, "may God crown all your days with glory and magnificence! Your son-in-law is a knave."

"What! a knave! how dare you speak in such terms? Is that a proper way of speaking to a duke of Cachemire of a son-in-law of whom he has made choice?"

"Yes, he is a knave," continued Rustan; "and to prove it to your highness, I have brought you back your diamond."

The duke, surprised at what he heard, compared the two diamonds; and as he was no judge of precious stones, he could not determine which was the true one.

"Here are two diamonds," said he, "and I have but one daughter. I am in a strange perplexity."

He sent for Barbabou, and asked him if he had not imposed upon him. Barbabou swore he had bought his diamond from an Armenian: the other did not tell him who he had his from; but he proposed an expedient, which was that he should engage his rival in single combat.

"It is not enough for your son-in-law to give a diamond," said he, "he should also give proofs of valor. Do not you think it just that he who kills his rival should marry the princess?"

"Undoubtedly," answered the prince. "It will be a fine sight for the court. Fight directly. The conqueror shall take the arms of the conquered according to the customs of Cachemire, and he shall marry my daughter."

The two pretenders to the hand of the princess go down into the court. Upon the stairs there was a jay and a raven. The raven cried, "Fight, fight." The jay cried, "Don't fight."

This made the prince laugh; the two rivals scarce took any notice of it. They begin the combat. All the courtiers made a circle round them. The princess, who kept to herself constantly shut up in her tower, did not choose to behold this sight. She never dreamt that her lover was at Cachemire, and she hated Barbabou to such a degree, that she could not bear the sight of him. The combat had the happiest result imaginable. Barbabou was killed outright; and this greatly rejoiced the people, because he was ugly and Rustan was very handsome. The favor of the public is almost always determined by this circumstance.

The conqueror put on the coat of mail, scarf, and the casque of the conquered, and came, followed by the whole court, to present himself under the windows of his mistress. The multitude cried aloud: "Beautiful princess, come and see your handsome lover, who has killed his ugly rival." These words were re-echoed by her women. The princess unluckily looked out of the window, and seeing the armor of a man she hated, she ran like one frantic to her strong box, and took out the fatal javelin, which flew to pierce Rustan, notwithstanding his cuirass. He cried out loudly, and at this cry the princess thought she again knew the voice of her unhappy lover.

She ran down stairs, with her hair disheveled, and death in her eyes as well as her heart. Rustan had already fallen, all bloody, into the arms of his attendants. She sees him. Oh, moment! oh, sight! oh, discovery of inexpressible grief, tenderness and horror! She throws herself upon him, and embraces him.

"You receive," said she, "the first and last kisses of your mistress and your murderer."

She pulls the dart from the wound, plunges it in her heart, and dies upon the body of the lover whom she adores. The father, terrified, in despair, and ready to die like his daughter, tries in vain to bring her to life. She was no more. He curses the fatal dart, breaks it to pieces, throws away the two fatal diamonds; and whilst he prepared the funeral of his daughter instead of her marriage, he caused Rustan, who weltered in his blood and had still some remains of life, to be carried to his palace.

He was put into bed. The first objects he saw on each side of his deathbed were Topaz and Ebene. This surprise made him in some degree recover his strength.

"Cruel men," said he, "why did you abandon me? Perhaps the princess would still be alive if you had been with the unhappy Rustan."

"I have not forsaken you a moment," said Topaz.

"I have always been with you," said Ebene.

"Ah! what do you say? why do you insult me in my last moments?" answered Rustan, with a languishing voice.

"You may believe me," said Topaz. "You know I never approved of this fatal journey, the dreadful consequences of which I foresaw. I was the eagle that fought with the vulture and stripped it of its feathers; I was the elephant that carried away the baggage, in order to force you to return to your own country; I was the streaked ass that carried you, whether you would or no, to your father; it was I that made your horses go astray; it was I that caused the torrent that prevented your passage; it was I that raised the mountain which stopped up a road so fatal to you; I was the physician that advised you to return to your own country; I was the jay that cried to you not to fight."

"And I," said Ebene, "was the vulture that he stripped of his feathers, the rhinoceros who gave him a hundred strokes with the horn, the clown that beat the streaked ass, the merchant who made you a present of camels to hasten you to your destruction; I dug the cavern that you crossed, I am the physician that encouraged you to walk, the raven that cried out to you to combat."

"Alas!" said Topaz, "remember the oracles: 'If you go to the east you will be at the west.'"

"Yes," said Ebene, "here the dead are buried with their faces turned to the west. The oracle was plain enough, though you did not understand it. You possessed, and you did not possess; for though you had the diamond, it was a false one, and you did not know it. You are conqueror, and you die; you are Rustan, and you cease to be so: all has been accomplished."

Whilst he spoke thus, four white wings covered the body of Topaz, and four black ones that of Ebene.

"What do I see?" cried Rustan.

Topaz and Ebene answered together: "You see your two geniuses."

"Good gentlemen," cried the unhappy Rustan, "how came you to meddle; and what occasion had a poor man for two geniuses?"

"It is a law," answered Topaz; "every man has two geniuses. Plato was the first man who said so, and others have repeated it after him. You see that nothing can be more true. I who now speak to you, am your good genius. I was charged to watch over you to the last moment of your life. Of this task I have faithfully acquitted myself."

"But," said the dying man, "if your business was to serve me, I am of a nature much superior to yours. And then how can you have the assurance to say you are my good genius, since you have suffered me to be deceived in everything I have undertaken, and since you suffer both my mistress and me to die miserably?"

"Alas!" said Topaz, "it was your destiny."

"If destiny does all," answered the dying man, "what is a genius good for? And you, Ebene, with your four black wings, you are, doubtless, my evil genius."

"You have hit it," answered Ebene.

"Then I suppose you were the evil genius of my princess likewise," said Rustan.

"No," replied Ebene, "she had an evil genius of her own, and I seconded him perfectly."

"Ah! cursed Ebene," said Rustan, "if you are so malicious, you don't belong to the same master with Topaz: you have been formed by two different principles, one of which is by nature good, the other evil."

"That does not follow," said Ebene, "this is a very knotty point."

"It is not possible," answered the dying man, "that a benevolent being could create so destructive a genius."

"Possible or not possible," replied the genius, "the thing is just as I say."

"Alas!" said Topaz, "my poor unfortunate friend, don't you see that that rogue is so malicious as to encourage you to dispute, in order to inflame your blood and hasten your death?"

"Get you gone," said the melancholy Rustan, "I am not much better satisfied with you than with him. He at least acknowledges that it was his intention to hurt me; and you, who pretended to defend me, have done me no service at all."

"I am very sorry for it," said the good genius.

"And I too," said the dying man; "there is something at the bottom of all this which I cannot comprehend."

"Nor I neither," said the good genius.

"I shall know the truth of the matter in a moment," said Rustan. "We shall see that," said Topaz.

The whole scene then vanished. Rustan again found himself in the house of his father, which he had not quitted, and in his bed, where he had slept an hour.

He awakes in astonishment, perspiring all over, and quite wild. He rubs himself, he calls, he rings the bell. His valet de chambre, Topaz, runs in, in his nightcap, and yawning.

"Am I dead or alive?" cried out Rustan, "shall the beauteous princess of Cachemire escape?"

"Does your lordship rave?" answered Topaz, coldly.

"Ah!" cried Rustan, "what then is become of this barbarous Ebene, with his four black wings! It is he that makes me die by so cruel a death."

"My lord," answered Topaz, "I left him snoring up stairs. Would you have me bid him come down?"

"The villain," said Rustan, "has persecuted me for six months together. It was he who carried me to the fatal fair of Kaboul; it is he that cheated me of the diamond which the princess presented me; he is the sole cause of my journey, of the death of my princess, and of the wound with a javelin, of which I die in the flower of my age."

"Take heart," said Topaz, "you were never at Kaboul; there is no princess of Cachemire; her father never had any children but two boys, who are now at college; you never had a diamond; the princess cannot be dead, because she never was born; and you are in perfect health."

"What! is it not then true that you attended me whilst dying, and in the bed of the prince of Cachemire? Did you not acknowledge to me, that, in order to preserve me from so many dangers, you were an eagle, an elephant, a streaked ass, a physician, and a jay?"

"My lord, you have dreamt all this," answered Topaz; "our ideas are no more of our own creating whilst we are asleep than whilst we are awake. God has thought proper that this train of ideas should pass in your head, most probably to convey some instruction to you, of which you may make a good use."

"You make a jest of me," replied Rustan, "how long have I slept?"

"My lord," said Topaz, "you have not yet slept an hour."

"Cursed reasoner," returned Rustan, "how is it possible that I could be in the space of an hour at the fair of Kaboul six months ago; that I could have returned from thence, have traveled to Cachemire, and that Barbabou, the princess, and I, should have died?"

"My lord," said Topaz, "nothing can be more easy and more common; and you might have traveled around the world, and have met with a great many more adventures in much less time. Is it not true that you can, in an hour's time, read the abridgment of the Persian history, written by Zoroaster? yet this abridgment contains eight hundred thousand years. All these events pass before your eyes one after another, in an hour's time. Now you must acknowledge, that it is as easy to Brahma to confine them to the space of an hour, as to extend them to the space of eight hundred thousand years. It is exactly the same thing. Imagine to yourself that time turns upon a wheel whose diameter is infinite. Under this vast wheel is a numerous multitude of wheels one within another. That in the centre is imperceptible, and goes round an infinite number of times, whilst the great wheel performs but one revolution. It is evident that all the events which have happened from the beginning of the world, to its end, might have happened in much less time than the hundred thousandth part of a second; and one may even go so far as to assert that the thing is so."

"I cannot comprehend all this," said Rustan.

"If you want information," said Topaz, "I have a parrot that will easily explain it to you. He was born some time before the deluge; he has been in the ark; he has seen a great deal; yet he is but a year and a half old. He will relate to you his history, which is extremely interesting."

"Go fetch your parrot," said Rustan, "it will amuse me till I again find myself disposed to sleep."

"It is with my sister," said Topaz: "I will go and fetch it. It will please you; its memory is faithful; it relates in a simple manner, without endeavoring to show wit at every turn."

"So much the better," said Rustan, "I like that manner of telling stories."

The parrot being brought to him, spoke in this manner:

N. B. Mademoiselle Catherine Vade could never find the history of the parrot in the commonplace-book of her late cousin Anthony Vade, author of that tale. This is a great misfortune, considering what age that parrot lived in.

MEMNON, THE PHILOSOPHER

MEMNON one day took it into his head to become a great philosopher. "To be perfectly happy," said he to himself, "I have nothing to do but to divest myself entirely of passions; and nothing is more easy, as everybody knows. In the first place, I will never be in love; for, when I see a beautiful woman, I will say to myself,—these cheeks will one day grow sallow and wrinkled, these eyes be encircled with vermilion, that bosom become lean and emaciated, that head bald and palsied. Now I have only to consider her at present in imagination as she will afterwards appear in reality, and certainly a fair face will never turn my head.

"In the second place, I shall always be temperate. It will be in vain to tempt me with good cheer, with delicious wines, or the charms of society. I will have only to figure to myself the consequences of excess—an aching head, a loathing stomach, the loss of reason, of health, and of time: I will then only eat to supply the waste of nature; my health will be always equal, my ideas pure and luminous. All this is so easy that there is no merit in accomplishing it.

"But," says Memnon, "I must think a little of how I am to regulate my fortune: why, my desires are moderate, my wealth is securely placed with the Receiver General of the finances of Nineveh. I have wherewithal to live independent; and that is the greatest of blessings. I shall never be under the cruel necessity of dancing attendance at court. I will never envy any one, and nobody will envy me. Still all this is easy. I have friends, and I will preserve them, for we shall never have any difference. I will never take amiss anything they may say or do; and they will behave in the same way to me. There is no difficulty in all this."

Having thus laid this little plan of philosophy in his closet, Memnon put his head out of the window. He saw two women walking under the plane-trees near his house. The one was old, and appeared quite at her ease. The other was young, handsome, and seemingly much agitated. She sighed, she wept, and seemed on that account still more beautiful. Our philosopher was touched, not, to be sure, with the lady (he was too much determined not to feel any uneasiness of that kind), but with the distress which he saw her in. He came down stairs, and accosted the young Ninevite, designing to console her with philosophy. That lovely person related to him, with an air of the greatest simplicity, and in the most affecting manner, the injuries she sustained from an imaginary uncle—with what art he had deprived her of some imaginary property, and of the violence which she pretended to dread from him.

"You appear to me," said she, "a man of such wisdom, that if you will come to my house and examine into my affairs, I am persuaded you will be able to relieve me from the cruel embarrassment I am at present involved in."

Memnon did not hesitate to follow her, to examine her affairs philosophically, and to give her sound counsel.

The afflicted lady led him into a perfumed chamber, and politely made him sit down with her on a large sofa, where they both placed themselves opposite to each other, in the attitude of conversation; the one eager in telling her story, the other listening with devout attention. The lady spoke with downcast eyes, whence there sometimes fell a tear, and which, as she now and then ventured to raise them, always met those of the sage Memnon. Their discourse was full of tenderness, which redoubled as often as their eyes met. Memnon took her affairs exceedingly to heart, and felt himself every instant more and more inclined to oblige a person so virtuous and so unhappy. By degrees, in the warmth of conversation they drew nearer. Memnon counseled her with great wisdom, and gave her most tender advice.

At this interesting moment, as may easily be imagined, who should come in but the uncle. He was armed from head to foot, and the first thing he said was, that he would immediately sacrifice, as was just, both Memnon and his niece. The latter, who made her escape, knew that he was disposed to pardon, provided a good round sum were offered to him. Memnon was obliged to purchase his safety with all he had about him. In those days people were happy in getting so easily quit. America was not then discovered, and distressed ladies were not then so dangerous as they are now.

Memnon, covered with shame and confusion, got home to his own house. He there found a card inviting him to dinner with some of his intimate friends.

"If I remain at home alone," said he, "I shall have my mind so occupied with this vexatious adventure, that I shall not be able to eat a bit, and I shall bring upon myself some disease. It will therefore be prudent in me to go to my intimate friends and partake with them of a frugal repast. I shall forget, in the sweets of their society, the folly I have this morning been guilty of."

Accordingly he attends the meeting; he is discovered to be uneasy at something, and he is urged to drink and banish care.

"A little wine, drank in moderation, comforts the heart of God and man:" so reasoned Memnon the philosopher, and he became intoxicated. After the repast, play is proposed.

"A little play, with one's intimate friends, is a harmless pastime." He plays and loses all in his purse, and four times as much on his word. A dispute arises on some circumstance in the game, and the disputants grow warm. One of his intimate friends throws a dice-box at his head, and strikes out one of his eyes. The philosopher Memnon is carried home drunk and penniless, with the loss of an eye.

He sleeps out his debauch, and, when his head becomes clear, he sends his servant to the Receiver General of the finances of Nineveh, to draw a little money to pay his debt of honor to his intimate friends. The servant returns and informs him, that the Receiver General had that morning been declared a fraudulent bankrupt, and that by this means an hundred families are reduced to poverty and despair. Memnon, almost beside himself, puts a plaster on his eye and a petition in his pocket, and goes to court to solicit justice from the king against the bankrupt. In the saloon he meets a number of ladies, all in the highest spirits, and sailing along with hoops four-and-twenty feet in circumference. One of them, slightly acquainted with him, eyed him askance, and cried aloud: "Ah! what a horrid monster!"

Another, who was better acquainted with him, thus accosts him: "Good-morrow, Mr. Memnon, I hope you are well, Mr. Memnon. La! Mr. Memnon, how did you lose your eye?" and turning upon her heel, she tripped uncon-cernedly away.

Memnon hid himself in a corner, and waited for the moment when he could throw himself at the feet of the monarch. That moment at last arrived. Three times he kissed the earth, and presented his petition. His gracious majesty received him very favorably, and referred the paper to one of his satraps. The satrap takes Memnon aside, and says to him with a haughty air and satirical grin:

"Hark ye, you fellow with the one eye, you must be a comical dog indeed, to address yourself to the king rather than to me: and still more so, to dare to demand justice against an honest bankrupt, whom I honor with my protec-tion, and who is also a nephew to the waiting-maid of my mistress. Proceed no further in this business, my good friend, if you wish to preserve the eye you have left."

Memnon having thus, in his closet, resolved to renounce women, the excess of the table, play, and quarreling, but especially having determined never to go to court, had been in the short space of four-and-twenty hours duped and robbed by a gentle dame, had got drunk, had gamed, had been engaged in a quarrel, had got his eye knocked out, and had been at court, where he was sneered at and insulted.

Petrified with astonishment, and his heart broken with grief, Memnon returns homeward in despair. As he was about to enter his house, he is repulsed by a number of officers who are carrying off his furniture for the benefit of his creditors. He falls down almost lifeless under a plane-tree. There he finds the fair dame of the morning, who was walking with her dear uncle; and both set up a loud laugh on seeing Memnon with his plaster. The night approached, and Memnon made his bed on some straw near the walls of his house. Here the ague seized him, and he fell asleep in one of the fits, when a celestial spirit appeared to him in a dream.

It was all resplendent with light: it had six beautiful wings, but neither feet, nor head, and could be likened to nothing.

"What art thou?" said Memnon.

"Thy good genius," replied the spirit.

"Restore me then my eye, my health, my fortune, my reason," said Memnon, and he related how he had lost them all in one day. "These are adventures which never happen to us in the world we inhabit," said the spirit.

"And what world do you inhabit?" said the man of affliction.

"My native country," replied the other, "is five hundred millions of leagues distant from the sun, in a little star near Sirius, which you see from hence."

"Charming country!" said Memnon. "And are there indeed with you no jades to dupe a poor devil, no intimate friends that win his money and knock out an eye for him, no fraudulent bankrupts, no satraps, that make a jest of you while they refuse you justice?"

"No," said the inhabitant of the star, "we have nothing of the kind. We are never duped by women, because we have none among us; we never commit excesses at table, because we neither eat nor drink; we have no bankrupts, because with us there is neither silver nor gold; our eyes cannot be knocked out, because we have not bodies in the form of yours; and satraps never do us injustice, because in our world we are all equal."

"Pray my lord," said Memnon, "without women and without eating how do you spend your time?"

"In watching over the other worlds that are entrusted to us; and I am now come to give you consolation."

"Alas!" said Memnon, "why did you not come yesterday to hinder me from committing so many indiscretions?"

"I was with your elder brother Hassan," said the celestial being. "He is still more to be pitied than you are. His most gracious majesty, the sultan of the Indies, in whose court he has the honor to serve, has caused both his eyes to be put out for some small indiscretion; and he is now in a dungeon, his hands and feet loaded with chains."

" 'Tis a happy thing, truly," said Memnon, "to have a good genius in one's family, when out of two brothers one is blind of an eye, the other blind of both; one stretched upon straw, the other in a dungeon."

"Your fate will soon change," said the spirit of the star. "It is true you will never recover your eye; but, except that, you may be sufficiently happy if you never again take it into your head to be a perfect philosopher."

"Is it then impossible?" said Memnon.

"As impossible as to be perfectly wise, perfectly strong, perfectly powerful, perfectly happy. We ourselves are very far from it. There is a world indeed where all this takes place; but, in the hundred thousand millions of worlds dispersed over the regions of space, everything goes on by degrees. There is less philosophy and less enjoyment in the second than in the first, less in the third than in the second, and so forth till the last in the scale, where all are completely fools."

"I am afraid," said Memnon, "that our little terraqueous globe here is the madhouse of those hundred thousand millions of worlds, of which your lordship does me the honor to speak."

"Not quite," said the spirit, "but very nearly; everything must be in its proper place."

"But are those poets and philosophers wrong, then, who tell us that everything is for the best?"

"No, they are right, when we consider things in relation to the gradation of the whole universe."

"Oh! I shall never believe it till I recover my eye again," said the unfortunate Memnon.

ANDRE DES TOUCHES AT SIAM

ANDRE DES TOUCHES was a very agreeable musician in the brilliant reign of Louis XIV. before the science of music was perfected by Rameau; and before it was corrupted by those who prefer the art of surmounting difficulties to nature and the real graces of composition.

Before he had recourse to these talents he had been a musketeer, and before that, in 1688, he went into Siam with the cleric Tachard, who gave him many marks of his affection, for the amusement he afforded on board the ship; and Des Touches spoke with admiration of Tachard for the rest of his life.

At Siam he became acquainted with the first commissary of Barcalon, whose name was Croutef; and he committed to writing most of those questions which he asked of Croutef, and the answers of that Siamese. They are as follows:

DES TOUCHES.—How many soldiers have you?

CROUTEF.—Fourscore thousand, very indifferently paid.

DES TOUCHES.—And how many Talapolins?

CROUTEF.—A hundred and twenty thousand, very idle and very rich. It is true that in the last war we were beaten, but our Talapolins have lived sumptuously, and built fine houses.

DES TOUCHES.—Nothing could have discovered more judgment. And your finances, in what state are they?

CROUTEF.—In a very bad state. We have, however, about ninety thousand men employed to render them prosperous, and if they have not succeeded, it has not been their fault; for there is not one of them who does not honorably seize all that he can get possession of, and strip and plunder those who cultivate the ground for the good of the state.

DES TOUCHES.—Bravo! And is not your jurisprudence as perfect as the rest of your administration?

CROUTEF.—It is much superior. We have no laws, but we have five or six thousand volumes on the laws. We are governed in general by customs; for it is known that a custom, having been established by chance, is the wisest principle that can be imagined. Besides, all customs being necessarily different in different provinces, the judges may choose at their pleasure a custom which prevailed four hundred years ago, or one which prevailed last year. It occasions a variety in our legislation, which our neighbors are forever admiring. This yields a certain fortune to practitioners. It is a resource for all pleaders who are destitute of honor, and a pastime of infinite amusement for the judges, who can with safe consciences decide causes without understanding them.

DES TOUCHES.—But in criminal cases—you have laws which may be depended upon.

CROUTEF.—God forbid! We can condemn men to exile, to the galleys, to be hanged; or we can discharge them, according to our own fancy. We sometimes complain of the arbitrary power of the Barcalon; but we choose that all our decisions should be arbitrary.

DES TOUCHES.—That is very just. And the torture—do you put people to the torture?

CROUTEF.—It is our greatest pleasure. We have found it an infallible secret to save a guilty person, who has vigorous muscles, strong and supple hamstrings, nervous arms, and firm loins; and we gaily break on the wheel all those innocent persons to whom nature has given feeble organs. It is thus we conduct ourselves with wonderful wisdom and prudence. As there are half proofs, I mean half truths, it is certain there are persons who are half innocent and half guilty. We commence, therefore, by rendering them half dead; we then go to breakfast; afterwards ensues entire death, which gives us great consideration in the world, which is one of the most valuable advantages of our offices.

DES TOUCHES.—It must be allowed that nothing can be more prudent and humane. Pray tell me what becomes of the property of the condemned?

CROUTEF.—The children are deprived of it. For you know that nothing can be more equitable than to punish the single fault of a parent on all his descendants.

DES TOUCHES.—Yes. It is a great while since I have heard of this jurisprudence.

CROUTEF.—The people of Laos, our neighbors, admit neither the torture, nor arbitrary punishments, nor the different customs, nor the horrible deaths which are in use among us; but we regard them as barbarians who have no idea of good government. All Asia is agreed that we dance the best of all its inhabitants, and that, consequently, it is impossible they should come near us in jurisprudence, in commerce, in finance, and, above all, in the military art.

DES TOUCHES.—Tell me, I beseech you, by what steps men arrive at the magistracy in Siam.

CROUTEF.—By ready money. You perceive that it may be impossible to be a good judge, if a man has not by him thirty or forty thousand pieces of silver. It is in vain a man may be perfectly acquainted with all our customs; it is to no purpose that he has pleaded five hundred causes with success—that he has a mind which is the seat of judgment, and a heart replete with justice; no man can become a magistrate without money. This, I say, is the circumstance which distinguishes us from all Asia, and particularly from the barbarous inhabitants of Laos, who have the madness to recompense all kinds of talents, and not to sell any employment.

Andre des Touches, who was a little off his guard, said to the Siamese, that most of the airs which he had just sung sounded discordant to him; and wished to receive information concerning real Siamese music. But Croutef, full of his subject, and enthusiastic for his country, continued in these words:

"What does it signify that our neighbors, who live beyond our mountains, have better music than we have, or better pictures; provided we have always wise and humane laws? It is in that circumstance we excel. For example:

"If a man has adroitly stolen three or four hundred thousand pieces of gold, we respect him, and we go and dine with him. But if a poor servant gets awkwardly into his possession three or four pieces of copper out of his mistress's box, we never fail of putting that servant to a public death; first, lest he should not correct himself; secondly, that he may not have it in his power to produce a great number of children for the state, one or two of whom might possibly steal a few little pieces of copper, or become great men; thirdly, because it is just to proportion the punishment to the crime, and that it would be ridiculous to give any useful employment in a prison to a person guilty of so enormous a crime.

"But we are still more just, more merciful, more reasonable in the chastisements which we inflict on those who have the audacity to make use of their legs to go wherever they choose. We treat those warriors so well who sell us their lives, we give them so prodigious a salary, they have so considerable a part in our conquests, that they must be the most criminal of all men to wish to return to their parents on the recovery of their reason, because they had been enlisted in a state of intoxication. To oblige them to remain in one place, we lodge about a dozen leaden balls in their heads; after which they become infinitely useful to their country.

"I will not speak of a great number of excellent institutions, which do not go so far as to shed the blood of men, but which render life so pleasant and agreeable that it is impossible the guilty should avoid becoming virtuous. If a farmer has not been able to pay promptly a tax which exceeds his ability, we sell the pot in which he dresses his food; we sell his bed, in order that, being relieved of all his superfluities, he may be in a better condition to cultivate the earth."

DES TOUCHES.—That is extremely harmonious!

CROUTEF.—To comprehend our profound wisdom, you must know that our fundamental principle is to acknowledge in many places as our sovereign a foreigner who lives at the distance of nine hundred miles from us. When we assign some of our best territories to any of our Talapolins, which it is very prudent in us to do, that Siamese Talapolin must pay the revenue of his first year to that Tartar, without which it is clear our lands would be unfruitful.

But the time, the happy time, is no more, when that Tartar induced one-half of the nation to cut the throats of the other half, in order to decide whether Sammonocodom had played at leap-frog or at some other game; whether he had been disguised in an elephant or in a cow; if he had slept three hundred and ninety days on the right side, or on the left. Those grand questions, which so essentially affect morality, agitated all minds; they shook the world; blood flowed plentifully for it; women were massacred on the bodies of their husbands; they dashed out the brains of their little infants on the stones, with a devotion, with a grace, with a contrition truly angelic. Woe to us! degenerate offspring of pious ancestors, who never offer such holy sacrifices! But, heaven be praised, there are yet among us at least a few good souls, who would imitate them if they were permitted.

DES TOUCHES.—Tell me, I beseech you, sir, if at Siam you divide the tone major into two commas, or into two semicommas; and if the progress of the fundamental sounds are made by one, three, and nine?

CROUTEF.—By Sammonocodom, you are laughing at me. You observe no bounds. You have interrogated me on the form of our government, and you speak to me of music!

DES TOUCHES.—Music is everything. It was at the foundation of all the politics of the Greeks. But I beg your pardon; you have not a good ear; and we will return to our subject. You said, that in order to produce a perfect harmony—

CROUTEF.—I was telling you, that formerly the Tartar pretended to dispose of all the kingdoms of Asia; which occasioned something very different from perfect harmony. But a very considerable benefit resulted from it; for people were then more devout toward Sammonocodom and his elephant than they are now; for, at the present time, all the world pretends to common sense, with an indiscretion truly pitiable. However, all things go on; people divert themselves, they dance, they play, they dine, they sup, they make love; this makes every man shudder who entertains good intentions.

DES TOUCHES.—And what would you have more? You only want good music. If you had good music, you might call your nation the happiest in the world.

THE BLIND PENSIONERS AT QUINZE VINGT

WHEN the hospital of the Quinze Vingt was first founded, the pensioners were all equal, and their little affairs were concluded upon by a majority of votes. They distinguished perfectly by the touch between copper and silver coin; they never mistook the wine of Brie for that of Burgundy. Their sense of smelling was finer than that of their neighbors who had the use of two eyes. They reasoned very well on the four senses; that is, they knew everything they were permitted to know, and they lived as peaceably and as happily as blind people could be supposed to do. But unfortunately one of their professors pretended to have clear ideas in respect to the sense of seeing; he drew attention; he intrigued; he formed enthusiasts; and at last he was acknowledged chief of the community. He pretended to be a judge of colors, and everything was lost.

This dictator of the Quinze Vingt chose at first a little council, by the assistance of which he got possession of all the alms. On this account, no person had the resolution to oppose him. He decreed that all the inhabitants of the Quinze Vingt were clothed in white. The blind pensioners believed him; and nothing was to be heard but their talk of white garments, though, in fact, they possessed not one of that color. All their acquaintance laughed at them. They made their complaints to the dictator, who received them very ill; he rebuked them as innovators, freethinkers, rebels, who had suffered themselves to be seduced by the errors of those who had eyes, and who presumed to doubt that their chief was infallible. This contention gave rise to two parties.

To appease the tumult, the dictator issued a decree, importing that all their vestments were red. There was not one vestment of that color in the Quinze Vingt. The poor men were laughed at more than ever. Complaints were again made by the community. The dictator rushed furiously in; and the other blind men were as much enraged. They fought a long time; and peace was not restored until the members of the Quinze Vingt were permitted to suspend their judgments in regard to the color of their dress.

A deaf man, reading this little history, allowed that these people, being blind, were to blame in pretending to judge of colors; but he remained steady to his own opinion, that those persons who were deaf were the only proper judges of music.

BABABEC

When I was in the city of Benarez, on the borders of the Ganges, the country of the ancient Brahmins, I endeavored to instruct myself in their religion and manners. I understood the Indian language tolerably well. I heard a great deal, and remarked everything. I lodged at the house of my correspondent Omri, who was the most worthy man I ever knew. He was of the religion of the Brahmins: I have the honor to be a Mussulman. We never exchanged one word higher than another about Mahomet or Brahma. We performed our ablutions each on his own side; we drank of the same sherbet, and we ate of the same rice, as if we had been two brothers.

One day we went together to the pagoda of Gavani. There we saw several bands of Fakirs. Some of whom were Janguis, that is to say, contemplative Fakirs; and others were disciples of the ancient Gymnosophists, who led an active life. They all have a learned language peculiar to themselves; it is that of the most ancient Brahmins; and they have a book written in this language, which they call the *Shasta*. It is, beyond all contradiction, the most ancient book in all Asia, not excepting the *Zend*.

I happened to cross in front of a Fakir, who was reading in this book. "Ah! wretched infidel!" cried he, "thou hast made me lose a number of vowels that I was counting, which will cause my soul to pass into the body of a hare instead of that of a parrot, with which I had before the greatest reason to flatter myself."

I gave him a rupee to comfort him for the accident. In going a few paces farther, I had the misfortune to sneeze. The noise I made roused a Fakir, who was in a trance.

"Heavens!" cried he, "what a dreadful noise. Where am I? I can no longer see the tip of my nose,—the heavenly light has disappeared."

"If I am the cause," said I, "of your not seeing farther than the length of your nose, here is a rupee to repair the great injury I have done you. Squint again, my friend, and resume the heavenly light."

Having thus brought myself off discreetly enough, I passed over to the side of the Gymnosophists, several of whom brought me a parcel of mighty pretty nails to drive into my arms and thighs, in honor of Brahma. I bought their nails, and made use of them to fasten down my boxes. Others were dancing upon their hands, others cut capers on the slack rope, and others went always upon one foot. There were some who dragged a heavy chain about with them, and others carried a packsaddle; some had their heads always in a bushel— the best people in the world to live with. My friend Omri took me to the cell of one of the most famous of these. His name was Bababec: he was as naked as he was born, and had a great chain about his neck, that weighed upwards of sixty pounds. He sat on a wooden chair, very neatly decorated with little points of nails that penetrated into his flesh; and you would have thought he had been sitting on a velvet cushion. Numbers of women flocked to him to consult him. He was the oracle of all the families in the neighborhood; and

271

was, truly speaking, in great reputation. I was witness to a long conversation that Omri had with him.

"Do you think, father," said my friend, "that after having gone through seven metempsychoses, I may at length arrive at the habitation of Brahma?"

"That is as it may happen," said the Fakir. "What sort of life do you lead?"

"I endeavor," answered Omri, "to be a good subject, a good husband, a good father, and a good friend. I lend money without interest to the rich who want it, and I give it to the poor: I always strive to preserve peace among my neighbors."

"But have you ever run nails into your flesh?" demanded the Brahmin.

"Never, reverend father."

"I am sorry for it," replied the father; "very sorry for it, indeed. It is a thousand pities; but you will certainly not reach above the nineteenth heaven."

"No higher!" said Omri. "In truth, I am very well contented with my lot. What is it to me whether I go into the nineteenth or the twentieth, provided I do my duty in my pilgrimage, and am well received at the end of my journey? Is it not as much as one can desire, to live with a fair character in this world, and be happy with Brahma in the next? And pray what heaven do you think of going to, good master Bababec, with your chain?"

"Into the thirty-fifth," said Bababec.

"I admire your modesty," replied Omri, "to pretend to be better lodged than me. This is surely the result of an excessive ambition. How can you, who condemn others that covet honors in this world, arrogate such distinguished ones to yourself in the next? What right have you to be better treated than me? Know that I bestow more alms to the poor in ten days, than the nails you run into your flesh cost for ten years? What is it to Brahma that you pass the whole day stark naked with a chain about your neck? This is doing a notable service to your country, doubtless! I have a thousand times more esteem for the man who sows pulse or plants trees, than for all your tribe, who look at the tips of their noses, or carry packsaddles, to show their magnanimity."

Having finished this speech, Omri softened his voice, embraced the Brahmin, and, with an endearing sweetness, besought him to throw aside his nails and his chain, to go home with him, and live in comfort.

The Fakir was persuaded: he was washed clean, rubbed with essences and perfumes, and clad in a decent habit; he lived a fortnight in this manner, behaved with prudence and wisdom, and acknowledged that he was a thousand times happier than before; but he lost his credit among the people; the women no longer crowded to consult him; he therefore quitted the house of the friendly Omri, and returned to his nails and his chain, *to regain his reputation.*

A CONVERSATION WITH A CHINESE

In the year 1723, there was a Chinese in Holland, who was both a learned man and a merchant, two things that ought by no means to be incompatible; but which, thanks to the profound respect that is shown to money, and the little regard that the human species pay to merit, have become so among us.

This Chinese, who spoke a little Dutch, happened to be in a book-seller's shop at the same time that some literati were assembled there. He asked for a book; they offered him *Universal History*, badly translated. At the title *Universal History*—

"How pleased am I," cried the Oriental, "to have met with this book. I shall now see what is said of our great empire; of a nation that has subsisted for upwards of fifty thousand years; of that long dynasty of emperors who have governed us for such a number of ages. I shall see what these Europeans think of the religion of our literati, and of that pure and simple worship we pay to the Supreme Being. What a pleasure will it be for me to find how they speak of our arts, many of which are of a more ancient date with us than the eras of all the kingdoms of Europe! I fancy the author will be greatly mistaken in relation to the war we had about twenty-two thousand five hundred and fifty-two years ago, with the martial people of Tonquin and Japan, as well as the solemn embassy that the powerful emperor of Mogulitian sent to request a body of laws from us in the year of the world 5000000000000079123450000."

"Lord bless you," said one of the literati, "there is hardly any mention made of that nation in this world. The only nation considered is that marvelous people, the Jews."

"The Jews!" said the Chinese, "those people then must be masters of three parts of the globe at least."

"They hope to be so some day," answered the other; "but at present they are those pedlars you see going about here with toys and nicknacks, and who sometimes do us the honor to clip our gold and silver."

"Surely you are not serious," exclaimed the Chinese. "Could those people ever have been in possession of a vast empire?"

Here I joined in the conversation, and told him that for a few years they were in possession of a small country to themselves; but that we were not to judge of a people from the extent of their dominions, any more than of a man by his riches.

"But does not this book take notice of some other nations?" demanded the man of letters.

"Undoubtedly," replied a learned gentleman who stood at my elbow; "it treats largely of a small country about sixty leagues wide, called Egypt, in which it is said that there is a lake of one hundred and fifty leagues in circumference, made by the hands of man."

"My God!" exclaimed the Chinese, "a lake of one hundred and fifty leagues in circumference within a spot of ground only sixty leagues wide! This is very curious!"

"The inhabitants of that country," continued the doctor. "were all sages.

"What happy times were those!" cried the Chinese; "but is that all?"

"No," replied the other, "there is mention made of those famous people the Greeks."

"Greeks! Greeks!" said the Asiatic, "who are those Greeks?"

"Why," replied the philosopher, "they were masters of a little province, about the two hundredth part as large as China, but whose fame spread over the whole world."

"Indeed!" said the Chinese, with an air of openness and ingenuousness; "I declare I never heard the least mention of these people, either in the Mogul's country, in Japan, or in Great Tartary."

"Oh, the barbarian! the ignorant creature!" cried out our sage very politely. "Why then, I suppose you know nothing of Epaminondas the Theban, nor of the Pierian Heaven, nor the names of Achilles's two horses, nor of Silenus's ass? You have never heard speak of Jupiter, nor of Diogenes, nor of Lais, nor of Cybele, nor of——"

"I am very much afraid," said the learned Oriental, interrupting him, "that you know nothing of that eternally memorable adventure of the famous Xixofon Concochigramki, nor of the mysteries of the great Fi-psi-hi-hi! But pray tell me what other unknown things does this *Universal History* treat of?"

Upon this my learned neighbor harangued for a quarter of an hour together about the Roman republic, and when he came to Julius Cæsar the Chinese stopped him, and very gravely said:

"I think I have heard of him, was he not a Turk?"

"How!" cried our sage in a fury, "don't you so much as know the difference between Pagans, Christians, and Mahometans? Did you never hear of Constantine? Do you know nothing of the history of the popes?"

"We have heard something confusedly of one Mahomet," replied the Asiatic.

"It is surely impossible," said the other, "but that you must have heard at least of Luther, Zuinglius, Bellarmin, and Oecolampadius."

"I shall never remember all those names," said the Chinese, and so saying he quitted the shop, and went to sell a large quantity of Pekoa tea, and fine calico, and then after purchasing what merchandise he required, set sail for his own country, adoring *Tien*, and recommending himself to Confucius.

As to myself, the conversation I had been witness to plainly discovered to me the nature of vain glory; and I could not forbear exclaiming:

"Since Cæsar and Jupiter are names unknown to the finest, most ancient, most extensive, most populous, and most civilized kingdom in the universe, it becomes ye well, O ye rulers of petty states! ye pulpit orators of a narrow parish, or a little town! ye doctors of Salamanca, or of Bourges! ye trifling authors, and ye heavy commentators!—it becomes you well, indeed, to aspire to fame and immortality."

PLATO'S DREAM

PLATO was a great dreamer, as many others have been since his time. He dreamed that mankind were formerly double; and that, as a punishment for their crimes, they were divided into male and female.

He undertook to prove that there can be no more than five perfect worlds, because there are but five regular mathematical bodies. His Republic was one of his principal dreams. He dreamed, moreover, that watching arises from sleep, and sleep from watching; and that a person who should attempt to look at an eclipse, otherwise than in a pail of water, would surely lose his sight. Dreams were, at that time, in great repute.

Here follows one of his dreams, which is not one of the least interesting. He thought that the great Demiurgos, the eternal geometer, having peopled the immensity of space with innumerable globes, was willing to make a trial of the knowledge of the genii who had been witnesses of his works. He gave to each of them a small portion of matter to arrange, nearly in the same manner as Phidias and Zeuxis would have given their scholars a statue to carve, or a picture to paint, if we may be allowed to compare small things to great.

Demogorgon had for his lot the lump of mould, which we call the Earth; and having formed it, such as it now appears, he thought he had executed a masterpiece. He imagined he had silenced Envy herself, and expected to receive the highest panegyrics, even from his brethren: but how great was his surprise, when, at his next appearing among them, they received him with a general hiss.

One among them, more satirical than the rest, accosted him thus:

"Truly you have performed mighty feats! you have divided your world into two parts; and, to prevent the one from having communication with the other, you have carefully placed a vast collection of waters between the two hemispheres. The inhabitants must perish with cold under both your poles, and be scorched to death under the equator. You have, in your great prudence, formed immense deserts of sand, so that all who travel over them may die with hunger and thirst. I have no fault to find with your cows, your sheep, your cocks, and your hens; but can never be reconciled to your serpents and your spiders. Your onions and your artichokes are very good things, but I cannot conceive what induced you to scatter such a heap of poisonous plants over the face of the earth, unless it was to poison its inhabitants. Moreover, if I am not mistaken, you have created about thirty different kinds of monkeys, a still greater number of dogs, and only four or five species of the human race. It is true, indeed, you have bestowed on the latter of these animals a faculty by you called Reason; but, in truth, this same reason is a very ridiculous thing, and borders very near upon folly. Besides, you do not seem to have shown any very great regard to this two-legged creature, seeing you have left him with so few means of defense; subjected him to so many disorders, and provided him with so few remedies; and formed him with such a multitude of passions, and so small a portion of wisdom or prudence to resist them. You certainly were not willing that there should remain any great number of these animals on the earth at once; for, without reckoning the dangers to which you have exposed them, you have so ordered matters that, taking every day through the year, the small pox will regularly carry off the tenth part of the species, and sister maladies will taint the springs of life in the nine remaining parts; and then, as if this was not sufficient, you have so disposed things, that one-half of those who survive will be occupied in going to law with each other, or cutting one another's throats.

"Now, they must be under infinite obligations to you, and it must be owned you have executed a masterpiece."

Demogorgon blushed. He was sensible there was much moral and physical evil in this affair; but still he insisted there was more good than ill in it.

"It is an easy matter to find fault, good folks," said the genii; "but do you imagine it is so easy to form an animal, who, having the gift of reason and free-will, shall not sometimes abuse his liberty? Do you think that, in rearing between nine and ten thousand different plants, it is so easy to prevent some few from having noxious qualities? Do you suppose that, with a certain quantity of water, sand, and mud, you could make a globe that should have neither seas nor deserts?

"As for you, my sneering friend, I think you have just finished the planet Jupiter. Let us see now what figure you make with your great belts, and your long nights, with four moons to enlighten them. Let us examine your worlds, and see whether the inhabitants you have made are exempt from follies or diseases."

Accordingly the genii fell to examining the planet Jupiter, when the laugh went strongly against the laughter. The serious genii who had made the planet Saturn did not escape without his share of the censure, and his brother operators, the makers of Mars, Mercury, and Venus, had each in his turn some reproaches to undergo.

Several large volumes, and a great number of pamphlets, were written on this occasion; smart sayings and witty repartees flew about on all sides; they railed against and ridiculed each other; and, in short, the disputes were carried on with all the warmth of party heat, when the eternal Demiurgos thus imposed silence on them all:

"In your several performances there is both good and bad, because, you have a great share of understanding, but at the same time fall short of perfection. Your works will not endure above an hundred millions of years, after which you will acquire more knowledge, and perform much better. It belongs to me alone to create things perfect and immortal."

This was the doctrine Plato taught his disciples. One of them, when he had finished his harangue, cried out, "*And so you then awoke?*"

AN ADVENTURE IN INDIA

ALL THE world knows that Pythagoras, while he resided in India, attended the school of the Gymnosophists, and learned the language of beasts and plants. One day, while he was walking in a meadow near the sea-shore, he heard these words:

"How unfortunate that I was born an herb! I scarcely attain two inches in height, when a voracious monster, an horrid animal, tramples me under his large feet; his jaws are armed with rows of sharp scythes, by which he cuts, then grinds, and then swallows me. Men call this monster a sheep. I do not suppose there is in the whole creation a more detestable creature."

Pythagoras proceeded a little way and found an oyster yawning on a small rock. He had not yet adopted that admirable law, by which we are enjoined not to eat those animals which have a resemblance to us. He had scarcely taken up the oyster to swallow it, when it spoke these affecting words:

"O, Nature, how happy is the herb, which is, as I am, thy work! though it be cut down, it is regenerated and immortal, and we, poor oysters, in vain are defended by a double cuirass: villains eat us by the dozens at their breakfast, and all is over with us forever. What an horrible fate is that of an oyster, and how barbarous are men!"

Pythagoras shuddered; he felt the enormity of the crime he had nearly committed; he begged pardon of the oyster with tears in his eyes, and replaced it very carefully on the rock.

As he was returning to the city, profoundly meditating on this adventure, he saw spiders devouring flies; swallows eating spiders, and sparrow-hawks eating swallows. "None of these," said he, "are philosophers."

On his entrance, Pythagoras was stunned, bruised, and thrown down by a lot of tatterdemalions, who were running and crying: "Well done, he fully deserved it." "Who? What?" said Pythagoras, as he was getting up. The people continued running and crying: "O how delightful it will be to see them boiled!"

Pythagoras supposed they meant lentils, or some other vegetables: but he was in an error; they meant two poor Indians. "Oh!" said Pythagoras, "these Indians, without doubt, are two great philosophers weary of their lives; they are desirous of regenerating under other forms; it affords pleasure to a man to change his place of residence, though he may be but indifferently lodged: there is no disputing on taste."

He proceeded with the mob to the public square, where he perceived a lighted pile of wood, and a bench opposite to it, which was called a tribunal. On this bench judges were seated, each of them had a cow's tail in his hand, and a cap on his head, with ears resembling those of the animal which bore Silenus when he came into that country with Bacchus, after having crossed the Erytrean sea without wetting a foot, and stopping the sun and moon; as it is recorded with great fidelity in the Orphicks.

Among these judges there was an honest man with whom Pythagoras was acquainted. The Indian sage explained to the sage of Samos the nature of that festival to be given to the people of India.

"These two Indians," said he, "have not the least desire to be committed to the flames. My grave brethren have adjudged them to be burnt; one for saying that the substance of Xaca is not that of Brahma; and the other for supposing that the approbation of the Supreme Being was to be obtained at the point of death without holding a cow by the tail; 'Because,' said he, 'we may be virtuous at all times, and we cannot always have a cow to lay hold of just when we may have occasion.' The good women of the city were greatly terrified at two such heretical opinions; they would not allow the judges a moment's peace until they had ordered the execution of those unfortunate men."

Pythagoras was convinced that from the herb up to man, there were many causes of chagrin. However, he obliged the judges and even the devotees to listen to reason, which happened only at that time.

He went afterwards and preached toleration at Crotona; but a bigot set fire to his house, and he was burnt—the man who had delivered the two Hindoos from the flames? Let those save themselves who can!

JEANNOT AND COLIN

MANY persons, worthy of credit, have seen Jeannot and Colin at school in the town of Issoire, in Auvergne, France,—a town famous all over the world for its college and its caldrons.

Jeannot was the son of a dealer in mules of great reputation; and Colin owed his birth to a good substantial farmer in the neighborhood, who cultivated the land with four mules; and who, after he had paid all taxes and duties at the rate of a sol per pound, was not very rich at the year's end.

Jeannot and Colin were very handsome, considering they were natives of Auvergne: they dearly loved each other. They had many enjoyments in common, and certain little adventures of such a nature as men always recollect with pleasure when they afterwards meet in the world.

Their studies were nearly finished, when a tailor brought Jeannot a velvet suit of three colors, with a waistcoat from Lyons, which was extremely well fancied. With these came a letter addressed to Monsieur de la Jeannotiere.

Colin admired the coat, and was not at all jealous; but Jeannot assumed an air of superiority, which gave Colin some uneasiness. From that moment Jeannot abandoned his studies; he contemplated himself in a glass, and despised all mankind.

Soon after, a valet-de-chambre arrived post-haste, and brought a second letter to the Marquis de la Jeannotiere; it was an order from his father, who desired the young marquis to repair immediately to Paris. Jeannot got into his chaise, giving his hand to Colin with a smile, which denoted the superiority of a patron. Colin felt his littleness, and wept. Jeannot departed in all the pomp of his glory.

Such readers as take a pleasure in being instructed should be informed that Monsieur Jeannot the father, had, with great rapidity, acquired an immense fortune by business. You will ask how such great fortunes are made? My answer is, by luck. Monsieur Jeannot had a good person, so had his wife; and she had still some freshness remaining. They went to Paris on account of a law-suit, which ruined them; when fortune, which raises and depresses men at her pleasure, presented them to the wife of an undertaker belonging to one of the hospitals for the army. This undertaker, a man of great talents, might make it his boast that he had buried more soldiers in a year than cannons destroy in ten. Jeannot pleased the wife; the wife of Jeannot interested the undertaker. Jeannot was employed in the undertaker's business; this introduced him to other business. When our boat runs with wind and stream, we have nothing to do but let it sail on. We then make an immense fortune with ease. The poor creatures who from the shore see you pursue your voyage with full sail, stare with astonishment; they cannot conceive to what you owe your success; they envy you instinctively, and write pamphlets against you which you never read.

This is just what happened to Jeannot the father, who soon became Monsieur de la Jeannotiere; and who having purchased a Marquisate in six months time, took the young marquis, his son, from school, in order to introduce him to the polite world at Paris.

Colin, whose heart was replete with tenderness, wrote a letter of compliments to his old companion, and congratulated him on his good fortune. The little marquis did not reply. Colin was so much affected at this neglect that he was taken ill.

The father and mother immediately consigned the young marquis to the care of a governor. This governor, who was a man of fashion, and who knew nothing, was not able to teach his pupil anything.

The marquis would have had his son learn Latin; this his lady opposed. They then referred the matter to the judgment of an author, who had at that time acquired great reputation by his entertaining writings. This author was invited to dinner. The master of the house immediately addressed him thus:

"Sir, as you understand Latin, and are a man acquainted with the court,—"

"I understand Latin! I don't know one word of it," answered the wit, "and I think myself better for being unacquainted with it. It is very evident that a man speaks his own language in greater perfection when he does not divide his application between it and foreign languages. Only consider our ladies; they have a much more agreeable turn of wit than the men; their letters are written with a hundred times the grace of ours. This superiority they owe to nothing else but their not understanding Latin."

"Well, was I not in the right?" said the lady. "I would have my son prove a notable man, I would have him succeed in the world; and you see that if he was to understand Latin he would be ruined. Pray, are plays and operas performed in Latin? Do lawyers plead in Latin? Do men court a mistress in Latin?"

The marquis, dazzled by these reasons, gave up the point, and it was resolved that the young marquis should not mis-spend his time in endeavoring to become acquainted with Cicero, Horace and Virgil.

"Then," said the father, "what shall he learn? For he must know something. Might not one teach him a little geography?"

"Of what use will that be?" answered the governor. "When the marquis goes to his estate, won't the postillion know the roads? They certainly will not carry him out of his way. There is no occasion for a quadrant to travel thither; and one can go very commodiously from Paris to Auvergne without knowing what latitude one is in."

"You are in the right," replied the father; "but I have heard of a science, called astronomy, if I am not mistaken."

"Bless me!" said the governor, "do people regulate their conduct by the influence of the stars in this world? And must the young gentleman perplex himself with the calculation of an eclipse, when he finds it ready calculated to his hand in an almanac, which, at the same time, shows him the movable feasts, the age of the moon, and also that of all the princesses in Europe?"

The lady agreed perfectly with the governor; the little marquis was transported with joy; the father remained undetermined. "What then is my son to learn?" said he.

"To become amiable," answered the friend who was consulted, "and it ne knows how to please, he will know all that need be known. This art he will learn in the company of his mother, without either he or she being at any trouble."

The lady, upon hearing this, embraced the ignorant flatterer, and said: "It is easy to see, sir, that you are the wisest man in the world. My son will be entirely indebted to you for his education. I think, however, it would not be amiss if he was to know something of history."

"Alas, madam, what is that good for," answered he; "there certainly is no useful or entertaining history but the history of the day; all ancient histories, as one of our wits has observed, are only fables that men have agreed to admit as true. With regard to modern history, it is a mere chaos, a confusion which it is impossible to make anything of. Of what consequence is it to the young marquis, your son, to know that Charlemagne instituted the twelve peers of France and that his successor stammered?"

"Admirably said," cried the governor; "the genius of young persons is smothered under a heap of useless knowledge; but of all sciences, the most absurd, and that which, in my opinion, is most calculated to stifle genius of every kind, is geometry. The objects about which this ridiculous science is conversant, are surfaces, lines, and points, that have no existence in nature. By the force of imagination, the geometrician makes a hundred thousand curved lines pass between a circle and a right line that touches it, when, in reality, there is not room for a straw to pass there. Geometry, if we consider it in its true light, is a mere jest, and nothing more."

The marquis and his lady did not well understand the governor's meaning, yet they were entirely of his opinion.

"A man of quality, like the young marquis," continued he, "should not rack his brains with useless sciences. If he should ever have occasion for a plan of the lands of his estate, he may have them correctly surveyed without studying geometry. If he has a mind to trace the antiquity of his noble family, which leads the inquirer back to the most remote ages, he will send for a Benedictine. It will be the same thing with regard to all other wants. A young man of quality, endowed with a happy genius, is neither a painter, a musician, an architect, nor a graver; but he makes all these arts flourish by generously encouraging them. It is, doubtless, better to patronize than to practice them. It is enough for the young marquis to have a taste; it is the business of artists to exert themselves for him; and it is in this sense that it is said very justly of people of quality, (I mean those who are very rich), that they know all things without having learnt anything; for they, in fact, come at last to know how to judge concerning whatever they order or pay for."

The ignorant man of fashion then spoke to this purpose:

"You have very justly observed, madam, that the grand end which a man should have in view is to succeed in the world. Can it possibly be said that this success is to be obtained by cultivating the sciences? Did anybody ever so much as think of talking of geometry in good company? Does anyone ever inquire of a man of the world, what star rises with the sun? Who enquires at supper, whether the long-haired Clodio passed the Rhine?"

"No, doubtless," cried the marchioness, whom her charms had in some measure initiated into the customs of the polite world; "and my son should not extinguish his genius by the study of all this stuff. But what is he, after all, to learn? for it is proper that a young person of quality should know how to shine upon an occasion, as my husband observes. I remember to have heard a cleric say, that the most delightful of all the sciences, is something that begins with a B."

"With a B, madam? Is it not botany you mean?"

"No, it was not botany he spoke of; the name of the science he mentioned began with B, and ended with *on.*"

"Oh, I comprehend you, madam," said the man of fashion; "it is *Blason* you mean. It is indeed a profound science; but it is no longer in fashion, since the people of quality have ceased to cause their arms to be painted upon the doors of their coaches. It was once the most useful thing in the world, in a well regulated state. Besides, this study would be endless. Now-a-days there is hardly a barber that has not his coat of arms; and you know that whatever becomes common is but little esteemed."

In fine, after they had examined the excellencies and defects of all the sciences, it was determined that the young marquis should learn to dance.

Nature, which does all, had given him a talent that quickly displayed itself surprisingly; it was that of singing ballads agreeably. The graces of youth, joined to this superior gift, caused him to be looked upon as a young man of the brightest hopes. He was admired by the women; and having his head full of songs, he composed some for his mistress. He stole from the song "*Bacchus and Love*" in one ballad; from that of "*Night and Day*" in another; from that of "*Charms and Alarms*" in a third. But as there were always in his verses some superfluous feet, or not enough, he had them corrected for twenty louis-d'ors a song; and in the annals of literature he was put upon a level with the La Fares, Chaulieus, Hamiltons, Sarrazins, and Voitures.

The marchioness then looked upon herself as the mother of a wit, and gave a supper to the wits of Paris. The young man's brain was soon turned; he acquired the art of speaking without knowing his own meaning, and he became perfect in the habit of being good for nothing. When his father found he was so eloquent, he very much regretted that his son had not learned Latin; for he would have bought him a lucrative place among the gentry of the long robe. The mother, who had more elevated sentiments, undertook to procure a regiment for her son; and in the meantime, courtship was his occupation. Love is sometimes more expensive than a regiment. He was very improvident, whilst his parents exhausted their finances still more, by expensive living.

A young widow of fashion, their neighbor, who had but a moderate fortune, had an inclination to secure the great wealth of Monsieur and Madame de la Jeannotiere, and appropriating it to herself, by a marriage with the young marquis. She allured him to visit her; she admitted his addresses; she showed that she was not indifferent to him; she led him on by degrees; she enchanted and captivated him without much difficulty. Sometimes she lavished praises upon him, sometimes she gave him advice. She became the most intimate friend of both the father and mother.

An elderly lady, who was their neighbor, proposed the match. The parents, dazzled by the glory of such an alliance, accepted the proposal with joy. They gave their only son to their intimate friend.

The young marquis was now on the point of marrying a woman whom he adored, and by whom he was beloved; the friends of the family congratulated them; the marriage articles were just going to be drawn up, whilst wedding clothes were being made for the young couple, and their epithalamium composed.

The young marquis was one day upon his knees before his charming mistress, whom love, esteem, and friendship were going to make all his own. In a tender and spirited conversation, they enjoyed a foretaste of their coming happiness; they concerted measures to lead a happy life. When all on a sudden a valet-de-chambre belonging to the old marchioness arrived in a great fright.

"Here is sad news," said he. "Officers have removed the effects of my master and mistress; the creditors have seized upon all by virtue of an execution; and I am obliged to make the best shift I can to have my wages paid."

"Let's see," said the marquis, "what is this? What can this adventure mean?"

"Go," said the widow, "go quickly, and punish those villains."

He runs, he arrives at the house; his father is already in prison; all the servants have fled in different ways, each carrying off whatever he could lay his hands upon. His mother is alone, without assistance, without comfort, drowned in tears. She has nothing left but the remembrance of her fortune, of her beauty, her faults, and her extravagant living.

After the son had wept a long time with his mother, he at length said to her:

"Let us not give ourselves up to despair. This young widow loves me to excess; she is more generous than rich, I can answer for her; I will go and bring her to you."

He returns to his mistress, and finds her in company with a very amiable young officer.

"What, is it you, M. de la Jeannotiere," said she; "what brings you here? Is it proper to forsake your unhappy mother in such a crisis? Go to that poor, unfortunate woman, and tell her I still wish her well. I have occasion for a chamber-maid, and will give her the preference."

"My lad," said the officer, "you are well shaped. Enlist in my company; you may depend on good usage."

The marquis, thunderstruck, and with a heart enraged, went in quest of his old governor, made him acquainted with his misfortune, and asked his advice. The governor proposed that he should become a tutor, like himself.

"Alas!" said the marquis, "I know nothing; you have taught me nothing, and you are the first cause of my misfortunes." He sobbed when he spoke thus.

"Write romances," said a wit who was present; "it is an admirable resource at Paris."

The young man, in greater despair than ever, ran to his mother's confessor. This confessor was a Theatin of great reputation, who directed the consciences only of women of the first rank. As soon as he saw Jeannot, he ran up to him:

"My God, Mr. Marquis," said he, "where is your coach? How is the good lady your mother?"

The poor unfortunate young man gave him an account of what had befallen his family. In proportion as he explained himself the Theatin assumed an air more grave, more indifferent, and more defiant.

"My son," said he, "it is the will of God that you should be reduced to this condition; riches serve only to corrupt the heart. God, in his great mercy, has then reduced your mother to beggary?"

"Yes, sir," answered the marquis.

"So much the better," said the confessor, "her election is the more certain."

"But father," said the marquis, "is there in the mean time no hopes of some assistance in this world?"

"Farewell, my son," said the confessor; "a court lady is waiting for me."

The marquis was almost ready to faint. He met with much the same treatment from all; and acquired more knowledge of the world in half a day than he had previously learned in all the rest of his life.

Being quite overwhelmed with despair, he saw an old-fashioned chaise advance, which resembled an open wagon with leather curtains; it was followed by four enormous carts which were loaded. In the chaise there was a young man, dressed in the rustic manner, whose fresh countenance was replete with sweetness and gaiety. His wife, a little woman of a brown complexion and an agreeable figure, though somewhat stout, sat close by him. As the carriage did not move on like the chaise of a petit-maitre, the traveler had sufficient time to contemplate the marquis, who was motionless and immersed in sorrow.

"Good God," cried he, "I think that is Jeannot." Upon hearing this name the marquis lifts up his eyes, the carriage stops, and Colin cries out, " 'Tis Jeannot, 'tis Jeannot himself."

The little fat bumpkin gave but one spring from the chaise and ran to embrace his old companion. Jeannot recollected his friend Colin, while his eyes were blinded with tears of shame.

"You have abandoned me," said Colin; "but, though you are a great man, I will love you forever."

Jeannot, confused and affected, related to him with emotion a great part of his history.

"Come to the inn where I lodge, and tell me the rest of it," said Colin; "embrace my wife here, and let us go and dine together." They then went on foot, followed by their baggage.

"What is all this train," said Jeannot; "is it yours?"

"Yes," answered Colin, "it all belongs to me and to my wife. We have just come in from the country. I am now at the head of a large manufactory of tin and copper. I have married the daughter of a merchant well provided with all things necessary for the great as well as the little. We work a great deal; God blesses us; we have not changed our condition; we are happy; we will assist our friend Jeannot. Be no longer a marquis; all the grandeur in the world is not to be compared to a good friend. You shall return with me to the country. I will teach you the trade; it is not very difficult; I will make you my partner, and we will live merrily in the remote corner where we were born."

Jeannot, quite transported, felt emotions of grief and joy, tenderness and shame; and he said within himself: "My fashionable friends have betrayed me, and Colin, whom I despised, is the only one who comes to relieve me." What instruction does not this narrative afford!

Colin's goodness of heart caused the seeds of a virtuous disposition, which the world had not quite stifled in Jeannot, to revive. He was sensible that he could not forsake his father and mother.

"We will take care of your mother," said Colin; "and as to the good man your father, who is now in jail, his creditors, seeing he has nothing, will compromise matters for a trifle. I know something of business, and will take the whole affair upon myself."

Colin found means to procure the father's enlargement. Jeannot returned to the country with his relatives, who resumed their former way of life. He married a sister of Colin, and she, being of the same temper with her brother, made him completely happy.

Jeannot the father, Jeannote the mother, and Jeannot the son, were thus convinced that happiness is not the result of vanity.

THE TRAVELS OF SCARMENTADO

I was born in Candia, in the year 1600. My father was governor of the city; and I remember that a poet of middling parts, and of a most unmusical ear, whose name was Iro, composed some verses in my praise, in which he made me to descend from Minos in a direct line; but my father being afterwards disgraced, he wrote some other verses, in which he derived my pedigree from no nobler an origin than the amours of Pasiphæ and her gallant. This Iro was a most mischievous rogue, and one of the most troublesome fellows in the island.

My father sent me at fifteen years of age to prosecute my studies at Rome. There I arrived in full hopes of learning all kinds of truth; for I had hitherto been taught quite the reverse, according to the custom of this lower world from China to the Alps. Monsignor Profondo, to whom I was recommended, was a man of a very singular character, and one of the most terrible scholars in the world. He was for teaching me the categories of Aristotle; and was just on the point of placing me in the category of his minions; a fate which I narrowly escaped. I saw processions, exorcisms, and some robberies.

It was commonly said, but without any foundation, that la Signora Olympia, a lady of great prudence, had deceived many lovers, she being both inconstant and mercenary. I was then of an age to relish such comical anecdotes.

A young lady of great sweetness of temper, called la Signora Fatelo, thought proper to fall in love with me.

I traveled to France. It was during the reign of Louis the Just. The first question put to me was, whether I chose to breakfast on a slice of the Marshal D'Ancre, whose flesh the people had roasted and distributed with great liberality to such as chose to taste it.

This kingdom was continually involved in civil wars, sometimes for a place at court, sometimes for two pages of theological controversy. This fire, which one while lay concealed under the ashes, and at another burst forth with great violence, had desolated these beautiful provinces for upwards of sixty years. The pretext was, defending the liberties of the Gallican church. "Alas!" said I, "these people are nevertheless born with a gentle disposition. What can have drawn them so far from their natural character? They joke and keep holy days. Happy the time when they shall do nothing but joke!"

I went over to England, where the same disputes occasioned the same barbarities. Some pious Catholics had resolved, for the good of the church, to blow up into the air with gunpowder the king, the royal family, and the whole parliament, and thus to deliver England from all these heretics at once. They showed me the place where Queen Mary of blessed memory, the daughter of Henry VIII., had caused more than five hundred of her subjects to be burnt.

From thence I went to Holland, where I hoped to find more tranquillity among a people of a more cold and phlegmatic temperament. Just as I arrived at the Hague, the people were cutting off the head of a venerable old man. It was the bald head of the prime minister Barnevelt; a man who deserved better treatment from the republic. Touched with pity at this affecting scene, I asked what was his crime, and whether he had betrayed the state.

"He has done much worse," replied a preacher in a black cloak; "he be⸱ lieved that men may be saved by good works as well as by faith. You must be sensible," adds he, "that if such opinions were to gain ground, a republic could not subsist; and that there must be severe laws to suppress such scandalous and horrid blasphemies."

A profound politician said to me with a sigh: "Alas! sir, this happy time will not last long; it is only by chance that the people are so zealous. They are naturally inclined to the abominable doctrine of toleration, and they will certainly at last grant it." This reflection set him a groaning.

For my own part, in expectation of that fatal period when moderation and indulgence should take place, I instantly quitted a country where severity was not softened by any lenitive, and embarked for Spain.

The court was then at Seville. The galleons had just arrived; and everything breathed plenty and gladness, in the most beautiful season of the year. I observed at the end of an alley of orange and citron trees, a kind of large ring, surrounded with steps covered with rich and costly cloth. The king, the queen, the infants, and the infantas, were seated under a superb canopy. Opposite to the royal family was another throne, raised higher than that on which his majesty sat. I said to a fellow-traveler: "Unless this throne be reserved for God, I don't see what purpose it can serve."

This unguarded expression was overheard by a grave Spaniard, and cost me dear. Meanwhile, I imagined we were going to a carousal, or a match of bullbaiting, when the grand inquisitor appeared in that elevated throne, from whence he ruled the king and the people.

As I was going to bed in the evening, two members of the inquisition came to my lodging with a figure of St. Hermandad. They embraced me with great tenderness, and conducted me in solemn silence to a well-aired prison, furnished with a bed of mat. There I remained for six weeks; at the end of which time the Inquisitor sent for me. He pressed me in his arms for some time with the most paternal affection, and told me that he was sorry to hear that I had been so ill lodged; but that all the apartments of the house were full, and hoped I should be better accommodated the next time. He then asked me with great cordiality if I knew for what reason I was imprisoned.

I told him that it was evidently for my sins.

"Very well," said he, "my dear child; but for what particular sin? Speak freely."

I racked my brain with conjectures, but could not possibly guess. He then charitably dismissed me. At last I remembered my unguarded expression. I escaped with a little bodily correction, and a fine of thirty thousand reals. I was led to make my obeisance to the grand Inquisitor, who was a man of great politeness. He asked me how I liked his little feast. I told him it was a most delicious one; and then went to press my companions to quit the country, beautiful as it was.

The impulse for traveling still possessed me. I had proposed to finish the tour of Europe with Turkey, and thither we now directed our course. I made a firm resolution not to give my opinion of any public feasts I might see in the future. "These Turks," said I to my companions, "are a set of miscreants that have not been baptized, and therefore will be more cruel than the reverend fathers the inquisitors. Let us observe a profound silence while we are among the Mahometans." When we arrived there, I was greatly surprised to see more Christian churches in Turkey than in Candia. I saw also numerous troops of monks, who were allowed to pray with great freedom, and to curse Mahomet —some in Greek, some in Latin, and others in Armenian. "What good-natured people are these Turks," cried I.

The Greek christians and the Latin christians in Constantinople were mortal enemies. These sectarians persecuted each other in much the same manner as dogs fight in the streets, till their masters part them with a cudgel.

The grand vizier was at that time the protector of the Greeks. The Greek patriarch accused me of having supped with the Latin patriarch; and I was condemned in full divan to receive an hundred blows on the soles of my feet, redeemable for five hundred sequins. Next day the grand vizier was strangled. The day following his successor, who was for the Latin party, and who was not strangled till a month after, condemned me to suffer the same punishment, for having supped with the Greek patriarch. Thus was I reduced to the sad necessity of absenting myself entirely from the Greek and Latin churches.

In order to console myself for this loss, I frequently visited a very handsome Circassian. She was the most entertaining lady I ever knew in a private conversation, and the most devout at the mosque. One evening she received me with tenderness and sweetly cried, "Alla, Illa, Alla."

These are the sacramental words of the Turks. I imagined they were the expressions of love, and therefore cried in my turn and with a very tender accent, "Alla, Illa, Alla."

"Ah!" said she, "God be praised, thou art then a Turk?"

I told her that I was blessing God for having given me so much enjoyment, and that I thought myself extremely happy.

In the morning the inman came to enroll me among the circumcised, and as I made some objection to the initiation, the cadi of that district, a man of great loyalty, proposed to have me impaled. I preserved my freedom by paying a thousand sequins, and then fled directly into Persia, resolved for the future never to hear Greek or Latin mass, nor to cry "Alla, Illa, Alla," in a love encounter.

On my arrival at Ispahan, the people asked me whether I was for white or black mutton? I told them it was a matter of indifference to me, provided it was tender. It must be observed that the Persian empire was at that time split into two factions, that of the white mutton and that of the black. The two parties imagined that I had made a jest of them both; so that I found myself engaged in a very troublesome affair at the gates of the city, and it cost me a great number of sequins to get rid of the white and the black mutton.

I proceeded as far as China, in company with an interpreter, who assured me that this country was the seat of gaiety and freedom. The Tartars had made themselves masters of it, after having destroyed everything with fire and sword.

I happened unluckily to be seized by the clerics. They represented me to his Tartarian majesty as a spy of the pope. The supreme council charged a prime mandarin, who ordered a sergeant, who commanded four shires of the country, to seize me and bind me with great ceremony. In this manner I was conducted before his majesty, after having made about an hundred and forty genuflections. He asked me if I was a spy of the pope's, and if it was true that that prince was to come in person to dethrone him. I told him that the pope was a priest of seventy years of age; that he lived at the distance of four thousand leagues from his sacred Tartaro-Chinese majesty; that he had about two thousand soldiers, who mounted guard with umbrellas; that he never dethroned anybody; and that his majesty might sleep in perfect security.

Of all the adventures of my life this was the least fatal. I was sent to Macao, and there I took shipping for Europe.

My ship required to be refitted on the coast of Golconda. I embraced this opportunity to visit the court of the great Aureng-Zeb, of whom such wonderful things have been told, and which was then in Delphi. I had the pleasure to see him on the day of that pompous ceremony in which he receives the celestial present sent him by the Sherif of Mecca. This was the besom with which they had swept the holy house, the Caaba, and the Beth Alla. It is a symbol that sweeps away all the pollutions of the soul.

Aureng-Zed seemed to have no need of it. He was the most pious man in all Indostan. It is true, he had cut the throat of one of his brothers, and poisoned his father. Twenty Rayas, and as many Omras, had been put to death; but that was a trifle. Nothing was talked of but his devotion. No king was thought comparable to him, except his sacred majesty Muley Ismael, the most serene emperor of Morocco, who always cut off some heads every Friday after prayers.

I spoke not a word. My travels had taught me wisdom. I was sensible that it did not belong to me to decide between these august sovereigns. A young Frenchman, a fellow-lodger of mine, was, however, greatly wanting in respect to both the emperor of the Indies and to that of Morocco. He happened to say very imprudently, that there were sovereigns in Europe who governed their dominions with great equity, and even went to church without killing their fathers or brothers, or cutting off the heads of their subjects.

This indiscreet discourse of my young friend the interpreter at once translated. Instructed by former experience, I instantly caused my camels to be saddled, and set out with my Frenchman. I was afterwards informed that the officers of the great Aureng-Zeb came that very night to seize me, but finding only the interpreter, they publicly executed him; and the courtiers all claimed, very justly, that his punishment was well deserved.

I had now only Africa to visit in order to enjoy all the pleasures of our continent; and thither I went to complete my voyage. The ship in which I embarked was taken by the Negro corsairs. The master of the vessel complained loudly, and asked why they thus violated the laws of nations. The captain of the Negroes thus replied:

"You have a long nose and we have a short one. Your hair is straight and ours is curled; your skin is ash-colored and ours is of the color of ebon; and therefore we ought, by the sacred laws of nature, to be always at enmity. You buy us in the public markets on the coast of Guinea like beasts of burden, to make us labor in I don't know what kind of drudgery, equally hard and ridiculous. With the whip held over our heads, you make us dig in mines for a kind of yellow earth, which in itself is good for nothing, and is not so valuable as an Egyptian onion. In like manner wherever we meet you, and are superior to you in strength, we make you slaves, and oblige you to cultivate our fields, or in case of refusal we cut off your nose and ears."

To such a learned discourse it was impossible to make any answer. I submitted to labor in the garden of an old negress, in order to save my nose and ears. After continuing in slavery for a whole year, I was at length happily ransomed.

As I had now seen all that was rare, good, or beautiful on earth, I resolved for the future to see nothing but my own home. I took a wife, and soon suspected that she deceived me; but, notwithstanding this doubt, I still found that of all conditions of life this was much the happiest.

THE GOOD BRAHMIN

DOES HAPPINESS RESULT FROM IGNORANCE OR FROM KNOWLEDGE?

IN MY travels I once happened to meet with an aged Brahmin. This man had a great share of understanding and prudence, and was very learned. He was also very rich, and his riches added greatly to his popularity; for, wanting nothing that wealth could procure, he had no desire to defraud anyone. His family was admirably managed by three handsome wives, who always studied to please him; and when he was weary of their society, he had recourse to the study of philosophy.

Not far from his house, which was handsome, well-furnished and embellished with delightful gardens, dwelt an old Indian woman who was a great bigot, ignorant, and withal very poor.

"I wish," said the Brahmin to me one day, "I had never been born!"

"Why so?" said I.

"Because," replied he, "I have been studying these forty years, and I find it has been so much time lost. While I teach others I know nothing myself. The sense of my condition is so humiliating, it makes all things so distasteful to me, that life has become a burden. I have been born, and I exist in time, without knowing what time is. I am placed, as our wise men say, in the confines between two eternities, and yet I have no idea of eternity. I am composed of matter, I think, but have never been able to satisfy myself what it is that produces thought. I even am ignorant whether my understanding is a simple faculty I possess, like that of walking and digesting, or if I think with my head in the same manner as I take hold of a thing with my hands. I am not only thus in the dark with relation to the principles of thought, but the principles of my motions are entirely unknown to me. I do not know why I exist, and yet I am applied to every day for a solution of the enigma. I must return an answer, but can say nothing satisfactory on the subject. I talk a great deal, and when I have done speaking remain confounded and ashamed of what I have said.

"I am in still greater perplexity when I am asked if Brahma was produced by Vishnu, or if they have both existed from eternity. God is my judge that I know nothing of the matter, as plainly appears by my answers. 'Reverend father,' says one, 'be pleased to inform me how evil is spread over the face of the earth.' I am as much at a loss as those who ask the question. Sometimes I tell them that every thing is for the best; but those who have the gout or the stone—those who have lost their fortunes or their limbs in the wars—believe as little of this assertion as I do myself. I retire to my own house full of curiosity, and endeavor to enlighten my ignorance by consulting the writings of our ancient sages, but they only serve to bewilder me the more. When I talk with my brethren upon this subject, some tell me we ought to make the most of life and laugh at the world. Others think they know something, and lose themselves in vain and chimerical hypotheses. Every effort I make to solve the mystery adds to the load I feel. Sometimes I am ready to fall into despair when

I reflect that, after all my researches, I neither know from whence I came, what I am, whither I shall go, or what is to become of me."

The condition in which I saw this good man gave me real concern. No one could be more rational, no one more open and honest. It appeared to me that the force of his understanding and the sensibility of his heart were the causes of his misery.

The same day I had a conversation with the old woman, his neighbor. I asked her if she had ever been unhappy for not understanding how her soul was made? She did not even comprehend my question. She had not, for the briefest moment in her life, had a thought about these subjects with which the good Brahmin had so tormented himself. She believed from the bottom of her heart in the metamorphoses of her god Vishnu, and, provided she could get some of the sacred water of the Ganges in which to make her ablutions, she thought herself the happiest of women.

Struck with the happiness of this poor creature, I returned to my philosopher, whom I thus addressed:

"Are you not ashamed to be thus miserable when, not fifty yards from you, there is an old automaton who thinks of nothing and lives contented?"

"You are right," he replied. "I have said to myself a thousand times that I should be happy if I were but as ignorant as my old neighbor, and yet it is a happiness I do not desire."

This reply of the Brahmin made a greater impression on me than anything that had passed. I consulted my own heart and found that I myself should not wish to be happy on condition of being ignorant.

I submitted this matter to some philosophers, and they were all of my opinion: and yet, said I, there is something very contradictory in this manner of thinking; for, after all, what is the question? Is it not to be happy? What signifies it then whether we have understandings or whether we are fools? Besides, there is this to be said: those who are contented with their condition are sure of that content; while those who have the faculty of reasoning are not always sure of reasoning right. It is evident then, I continued, that we ought rather to wish not to have common sense, if that common sense contributes to our being either miserable or wicked.

They were all of my opinion, and yet not one of them could be found to accept of happiness on the terms of being ignorant. From hence I concluded, that although we may set a great value upon happiness, we set a still greater upon reason.

But after mature reflection upon this subject I still thought there was great madness in preferring reason to happiness. How is this contradiction to be explained? Like all other questions, a great deal may be said about it.

THE TWO COMFORTERS

THE great philosopher Citosile once said to a woman who was disconsolate, and who had good reason to be so: "Madame, the queen of England, daughter to Henry IV., was as wretched as you. She was banished from her kingdom, was in great danger of losing her life at sea, and saw her royal spouse expire on a scaffold."

"I am sorry for her," said the lady, and began again to lament her own misfortunes.

"But," said Citosile, "remember the fate of Mary Stuart. She loved (but with a most chaste and virtuous affection) an excellent musician, who played admirably on the bass-viol. Her husband killed her musician before her face; and in the sequel, her good friend and relative, Queen Elizabeth, who called herself a virgin, caused her head to be cut off on a scaffold covered with black, after having confined her in prison for the space of eighteen years."

"That was very cruel," replied the lady, and presently relapsed into her former melancholy.

"Perhaps," said the comforter, "you have heard of the beautiful Joan of Naples, who was taken prisoner and strangled."

"I have a dim remembrance of her," said the afflicted lady.

"I must relate to you," continued the other, "the adventure of a sovereign princess who, within my recollection, was dethroned after supper, and who died in a desert island."

"I know her whole history," replied the lady.

"Well, then," said Citosile, "I will tell you what happened to another great princess whom I instructed in philosophy. She had a lover as all great and beautiful princesses have. Her father surprised this lover in her company, and was so displeased with the young man's confused manner and excited countenance, that he gave him one of the most terrible blows that had ever been given in his province. The lover seized a pair of tongs and broke the head of the angry parent, who was cured with great difficulty, and who still bears the marks of the wound. The lady in a fright leaped out of the window and dislocated her foot, in consequence of which she habitually halts, though still possessed in other respects of a very handsome person. The lover was condemned to death for having broken the head of a great prince. You can imagine in what a deplorable condition the princess must have been when her lover was led to the gallows. I have seen her long ago when she was in prison, and she always spoke to me of her own misfortunes."

"And why will you not allow me to think of mine?" said the lady.

"Because," said the philosopher, "you ought not to think of them; and since so many great ladies have been so unfortunate, it ill becomes you to despair. Think of Hecuba,—think of Niobe."

"Ah!" said the lady, "had I lived in their time, or in that of so many beautiful princesses, and had you endeavored to console them by a relation of my misfortunes, would they have listened to you, do you imagine?"

Next day the philosopher lost his only son, and was entirely prostrated with grief. The lady caused a catalogue to be drawn up of all the kings who had lost their children, and carried it to the philosopher. He read it—found it very exact—and wept nevertheless.

Three months afterwards they chanced to renew their acquaintance, and were mutually surprised to find each other in such a gay and sprightly humor. To commemorate this event, they caused to be erected a beautiful statue to Time, with this inscription: "To HIM WHO COMFORTS."

ANCIENT FAITH AND FABLE

IN ORDER to be successful in their efforts to govern the multitude, rulers have endeavored to instill all the visionary notions possible into the minds of their subjects.

The good people who read *Virgil*, or the *Provincial Letters*, do not know that there are twenty times more copies of the *Almanac of Liege* and of the *Courier Boiteux* printed, than of all the ancient and modern books together. No one can have a greater admiration than myself for the illustrious authors of these *Almanacs* and their brethren. I know that ever since the time of the ancient Chaldeans there have been fixed and stated days for taking physic, paring our nails, giving battle, and cleaving wood. I know that the best part of the revenue of an illustrious academy consists in the sale of these *Almanacs*. May I presume to ask, with all possible submission, and a becoming diffidence of my own judgment, what harm it would do to the world if some powerful astrologer were to assure the peasants and the good inhabitants of little villages that they might safely pare their nails when they please, provided it be done with a good intention? The people, I shall be told, would not buy the *Almanacs* of this new astrologer. On the contrary, I will venture to affirm, that there would be found among your great geniuses many who would make a merit in following this novelty. Should it be alleged, however, that these geniuses, in their new-born zeal, would form factions and kindle a civil war, I would have nothing farther to say on the subject, but readily give up for the sake of peace my too radical and dangerous opinion.

Everybody knows the king of Boutan. He is one of the greatest princes in the universe. He tramples under his feet the thrones of the earth; and his shoes (if he has any) are provided with sceptres instead of buckles. He adores the devil, as is well known, and his example is followed by all his courtiers. He one day sent for a famous sculptor of my country, and ordered him to make a beautiful statue of Beelzebub. The sculptor succeeded admirably. Never before was there seen such an interesting and handsome devil. But, unhappily, our Praxiteles had only given five clutches to his statue, whereas the devout Boutaniers always gave him six. This serious blunder of the artist was aggravated by the grand master of ceremonies to the devil with all the zeal of a man justly jealous of his master's acknowledged rights, and also of the established and sacred customs of the kingdom of Boutan. He insisted that the sculptor should be punished for his thoughtless innovation by the loss of his head. The anxious sculptor explained that his five clutches were exactly equal in weight to six ordinary clutches; and the king of Boutan, who was a prince of great clemency, granted him a pardon. From that time the people of Boutan no longer believed the dogma relating to the devil's six clutches.

The same day it was thought necessary that his majesty should be bled, and a surgeon of Gascony, who had come to his court in a ship belonging to our East India Company, was appointed to take from him five ounces of his precious blood. The astrologer of that quarter cried out that the king would be in danger of losing his life if the surgeon opened a vein while the heavens were in their present state. The Gascon might have told him that the only question was about the king's health; but he prudently waited a few moments and then, taking an *Almanac* in his hand, thus addressed the astrologer:

"You were in the right, great man! The king would have died had he been bled at the instant you mentioned; but the heavens have since changed their aspect, and now is the favorable moment."

The astrologer assented to the surgeon's observation. The king was cured; and by degrees it became an established custom among the Boutaniers to bleed their kings whenever it was considered necessary.

Although the Indian astronomers understood the method of calculating eclipses, yet the common people obstinately held to the old belief that the sun, when obscured, had fallen into the throat of a great dragon, and that the only way to free him from thence was by standing naked in the water and making a hideous noise to frighten away the monster, and oblige him to release his hold. This notion, which is quite prevalent among the orientals, is an evident proof how much the symbols of religion and natural philosophy have at all times been perverted by the common people. The astronomers of all ages have been wont to distinguish the two points of intersection, upon which every eclipse happens, and which are called the Lunar Nodes, by marking them with a dragon's head and tail. Now the vulgar, who are equally ignorant in every part of the world, took the symbol or sign for the thing itself. Thus, when the astronomers said the sun is in the dragon's head, the common people said the dragon is going to swallow up the sun; and yet these people were remarkable for their fondness for astrology. But while we laugh at the ignorance and credulity of the Indians, we do not reflect that there are no less than 300,000 *Almanacs* sold yearly in Europe, all of them filled with observations and predictions equally as false and absurd as any to be met with among the Indians. It is surely as reasonable to say that the sun is in the mouth or the claws of a dragon, as to tell people every year in print that they must not sow, nor plant, nor take physic, nor be bled, but on certain days of the moon. It is high time, in an age like ours, that some men of learning should think it worth their while to compose a calendar that might be of use to the industrious classes by instructing instead of deceiving them.

A blustering cleric at Rome said to an English philosopher with whom he was disputing:

"You are a dog; you say that it is the earth that turns round, never reflecting that Joshua made the sun to stand still!"

"Well! my reverend father," replied the philosopher, "ever since that time hath not the sun been immovable?"

The dog and the cleric embraced each other, and even the devout Italians were at length convinced that the earth turns round.

An augur and a senator lamented, in the time of Cæsar, the declining state of the republic.

"The times, indeed, are very bad," said the senator, "we have reason to tremble for the liberty of Rome."

"Ah!" said the augur, "that is not the greatest evil; the people now begin to lose the respect which they formerly had for our order. We seem barely to be tolerated—we cease to be necessary. Some generals have the assurance to give battle without consulting us. And, to complete our misfortunes, even those who sell us the sacred pullets begin to reason."

"Well, and why don't you reason likewise?" replied the senator, "and since the dealers in pullets in the time of Cæsar are more knowing than they were in the time of Numa, ought not you modern augurs to be better philosophers than those who lived in former ages?"

THE STUDY OF NATURE

I

THERE can be no doubt that everything in the world is governed by fatality. My own life is a convincing proof of this doctrine. An English lord, with whom I was a great favorite, had promised me that I should have the first living that fell to his gift. An old incumbent of eighty happened to die, and I immediately traveled post to London to remind the earl of his promise. I was honored with an immediate interview, and was received with the greatest kindness. I informed his lordship of the death of the rector, and of the hope I cherished relative to the disposal of the vacant living. He replied that I really looked very ill. I answered that, thanks to God, my greatest affliction was poverty. I am sorry for you, said his lordship, and he politely dismissed me with a letter of introduction to a Mr. Sidrac, who dwelt in the vicinity of Guildhall. I ran as fast as I could to this gentleman's house, not doubting but that he would immediately install me in the wished-for living. I delivered the earl's letter, and Mr. Sidrac, who had the honor to be my lord's surgeon, asked me to sit down; and, producing a case of surgical instruments, began to assure me that he would perform an operation which he trusted would very soon relieve me.

You must know, that his lordship had understood that I was suffering from some dreadful complaint, and that he generously intended to have me cured at his own expense. The earl had the misfortune to be as deaf as a post, a fact with which I, alas! had not been previously acquainted.

During the time which I lost in defending myself against the attacks of Mr. Sidrac, who insisted positively upon curing me, whether I would or no, one out of the fifty candidates who were all on the lookout, came to town, flew to my lord, begged the vacant living and obtained it.

I was deeply in love with an interesting girl, a Miss Fidler, who had promised to marry me upon condition of my being made rector. My fortunate rival not only got the living, but also my mistress into the bargain!

My patron, upon being told of his mistake, promised to make me ample amends, but alas! he died two days afterwards.

Mr. Sidrac demonstrated to me that, according to his organic structure, my good patron could not have lived one hour longer. He also clearly proved that the earl's deafness proceeded entirely from the extreme dryness of the drums of his ears, and kindly offered, by an application of spirits of wine, to harden both of my ears to such a degree that I should, in one month only, become as deaf as any peer of the realm.

I discovered Mr. Sidrac to be a man of profound knowledge. He inspired me with a taste for the study of nature, and I could not but be sensible of the valuable acquisition I had made in acquiring the friendship of a man who was capable of relieving me, should I need his services. Following his advice, I applied myself closely to the study of nature, to console myself for the loss of the rectory and of my enchanting Miss Fidler.

II

THE STUDY OF NATURE

AFTER making many profound observations upon nature (having employed in the research, my five senses, my spectacles, and a very large telescope) I said one day to Mr. Sidrac, "Unless I am much deceived, philosophy laughs at us. I cannot discover any trace of what the world calls nature; on the contrary, everything seems to me to be the result of art. By art the planets are made to revolve around the sun, while the sun revolves on its own axis. I am convinced that some genius has arranged things in such a manner, that the square of the revolutions of the planets is always in proportion to the cubic root from their distance to their centre, and one had need be a magician to find out how this is accomplished. The tides of the sea are the result of art no less profound and no less difficult to explain.

"All animals, vegetables and minerals are arranged with due regard to weight and measure, number and motion. All is performed by springs, levers, pullies, hydraulic machines, and chemical combinations, from the insignificant flea to the being called man, from the grass of the field to the far-spreading oak, from a grain of sand to a cloud in the firmament of heaven. Assuredly, everything is governed by art, and the word *nature* is but a chimera."

"What you say," answered Mr. Sidrac, "has been said many years ago, and so much the better, for the probability is greater that your remark is true. I am always astonished when I reflect that a grain of wheat cast into the earth will produce in a short time above a handful of the same corn. Stop, said I, foolishly, you forget that wheat must die before it can spring up again, at least so they say at college. My friend Sidrac, laughing heartily at this interruption, replied: That assertion went down very well a few years ago, when it was first published by an apostle called Paul; but in our more enlightened age, the meanest laborer knows that the thing is altogether too ridiculous even for argument."

"My dear friend," said I, "excuse the absurdity of my remark, I have hitherto been a theologian, and one cannot divest one's self in a moment of every silly opinion."

III

GOOD ADVICE

SOME time after this conversation between the disconsolate person, whom we shall call Goodman, and the clever anatomist, Mr. Sidrac, the latter, one fine morning, observed his friend in St. James's Park, standing in an attitude of deep thought. "What is the matter?" said the surgeon. "Is there anything amiss?"

"No," replied Goodman, "but I am left without a patron in the world since the death of my friend, who had the misfortune to be so deaf. Now supposing there be only ten thousand clergymen in England, and granting these ten thousand have each two patrons, the odds against my obtaining a bishopric are twenty thousand to one; a reflection quite sufficient to give any man the blue-devils. I remember, it was once proposed to me, to go out as cabin-boy to the East Indies. I was told that I should make my fortune. But as I did not think I should make a good admiral, whenever I should arrive at the distinction, I declined; and so, after turning my attention to every profession under the sun, I am fixed for life as a poor clergyman, good for nothing."

"Then be a clergyman no longer!" cried Sidrac, "and turn philosopher: what is your income?"

"Only thirty guineas a year," replied Goodman; "although at the death of my mother, it will be increased to fifty."

"Well, my dear Goodman," continued Sidrac, "that sum is quite sufficient to support you in comfort. Thirty guineas are six hundred and thirty shillings, almost two shillings a day. With this fixed income, a man need do nothing to increase it, but is at perfect liberty to say all he thinks of the East India Company, the House of Commons, the king and all the royal family, of man generally and individually, and lastly, of God and his attributes; and the liberty we enjoy of expressing our thoughts upon these most interesting topics, is certainly very agreeable and amusing.

"Come and dine at my table every day. That will save you some little money. We will afterwards amuse ourselves with conversation, and your thinking faculty will have the pleasure of communicating with mine by means of speech, which is certainly a very wonderful thing, though its advantages are not duly appreciated by the greater part of mankind."

IV

DIALOGUE UPON THE SOUL AND OTHER TOPICS

GOODMAN.—But my dear Sidrac, why do you always say *my thinking faculty* and not *my soul?* If you used the latter term I should understand you much better.

SIDRAC.—And for my part, I freely confess, I should not understand myself. I *feel*, I *know*, that God has endowed me with the faculties of thinking and speaking, but I can neither *feel* nor *know* that God has given me a thing called a soul.

GOODMAN.—Truly upon reflection, I perceive that I know as little about the matter as you do, though I own that I have, all my life, been bold enough to believe that I knew. I have often remarked that the eastern nations apply to the soul the same word they use to express life. After their example, the

Latins understood the word *anima* to signify the life of the animal. The Greeks called the breath the soul. The Romans translated the word breath by *spiritus,* and thence it is that the word spirit or soul is found in every modern nation. As it happens that no one has ever seen this spirit of breath, our imagination has converted it into a being, which it is impossible to see or touch. The learned tell us, that the soul inhabits the body without having any place in it, that it has the power of setting our different organs in motion without being able to reach and touch them, indeed, what has not been said upon the subject? The great Locke knew into what a chaos these absurdities had plunged the human understanding. In writing the only reasonable book upon metaphysics that has yet appeared in the world, he did not compose a single chapter on the soul; and if by chance he now and then makes use of the word, he only introduces it to stand for intellect or mind.

In fact, every human being, in spite of Bishop Berkeley, is sensible that he has a mind, and that this mind or intellect is capable of receiving ideas; but no one can feel that there is another being—a soul,—within him, which gives him motion, feeling and thought. It is, in fact, ridiculous to use words we do not understand, and to admit the existence of beings of whom we cannot have the slightest knowledge.

SIDRAC.—We are then agreed upon a subject which, for so many centuries, has been a matter of dispute.

GOODMAN.—And I must observe that I am surprised we should have agreed upon it so soon.

SIDRAC.—Oh! that is not so astonishing. We really wish to know what is truth. If we were among the Academies, we should argue like the characters in Rabelais. If we had lived in those ages of darkness, the clouds of which so long enveloped Great Britain, one of us would very likely have burned the other. We are so fortunate as to be born in an age comparatively reasonable; we easily discover what appears to us to be truth, and we are not afraid to proclaim it.

GOODMAN.—You are right, but I fear, that, after all, the truth we have discovered is not worth much. In mathematics, indeed, we have done wonders; from the most simple causes we have produced effects that would have astonished Apollonius or Archimedes: but what have we proved in metaphysics? Absolutely nothing but our own ignorance.

SIDRAC.—And do you call that nothing? You grant the supreme Being has given you the faculties of feeling and thinking, he has in the same manner given your feet the faculty of walking, your hands their wonderful dexterity, your stomach the capability of digesting food, and your heart the power of throwing arterial blood into all parts of your body. Everything we enjoy is derived from God, and yet we are totally ignorant of the means by which he governs and conducts the universe. For my own part, as Shakespeare says, I thank him for having taught me that, of the principles of things, I know absolutely nothing. It has always been a question, in what manner the soul acted upon the body. Before attempting to answer this question, I must be convinced that I have a soul. Either God has given us this wonderful spark of intellect, or he has gifted us with some principle that answers equally well. In either case, we are still the creatures of his divine will and goodness, and that is all I know about the matter.

GOODMAN.—But if you do not know, tell me at least what you are inclined to think upon the subject. You have opened skulls, and dissected the human fœtus. Have you ever, in these dissections, discovered any appearance of a soul?

SIDRAC.—Not the least, and I have not been able to understand how an immortal and spiritual essence could dwell for months together in a membrane. It appears to me difficult to conceive that this pretended soul existed before the foundation of the body; for in what could it have been employed during the many ages previous to its mysterious union with flesh? Again! how can we imagine a spiritual principle waiting patiently in idleness during a whole eternity, in order to animate a mass of matter for a space of time, which, compared with eternity, is less than a moment?

It is worse still, when I am told that God forms immortal souls out of nothing, and then cruelly dooms them to an eternity of flames and torments. What? burn a spirit, in which there can be nothing capable of burning; how can he burn the sound of a voice, or the wind that blows? though both the sound and wind were material during the short time of their existence; but a pure spirit —a thought—a doubt—I am lost in the labyrinth; on whichever side I turn, I find nothing but obscurity and absurdity, impossibility and contradiction. But I am quite at ease when I say to myself God is master of all. He who can cause each star to hold its particular course through the broad expanse of the firmament, can easily give to us sentiments and ideas, without the aid of this atom, called the soul. It is certain that God has endowed all animals, in a great or lesser degree, with thought, memory and judgment; he has given them life; it is demonstrated that they have feeling, since they possess all the organs of feeling; if then they have all this without a soul, why is it improbable that we have none? and why do mankind flatter themselves that they alone are gifted with a spiritual and immortal principle?

GOODMAN.—Perhaps this idea arises from their inordinate vanity. I am persuaded that if the peacock could speak, he would boast of his soul, and would affirm that it inhabited his magnificent tail. I am very much inclined to believe with you, that God has created us thinking creatures, with the faculties of eating, drinking, feeling, &c., without telling us one word about the matter. We are as ignorant as the peacock I just mentioned, and he who said that we live and die without knowing how, why, or wherefore, spoke nothing but the truth.

SIDRAC.—A celebrated author, whose name I forget, calls us nothing more than the puppets of Providence, and this seems to me to be a very good definition. An infinity of movements are necessary to our existence, but we did not ourselves invent and produce motion. There is a Being who has created light, caused it to move from the sun to our eyes in about seven minutes. It is only by means of motion that my five senses are put in action, and it is only by means of my senses that I have ideas, hence it follows that my ideas are derived from the great author of motion, and when he informs me how he communicates these ideas to me, I will most sincerely thank him.

GOODMAN.—And so will I. As it is I constantly thank him for having permitted me, as Epictetus says, to contemplate for a period of some years this beautiful and glorious world. It is true that he could have made me happier by putting me in possession of Miss Fidler and a good rectory; but still, such as I am, I consider myself as under a great obligation to God's parental kindness and care.

SIDRAC.—You say that it is in the power of God to give you a good living, and to make you still happier than you are at present. There are many persons who would not scruple flatly to contradict this proposition of yours. Do you forget that you yourself sometimes complain of fatality? A man, and particularly a priest, ought never to contradict one day an assertion he has perhaps made the day before. All is but a succession of links, and God is wiser than to break the eternal chain of events, even for the sake of my dear friend Goodman.

GOODMAN.—I did not foresee this argument when I was speaking of fatality; but to come at once to the point, if it be so, God is as much a slave as myself.

SIDRAC.—He is the slave of his will, of his wisdom, and of the laws which he has himself instituted; and it is impossible that he can infringe upon any of them; because it is impossible that he can become either weak or inconsistent.

GOODMAN.—But, my friend, what you say would tend to make us irreligious, for, if God cannot change any of the affairs of the world, what is the use of teasing him with prayers, or of singing hymns to his praise?

SIDRAC.—Well! who bids you worship or pray to God? We praise a man because we think him vain; we entreat of him when we think him weak and likely to change his purpose on account of our petitions. Let us do our duty to God, by being just and true to each other. In that consists our real prayers, and our most heartfelt praises.

THE MAN OF FORTY CROWNS

I

NATIONAL POVERTY

AN OLD MAN, who is forever *pitying the present times, and extolling the past,* was saying to me: "Friend, France is not so rich as it was under Henry the IVth."

"And why?"

"Because the lands are not so well cultivated; because hands are wanting for the cultivation; and because the day-laborer having raised the price of his work, many landowners let their inheritances lie fallow."

"Whence comes this scarcity of hands?"

"From this, that whoever finds in himself anything of a spirit of industry, takes up the trades of embroiderer, chaser, watchmaker, silk weaver, attorney, or divine. It is also because the revocation of the Edict of Nantes has left a great void in the kingdom; because beggars of all kinds have greatly multiplied, because the people in general avoid as much as possible the hard labor of cultivation, for which we are born by God's destination, and which we have rendered ignominious by our own opinions; so very wise are we!

"Another cause of our poverty lies in our new wants. We pay our neighbors four millions of livres on one article, and five or six upon another; such, for example, as a stinking powder for stuffing up our noses brought from America. Our coffee, tea, chocolate, cochineal, indigo, spices, cost us above sixty millions a year. All these were unknown to us in the reign of Henry the IVth, except the spices, of which, however, the consumption was not so great as it is now. We burn a hundred times more wax-lights than were burnt then; and get more than the half of the wax from foreign countries, because we neglect our own hives. We see a hundred times more diamonds in the ears, round the necks, and on the hands of our city ladies of Paris, and other great towns, than were worn by all the ladies of Henry the IVth's court, the Queen included. Almost all the superfluities are necessarily paid for with ready specie.

"Observe especially that we pay to foreigners above fifteen millions of annuities on the *Hôtel-de-Ville;* and that Henry the IVth, on his accession, having found two millions of debt in all on this imaginary *Hôtel,* very wisely paid off a part, to ease the state of this burden.

"Consider that our civil wars were the occasion of the treasures of Mexico being poured into the kingdom, when Don Philip *el Discreto* took it into his head to buy France, and that since that time our foreign wars have eased us of a good half of our money.

"These are partly the causes of our poverty; a poverty which we hide under varnished ceilings, or with the help of our dealers in fashion. We are poor with taste. There are some officers of revenue, there are contractors or jobbers, there are merchants, very rich; their children, their sons-in-law, are also very rich; but the nation in general is unfortunately not so."

This old man's discourse, well or ill grounded, made a deep impression on me; for the curate of my parish, who had always had a friendship for me, had taught me a little of geometry and of history: and I begin to reflect a little, which is very rare in my province. I do not know whether he was right or not in every thing, but being very poor, I could very easily believe that I had a great many companions of my misery.

II

DISASTER OF THE MAN OF FORTY CROWNS

I VERY readily make known to the *universe*, that I have a landed estate which would yield me forty crowns a year, were it not for the tax laid on it.

There came forth several edicts from certain persons, who, having nothing better to do, govern the state at their fire-side. The preamble of these edicts was, "that the legislative and executive was born, *jure divino*, the co-proprietor of my land;" and that I owe it at least the half of what I possess. The enormity of this legislative and executive power made me bless myself. What would it be if that power which presides over "the essential order of society," were to take the whole of my little estate? The one is still more divine than the other.

The comptroller general knows that I used to pay, in all, but twelve livres; that even this was a heavy burden on me, and that I should have sunk under it if God had not given me the talent of making wicker baskets, which helped to carry me through my trials. But how should I, on a sudden, be able to give the king twenty crowns?

The new ministers also said in their preamble, that it was not fit to tax anything but the land, because everything arises from the land, even rain itself, and consequently that nothing was properly liable to taxation but the fruits of the land.

During the last war, one of their collectors came to my house, and demanded · of me, for my quota, three measures of corn and a sack of beans, the whole worth twenty crowns, to maintain the war—of which I never knew the reason, having only heard it said that there was nothing to be got by it for our country, and a great deal to lose. As I had not at that time either corn, or beans, or money, the legislative and executive power had me dragged to prison; and the war went on as well as it could.

On my release from the dungeon, being nothing but skin and bone, whom should I meet but a jolly fresh-colored man in a coach and six? He had six footmen, to each of whom he gave for his wages more than the double of my revenue. His head-steward, who, by the way, looked in as good plight as himself, had of him a salary of two thousand livres, and robbed him every year of twenty thousand more. His mistress had in six months stood him in forty thousand crowns. I had formerly known him when he was less well to pass than myself. He owned, by way of comfort to me, that he enjoyed four hundred thousand livres a year.

"I suppose, then," said I, "that you pay out of this income two hundred thousand to the state, to help to support that advantageous war we are carrying on; since I, who have but just a hundred and twenty livres a year, am obliged to pay half of them."

"I," said he, "I contribute to the wants of the state? You are surely jesting. my friend. I have inherited from an uncle his fortune of eight millions, which he got at Cadiz and at Surat; I have not a foot of land: my estate lies in government contracts, and in the funds. I owe the state nothing. It is for you to give half of your substance,—you who are a proprietor of land. Do you not see, that if the minister of the revenue were to require anything of me in aid of our country, he would be a blockhead, that could not calculate? for everything is the produce of the land. Money and the paper currency are nothing but pledges of exchange. If, after having laid the sole tax, the tax that is to supply the place of all others, on those commodities, the government were to ask money of me; do you not see, that this would be a double load? that it would be asking the same thing twice over? My uncle sold at Cadiz to the amount of two millions of your corn, and of two millions of stuffs made of your wool; upon these two articles he gained cent. per cent. You must easily think that this profit came out of lands already taxed. What my uncle bought for tenpence of you, he sold again for above fifty livres at Mexico; and thus he made a shift to return to his own country with eight millions clear.

"You must be sensible, then, that it would be a horrid injustice to re-demand of him a few farthings on the tenpence he paid you. If twenty nephews like me, whose uncles had gained each eight millions at Buenos Ayres, at Lima, at Surat, or at Pondicherry, were, in the urgent necessities of the state, each to lend to it only two hundred tnousand livres, that would produce four millions. But what horror would that be! Pay then thou, my friend, who enjoyest quietly the neat and clear revenue of forty crowns; serve thy country well, and come now and then to dine with my servants in livery."

This plausible discourse made me reflect a good deal, but I cannot say it much comforted me.

III

CONVERSATION WITH A GEOMETRICIAN

IT SOMETIMES happens that a man has no answer to make, and yet is not persuaded. He is overthrown without the feeling of being convinced. He feels at the bottom of his heart a scruple, a repugnance, which hinders him from believing what has been proved to him. A geometrician demonstrates to you that between a circle and a tangent you may thread a number of curves, and yet cannot get one straight line to pass. Your eyes, your reason, tell you the contrary. The geometrician gravely answers you, that it is an infinitesimal of the second order. You stare in stupid silence, and quit the field all astonished, without having any clear idea, without comprehending anything, and without having any reply to make.

Consult but a geometrician of more candor, and he explains the mystery to you.

"We suppose," says he, "what cannot be in nature, lines which have length without breadth. Naturally and philosophically speaking, it is impossible for one real line to penetrate another. No curve nor no right line can pass between two real lines that touch one another. These theorems that puzzle you are but sports of the imagination, ideal chimeras. Whereas true geometry is the art of measuring things actually existent."

I was perfectly well satisfied with the confession of the sensible mathematician, and, with all my misfortune, could not help laughing on learning that there was a quackery even in that science, which is called the sublime science. My geometrician was a kind of philosophical patriot, who had deigned to chat with me sometimes in my cottage. I said to him:

"Sir, you have tried to enlighten the cockneys of Paris, on a point of the greatest concern of mankind, that of the duration of human life. It is to you alone that the ministry owes its knowledge of the due rate of annuities for lives, according to different ages. You have proposed to furnish the houses in town with what water they may want, and to deliver us at length from the shame and ridicule of hearing water cried about the streets, and of seeing women inclosed within an oblong hoop, carrying two pails of water, both together of about thirty pounds weight, up to a fourth story. Be so good, in the name of friendship, to tell me, how many two-handed bipeds there may be in France?

THE GEOMETRICIAN.—It is assumed, that there may be about twenty millions, and I am willing to adopt this calculation as the most probable, till it can be verified, which it would be very easy to do, and which, however, has not hitherto been done, because *one does not always think of everything*.

THE MAN OF FORTY CROWNS.—How many acres, think you, the whole territory of France contains?

THE GEOMETRICIAN.—One hundred and thirty millions, of which almost the half is in roads, in towns, villages, moors, heaths, marches, sands, barren lands, useless convents, gardens of more pleasure than profit, uncultivated grounds, and bad grounds ill cultivated. We might reduce all the land which yields good returns to seventy-five millions of square acres; but let us state them at fourscore millions. One cannot do too much for one's country.

THE MAN OF FORTY CROWNS.—How much may you think each acre brings in yearly, one year with another, in corn, seeds of all kinds, wine, fishponds, wood, metals, cattle, fruit, wool, silk, oil, milk, clear of all charges, without reckoning the tax?

THE GEOMETRICIAN.—Why, if they produce each twenty-five livres (about twenty English shillings), it is a great deal; but not to discourage our countrymen, let us put them at thirty livres. There are acres which produce constantly regenerating value, and which are estimated at three hundred livres: there are others which only produce three livres. The mean proportion between three and three hundred is thirty; for you must allow that three is to thirty as thirty is to three hundred. If, indeed, there were comparatively many acres at thirty livres, and very few at three hundred, our account would not hold good; but, once more, I would not be over punctilious.

THE MAN OF FORTY CROWNS.—Well, sir; how much will these fourscore millions of acres yield of revenue, estimated in money?

THE GEOMETRICIAN.—The account is ready made; they will produce two thousand four hundred millions of livres of the present currency.

THE MAN OF FORTY CROWNS.—I have read that Solomon possessed, of his own property, twenty-five thousand millions of livres, in ready money; and certainly there are not two thousand four hundred millions of specie circulating in France, which, I am told, is much greater and much richer than Solomon's country.

THE GEOMETRICIAN.—There lies the mystery. There may be about nine hundred millions circulating throughout the kingdom; and this money, passing from hand to hand, is sufficient to pay for all the produce of the land, and of industry. The same crown may pass ten times from the pocket of the cultivator into that of the ale-housekeeper and of the tax-gatherer.

THE MAN OF FORTY CROWNS.—I apprehend you. But you told me that we are, in all, about twenty millions of inhabitants, men, women, old and young. How much, pray, do you allow for each?

THE GEOMETRICIAN.—One hundred and twenty livres, or forty crowns.

THE MAN OF FORTY CROWNS.—You have just guessed my revenue. I have four acres, which, reckoning the fallow years with those of produce, bring me in one hundred and twenty livres; which is little enough, God knows.

But if every individual were to have his contingent, would that be no more than five louis d'ors a year?

THE GEOMETRICIAN.—Certainly not, according to our calculation, which I have a little amplified. Such is the state of human nature. Our life and our fortune have narrow limits. In Paris, they do not, one with another, live above twenty-two or twenty-three years, and, one with another, have not, at the most, above a hundred and twenty livres a year to spend. So that your food, your raiment, your lodging, your movables, are all represented by the sum of one hundred and twenty livres.

THE MAN OF FORTY CROWNS.—Alas! What have I done to you, that you thus abridge me of my fortune and life? Can it then be true, that I have but three and twenty years to live, unless I rob my fellow-creatures of their share?

THE GEOMETRICIAN.—This is incontestable in the good city of Paris. But from these twenty-three years you must deduct ten, at the least, for your childhood, as childhood is not an enjoyment of life; it is a preparation; it is the porch of the edifice; it is the tree that has not yet given fruits; it is the dawn of a day. Then again, from the thirteen years which remain to you, deduct the time of sleep, and that of tiresomeness of life, and that will be at least a moiety. You will then have six years and a half left to pass in vexation, in pain, in some pleasures, and in hopes.

THE MAN OF FORTY CROWNS.—Merciful heaven! At this rate, your account does not allow us above three years of tolerable existence.

THE GEOMETRICIAN.—That is no fault of mine. Nature cares very little for individuals. There are insects which do not live above one day, but of which the species is perpetual. Nature resembles those great princes, who reckon as nothing the loss of four hundred thousand men, so they but accomplish their august designs.

THE MAN OF FORTY CROWNS.—Forty crowns and three years of life! What recourse can you imagine against two such curses?

THE GEOMETRICIAN.—As to life, it would be requisite to render the air of Paris more pure—that men should eat less and take more exercise—that mothers should suckle their own children—that people should be no longer so ill-advised as to dread inoculation. This is what I have already said; and as to fortune, why, even marry and rear a family.

THE MAN OF FORTY CROWNS.—How! Can the way to live more at ease be to associate to my own bad circumstances those of others?

THE GEOMETRICIAN.—Five or six bad circumstances put together form a tolerable establishment. Get a good wife, and we will say only two sons and two daughters; this will make seven hundred and twenty livres for your little family, that is to say, if distributive justice were to take place, and that each individual had an hundred and twenty livres a year. Your children, in their infancy, stand you in almost nothing; when grown up they will ease and help you. Their mutual aid will save you a good part of your expenses, and you may live very happy, like a philosopher. Always provided, however, that those worthy gentlemen who govern the state have not the barbarity to extort from each of you twenty crowns a year. But the misfortune is, we are no longer in the golden age, where the men, born all equals, had an equal part in the nutritive productions of uncultivated land. The case is now far from being so good a one, as that every two-handed biped possesses land to the value of an hundred and twenty livres a year.

THE MAN OF FORTY CROWNS.—'Sdeath! You ruin us. You said but just now, that in a country of fourscore millions of inhabitants, each of them ought to enjoy an hundred and twenty livres a year, and now you take them away from us again!

THE GEOMETRICIAN.—I was computing according to the registers of the golden age, but we must reckon according to that of iron. There are many inhabitants who have but the value of ten crowns a year, others no more than four or five, and above six millions of men who have absolutely nothing.

THE MAN OF FORTY CROWNS.—Nothing? Why they would perish of hunger in three days' time.

THE GEOMETRICIAN.—Not in the least. The others, who possess their portions, set them to work, and share with them. It is from this arrangement that the pay comes for the divine, the confectioner, the apothecary, the preacher, the actor, the attorney, and the hackney-coachman. You thought yourself very ill off to have no more than a hundred and twenty livres a year, reduced to a hundred and eight by your tax of twelve livres. But consider the soldiers who devote their blood to their country at the rate of fourpence a day. They have not above sixty-three livres a year for their livelihood, and yet they make a comfortable shift, by a number of them joining their little stock and living in common.

THE MAN OF FORTY CROWNS.—A pretty way of flourishing, truly!

THE GEOMETRICIAN.—And yet there is no other. In every country it is the rich that enable the poor to live. This is the sole source of the industry of commerce. The more industrious a nation itself is, the more it gains from foreign countries. Could we, on our foreign trade, get ten millions a year by the balance in our favor, there would, in twenty years, be two hundred millions more in the nation. This would afford ten livres a head more, on the supposition of an equitable distribution; that is to say, that the dealers would make each poor person earn ten livres the more, once paid, in the hopes of making still more considerable gains. But commerce, like the fertility of the earth, has its bounds, otherwise its progression would be *ad infinitum*. Nor, besides, is it clear, that the balance of our trade is constantly favorable to us; there are times in which we lose.

THE MAN OF FORTY CROWNS.—I have heard much talk of population. If our inhabitants were doubled, so that we numbered forty millions of people instead of twenty, what would be the consequence?

THE GEOMETRICIAN.—It would be this: that, one with another, each would have, instead of forty, but twenty crowns to live upon; or that the land should produce double the crops it now does; or that there should be double the national industry, or of gain from foreign countries; or that half of the people should be sent to America; or that one-half of the nation should eat the other.

THE MAN OF FORTY CROWNS.—Let us then remain satisfied with our twenty millions of inhabitants, and with our hundred and twenty livres a head, distributed as it shall please the Lord. Yet this situation is a sad one, and your iron age is hard indeed.

THE GEOMETRICIAN.—There is no nation that is better off; and there are many that are worse. Do you believe that there is in the North wherewithal to afford to each inhabitant the value of an hundred and twenty of our livres a year? If they had had the equivalent of this, the Huns, the Vandals, and the Franks would not have deserted their country, in quest of establishments elsewhere, which they conquered, fire and sword in hand.

THE MAN OF FORTY CROWNS.—If I were to listen to you, you would persuade me presently that I am happy with my hundred and twenty livres.

THE GEOMETRICIAN.—If you would but think yourself happy, you would then be so.

THE MAN OF FORTY CROWNS.—A man cannot imagine what actually is not, unless he be mad.

THE GEOMETRICIAN.—I have already told you, that in order to be more at your ease, and more happy than you are, you should take a wife; to which I tack, however, this clause, that she has, as well as you, one hundred and twenty livres a year; that is to say, four acres at ten crowns an acre. The ancient Romans had each but one. If your children are industrious, they can each earn as much by their working for others.

THE MAN OF FORTY CROWNS.—So that they may get money, without others losing it.

THE GEOMETRICIAN.—Such is the law of all nations: there is no living but on these terms.

THE MAN OF FORTY CROWNS.—And must my wife and I give each of us the half of our produce to the legislative and executive power, and the new ministers of state rob us of the price of our hard labor, and of the substance of our poor children, before they are able to get their livelihood? Pray, tell me, how much money will these new ministers of ours bring into the king's coffers, by this *jure divino* system?

THE GEOMETRICIAN.—You pay twenty crowns on four acres, which bring you in forty. A rich man, who possesses four hundred acres will, by the new tariff, pay two thousand crowns; and the whole fourscore millions of acres will yield to the king twelve hundred millions of livres a year, or four hundred millions of crowns.

THE MAN OF FORTY CROWNS.—That apears to me impracticable and impossible.

THE GEOMETRICIAN.—And very much you are in the right to think so: and this impossibility is a geometrical demonstration that there is a fundamental defect in the calculation of our new ministers..

THE MAN OF FORTY CROWNS.—Is not there also demonstrably a prodigious injustice in taking from me the half of my corn, of my hemp, of the wool of my sheep, etc., and, at the same time, to require no aid from those who shall have gained ten, twenty, or thirty thousand livres a year, by my hemp, of which they will have made linen,—by my wool, of which they will have made cloth,—by my corn, which they will have sold at so much more than it cost them?

THE GEOMETRICIAN.—The injustice of this administration is as evident as its calculation is erroneous. It is right to favor industry; but opulent industry ought to contribute to support the state. This industry will have certainly taken from you a part of your one hundred and twenty livres, and appropriated that part to itself, in selling you your shirts and your coat twenty times dearer than they would have cost you, if you had made them yourself. The manufacturer who shall have enriched himself, at your expense, will, I allow, have also paid wages to his workmen, who had nothing of themselves, but he will, every year, have sunk, and put by a sum that will, at length, have produced to him thirty thousand livres a year. This fortune then he will have acquired at your expense. Nor can you ever sell him the produce of your land dear enough to reimburse you for what he will have got by you; for were you to attempt such an advance of your price, he would procure what he wanted cheaper from other countries. A proof of which is, that he remains constantly possessor of his thirty thousand livres a year, and you of your one hundred and twenty livres, that often diminish instead of increasing. It is then necessary and equitable that the refined industry of the trader should pay more than the gross industry of the farmer. The same is to be said of the collectors of the revenue. Your tax had previously been but twelve livres, before our great ministers were pleased to take from you twenty crowns. On these twelve livres, the collector retained tenpence, or ten *sols* for himself. If in your province there were five hundred thousand souls, he will have gained two hundred and fifty thousand livres a year. Suppose he spends fifty thousand, it is clear that at the end of ten years he will be two millions in pocket. It is then but just that he should contribute his proportion, otherwise, everything would be perverted, and go to ruin.

THE MAN OF FORTY CROWNS.—I am very glad you have taxed the officer of the revenue. It is some relief to my imagination. But since he has so well increased his superfluity, what shall I do to augment my small modicum?

THE GEOMETRICIAN.—I have already told you, by marrying, by laboring, by trying to procure from your land some sheaves of corn in addition to what it previously produced.

THE MAN OF FORTY CROWNS.—Well! granted then that I shall have been duly industrious; that all my countrymen will have been so too; and that the legislative and executive power shall have received a good round tax; how much will the nation have gained at the end of the year?

THE GEOMETRICIAN.—Nothing at all; unless it shall have carried on a profitable foreign trade. But life will have been more agreeable in it. Everyone will, respectively, in proportion, have had more clothes, more linen, more movables than he had before. There will have been in the nation a more abundant circulation. The wages would have been, in process of time, augmented, nearly in proportion to the number of the sheaves of corn, of the tods of wool, of the ox-hides, of the sheep and goats, that will have been added, of the clusters of grapes that will have been squeezed in the winepress. More of the value of commodities will have been paid to the king in money, and the king will have returned more value to those he will have employed under his orders; but there will not be half a crown the more in the kingdom.

THE MAN OF FORTY CROWNS.—What will then remain to the government at the end of the year?

THE GEOMETRICIAN.—Once more, nothing. This is the case of government in general. It never lays by anything. It will have got its living, that is to say, its food, raiment, lodging, movables. The subject will have done so too. Where a government amasses treasure, it will have squeezed from the circulation so much money as it will have amassed. It will have made so many wretched, as it will have put by forty crowns in its coffers.

THE MAN OF FORTY CROWNS.—At this rate, then, Henry IV. was but a mean-spirited wretch, a miser, a plunderer; for I have been told that he had chested up in the Bastile above fifty millions of livres according to our present currency.

THE GEOMETRICIAN.—He was a man as good, and as prudent, as he was ʌrave. He was preparing to make a just war, and by amassing in his coffers twenty-two millions of the currency of that time, besides which he had twenty more to receive, which he left in circulation, he spared the people above a hundred millions that it would have cost, if he had not taken those useful measures. He made himself morally sure of success against an enemy who had not taken the like precaution. The probabilities were prodigiously in his favor. His twenty-two millions, in bank, proved that there was then in this kingdom twenty-two millions of surplusage of the territorial produce, so that no one was a sufferer.

THE MAN OF FORTY CROWNS.—My father then told me the truth, when he said that the subject was in proportion more rich under the administration of the Duke of Sully than under that of our new ministers, who had laid on the *single* tax, the *sole* tax, and who, out of my forty crowns, have taken away twenty. Pray, tell me, is there another nation in the world that enjoys this precious advantage of the *sole tax?*

THE GEOMETRICIAN.—Not one opulent nation. The English, who are not much given to laughter, could not, however, help bursting out, when they heard that men of intelligence among us had proposed this kind of administration. The Chinese exact a tax from all the foreign trading ships that resort to Canton. The Dutch pay, at Nangazaqui, when they are received in Japan, under pretext, that they are not Christians. The Laplanders, and the Samoieds, are indeed subjected to a sole tax in sables or marten-skins. The republic of St. Marino pays nothing more than tithes for the maintenance of that state in its splendor.

There is, in Europe, a nation celebrated for its equity and its valor, that pays no tax. This is Switzerland. But thus it has happened. The people have put themselves in the place of the Dukes of Austria and of Zeringue. The small cantons are democratical, and very poor. Each inhabitant pays but a trifling sum toward the support of this little republic. In the rich cantons, the people are charged, for the state, with those duties which the Archdukes of Austria and the lords of the land used to exact. The protestant cantons are, in proportion, twice as rich as the catholic, because the state, in the first, possesses the lands of the monks. Those who were formerly subjects to the Archdukes of Austria, to the Duke of Zeringue, and to the monks, are now the subjects of their own country. They pay to that country the same tithes, the same fines of alienation, that they paid to their former masters; and as the subjects, in general, have very little trade, their merchandise is liable to no charges, except some small staple duties. The men make a trade of their courage, in their dealings with foreign powers, and sell themselves for a certain term of years, which brings some money into their country at our expense: and this example is as singular a one in the civilized world as is the sole tax now laid by our new legislators.

THE MAN OF FORTY CROWNS.—So, sir, the Swiss are not plundered, *jure divino*, of one-half of their goods; and he that has four cows in Switzerland is not obliged to give two of them to the state?

THE GEOMETRICIAN.—Undoubtedly not. In one canton, upon thirteen tons of wine, they pay one, and drink the other twelve. In another canton, they pay the twelfth, and drink the remaining eleven.

THE MAN OF FORTY CROWNS.—Why am not I a Swiss? That cursed tax, that single and singularly iniquitous tax, that has reduced me to beggary! But then again, three or four hundred taxes, of which it is impossible for me to retain or pronounce the bare names, are they more just and more tolerable? Was there ever a legislator, who, in founding a state, wished to create counselors to the king, inspectors of coal-meters, gaugers of wine, measurers of wood, searchers of hog-tongues, comptrollers of salt butter? or to maintain an army of rascals, twice as numerous as that of Alexander, commanded by sixty generals, who lay the country under contribution, who gain, every day, signal victories, who take prisoners, and who sometimes sacrifice them in the air, or on a boarded stage, as the ancient Scythians did, according to what my vicar told me?

Now, was such a legislation, against which so many outcries were raised, and which caused the shedding of so many tears, much better than the newly imposed one, which at one stroke cleanly and quietly takes away half of my subsistence? I am afraid that on a fair liquidation it will be found that under the ancient system of the revenue they used to take, at times and in detail, three-quarters of it.

THE GEOMETRICIAN.—*Iliacos intra muros peccatur et extra. Est modus in rebus. Caveas ne quid nimie.*

THE MAN OF FORTY CROWNS.—I have learned a little of history, and something of geometry; but I do not understand a word of Latin.

THE GEOMETRICIAN.—The sense is, pretty nearly, as follows. *There is wrong on both sides. Keep to a medium in everything. Nothing too much.*

THE MAN OF FORTY CROWNS.—I say, nothing too much; that is really my situation; but the worst of it is, I have not enough.

THE GEOMETRICIAN.—I allow that you must perish of want, and I too, and the state too, if the new administration should continue only two years longer; but it is to be hoped heaven will have mercy on us.

THE MAN OF FORTY CROWNS.—We pass our lives in hope, and die hoping to the last. Adieu, sir, you have enlightened me, but my heart is grieved.

THE GEOMETRICIAN.—This is, indeed, often the fruit of knowledge.

IV

AUDIENCE OF THE COMPTROLLER GENERAL

I WENT with my half-crown, to present a petition to the comptroller general, who was that day giving audience.

His ante-chamber was filled with people of all kinds. There were there especially some with more bluff faces, more prominent bellies, and more arrogant looks than my man of eight millions. I durst not draw near to them; I saw them, but they did not observe me.

A squire, a great man for tithes, had begun a suit at law against certain subjects of the state, whom he called his tenants. He had already a larger income than the half of his villagers put together, and was moreover lord of the manor. His claim was, that whereas his vassals had, with infinite pains, converted their heaths into vineyards, they owed him a tithe of the wine, which, taking into the account the price of labor, of the vine-props, of the casks and cellarage, would carry off above a quarter of the produce.

"But," said he, "as the tithes are due, *jure divino,* I demand the quarter of the substance of my tenants, in the name of God."

The minister of the revenue said to him, "I see how charitable you are."

A farmer-general, extremely well-skilled in assessments, interposed, saying: "Sir, that village can afford nothing to this squire; as I have, but the last year, made the villagers pay thirty-two taxes on their wine beside their over-consumption of the allowance for their own drinking. They are entirely ruined. I have seized and sold their cattle and movables, and yet they are still my debtors. I protest, then, against the claim of the reverend father."

"You are in the right," answered the minister of the revenue, "to be his rival; you both equally love your neighbor, and you both edify me."

A third, a lord of the manor, whose tenants were in mortmain, was waiting for a decree of the council that should put him in possession of all the estate of a Paris cockney, who having, inadvertently, lived a year and a day in a house subject to this servitude, and inclosed within the hands of this priest, had died at the year's end. The lord was claiming all the estate of this cockney, and claiming it *jure divino.*

The minister found by this that the heart of this lord was as just and as tender as those of the others.

A fourth, who was comptroller of the royal domains, presented a specious memorial, in which he justified himself for his having reduced twenty families to beggary. They had inherited from their uncles, their aunts, their brothers, or cousins; and were liable to pay the duties. The officers of the domain had generously proved to them that they had not set the full value on their inherit-ances,—that they were much richer than they believed; and, consequently, having condemned them to a triple fine, ruined them in charges, and threw the heads of the families into jail, he had bought their best possessions without untying his purse-strings.

The comptroller general said to him in a tone indeed rather bitter:

"*Euge, controlleur bone et fidelis, quia supra pauca fuisti fidelis, fermier-general te constituam.*" (Well done.)

But to a master of the requests, who was standing at his side, he said in a low voice:

"We must make these blood-suckers disgorge. It is time to give some relief to the people, who, without our care, and our equity, would have nothing to live upon in this world at least, however they might fare in the other."

Some, of profound genius, presented projects to him. One of them had imagined a scheme to lay a tax on wit. "All the world," said he, "will be eager to pay, as no one cares to pass for a fool."

The minister declared to him, "I exempt you from the tax."

Another proposed to lay the *only* tax upon songs and laughing, in considera-tion that we were the merriest nation under the sun, and that a song was a relief and comfort for every thing. But the minister observed that of late there were hardly any songs of pleasantry made; and he was afraid that, to escape the tax, we would become too serious.

The next that presented himself was a trusty and loyal subject, who offered to raise for the king three times as much, by making the nation pay three times less. The minister advised him to learn arithmetic.

A fourth proved to the king in the way of *friendship*, that he could not raise above seventy-five millions, but that he was going to procure him two hundred and twenty-five. "You will oblige me in this," said the minister, "as soon as we shall have paid the public debts."

At length, who should appear but a deputy of the new author, who makes the legislative power co-proprietor of all our lands, *jure divino*, and who was giving the king twelve hundred millions of revenue. I knew the man again who had flung me into prison for not having paid my twenty crowns, and throwing myself at the feet of the comptroller general, I implored his justice; upon which, he burst out a laughing, and telling me it was a trick that had been played me, he ordered the doers of this mischief in jest to pay me a hundred crowns damages, and exempted me from the land-tax for the rest of my life. I said to him, "God bless your honor!"

V

On Taxes Paid to a Foreign Power

The man of Forty Crowns having improved his understanding and having accumulated a moderate fortune, married a very pretty girl, who had an hundred crowns a year of her own. As soon as his son was born, he felt himself a man of some consequence in the state. He was famous for making the best baskets in the world, and his wife was an excellent seamstress.

About a month ago, the Man of Forty Crowns came to me, holding both his sides, which seemed ready to burst with laughing. In short, he laughed so heartily that I could not help laughing also, without knowing at what. So true it is, that man is born an imitative animal, that instinct rules us, and that the great emotions of the soul are catching. *Ut ridentibus arrident, ita flentibus adfient, Humani vultus.* (Our faces reflect.)

When he had had his laugh out, he told me that he had just come from meeting with a man who called himself a foreign envoy, and that this per-sonage was sending away a great sum of money to an Italian, three hundred leagues off, in the name and behalf of a Frenchman, on whom the king had bestowed a small fief or fee; because the said Frenchman could never enjoy this benefit of the king's conferring, if he did not give to this Italian the first year's income.

"The thing," said I, "is very true; but it is not quite such a laughing matter either. It costs France about four hundred thousand livres a year, in petty duties of this kind; and in the course of two centuries and a half, that this custom has lasted, we have already sent to Italy fourscore millions."

"Heavenly father!" he exclaimed, "how many forty crowns would that make? Some Italian, then, subdued us, I suppose, two centuries and a half ago, and laid that tribute upon us!"

"In good faith," answered I, "he used to impose on us in former times, in a much more burthensome way. That is but a trifle in comparison to what, for a long time, he levied on our poor nations of Europe."

Then I related to him how those holy usurpations had taken place, and, came to be established. He knows a little of history, and does not want for sense. He easily conceived that we had been slaves, and that we were still dragging a little bit of our chain that we could not get rid of. He spoke much and with energy, against this abuse; but with what respect for religion in general. With what reverence did he express himself for the bishops! How heartily did he wish them many forty crowns a year, that they might spend them in their dioceses in good works.

He also wished that all the country vicars might have a number of forty crowns, that they might live with decency.

"It is a sad thing," said he, "that a vicar should be obliged to dispute with his flock for two or three sheaves of corn, and that he should not be amply paid by the country. These eternal contests for imaginary rights, for the tithes, destroy the respect that is owing to them. The unhappy cultivator who shall have already paid to the collectors his tenth penny, and the twopence a livre, and the tax, and the capitation, and the purchase of his exemption from lodging soldiers,–after he shall have lodged soldiers,–for this unfortunate man, I say, to see the vicar take away in addition the tithe of his produce, he can no longer look on him as his pastor, but as one that flays him alive,–that tears from him the little skin that is left him. He feels but too sensible, that while they are, *jure divino*, robbing him of his tenth sheaf, they have the diabolical cruelty not to give him credit for all that it will have cost him to make that sheaf grow. What then remains to him for himself and family? Tears, want, discouragement, despair, and thus he dies of fatigue and misery. If the vicar were paid by the country, he would be a comfort to his parishioners, instead of being looked on by them as their enemy."

The worthy man melted as he uttered these words; he loved his country, and the public good was his idol. He would sometimes emphatically say, "What a nation would the French be if it pleased!" We went to see his son, whom the mother, a very neat and clean woman, was nursing. "Alas!" said the father, "here thou art, poor child, and hast nothing to pretend to but twenty-three years of life, and forty crowns a year."

VI

ON PROPORTIONS

THE produce of the extremes is equal to the produce of the means: but two sacks of corn stolen are not, to those who stole them, as the loss of their lives is to the interest of the person from whom they were stolen.

The squire of ———, from whom two of his domestic servants in the country had stolen two measures of corn, has just had the two delinquents hanged. This execution has cost him more than all his harvest has been worth to him: and since that time he has not been able to get a servant.

If the laws had ordained that such as stole their master's corn should work in his grounds, during their lives in fetters, and with a bell at their neck fixed to a collar, the squire would have been a considerable gainer by it.

"Terror should be preventively employed against crimes;" very true: but work, on compulsion, and lasting shame, strike more terror than the gallows.

There was, some months ago at London, a malefactor who had been condemned to be transported to America to work there at the sugar works with the Negroes. In England, any criminal, as in many other countries, may get a petition presented to the king, either to obtain a free pardon, or a mitigation of the sentence. This one presented a petition to be hanged, alleging that he mortally hated work, and that he had rather suffer strangling for a minute than to make sugar all his lifetime.

Others may think otherwise: every one to his taste. But it has been already said, and cannot be too often repeated, that a man hanged is good for nothing, and that punishments ought to be useful.

Some years ago, in Turkey, two young men were condemned to be impaled, for having (without taking off their caps) stood to see the procession of the Lama pass by. The Emperor of China, who is a man of very good sense, said, that for his part, he should have condemned them to walk bareheaded, in every public procession, for three months afterwards.

"Proportion punishments to crimes," says the Marquis Beccaria; but those who made the laws were not geometricians.

I hate the laws of Draco, which punish equally crimes and faults, wickedness and folly. Let us,—especially in all litigations, in all dissensions, in all quarrels,—distinguish the aggressor from the party offended, the oppressor from the oppressed. An offensive war is the procedure of a tyrant; he who defends himself is in the character of a just man.

As I was absorbed in these reflections, the Man of Forty Crowns came to me all in tears. I asked, with emotion, if his son, who was by right to live twenty-three years, was dead?

"No," said he, "the little one is very well, and so is my wife; but I was summoned to give evidence against a miller, who has been put to the torture, ordinary and extraordinary, and who has been found innocent. I saw him faint away under redoubled tortures. I heard the crash of his bones. His outcries and screams of agony are not yet out of my ears; they haunt me. I shed tears for pity, and shudder with horror."

His tears drew mine. I trembled, too, like him; for I have naturally an extreme sensibility.

My memory then represented to me the dreadful fate of the Calas family: A virtuous mother in irons,—her children in tears, and forced to fly,—her house given up to pillage,—a respectable father of a family broken with torture, agonizing on a wheel, and expiring in the flames; a son loaded with chains, and dragged before the judges, one of whom said to him:

"We have just now broken your father on the wheel; we will break you alive too."

I remembered the family of Sirven, who one of my friends met with among the mountains covered with ice, as they were flying from the persecution of a judge as ignorant as he was unjust. This judge (he told me) had condemned an innocent family to death on a supposition, without the least shadow of proof, that the father and mother, assisted by two of their daughters, had cut the throat of the third, and drowned her besides, for going to mass. I saw in judgments of this kind at once an excess of stupidity, of injustice, and of barbarity.

The Man of Forty Crowns joined with me in pitying human nature. I had in my pockets the discourse of an attorney-general of Dauphiny, which turned upon very important matters. I read to him the following passages:

"Certainly those must have been truly great men, who, at first, dared to take upon themselves the office of governing their fellow creatures, and to set their shoulders to the burthen of the public welfare; who, for the sake of the good they meant to do to men, exposed themselves to their ingratitude, and for the public repose renounced their own; who made themselves, as one may say, middlemen between their fellow-creatures and Providence, to compose for them, by artifice, a happiness which Providence seems otherwise to have refused to them by any other means.

"What magistrate was ever so careless of his responsibilities and duties to humanity as to entertain such ideas? Could he, in the solitude of his closet, without shuddering with horror and pity, cast his eyes on those papers, the unfortunate monuments of gilt or of innocence? Should he not think he hears a plaintive voice and groans issue from those fatal writings, and press him to decide the destiny of a subject, of a husband, of a father, or of a whole family? What judge can be so unmerciful (if he is charged with but one single process) as to pass in cold blood before the door of a prison? Is it I (must he say to himself) who detain in that execrable place my fellow-creature, perhaps my countryman, one of humankind, in short? Is it I that confine him every day,—that shut those execrable doors upon him? Perhaps despair will have seized him. He sends up to heaven my name loaded with his curses; and doubtless calls to witness against me that great Judge of the world, who observes us, and will judge us both.

"Here a dreadful sight presents itself on a sudden to my eyes: The judge, tired with interrogating by words, has recourse to interrogation by tortures. Impatient in his inquiries and researches, and perhaps irritated at their inutility, he has brought to him torches, chains, levers, and all those instruments invented for producing pain. An executioner comes to interpose in the functions of the magistracy, and terminates by violence a judicial interrogation.

"Gentle philosophy! Thou who never seekest truth but with attention and patience, couldst thou expect, in an age that takes thy name, that such instruments would be employed to discover that truth?

"Can it be really true, that our laws approve this inconceivable method, and that custom consecrates it?

"Their laws imitate their prejudices; their public punishments are as cruel as their private vengeance; and the acts of their reason are scarce less unmerciful than those of their passions. What can be the cause of this strange contrariety? It is because our prejudices are ancient, and our morality new; it is because we are as penetrated with our opinions as we are inattentive to our ideas; it is because our passion for pleasures hinders us from reflecting on our wants, and that we are more eager to live than to direct ourselves right; it is, in a word, because our morals are gentle without being good; it is because we are polite, and are not so much as humane."

These fragments, which eloquence had dictated to humanity, filled the heart of my friend with a sweet consolation. He admired with tenderness.

"What!" said he, "are such masterpieces as these produced in a province? I had been told that Paris was all the world, or the only place in it!"

"It is," said I, "the only place for producing comic operas; but there are at this time, in the provinces, magistrates who think with the same virtue and express themselves with the same force. Formerly, the oracles of justice, like those of morality, were nothing but matter of mere ridicule. Dr. Balordo declaimed at the bar, and Harlequin in the pulpit. Philosophy has at length come, and has said, 'Do not speak in public, unless to set forth new and useful truths, with the eloquence of sentiment and of reason.'"

But, say the praters, if we have nothing new to say, what then? Why, hold your tongues, replies philosophy. All those vain discourses for parade, that contain nothing but phrases, are like the fire on the eve of St. John's, kindled on that day of the year in which there is the least want of it to heat one's self— it causes no pleasure, and not so much as the ashes of it remain.

Let all France read good books. But notwithstanding all the progress of the human understanding, there are few that read; and among those who sometimes seek instruction, the reading for the most part is very ill chosen. My neighbors, men and women, pass their time, after dinner, at playing an English game, which I have much difficulty to pronounce, since they call it whist. Many good citizens, many thick heads, who take themselves for good heads, tell you, with an air of importance, that books are good for nothing. But, Messieurs, the critics, do not you know that you are governed only by books? Do not you know that the statutes, the military code, and the gospel, are books on which you continually depend? Read; improve yourselves. It is reading alone that invigorates the understanding; conversation dissipates it; play con- tracts it.

Thus it was that the Man of Forty Crowns proceeded to form, as one may say, his head and his heart. He not only succeeded to the inheritance of his two fair cousins, but he came also to a fortune left by a very distant relation, who had been a sub-farmer of the military hospitals, where he had fattened himself on the strict abstinence to which he had put the wounded soldiers. This man never would marry. He never would own any of his relations. He lived in the height of debauchery, and died at Paris of a surfeit. He was, as any- one may see, a very useful member of the state.

Our new philosopher was obliged to go to Paris to get possession of the inheritance of this relative. At first, the farmers of the domain disputed it with him. He had the good luck, however, to gain his cause, and the generosity to give to the poor of his neighborhood, who had not their contingent of forty crowns a year, a part of the spoils of the deceased son of fortune. After which he set himself about satisfying his passion for having a library.

He read every morning and made extracts. In the evening, he consulted the learned to know in what language the serpent had talked to our good mother; whether the soul is in the callous body, or in the pineal gland; whether St. Peter lived five and twenty years at Rome; what specific difference there is between a throne and a dominion; and why the Negroes have a flat nose. He proposed to himself, besides, never to govern the state, nor to write any pamphlets against new dramatic pieces. He was called Mr. Andrew, which was his Christian name. Those who have known him, do justice to his modesty and to his qualities, both natural and acquired.

VII

A Great Quarrel

During the stay of Mr. Andrew at Paris, there happened a very important quarrel. The point was, to decide whether Marcus Antoninus was an honest man, and whether he was in hell, or in purgatory, or in limbo, waiting till the day of resurrection. All the men of sense took the part of Marcus Antoninus. They said: Antoninus has been always just, temperate, chaste, and beneficent. It is true, he has not so good a place in paradise as St. Anthony; for proportions ought to be observed, as has been before recommended. But certainly the soul of Antoninus is not roasting on a spit in hell.

The party opposed to these good people pretended, on the contrary, that no compounding for salvation ought to be allowed to Marcus Antoninus; that he was a heretic; that the Carpocratians and the Alcgi were not so bad as he; that he had died without confession; that it was necessary to make an example; that it was right to damn him, if but to teach better manners to the emperors of China and Japan,—to those of Persia, Turkey, and Morocco,—to the kings of England, Sweden, Denmark, and Prussia,—to the stadtholder of Holland,—to the avoyers of the Canton of Berne, who no more go to confession than did the Emperor Marcus Antoninus; that, in short, there is an unspeakable pleasure in passing sentence against a dead sovereign, which one could not fulminate against him in his lifetime, for fear of losing one's ears.

This quarrel became as furious as was formerly that of the Ursulines and the Annonciades. In short, it was feared that it would come to a schism, as in the time of the hundred and one Mother Goose's tales, and of certain bills payable to the bearer in the other world. To be sure, a schism is something very terrible. The meaning of the word is a division in opinion, and till this fatal moment all men had been agreed to think the same thing.

Mr. Andrew, who was an excellent member of society, invited the chiefs of the two parties to sup with him. He is one of the best companions that we have. His humor is gentle and lively; his gaiety is not noisy; he is open, frank, and easy. He has not that sort of wit which seems to aim at stifling that of others. The authority which he conciliates to himself is due to nothing but his graceful manner, to his moderation, and to a round good-natured face, which is quite persuasive. He could have brought to sup cheerfully together a Corsican and a Genoese,—a representative of Geneva and a negative man,—the mufti and cleric. He managed so dextrously as to make the first stroke that the disputants of both parties aimed at each other fall to the ground, by turning off the discourse, and by telling a very diverting tale, which pleased equally the damning and the damned. In short, when they had got a little good-humored and elevated with wine, he made them sign an agreement that the soul of Marcus Antoninus should remain in *statu quo*—that is to say, nobody knows where,—till the day of final judgment.

The souls of the doctors of divinity returned quietly to their limbos after supper, and all was calm. This adjustment of the quarrel did great honor to the Man of Forty Crowns; and, since then, whenever any very peevish virulent dispute arose among men of letters, or among men not of letters, the advice given was, "*Gentlemen, go and sup at Master Andrew's!*"

VIII

A RASCAL REPULSED

THE reputation which Mr. Andrew had acquired for pacifying quarrels,—by giving good suppers,—drew upon him last week a singular visit. A dark complexioned man, shabbily enough dressed, rather crook-backed, with his head leaning toward one shoulder, a haggard eye, and dirty hands, asked to be invited to a supper with his enemies.

"Who are your enemies?" said Mr. Andrew, "and who are you?"

"Alas, sir," said he, "I am forced to confess that I am taken for one of those wretches that compose libels to get bread, and who are forever crying out,— 'Religion,—Religion,—Religion,' in order to come at some little benefice. I am accused of having calumniated some of the most truly religious subjects, the most sincere adorers of divinity, and the most honest men of the kingdom. It is true, sir, that in the heat of composition there often fall from the pen of those of my trade certain little inadvertencies or slips, which are taken for gross errors; and some liberties taken with the truth, which are termed impudent lies. Our zeal is looked upon in the light of a horrid mixture of villainy and fanaticism. It has been alleged, that while we are insnaring the easy faith of some silly old women, we are the scorn and execration of all the men of worth who can read.

"My enemies are the principal members of the most illustrious academies of Europe, writers much esteemed, and beneficent members of society. I have but just published a book under the title of *Anti-philosophical*. I had nothing but the best intentions, and yet no one would buy my book. Those to whom I made presents of it, threw it into the fire, telling me it was not only anti-reasonable, but anti-christian, and extremely anti-decent."

"Well, then!" said Mr. Andrew to him, "follow the example of those to whom you presented your libel, throw it into the fire, and let no more be said of it. It is unnecessary to ask you to sup with men of wit, who can never be your enemies, since they will never read you."

"Could not you, sir, at least," said the hypocrite to him, "reconcile me with the relations of the deceased Monsieur de Montesquieu, to whose memory I offered an indignity, that I might give honor and glory to the Reverend Rout?"

"Zounds!" said Mr. Andrew, "the Reverend Rout has been dead this long time; go and sup with him."

IX

THE GOOD SENSE OF MR. ANDREW

BUT how greatly did the sense of Mr. Andrew improve in vigor from the time he procured a library! He lives with books as with men, and is careful in his choice of them. What a pleasure it is to gain instruction, to enlarge one's mind by studying the best works of the greatest authors.

He congratulates himself on being born at a time when human reason is tending toward perfection. "How unhappy should I have been," he used to say, "if the age I live in had been that in which they used to condemn to the galleys those who wrote against the categories of Aristotle."

Distress had weakened the springs of Mr. Andrew's soul; but good fortune restored their elasticity. There are many Andrews in the world to whom nothing is wanting but a turn of the wheel of fortune to make of them men of true merit.

He is now well acquainted with all the affairs of Europe, and especially with the progress of the human understanding.

He recently remarked to me, that Reason travels by slow journeys from north to south, in company with her two intimate friends, Experience and Toleration. Agriculture and Commerce attend them. When Reason presented herself in Italy, the congregation of the Index sternly repulsed her. All she could do was to secretly send some of her agents, who, in spite of her enemies, do some good. Let but some years more pass, and it is to be hoped that the country of the Scipios will no longer be that of harlequins in monks' habits.

She has sometimes met with cruel foes in France; but she has now so many friends in that kingdom that she stands a good chance of at length becoming first minister there.

When she presented herself in Bavaria and Austria, she found two or three great wig-blocks that stared at her with stupid and astonished eyes. Their greeting was: "Madam, we never heard of you; we do not know you." Her answer to which was: "Gentlemen, in time you will come to know me, and to love me. I have been well received at Berlin, at Moscow, at Copenhagen, at Stockholm. It is long ago that I have been naturalized by Act of Parliament in England, through the labors of Locke, Gordon, Trenchard, Lord Shaftesbury, and a number of others of the same nation. You will, some day or other, confer on me the like grant. I am the daughter of Time. I expect every thing from my father."

When she passed over the frontiers of Spain and Portugal, she blessed God on observing that the fires of the Inquisition were less frequently kindled. She rejoiced on seeing the cleric expelled; but was afraid that, while the country had been cleared of the foxes, it was still left exposed to the ravages of wolves.

If she makes any fresh attempts to gain entrance into Italy it is thought she will begin by establishing herself at Venice; and that she will take up her abode in the kingdom of Naples, in spite of the liquefaction of the saint's blood in that country, which awakens in her mind mournful reflections on human credulity. It is pretended that she has an infallible secret for untying the strings of a crown, which are entangled, nobody knows how, in those of a mitre.

X

THE GOOD SUPPER AT MR. ANDREW'S

WE SUPPED at Mr. Andrew's yesterday, together with a Doctor Sorbonne with Monsieur Pinto, the celebrated Jew, with the Chaplain of the Protestant chapel of the Dutch Ambassador, the secretary of the Prince Galitzin of the Greek church, a Calvinist Swiss Captain, two Philosophers, and three Ladies of great wit.

The supper was a very long one; and yet, so polite it must be owned we are grown—so much is one afraid at supper to give any cause of offence to one's brethren, that there was no more disputing upon religion than as if not one of those at table had ever had any. It is not so with the Regent Coge, and the ex-cleric Patouillet, and with all the animals of that kind. Those pitiful creatures will say more stupidly abusive things in one pamphlet of two pages, than the best company in Paris can say agreeable and instructive ones in a supper of four hours. And what is stranger yet, they dare not tell a man to his face what they have the impudence to print.

The conversation turned at first on a piece of pleasantry in the Persian Letters, in which it is repeated, after a number of grave personages, that the world is not only growing worse, but that it is becoming depopulated, so that if the proverb should have any truth in it, that "the more fools there are, the more laughter," laughing is likely to be soon banished from the face of the earth.

The Doctor of Sorbonne assured us that, in fact, the world was almost reduced to nothing. He quoted Petavius, who demonstrates that in less than three hundred years the descendants of one of the sons of Noah (I forget whether it was Shem or Japhet) amounted to six hundred and twelve millions three hundred and fifty-eight thousand true believers within two hundred and eighty-five years after the universal deluge.

Mr. Andrew asked, why in the time of Philip de Bel, that is to say, about three hundred years after Hugh Capet, there were not six hundred and twenty-three thousand millions of princes of the royal family?

"It is," said the Doctor of Sorbonne, "because the stock of faith has greatly decreased."

A great deal was said about Thebes and its hundred gates, and of the million of soldiers that issued out of those gates with the twenty thousand chariots of war.

"Shut the book there," said Mr. Andrew: "Since I have taken to reading, I beg to suspect that the same genius that wrote Gargantua, used of yore to write all the histories."

"But, in short," said one of the company, "Thebes, Memphis, Babylon, Nineveh, Troy, Seleucia, were great cities once, and now no longer exist."

"Granted," answered the secretary of the Prince Galitzin; "but Moscow, Constantinople, London, Paris, Amsterdam, Lyons (which is better than ever Troy was) and all the towns of France, Germany, Spain, and the North, were then deserts."

The Swiss captain, a gentleman of great knowledge, owned to us, that when his ancestors took it into their heads to quit their mountains and their precipices, to go and take forcible possession, as was but reasonable, of a finer country, Cæsar, who saw with his own eyes the list of those emigrants, found that their number amounted to three hundred and sixty-eight thousand, inclusive of the old, the children, and the women. At this time, the single canton of Berne possesses as many inhabitants, which is not quite the half of Switzerland, and I can assure you that the thirteen cantons have above seven hundred and twenty thousand souls, including the natives who are serving or carrying on business in other countries. From such data, gentlemen of learning make absurd calculations, and they base fallacious systems on no better footing.

The question next agitated was, whether the citizens of Rome, in the time of the Cæsars, were richer than the citizens of Paris, in the time of Monsieur Silhouette?

"Oh," says Mr. Andrew, "this is a point on which I have some call to speak. I was a long time the Man of Forty Crowns; but I conceive that the citizens of Rome had more. Those illustrious robbers on the highway pillaged the finest countries of Asia, of Africa, and of Europe. They lived splendidly on the produce of their rapines; but yet there were doubtless some beggars at Rome. I am persuaded that, among those conquerors of the world, there were some reduced to an income of forty crowns a year, as I formerly was."

"Do you know," said a learned member of the Academy of Inscription and Belles Lettres, "that it cost Lucullus for every supper he gave in the saloon of Apollo thirty-nine thousand three hundred and twelve livres of our money; but that the celebrated epicurean Atticus did not expend above two hundred and thirty livres a month for his table."

"If that be true," said I, "he deserved to be president of the Miser-society, lately established in Italy. I have read as you have done, in Florus, that incredible anecdote; but perhaps Florus had never supped with Atticus, or else his text, like so many others, has been corrupted by copyists. No Florus shall ever make me believe that the friend of Cæsar and of Pompey, of Cicero and of Antony, all of whom were often entertained at his house, got off for something less than ten louis d'ors a month. *But thus exactly 'tis that history written.*"

Madam Andrew, for her part, told the learned member of the Academy, that if he would keep her table for ten times as much, she would be greatly obliged to him.

I am persuaded that this evening at Mr. Andrew's cost him as much as the monthly expense at Atticus. As for the ladies, they expressed a doubt whether the suppers of Rome were more agreeable than those of Paris. The conversation was very gay, though leaning a little to the learned. There was no talk of new fashions, nor of the ridiculous part of any one's character or conduct, nor of the scandalous history of the day.

The question upon luxury was discussed and searched to the bottom. It was mooted whether or not luxury had been the ruin of the Roman empire; and it was proved that the two empires of the east and west owed their destruction to nothing but to religious controversies, and to the monks; and, in fact, when Alaric took Rome, its whole attention was engrossed by theological disputes; when Mahomet took Constantinople, the monks defended much better the eternity of the light of Mount Thabor, than they defended the town against the Turks.

One of our men of learning made a very significant remark. It was that those two great empires were annihilated, but that the works of Virgil, Horace, and Ovid still exist.

From the age of Augustus, they made but one skip to the age of Louis the XIVth. A lady put the question, why it was that with a great deal of wit there was no longer produced scarcely any work of genius? Mr. Andrew answered that it was because such works had been produced in the last age. This idea was fine spun, and yet solidly true. It bore a thorough handling. After that, they fell with some harshness upon a Scotchman, who had taken it into his head to give rules to taste, and to criticise the most admirable passages of Racine, without understanding French. But there was one Denina still more severely treated. He had abused Montesquieu's *Spirit of Laws*, without comprehending him, and had especially censured what is the most liked and approved in that work.

This recalled to my mind Boileau's making a parade of his affected contempt of Tasso. One of the company advanced that Tasso, with all his faults, was as superior to Homer, as Montesquieu, with his still greater imperfections, was above the farrago of Grotius. But there was presently a strong opposition made to these false criticisms, dictated by national hatred and prejudice. The Seignior Denina was treated as he deserved, and as pedants ought to be by men of wit.

It was especially remarked, with much sagacity, that the greatest part of the literary works of this age, as well as of the conversations, turned on the examination of the masterpieces of the last century; in which we are like disinherited children, who are taking an estimate of their father's estate. It was confessed that philosophy had made great progress, but that the language and style was somewhat corrupted.

It is the nature of all these conversations to make transitions from one subject to another. All these objects of curiosity, of science, and of taste, soon vanished, to give way to the great scene which the Empress of Russia, and the King of Poland, were giving to the world. They had been just raising up and restoring the rights of oppressed humanity, and establishing liberty of conscience in a part of the globe of a much greater extent than the old Roman Empire. This service done to human kind, this example given to so many courts, was mentioned with the applause it deserved. Healths were drunk to the philosophical empress, to the royal philosopher, and to the philosophical primate, with the wish of their having many imitators. Even the doctors of Sorbonne admired them; for there are some persons of good sense in that body, as there were formerly some men of wit among the Bœotians.

The Russian secretary astonished us with a recital of the great establishments they were forming in Russia. It was asked, why people were in general more fond of reading the history of Charles the XIIth, who passed his life in destroying, than that of Peter the Great, who consumed his in creating? On this we concluded, that weakness and a frivolous turn of mind are the causes of this preference; that Charles the XIIth was the Don Quixote, and Peter the Solon of the North; that superficial understandings prefer a wild extravagant heroism, to the great views of a legislator: that the particulars of the foundation of a town are less pleasing to them, than the rashness of a man, who, at the head of only his domestics, braves an army of ten thousand Turks; and that, in short, most readers love amusement better than instruction. Thence it is, that a hundred women read *The Thousand and One Arabian Nights*, for one that reads two chapters of Locke.

What was not talked of at this supper? of which I shall long retain the remembrance. It was also in course to say a word of the actors and actresses, that eternal subject of the table-talk of Versailles and of Paris. It was agreed that a good declaimer was as rare as a good poet. For my part, I must own that Plato's banquet could not have given me more pleasure than that of Monsieur and Madame Andrew.

Our very pretty gentlemen, and our very fine ladies, would, doubtless, have found it dull, and been tired with it. They pretend to be the only good company: but neither Mr. Andrew nor I ever willingly sup with that kind of good company.

THE SAGE AND THE ATHEIST

INTRODUCTION

You request me, sir, to give you some account of our worthy friend, and his singular son. The leisure that the retirement of Lord Peterborough now affords me places it in my power to oblige you. You will be as astonished as I was, and perhaps adopt my opinion on the subject.

You scarcely knew the young and unfortunate John, Freind's only son, whom his father took with him to Spain when he received the appointment of chaplain to our armies, in 1705. You started for Aleppo, before my lord besieged Barcelona; yet you were right when you said John's countenance was amiable and interesting and that he gave proofs of intelligence and courage. It was quite true. Every one who knew him, loved him. At first he was intended for the church; but, as he manifested much aversion for that profession, which, indeed, requires great skill, management, and finesse, his prudent father considered it a folly and a crime to oppose his inclination.

John was not twenty years old when he assisted, as a volunteer, at the attack on Mont-Joui, which was captured, and where the Prince of Hesse lost his life. Our poor John was wounded, taken prisoner, and carried into the town. The following is an account of his adventures from the attack on Mont-Joui till the taking of Barcelona. It is as told by a Catalonian lady, a little too free and too simple. Such stories do not find a way to the hearts of your wise men. I received it from her when I entered Barcelona in the suite of Lord Peterborough. You must read it without offence, as a true description of the manners of the country.

I

ADVENTURES OF JOHN, A YOUNG ENGLISHMAN, WRITTEN BY DONNA LAS NALGAS

WHEN we were informed that the same savages who came through the air to seize on Gibraltar, were come to besiege our beautiful Barcelona, we began to offer prayers at Notre Dame de Manreze—assuredly the best mode of defence.

These people, who are come from so far, are called by a name very hard to pronounce, that is, English. The inquisitor, Don Jeronimo Bueno Caracu-carador, denounced these brigands. He assured us that the English had monkey-tails, bears' paws, and parrot-heads; that they sometimes spoke like men, but invariably made a great hissing; and that consequently they would all be infallibly exterminated, especially if they presumed to appear before Mont-Joui. He had scarcely finished his harangue when he heard that Mont-Joui was taken by storm.

The same evening we learned that a young Englishman, who had been wounded in the assault, was our prisoner. Throughout the town arose cries of victory! victory! And the illuminations were very general.

Donna Boca Vermeja, who had the honor to be the inquisitor's favorite, was very desirous to see what the English animal and heretic was like. She was my intimate friend. I shared her curiosity. We were obliged to wait till his wound was cured; and this did not take very long.

Soon after, we learned that he was in the habit of visiting daily at the residence of Elbob, my cousin german, who, as every one knows, is the best surgeon in the town. My friend Boca Vermeja's impatience to see this singular monster increased two-fold. We had no rest ourselves, and gave none to our cousin, the surgeon, till he allowed us to conceal ourselves in a small closet, which we entered on tiptoe without saying a word and scarcely venturing to breathe, just as the Englishman arrived. His face was not turned towards us. He took off a small cap which enclosed his light hair, which then fell in thick curls down the finest neck I ever beheld. His form presented a plumpness, a finish, an elegance, approaching, in my opinion, the Apollo Belvedere at Rome—a copy of which my uncle the sculptor possesses.

Donna Boca Vermeja was transported with surprise, and delighted. I shared her ecstasy, and could not forbear exclaiming: "O che hermoso Muchacho!"

These words made the young man turn round. We then saw the face of an Adonis on the body of a young Hercules. Donna Boca Vermeja nearly fell backwards at the sight:

"St. James!" she exclaimed. "Is it possible heretics are such fine men? How we have been deceived about them."

Donna Boca was soon violently in love with the English monster. She is handsomer than I am, I must confess; and I must also confess that I became doubly jealous of her on that account. I took care to show her that to forsake the inquisitor, Don Jeronimo Bueno Caracucarador, for an Englishman, would be a crime falling nothing short of damnation.

"Ah! my dear Las Nalgas," she said (Las Nalgas is my name), "I would forsake Melchizedek himself for so fine a young man."

One of the inquisitors whipped us both, and had our dear Englishman arrested by twenty-four Alguazils of St. Hermandad. John killed four; and was at length captured by the remaining twenty. He was confined in a very damp cellar, and sentenced to be burnt the following Sunday, in full ceremony, clothed in a San-bénito, wearing a sugar-loaf cap.

Here Donna Las Nalgas's tale terminates. This lady was not without a description of wit, which in Spain we call agudéza.

II

You know the skillful conduct of the Earl of Peterborough after he took Barcelona; how successfully he prevented pillage, restored order, and rescued the Duchess of Popoli from the hands of some drunken Germans, who robbed and abused her. Conceive the surprise, grief, rage, and tears, of our friend Freind, on learning that John was confined in the dungeons of the inquisition, and condemned to the stake. You know that cold temperaments are frequently most energetic when great events call them into action. You should have seen this distracted father, whom you were accustomed to think imperturbable, fly to the dungeon of his son more rapidly than the horses at Newmarket hasten to the goal. The fifty soldiers who went with him were soon out of breath, and always a hundred paces behind. At length he reached the cell and entered it. What a scene! what tears! what joy! Twenty victims, devoted to the same ceremony, are delivered. All the prisoners take arms and fight with our soldiers. The buildings of the office are destroyed in ten minutes, and they breakfasted beside the ruins, on the wine and ham of the inquisitors.

In the midst of the roar of cannon, the sound of trumpets and drums, announcing our victory to Catalonia, our friend Freind recovered his accustomed tranquillity of manner. He was as calm as the sky after a day of storm. He was raising to God a heart as serene as his countenance, when he perceived a black spectral figure, clad in a surplice, issue from a vault, and fall at his feet, crying for mercy.

"Who are you?" said our friend. "Do you come from Hades?"

"Almost," rejoined the other. "I am Don Jeronimo Bueno Caracucarador, inquisitor. I solicit most humbly your forgiveness for wishing to roast your son in public. I took him for a Jew."

"Supposing that to be the case," said our friend with his customary sang froid, "does it become you, Señor Caracucarador, to roast people alive because they are descended from a sect that formerly inhabited a rocky canton near the Syrian desert? What does it matter to you whether a man is circumcised or not? that he observe Easter at the full of the moon, or on the following Sunday? It is very bad reasoning to say, 'That man is a Jew; therefore I must have him burnt, and take his property.' The Royal Society of London do not reason in that way.

"Do you know, Señor Caracucarador, that Jesus Christ was a Jew—that he was born, lived, and died a Jew? that he observed the passover like a Jew, at the full of the moon? that all his apostles were Jews? that they went to the temple after his death, as we are expressly told? that the first fifteen secret bishops of Jerusalem were Jews? But my son is no Jew; he belongs to the established church. How came it into your head to burn him alive?"

The inquisitor, overawed by the learning of Monsieur Freind, and still prostrate at his feet, replied:

"Alas! sir, we know nothing about this at the University of Salamanca. Forgive me, once more. The true reason is, your son took from me my favorite, Donna Boca Vermeja."

"Ah! if he took your favorite, that's another thing. We should never take 'our neighbor's goods.' That is not, however, a sufficient reason for burning a young man to death. As Leibnitz says, 'The punishment should be in proportion to the crime.' As Christians on the other side of the British Channel, especially toward the South, make no more of roasting each other, be it the Counsellor Dubourg, M. Servetus, or those who were burned in the reign of Philippe II., surnamed El Discreto, than we do of roasting a joint of beef in London. But bring Miss Boca Vermeja before me, that I may learn the truth from her own mouth."

Boca Vermeja appeared weeping, looking the handsomer for her tears, as women generally do.

"Is it true, Miss, that you are devotedly attached to M. Caracucarador, and that my son has abducted you?"

"Abducted me? The English gentleman! I never met with any one so amiable and good-looking as your son. You are very fortunate in being his father. I could follow him to the world's end. I always hated that ugly inquisitor, who whipped me and Mademoiselle Las Nalgas till he nearly brought blood. If you wish to make me happy, you will cause the old fellow to be hanged at my bedroom window."

Just as Boca Vermeja was thus speaking, the Earl of Peterborough sent for the inquisitor Caracucarador, to have him hanged. You will not be surprised to hear that Mr. Freind firmly opposed this measure.

"Let your just displeasure," said he, "give way to generous feelings. A man should never be put to death but when it is absolutely necessary for the safety of others. The Spaniards say the English are barbarians, who kill all the priests that come in their way. This might have injured the cause of the arch-duke, for whom you have taken Barcelona. I have sufficient satisfaction in rescuing my son, and putting it out of the power of this rascally lord to exercise his inquisitorial functions."

In a word, the wise and charitable Freind was contented with getting Caracucarador flogged, as he had whipped Miss Boca Vermeja and Miss Las Nalgas.

Such clemency affected the Catalonians. The persons rescued from the inquisition felt that our religion was better than theirs. Nearly all requested to be admitted members of the established church; even some bachelors of the University of Salamanca, who chanced to be at Barcelona, requested instruction. The greater part soon became enlightened, with the exception of a certain Don Inigo-y-Medroso, y-Comodios, y-Papalamiendos, who obstinately adhered to his opinions.

I informed him that Mr. Freind was tolerant, or a quaker and a descendant
of the daughter of William Penn, who founded Philadelphia.
"Quaker, Philadelphia," he cried, "I never heard of those sects."
I gave him some information on the subject. He could scarcely believe me.
It seemed to him like another universe. And, indeed, he was in the right.

III

John Returns to London, and Is Led into Bad Company

WHILE our worthy philosopher Freind was enlightening the priests of Barcelona, and his son John delighting the ladies, Lord Peterborough lost all
favor with the queen and arch-duke for seizing Barcelona for them. The
courtiers censured him for taking the city contrary to all rule, with an army
less strong by half than the garrison. At first the arch-duke was highly incensed; and our friend was obliged to print an apology for the general. Yet
this arch-duke, who had come to conquer Spain, had not the worth of his
chocolate. All Queen Anne had given was squandered.

Montecuculi, in his *Memoirs,* says three things are necessary to maintain a
war; 1st, money, 2nd, money, and 3rd, money. The arch-duke wrote from
Guadalajara, where he was on the 11th of August, 1706, to Lord Peterborough, a long letter signed "Yo el Rey," in which he begged him to hasten to
Genoa and raise on credit £100,000. So our Sartorius, from general of an
army, thus became a Genoese banker. He communicated his distress to our
friend Freind. They started for Genoa. I went with them, for you know my
heart leads me thither. I admired the skill and spirit of conciliation my friend
displayed in this delicate business. I saw at once that intelligence may meet
every exigency. Our great Locke was a physician; he became the first metaphysician in Europe, and restored the value of the British coinage. In three
days Freind raised the £100,000: but the court of Charles the VI. contrived
to squander it in three weeks. After this, the general, accompanied by his
counsellor, was obliged to repair to London to justify himself before the parliament for conquering Catalonia against all rule, and for ruining himself in the
common cause. The affair was protracted and vexatious, as are all party disputes.

You know that Mr. Freind was a member of parliament before he became
a cleric; and he is the only person who has been allowed to combine functions
so opposed. One day, when Freind was thinking over a speech he intended
to deliver in the house (of which he was a most respectable member), a
Spanish lady was announced as desirous of seeing him on particular business.
It was Donna Boca Vermeja herself, and in tears. Our good friend ordered a
luncheon. She took some refreshment, dried her eyes, and thus began:

"You will remember, sir, when you went to Genoa, you ordered your son
John to leave Barcelona for London, and to commence his duties as a clerk
in the exchequer, a post which your influence had obtained for him. He em-

barked in the Triton with a young bachelor of arts, Don Papa Dexando, and others whom you had converted. You may well suppose that I, with my dear friend Las Nalgas, accompanied them."

Boca Vermeja then told him, again shedding tears, how John was jealous or affected to be jealous, of the bachelor,—how a certain Madame Clive-Hart, a very bold, spiteful, masculine, young married lady, had enslaved his mind,—how he lived with libertines who had no fear of God,—how, in a word, he neglected Boca Vermeja for the artful Clive-Hart; and all because Clive-Hart had a little more red and white in her complexion than poor Boca Vermeja.

"I will look into the matter at leisure," said the worthy Mr. Freind. "I must now attend parliament, to look after Lord Peterborough's business."

Accordingly, to parliament he went; where I heard him deliver a firm and concise discourse, free from commonplace epithets, and circumlocutions. He never *invoked* a law or a testimony. He quoted, enforced, and applied them. He did not say they had taken the religion of the court by surprise, by accusing Lord Peterborough of exposing Queen Anne's troops to risk; because it had nothing to do with religion. He did not call a conjecture a demonstration, nor forget his respect to an august parliament, by using common jokes. He did not call Lord Peterborough his client, because client signifies a plebeian protected by a senator. Freind spoke with confidence and modesty; he was listened to in silence, only disturbed by cries of "Hear him, hear him."

The House of Commons passed a vote of thanks to Earl Peterborough, instead of condemning him. His lordship obtained the same justice from the House of Peers, and prepared to set out with his dear Freind to deliver the kingdom of Spain to the arch-duke. This did not take place, solely because things do not always turn out as we wish them to.

On leaving the house, our first care was to enquire after the health of John. We learnt that he was leading a dissipated and debauched life with Mrs. Clive-Hart, and a party of young men,—intelligent, but atheists,—who believed:

"That man is in no respect superior to the brutes;—that he lives and dies as they do;—that both spring from and both return to the earth;—that wisdom and virtue consist in enjoyment and in living with those we love, as Solomon says at the end of the 'Coheleth,' which we call 'Ecclesiastes.'"

These sentiments were chiefly advanced among them by one Warburton,—a very forward licentious fellow. I have glanced at some of the poor author's MSS., which heaven grant may not one day be printed. Warburton pretends that Moses did not believe in the immortality of the soul, because he never speaks of it, and considers that to be the only proof of his divine mission. This absurd conclusion leads to the supposition that the religion of the Jews is false. Infidels thence argue that ours, being founded thereon, is false also; and *ours*, which is the best of all, being false, all others are, if possible, still more false: therefore there is no religion. Hence some conclude that there is no God. Let us add to these conclusions, that this little Warburton is an intriguing, slandering fellow. See what peril!

But worse than all, John was head over ears in debt, and had a strange way of paying. One of his creditors came to him with a claim for a hundred guineas, while we were in the house. John, who always appeared polite and gentle, fought his creditor, and paid him with a sword-wound. It was apprehended the wounded man would die; and John, notwithstanding Lord Peterborough's protection, ran the risk of imprisonment and hanging.

IV

THEY WANT TO GET JOHN MARRIED

You remember the anguish of the venerable Freind when he learned that John was in the prison of the inquisition at Barcelona. Imagine his rage when he learned of the debauchery and dissipation of the unfortunate lad, his way of paying debts, and his danger of getting hanged! Yet Freind restrained himself. This excellent man's self-command is really astonishing. His reason regulates his heart, as a good master rules his servants. He does every thing reasonably, and judges wisely with as much celerity as hasty people act rashly.

"This is no time to lecture John," said he. "We must snatch him from the precipice."

You must know that the day previously, our friend had come into a handsome sum, left him by George Hubert, his uncle. He went himself in search of our great surgeon, Cheselden. We found him at home, and then proceeded together to the wounded creditor. The wound was inspected. It was not dangerous. Freind gave the sufferer a hundred guineas as a first step, and fifty others by way of reparation, and then asked forgiveness for his son. Indeed, he expressed his regret so touchingly, that the poor man embraced him, and, weeping, wished to return the money.

This sight moved and surprised young Mr. Cheselden, whose reputation is becoming very great, and whose heart is as kind as his hand is skillful.

I was carried beyond myself; never had I admired and loved our friend so much.

On returning home, I asked him if he did not intend to send for his son, and to admonish him.

"No," said he. "Let him feel his faults before I speak of them. Let us sup together to-night. We will see what in honesty I ought to do. Examples correct better than reprimands."

While waiting for supper, I called on John. I found him in the state which all men experience after their first crime,—that is, pale, with sunken eyes and hoarse voice,—absent, and answering at random when spoken to.

I told him what his father had just done.

He looked at me steadily, then turned away to dash a tear from his eye. I argued well from this, and began to hope that John would yet prove a worthy man. I felt ready to clasp him in my arms, when Madame Clive-Hart came in, accompanied by a wild fellow, called Birton.

"Well," said the lady, laughing, "have you really killed a man to-day? Some tiresome fellow. 'Tis well to rid the world of such people. When you are next in the killing mood, pray think of my husband. He plagues me to death."

I surveyed this woman from head to foot. She was handsome, but there was something sinister in her countenance. John dared not reply, and, confused by my presence, looked downward.

"What's the matter?" said Birton. "You look as if you had done something wrong. I come to give you absolution. Here is a little book I have just bought at Lintot's. It proves as clearly as two and two make four, that there is neither God, nor vice, nor virtue,—a very consoling fact! So, let us drink together."

On hearing this singular discourse, I withdrew quickly, and represented to Mr. Freind how much his son required his advice.

"I see it as clearly as you do," said this kind father; "but let us begin by paying his debts."

They were all discharged the next day. John came and threw himself at his father's feet. Will you believe it? The father made no reproaches. He left him ro conscience; only observing, "Remember, my son, there is no happiness apart from virtue."

Mr. Freind then saw that the bachelor married Boca Vermeja, who really loved him, notwithstanding her tears for John. Women know how to confuse such feelings wonderfully. One would almost say that their hearts are a bundle of contradictions, perhaps because they were originally formed from one of our ribs.

Our generous Freind gave her also a dowry, and took care to secure places for his converts. It is not enough to take care of people's souls, if we neglect to provide for their present wants.

After performing these good actions, with his astonishing *sang froid*, he concluded he had nothing more to do to restore his son to virtue, than to marry him to a young person of beauty, virtue, talents, and some wealth. This, indeed, was the only way to wean him from the detestable Clive-Hart, and others, whom he frequented.

I had heard speak of a Miss Primerose, a young heiress, brought up by her relative, Lady Hervey. The Earl of Peterborough introduced me to Lady Hervey. I saw Miss Primerose and considered her a proper person to fulfill the wishes of my friend. John, in the midst of his dissipation, had great reverence and even affection for his father. He was chiefly affected that his father had never blamed him for his follies. Debts paid without informing him· wise counsels seasonably given, and without reprimand; proofs of friendship given from time to time, yet free from the familiarity which might depreciate them. All this went to John's heart, for he was both intelligent and sensitive.

Lord Peterborough introduced the father and son to Lady Hervey. I perceived that the extreme beauty of John soon made a favorable impression on Miss Primerose; for I saw her look stealthily at him and blush. John seemed only polite; and Primerose admitted to Lady Hervey that she wished his politeness might become love.

The young man soon discovered the worth of this charming girl, though he was the complete slave of Clive-Hart. He was like the Indian invited to gather celestial fruit, but restrained by the claws of a dragon.

But here the recollection of what I witnessed overwhelms me. Tears moisten my paper. When I recover, I will resume my tale.

V

A TERRIBLE ADVENTURE

THE marriage of John and the lovely Primerose was about to be celebrated. Freind never felt more joy. I shared it. But the occasion was changed into one of deep sorrow and suffering.

Clive-Hart loved John, though constantly faithless. They say this is the lot of those women who, violating modesty, renounce their honor. Especially she deceived John for her dear Birton and for another of the same school. They lived together in debauch; and, what is perhaps peculiar to our nation, they had all of them sense and worth. Unfortunately, they employed their sense against God. Madame Clive-Hart's house was a rendezvous for atheists. Well for them had they been such atheists as Epicurus, Leontium, Lucretius, Memmius, and Spinoza,—the most upright man of Holland,—or Hobbes, so faithful to his unfortunate king, Charles I.

But however it may be, Clive-Hart, jealous of the pure and gentle Primerose, could not endure the marriage. She devised a vengeance, which I conceive to be unsurpassed even in London, where I believe our fathers have witnessed crimes of every kind. She learned that Miss Primerose, returning from shopping, would pass by her door. She took advantage of the opportunity, and had a sewer opened, communicating with her premises.

Miss Primerose's carriage, on its return, was obliged to draw up at this obstruction. Clive-Hart goes out, and entreats her to alight and take some refreshment, while the passage is being cleared. This invitation made Miss Primerose hesitate; but she perceived John standing in the hall, and, yielding to an impulse stronger than her discretion, she got out. John offered her his hand. She enters. Clive-Hart's husband was a silly drunkard, as hateful to his wife as he was submissive and troublesome by his civility. He presents refreshments to the young lady, and drinks after her. Mrs. Clive-Hart takes them away instantly and brings others. By this time the street is cleared. Miss Primerose enters her carriage, and drives to her mother's.

She soon falls sick, and complains of giddiness. They suppose it is occasioned by the motion of the carriage. But the illness increased, and the next day she was dying.

Mr. Freind and I hastened to the house. We found the lovely creature pale and livid, a prey to convulsions,—her lips open, her eyes glazed, and always staring. Black spots disfigured her face and throat. Her mother had fainted on her bed. Cheselden employed in vain all the resources of his art. I will not attempt to describe Freind's anguish. It was intense. I hurried to Clive-Hart's house, and found that the husband was just dead, and that the wife had fled.

I sought John. He could not be found. A servant told me that his mistress had besought him not to leave her in her misfortune, and that they had gone off together, accompanied by Birton, no one knew whither.

Overcome by these rapid and numerous shocks, terrified at the frightful suspicions which haunted me, I hastened to the dying lady.

"Yet," said I to myself, "if this abominable woman threw herself on John's generosity, it does not follow that he is an accomplice. John is incapable of so horrible and cowardly a crime, which he had no interest in committing, which deprives him of a charming wife, and renders him odious to the human race. Weak, he has allowed himself to be drawn away by a wretch, of whose crime he was ignorant. He did not see, as I have done, Primerose dying; he never would have deserted her pillow to accompany the poisoner of his bride. Oppressed by these thoughts, I entered, shuddering, the room which I expected contained a corpse."

She was still living. Old Clive-Hart died soon, because his constitution was worn out by debauchery; but young Primerose was sustained by a temperament as robust as her blood was pure. She saw me, and enquired in a tender tone, after John. A flood of tears gushed from my eyes. I could not reply. I was unable to speak to the father. I was obliged to leave her to the faithful hands that served her.

We went to inform his lordship of this disaster. He is as kind to his friends as terrible to his foes. Never was there a more compassionate man with so stern a countenance. He took as much pains to assist the dying lady, and to overtake the abandoned woman, and discover John, as he had done to give Spain to the arch-duke. But all our search proved in vain. I thought it would kill Freind. Now we flew to the residence of Miss Primerose, whose dying was protracted, now to Rochester, Dover, Portsmouth. Couriers were dispatched everywhere. We wandered about at random, like dogs that have lost the scent;—while the unfortunate mother expected hourly the death of her child.

At length we learned that a handsome lady, accompanied by three young men and some servants, had embarked at Newport, in Monmouthshire, in a little smuggling vessel that was in the roads, and had sailed for North America.

Freind sighed deeply at this intelligence; then suddenly recovering himself, and pressing my hand, he said:

"I must go to America."

I replied, weeping with admiration: "I will not leave you. But what can you do?"

"Restore my only son," said he, "to virtue and his country, or bury myself with him."

Indeed, from our information, we could not doubt but he had fled thither with that horrible woman, Birton, and the other villains of the party.

The good father took leave of Lord Peterborough, who returned soon after to Catalonia; and we went to Bristol and freighted a ship for the Delaware and the bay of Maryland.

Freind, knowing these coasts to be in the heart of the English possessions, thought it right to go thither, to find out whether his son had sought concealment in the North or South.

He supplied himself with money, letters of credit, and provisions, and left a confidential servant in London, to write to him by ships that were leaving every week for Maryland or Pennsylvania.

We started. The crew, judging from the placid countenance of my friend, thought we were on an excursion of pleasure. But when he was alone with me, his sighs expressed the depth of his anguish. At times I congratulated myself on the happiness of consoling such a noble mind.

A west wind kept us a long time about the Sorlingues. We were obliged to steer for New England. What enquiries we made on every coast! What time and toil were thrown away! At length a northeast wind arising, we steered for Maryland. There, it was said, John and his companions had taken refuge.

The fugitives had sojourned on the coast more than a month, and had astonished the whole colony by indulgences in luxury and debauch, till then unknown in that part of the world. Then they disappeared; no one knew whither.

We advanced into the bay, intending to go to Baltimore for fresh information.

VI

What Happened in America

On the way we found, to the right, a very handsome house. It was low, but convenient and neat, placed between a spacious barn and a large stable; the whole enclosed by a garden, well stocked with fruits of the country. It belonged to an old man, who invited us to alight at his retreat. He did not look like an Englishman: his accent showed us he was a foreigner. We anchored and went on shore. The old man welcomed us cordially, and gave us the best cheer to be had in the New World.

We discreetly insinuated our wish to know to whom we were indebted for so kind a reception.

"I am," said he, "of the race you call savages. I was born on the Blue Mountains, which bound this country in the west. In my childhood I was bitten by a rattlesnake, and abandoned. I was on the point of death. The father of the present Lord Baltimore, falling in with me, confided me to his physician; and to him I owe my life. I soon discharged the debt; for I have saved his in a skirmish with the neighboring tribes. He gave me, in return, this habitation."

Mr. Freind enquired if he was of Lord Baltimore's religion?

"How," said he, "would you have me profess another man's religion? I have my own."

This short and energetic answer made us reflect a little.

"You have, then," said I, "your own law and your own God?"

"Yes," he replied, with an assurance wholly free from pride. "My God is there," and he pointed to heaven. "My law is here," and he put his hand on his breast.

My friend was struck with admiration, and, pressing my hand, he said:

"This simple nature reasons more wisely than all the bachelors with whom we conversed at Barcelona."

He was anxious to know if he could gain any information respecting his son John. It was a weight that oppressed him. He enquired if his host had heard speak of some young people, who had made a great noise in the neighborhood.

"Indeed I have," said he, "I received them in my house; and they were so satisfied with the reception I gave them, that they have carried away one of my daughters."

Judge of my friend's distress at this intelligence. In his emotion, he could not avoid exclaiming:

"What! Has my son run away with your daughter?"

"Good Englishman," said the host, "do not let that grieve you. I am glad to find he is your son. He is handsome, well made, and seems courageous. He did not run away with my dear Parouba; for you must know that Parouba is her name, because it is mine. Had he taken off Parouba, it would have been a robbery; and my five sons, who are now hunting some forty or fifty miles from here, would not have endured such an affront. It is a great sin to thieve. My daughter went of her own accord with these young people. She has gone to see the country, a pleasure one cannot deny to one of her age. These travelers will bring her back to me before a month is passed. I am sure of it. They promised to do so."

These words would have made me laugh, had not the evident distress of my friend severely afflicted me.

In the evening, just as we were about to start to take advantage of the wind, one of Parouba's sons arrived out of breath, his face expressing horror and despair.

"What is the matter, my son? I thought you were hunting far away. Are you wounded by some savage beast?"

"No, father,—not wounded, yet in pain."

"But whence do you come, son?"

"From a distance of forty miles, without stopping; and I am almost dead."

The aged father makes him sit down. They give him restoratives. Mr. Freind and I, his little brothers and sisters, with the servants, crowd around him. When he recovered his breath, he exclaimed:

"Alas, my sister Parouba is a prisoner of war, and will no doubt be killed."

The worthy Parouba was grieved at this recital. Mr. Freind, feeling for him as a father, was struck to the very heart. At last, the son informed us that a party of silly young Englishmen had attacked, for diversion, the people of the mountains. He said, they had with them a very beautiful lady and her maid;

and he knew not how his sister came to be with them. The handsome English lady had been scalped and killed; and his sister captured.

"I come here for aid against the people of the Blue Mountains. I will kill them too, and will retake my dear sister, or perish."

Mr. Freind's habits of self-command supported him in this trying moment.

"God has given me a son," said he. "Let him take both father and son, when the eternal decree shall go forth. My friend, I am tempted to think God sometimes acts by a special providence, since he avenges in America crimes committed in Europe, and since this wicked Clive-Hart died as she deserved. Perhaps the Sovereign of the universe does in his government punish even in this world crimes committed here. I dare not assert; I wish to think so; indeed I should believe it, were not such an opinion opposed to all metaphysical laws."

After these sad reflections on an event common in America, Freind resumed his usual demeanor.

"I have a good ship," said he to his host, "with abundant stores. Let us go up the gulf as near as we may to the Blue Mountains. My most anxious business now is to save your daughter. Let us go to your countrymen; say I bear the pipe of peace—that I am the grandson of Penn. That name alone will suffice."

At the name of Penn, so much revered throughout North America, the worthy Parouba and his son felt the greatest respect and the greatest hope. We embarked, and in thirty-six hours reached Baltimore.

We were scarcely in sight of this almost desert place, when we saw in the distance a numerous band of mountaineers descending to the plain, armed with axes, tomahawks, and those muskets which Europeans so foolishly sold to them, to procure skins. Already you might hear their frightful howlings. From another side we saw four persons approaching on horseback, accompanied by others on foot. We were taken for people of Baltimore, come there for the purpose of fighting. The horsemen galloped toward us, sword in hand. Our companions prepared to receive them. Mr. Freind, observing them steadily, shuddered for a moment; but soon resuming his sang-froid.

"Do not stir, my friends," said he. "Leave all to me."

He advanced alone and unarmed toward the party. In a moment, we saw the chief let fall the bridle from his horse, spring to the ground, and fall prostrate. We uttered a cry of surprise, and advanced. It was John himself, who, bathed in tears, had fallen at the feet of his father. Neither of them was able to speak. Birton, and the two horsemen with him, alighted. But Birton, in his characteristic way, said:

"My dear Freind, I did not expect to see you here. You and I seem born for adventures. I am glad to see you."

Freind, without deigning to reply, looked toward the army of mountaineers, now approaching us. He walked toward them, accompanied by Parouba, who acted as interpreter.

"Fellow countrymen," said Parouba, "behold a descendant of Penn, who brings you the pipe of peace."

At these words, the eldest of the tribe raising his hands and eyes to heaven, exclaimed:

"A son of Penn! He is welcomed! May the Penns live for ever! The great Penn is our Manitou, our god. He and his were the only Europeans who did not deceive us, and seize on our land. He bought the territory we gave up to him; he paid for it liberally; he maintained peace among us; he brought us remedies for the few diseases we had caught from the Europeans. He taught us new arts. We never dug up against him and against his children the hatchet of war. For the Penns we always entertain respect."

Freind immediately sent for thirty hams, as many pies and fowls, with two hundred bottles of Pontac, from the ship. He seated himself close to the chief of the Blue Mountains. John and his companions assisted at the festival. John would rather have been a hundred feet under the earth. His father said nothing to him; and this silence increased his confusion.

Birton, who cared for nothing, seemed very jovial. Freind, before he began to eat, said to Parouba:

"One person, very dear to you, is waiting here. I mean your daughter."

The chief of the Blue Mountains ordered her to be brought. She had suffered no injury; she smiled at her brother and father, as if she had only returned from a walk.

I took advantage of the freedom of the meal, to enquire why the warriors of the Blue Mountains had put to death Madame Clive-Hart, and had done nothing to Parouba's daughter.

"Because we are just," returned the chief. "That proud English woman belonged to the party that attacked us. She killed one of our men by firing a pistol behind him. We did nothing to Parouba, as soon as we ascertained that she was a daughter of our tribes, and only came here for diversion. Every one should be treated according to his desert."

Freind was affected by this maxim, but he represented to them that the custom of burning captives at the stake was degrading to worthy people; and that, with so much virtue, they should be less ferocious.

The chief then asked us what we did with those whom we killed in battle. "We bury them."

"I understand. You leave them for worms to eat. Cannibals think proper to give themselves the preference. Their stomachs are a more honorable grave."

Birton supported with pleasure the opinions of the mountaineer. He said the custom of boiling and roasting a neighbor must be both ancient and natural, since it prevailed in both hemispheres; and therefore it must be an innate idea;—that men were hunted before beasts, because it was easier to kill men than wolves;—that if the Jews, in their books, so long unknown, imagined that a certain Cain killed a certain Abel, it could only be with a view to eat him;— that the same Jews admit they had often fed on human flesh;—that the best historians describe the Jews as eating the bleeding flesh of Romans, whom they massacred in Egypt, Cyprus, and Asia, in their revolts against the emperors Trajan and Adrian.

We allowed him to indulge in these coarse jokes, which, though unfortunately true at the bottom, had neither Grecian wit nor Roman urbanity.

Freind, without answering him, addressed the natives. Parouba translated, phrase by phrase. Tillotson himself never spoke with more force. The insinuating Smaldridge never displayed more touching graces. The great secret of eloquence is to convince. He proved to them, accordingly, that the execrable custom of burning captives inspired a ferocity destructive to the human race; for this reason, they were strangers to the comforts of society and the tillage of the ground.

At last they all swore by their great Manitou that they would not burn men and women again.

Thus, from a single conversation, Freind became their legislator, like an Orpheus taming tigers.

After loading the chiefs of the Blue Mountains with presents, he conducted the worthy Parouba back to his residence. Young Parouba, with his sister, accompanied us. The others went hunting in the distant forest.

John, Birton, and his companions, also embarked in the ship.

Freind persisted in his plan of not reproaching his son, whenever the young scamp did wrong. He left him to self-examination, and to consume his heart, as Pythagoras has it. Nevertheless, he took up the letter thrice, which had been received from England, and looked at his son as he read it. The young man would then cast his eyes on the ground; and respect and repentance might be read on his face.

Birton continued as gay and noisy as if he had just returned from the play. He was in character like the late Duke of Rochester, extreme in debauchery, bravery, sentiments, language, and, in his Epicurean philosophy, attaching himself only to the extraordinary and soon disgusted even then; having the turn of mind that mistakes probabilities for demonstrations; more wise and eloquent than any young man of his age; but too indolent to be profound in any thing.

While dining with us on board, Mr. Freind said to me:

"Indeed, my dear friend, I hope God will inspire these young people with purer morals, and that Clive-Hart's terrible example will be a lesson to them."

Birton, hearing these words, said, in a disdainful tone:

"For a long time I had been dissatisfied with that wicked Clive-Hart. Indeed, I scarcely care more for her than I do for a trussed fowl. But do you believe there exists (I don't know where) a being perpetually occupied in punishing the wicked men and women who people and depopulate the four quarters of our little world? Where, then, is this just and avenging God?"

Mr. Freind with austerity and calmness replied:

"It seems to me, sir, you ought not to say 'there is no God.' Remember, Locke and Newton never pronounced that word but in a tone of reverence, that every one remarked."

"What care I?" returned Birton, "for two men's grimaces? How did Newton look, when he wrote his *Commentary on the Apocalypse?* Or Locke, when he wrote the *Dialogue between a Parrot and the Prince Maurice?*"

Then Freind repeated the golden words which should be graven on every heart:

"Let us forget the dreams of great men; and remember the truths they taught us."

This reply gave way to a well-sustained conversation. I sat in a corner and took notes. The company drew round the disputants. The worthy Parouba, his son, and daughter, John's debauched companions, and John himself, with his head resting on his hands,—all listened with eager attention.

VII

Dialogue between Freind and Birton on Atheism

Freind.—I will not repeat to you, sir, the metaphysical arguments of our celebrated Clarke; I only exhort you to read them again. They are rather intended to convince than affect you. I shall confine myself to arguments calculated to touch your heart.

Birton.—You will gratify me very much. I like to be amused and interested. I hate sophisms. Metaphysical arguments seem to me like balloons filled with air used between the disputants. The bladders burst; and nothing remains.

Freind.—It is possible there may be some obscurity—some bladders—in the deep things of Clarke, the respectable Arian. Perhaps he was deceived on the subject of actual infinity. Perhaps, when he took upon himself to comment on God, he follows too closely a commentator of Homer, who attributes ideas to his author which he never entertained.

At the words, "infinity," "Homer," "commentators," the worthy Parouba and his daughter, and even a few of the English, seemed disposed to go and take an airing on the deck. But Freind promising to be intelligible, they consented to remain. I explained in a whisper to Parouba scientific expressions, which a native of the Blue Mountains was not likely to understand so well as a doctor of Oxford or Cambridge.

Freind.—It would be sad, indeed, if we could not be sure of the existence of God without being metaphysicians. In all England, scarcely a hundred minds would be found capable of fathoming the mysteries of the *for* and *against;* and the rest of the world would be enveloped in ignorance,—a prey to brutal passions,—swayed by instinct alone,—and only capable of reasoning on the vulgar notions of their carnal interests. To find out God, I only require you to make one effort,—to open your eyes.

Birton.—I see your aim. You are returning to the worn-out arguments that the sun turns on its axis in twenty-five days and a half, in spite of the absurd inquisition of Rome;—that the light comes to us reflected from Saturn in fifteen minutes, in spite of the absurd supposition of Descartes;—that every fixed star is a sun, like ours, surrounded by planets;—that the countless stars, scattered through space, obey mathematical laws, discovered and proved by the great

THE SAGE AND THE ATHEIST

Newton;—that a catechist announces God to children, and that Newton reveals him to the sage, as a philosophical Frenchman said, who was persecuted in his own country for asserting as much. Do not trouble yourself to bring before me the ceaseless order which prevails in all parts of the universe. All that exists must have order of some sort. Rarefied matter must take a higher place than denser substances. The strongest press upon the weakest. Bodies moved with a greater impulse, progress more rapidly than those moved with less. Things arrange themselves in this way of their own accord. In vain, after drinking a pint of wine, like Esdras, would you talk to me for a hundred and sixty hours together without shutting the mouth, I should not be convinced. Do you wish me to adopt an eternal being, infinite and immutable, who saw fit (I do not know when) to create from nothing, things which change every moment, and spiders to disembowel flies? Would you have me suppose, with the gossip Niewentyt, that God gave us ears that we might have faith? since faith cometh by hearing. No! No! I will not believe these quacks who have sold their drugs at a good price to fools. I keep to the little book of a Frenchman, who maintains that nothing exists nor can exist but nature; that nature does all, and is *all;* that it is impossible and contradictory that any thing can exist beyond ALL. In a word, I only believe in nature.

FREIND.—What if I tell you there is no such thing as nature; and that in us, around us, a thousand millions of leagues from us, all is art, without any exception.

BIRTON.—What? All art! That's something new.

FREIND.—Few observe that. Nothing, however, is more true. I shall always say, make use of your eyes, and you will recognize and adore God. Think how those vast globes, whic.: you see revolve in their immense orbits, observe deep mathematical laws. There is then a great calculator whom Plato called the eternal geometrician. You admire those newly invented machines, called orreries, because Lord Orrery invented them by imitating the maker. It is a feeble copy of our planetary system and its revolutions; also the periods of the changes of the solstice and equinox which bring us from day to day a new polar planet. This period, this slow course of about twenty-six thousand years, could not be effected in our feeble hands by human orreries. The machine is very imperfect; it must be turned by a handle; yet it is a *chef-d'œuvre* of the skill of our artisans. Conceive, then, the power and patience, the genius, of the eternal architect, if we may apply such terms to the supreme being.

When I described an orrery to Parouba, he said:

"If the copy indicates genius, how much more must there be in the original?"

All present, English and American, felt the force of these words, and raised their hands to heaven.

Birton remained thoughtful. Then he cried:

"What, all art? Nature the result of art? Can it be possible?"

FREIND.—Now, consider yourself; examine with what art, never sufficiently explored, all is constructed within and without for all your wishes and actions. I do not pretend now to lecture on anatomy. You know well enough there is not one superfluous vessel, nor one that does not, in the exercise of its functions, depend on neighboring vessels. So artificial is the arrangement throughout the body, that there is not a single vein without valves and sluices, making a passage for the blood. From the roots of the hair to the toes, all is art, design, cause, and effect. Indeed, we cannot suppress feelings of indignation toward those who presume to deny final causes, and have the rashness to say that the mouth was not made to eat and speak with—that the eyes are not admirably contrived for seeing, the ears for hearing, the nerves for feeling. Such audacity is madness. I cannot conceive it.

Let us admit that every animal renders testimony to the supreme fabricator.

The smallest herb perplexes human intellect. So true is this that the aggregate toil of all men could not create a straw unless the seed be sown in the earth. Let it not be said that the seed must rot in the earth to produce. Such nonsense should not be listened to now.

The company felt the force of these proofs more forcibly than the others, because they were more palpable. Birton murmured: "Must I then acknowledge God? We shall see. It is not yet proved."

John remained thoughtful, and seemed affected.

FREIND.—No, my friends. We make nothing, we can do nothing. It is in our power to arrange, unite, calculate, weigh, measure, but, *to make!* What a word! The essential Being, existing by Himself, alone can make. This is why quacks, who labor at the philosopher's stone, prove themselves such fools. They boast that they create gold, and they cannot even create clay. Let us then confess, my friends, that there is a necessary and incomprehensible Being who made us.

BIRTON.—If he exist, where is he? Why is he concealed? Has any one ever seen him? Should the creator of good hide himself?

FREIND.—Did you ever see Sir Christopher Wren, the architect of Saint Paul's, when you were in London? Yet it is clear that church is the work of a great architect.

BIRTON.—Every one knows that Wren erected, at a great expense, the vast edifice in which Burgess, when he preaches, sends us to sleep. We know very well why and how our fathers built it. But why and how did God make the universe from nothing? You know well the ancient maxim: "Nothing can create nothing; nothing returns to nothing." No one ever doubted that truth. Your Bible itself says that your God made heaven and earth, though the heaven, that is, the assemblage of stars, is as superior to the earth, as the earth itself is to one blade of grass. But your Bible does not tell us that God made heaven and earth from nothing. It does not pretend that the Lord made woman from nothing. She was kneaded in a very singular way, from a rib taken from her husband's side. According to the Bible, chaos existed before the world; therefore matter must be as eternal as your God.

A slight murmur then went round the company; "Birton might be right," they said.

FREIND.—I think I have proved to you that there is a supreme intelligence; an eternal power to whom we owe our passing existence. I have not engaged to tell you the how and the why. God has given me sufficient reason to know that he exists, but not enough to discover whether matter has been subject to him from eternity, or whether he created it in time. What have you to do with the creation of matter, provided you acknowledge a God the ruler of matter and of yourself? You ask me where God is? I do not know. I ought not to know. I know that he is; I know that he is my maker; that he makes all, and that we ought to depend on his goodness.

BIRTON.—His goodness! Are you jesting with me? Did you not tell me to make use of my eyes? Make use of yours. Glance at the world, and then talk of the goodness of God.

Mr. Freind saw that he had now reached the most difficult part of the dispute, and that Birton was preparing a rude assault. He saw that the hearers, especially the Americans, together with himself, required a little respite. Recommending himself therefore to God, they went on deck for exercise. When tea was served, the disputation was renewed.

VIII

ON ATHEISM

BIRTON.—You must not expect such success, sir, on the subject of goodness, as you have had on ingenuity and power. First, I shall touch on the misconstructions of our globe, in many instances opposed to the cleverness so much boasted of; then I intend to dwell on the perpetual crimes and misfortunes of the inhabitants; and you will judge of the great ruler's paternal affection for them.

I shall begin by telling you that in Gloucestershire, my county, when we breed horses, we rear them with care, in fine pasturage and good stables, with hay and oats. Pray, what shelter and food had these poor Americans, when we discovered their continent? They were obliged to scour over thirty or forty miles for food. All the northern coast of the old world is exposed to the same cruel necessity; and from Swedish Laponia to the Sea of Japan, a hundred tribes spend a life as short as it is wretched, in the most complete want, amidst eternal snows.

Fine climates are continually exposed to destructive scourges. There we walk over burning precipices, covered by fertile plains, which prove but deadly snares. There is no hell but this, doubtless; and it opens a hundred times beneath our feet.

They tell us of an universal deluge, an event physically impossible, and at which all sensible people laugh. But they console us by saying it only lasted ten months. I wonder it did not put out the fires which have since destroyed so many flourishing towns. Your St. Augustin tells us of a hundred cities burnt or swallowed up in Lydia, by an earthquake. Volcanoes have several times devastated lovely Italy. As a crowning misfortune, the inhabitants of the Arctic Circle are not exempt from these subterranean fires. The Icelander, always in alarm, has hunger staring him in the face, and a hundred feet of flame or ice to the right or left, under their Mount Hecla; for the great volcanoes are always found among terrible mountains.

It is in vain to say that mountains of two thousand toises in elevation are nothing on a globe nine thousand miles in diameter, or like the irregularities of an orange compared with the bulk of that fruit—that it is scarcely one foot to every three thousand feet. Alas! What then are we, if high mountains are but as figures one foot high for every three thousand feet, or four inches for every nine thousand inches? We are then animals absolutely imperceptible; yet we are liable to be crushed by all that surround us, though our infinite littleness, so closely bordering on nothing, might seem to secure us from all accidents. Besides the countless cities destroyed and re-destroyed like as many ant-hills, what shall we say to the seas of sand that cross the centre of Africa, and whose burning waves, raised by the wind, have buried entire armies? What is the use of the vast deserts on the borders of Syria,—deserts so horrible that the zealous nation, called Jews, imagined they had reached Paradise when they passed from these scenes of horror into a little corner of land where they could cultivate a few acres? It is not enough that man, the noble creature, should be so ill lodged, clothed, and fed, for so many ages. He comes into the world to live for a few days, perplexed by deceitful hopes and real vexations. His body, contrived with useless art, is a prey to all the ills resulting from that very art. He lives between the dangers of poison and plague. No one can remember the list of ills we are subject to; and the modest doctors of Switzerland pretend they can cure them all.

While Birton said this, the company listened with attention and even emotion. Parouba said: "Let us see how the doctor will get over this."

Even John said in a low tone: "On my word, he is right. I was a fool to be so soon touched by my father's conversation."

Mr. Freind waited till their imaginations were a little recovered from the assault, and then resumed the discussion.

FREIND.—A young theologian would answer these sad truths by sophisms, backed with quotations from St. Basil and St. Cyril. For my part, I shall admit that there are many physical evils in the world. I will not even lessen the number, though Mr. Birton has seen fit to exaggerate. I ask you, my dear Parouba, is not your climate made for you? It cannot be injurious, since neither you nor your companions wish to leave it. Esquimaux, Icelanders, Laplanders, Asiatics and Indians, never think of leaving theirs. The reindeer, which God has sent to clothe and feed them, die when transported to another zone. Laplanders themselves die in southern climates. The south of Siberia is too warm for them; here they would be burnt. It is evident that God made every kind of animal and vegetable for the clime in which it thrives. Negroes, a race of men so different to ours, are so thoroughly formed for their country, that thousands of them have preferred death to slavery elsewhere. The camel and ostrich are quite at home in the sands of Africa. The bull abounds in fertile countries, where the grass is ever fresh for his nourishment. Cinnamon and spice only grow in India. Barley is only useful in those countries where God has appointed it to grow. From one end of America to the other, you have different kinds of food. The vine cannot be brought to perfection in England, nor in Sweden and Canada. This is the reason that in some countries the elements of religious rites consist in bread and wine: and they do well to thank God for the food and beverage his goodness has provided; and Americans would do well to thank him for their Indian corn and arrowroot. Throughout the world God has suited all animals, from the snail to man, to the countries in which he has placed them. Let us not reproach Providence when we owe him praises.

But to consider scourges, such as inundations, volcanoes, earthquakes. If you confine your attention to the accidents which sometimes happen to the wheels of the eternal machine, you may well consider God as a tyrant; but observe his ceaseless benefits, and he becomes a compassionate father. You have quoted Augustin and his account of the destruction of a hundred cities; but remember the African rhetorician often contradicts himself and was prodigal of exaggerations in his writings. He wrote of earthquakes as he did of the efficacy of grace, and the damnation of children dying without baptism. Has he not said in his thirty-seventh sermon, that he had seen people at Ethiopia with one eye in the middle of the forehead like the Cyclops, and a whole race without heads?

We, who are not fathers of the church, ought not to go beyond nor to stop short of truth; and the truth is, that of the houses destroyed, we cannot reckon that more than one out of every hundred thousand is destroyed by the fires necessary to the due performance of the operations of the world.

So essential to the nature of the universe is fire, that but for it there would be no sun nor stars, no animals, vegetables, or minerals. The fire, placed under the earth, is subject to fixed natural laws. Some disasters may nevertheless occur. You cannot say a man is a poor artisan when an immense machine, formed by him, lasts unimpaired for years. If a man invented a hydraulic engine to water a province, would you disparage his work because it destroys some insects?

I have shown you that the machine of the world is the work of an intelligent and powerful being; you, who are intelligent, ought to admire him,—you, who are laden with his gifts, ought to adore him.

But how, you inquire, can the wretches who are condemned to languish under incurable evils—how can they admire and love? I must tell you, that such ills are generally brought on ourselves, or come to us from our fathers, who abused their bodies, and not from the great fabricator. No disease but decrepitude was known in America till we introduced strong liquors, the source of all evils.

Let us remember that in Milton's Poem, the simple Adam is made to inquire if he will live long. Yes, is the reply, if you take nothing to excess. Observe this rule, my friends. Can you require that God should let you live for ages, as the reward for your gluttony, your drunkenness, your incontinence, and your indulgence in infamous passions, which corrupt the blood and necessarily shorten life?

I approved of this reply. Parouba liked it; but Birton was not moved. I read in John's eyes that he was still doubtful. Birton rejoined in these terms:

BIRTON.—Since you have made use of common arguments, with a few novel remarks, I may be allowed to follow your plan. If so good and powerful a God existed, surely he would not have suffered evil to enter the world, nor have devoted his creatures to grief and crime. If he cannot prevent evil, he is not almighty; if he will not, he is cruel.

The annals of the Brahmins only extend back 8,000 years; those of the Chinese only 5,000. Our knowledge is but of yesterday: but, in that brief space, all is horror. Murder has been the practice from one end of the earth to the other; and men have been weak enough to give to those men who slew the greatest number of their fellow creatures the titles of heroes, demigods, and even gods.

In America there were left two great nations, beginning to enjoy the sweets of peace and civilization, when the Spaniards came there to slay eleven millions. They hunted men down with dogs; and King Ferdinand of Castile gave those dogs pensions for their services.

They burned Atahualpa, as they had burned Guatimozin. They slew his people; and all to gain that hard and yellow earth which has only served to depopulate and impoverish Spain; for it has made her neglect the cultivation of the earth, which really nourishes man.

Now, my dear Mr. Freind, if the fantastic and ridiculous being men call the devil had wished to make men in his image, would he have made them otherwise? Do not, then, attribute such an abominable work to God.

This speech brought the party round again to Birton's views. I saw John rejoice in himself. I confess, I trembled for Freind. I despaired of his cause. He replied, however, without embarrassment.

FREIND.—Remember, my friends, there is a God. This I proved to you; you agreed to it, and after being driven to admit that he exists, you strive to find out his imperfections, vices, and wickedness.

I am far from asserting, with some reasoners, that private ills form the general good. This is too ridiculous a sentiment. I admit, with grief, that the world contains much moral and physical evil: but, since it is certain that God exists, it is also certain that all these evils cannot prevent God's existence. He cannot be cruel. What interest could make him so? There are horrible evils in the world, my friends. Let us not swell their number. It is impossible that God can be other than good; but men are perverse, and make a detestable use of the liberty that God has given and ought to have given,—that is, the power of exercising their wills, without which they would be simple machines, formed by a wicked being, to be broken at his caprice.

All enlightened Spaniards agree that a small number of their ancestors abused this liberty so far as to commit crimes that make human nature shudder.

The second Don Carlos did what he could to repair the atrocities committed by the Spaniards under Ferdinand and Charles V.

If there be crime in the world, my friends, there is virtue as well.

BIRTON.—Ah! ha! virtue! A good joke! I should like to see this virtue. Where is she to be found?

At these words I could not contain myself.

"You may find her," said I, "in the worthy Mr. Freind, in Parouba, even in yourself when your heart is cleansed of its vices."

He blushed; and John also. The latter looked down and seemed to feel remorse. His father surveyed him with compassion and resumed.

FREIND.—Yes, dear friends. If there have always been crimes; there have always been virtues too. Athens had such men as Socrates, as well as such as Anitus. Rome had Catos, as well as Syllas. Nero frightened the world by his atrocities, but Titus, Trajan, and the Antonines, consoled it by their benevolence. My friend will explain to Parouba who these great men were. Fortunately, I have Epictetus in my pocket. Epictetus was a slave, but the equal of Marcus Aurelius in mind. Listen; and may all who pretend to teach men hear what Epictetus says to himself,—"God made me; I feel this; and shall I dare to dishonor him by infamous thoughts, criminal actions, and base desires?" His mind agreed with his conversation. Marcus Aurelius, on the throne of Europe and two parts of our hemisphere, did not think otherwise than the slave Epictetus. The one was never humiliated by meanness, nor the other dazzled by greatness; and when they wrote their thoughts it was for the use of their disciples, and not to be extolled in the papers. Pray, in your opinion, were not Locke, Newton, Tillotson, Penn, Clarke, the good man called "The Man of Ross," and many others, in and beyond your island, models of virtue?

You have alluded to the cruel and unjust wars of which so many nations have been guilty. You have described the abominations of Christians in Mexico and Peru; you might add the St. Bartholomew of France and the Irish massacre. But are there not people who have always held in abhorrence the shedding of blood? Have not the Brahmins in all ages given this example to the world? and, even in this country, have we not near us, in Pennsylvania, our Philadelphians, whom they attempt in vain to ridicule by the name of Quakers, and who have always hated war?

Have we not the Carolinas, where the great Locke dictated laws? In these two lands of virtue, all citizens are equal; all consciences are free; all religions good; provided they worship God. There all men are brethren. You have seen, Mr. Birton, the inhabitants of the Blue Mountains lay down their arms before a descendant of Penn. They felt the force of virtue. You persist in disavowing it. Because the earth produces poisons as well as wholesome plants, will you prefer the poisons?

BIRTON.—Oh, sir, your poisons are not to the point. If God made them, they are his work. He is master, and does all. His hand directs Cromwell's, when he signs the death warrant of Charles I. His arm conducts the headsman's, who severs his head from the body. No, I cannot admit that God is a homicide.

FREIND.—Nor I. Pray, hear me. You will admit that God governs by general laws. According to these laws, Cromwell, a monster of fanaticism and envy, determines to sacrifice Charles I. to his own interest, which, no doubt, all men seek to promote, though they do not understand it alike. According to the laws of motion established by God, the executioner cuts off his head. But assuredly it is not God who commits the assassination by a particular act of his will. God was not Cromwell, nor Ravaillac, nor Balthazar Gerard. God does not permit, nor command, nor authorize crime. But he has made man; he has established laws of motion; and these eternal laws are equally executed by the good man who stretches out his hand to the poor, and by the hand of a villain who assassinates his brother. In the same way that God did not extinguish the sun, or swallow up Spain, to punish Cortez, and Pizarro, so, also, he does not send a company of angels to London, nor make a hundred thousand pipes of Burgundy to descend from heaven to delight the hearts of his dear Englishmen, when they do good. His general providence would become ridiculous, if thus made manifest to every individual; and this is so striking, that God never punishes a criminal immediately, by a decided stroke of his power. He lets the sun shine on the evil and the good. If some wretches expire in their crimes, it is by the general laws that govern the world. I have read in a great book, by a Frenchman called Mezeray, that God caused our Henry V. to suffer a painful death, because he dared to sit on the throne of a Christian king.

The physical part of a bad action is the effect of the primary laws given to the matter by the hand of God. All moral evil is the effect of the liberty which man abuses.

In a word, without plunging into the fogs of metaphysics, let us remember that the existence of God is proved. We have no longer to argue on that point. Take God from the world, and does the assassination of Charles I. become more lawful? Do you feel less aversion toward his executioner? God exists. Enough. If he exists, he is just. Be, then, just also.

BIRTON.—Your argument has strength and force, though it does not altogether exonerate God from being the author of physical and moral evil. I see your way of justifying him makes an impression on the assembly; but might it not be contrived that these laws should not involve such particular misfortunes? You have proved to me a powerful and eternal God, and I was almost on the point of believing. But I have some terrible objections to make. Come, John, courage; let us not be cast down.

IX

ON ATHEISM

NIGHT closed in beautifully. The atmosphere presented a vault of transparent azure, spangled with golden stars. Such a spectacle always affects man, and inspires him with pleasant reveries. The worthy Parouba admired the heavens, like a German when he beholds St. Peter's at Rome, or the Opera at Naples, for the first time.

"What a boldly arched vault," said he to Freind.

"It is no arch at all," replied Freind. "The blue dome you behold is nothing more than a collection of vapors, which God has so disposed and combined with the mechanism of your eyes, that, wherever you may be, you are still in the centre of your promenade, and perceive what is called heaven, arched above your head."

"And those stars, Mr. Freind?"

"As I have already said, they are so many suns, round which other worlds revolve. Far from being attached to that blue vault, remember that they are at various and prodigious distances from us. That star is twelve hundred millions of miles from our sun."

Then, showing him the telescope he had brought, he pointed out to him the planets;—Jupiter, with his four moons; Saturn, with his five moons and mysterious ring.

"It is the same light," said he, "which proceeds from all these luminaries, and comes to us from this planet, in a quarter of an hour, and from that star, in six months."

Parouba was deeply impressed, and said: "The heavens proclaim a God." All the crew looked on with admiration. But the pertinacious Birton, unmoved, continued as follows:

BIRTON.—Be it so! There is a God; I grant it. But what is that to you and me? What connection is there between the superior Being and worms of the earth? What relation is there between his essence and ours? Epicurus, when he supposed a God in the planets, did well to conclude that he took no part in our horrors and follies; that we could neither please nor offend him; that he had no need of us; nor we of him. You admit a God, more worthy of the human mind than the God of Epicurus, or the gods of the east and west: but if you assert, with so many others, that God made the world and man for his own glory; that he formerly required sacrifices of oxen for his glory; that he appeared for his glory in our biped form; you would, I think, be asserting an absurdity. The love of glory is nothing but pride. A proud man is a conceited fellow, such as Shakespeare would introduce in his plays. This epithet cannot suit God—it does not agree with the divine nature—any more than injustice, cruelty or inconstancy. If God condescended to regulate the universe, it could only be to make others happy. Has he done so?

FREIND.—He has doubtless succeeded with all just spirits. They will be happy one day; if they are not so now.

BIRTON.—Happy! How? When? Who told you so?

FREIND.—His justice.

BIRTON.—Will you tell me that we shall live eternally—that we have immortal souls, after admitting that the Jews, whom you boast of having succeeded, did not entertain this notion of immortality up to the time of Herod? This idea of an immortal soul was invented by the Brahmins, adopted by the Persians, Chaldeans, and Greeks, and was for a long time unknown to the insignificant and superstitious Jewish tribes. Alas! sir, how do we know that we have souls? or how do we know but other animals, who have similar passions, wills, appetites, and memories, so incomprehensible to us, have not souls as well?

Hitherto I have thought that there is in nature a power by which we have the faculty of life in all our body,—walking with our feet,—taking with our hands,—seeing with our eyes,—feeling with our nerves,—thinking with our brain,—and that all this is called the soul, which is merely a vague word, signifying the unknown principle of our faculties. With you, I will call God the intelligent principle animating nature; but has he condescended to reveal himself to us?

FREIND.—Yes, by his works.

BIRTON.—Has he revealed his laws, or spoken to us?

FREIND.—Yes, by the voice of conscience. Is it true, that, if you killed your father and mother, your conscience would be a prey to remorse as terrible as it would be involuntary? Is not this truth avowed and felt throughout the world? To come down to lesser crimes,—do they not all revolt us at the first glance,—make us turn pale when we commit them for the first time,—and leave in our hearts the stings of repentance?

BIRTON.—I must confess it.

FREIND.—God, in thus speaking to your heart, has commanded you to abstain from crime. As for equivocal actions, which some condemn and others approve, what can we do better than follow the grand rule of Zoroaster,—"When you are not sure whether the action you are about to commit is good or bad, abstain from it."

BIRTON.—An admirable maxim, and doubtless the most beautiful ever advanced in morals. I admit that, from time to time, God has raised up men to teach virtue to their degraded fellows. I apologize to you for speaking lightly of virtue.

FREIND.—Rather apologize to the Supreme Being, who can reward and punish eternally.

BIRTON.—What! will God punish me for yielding to passions he has given me?

FREIND.—He has given you passions, with which you can do both good and evil. I do not tell you he will punish eternally; nor how he will punish; for no one can know that. The Brahmins were the first to conceive a place of imprisonment for those who had revolted from God; they were shut up in a description of hell, called Onderah, but were gradually liberated at various periods. Hence we have our mixture of virtues, vices, pleasures, and calamities. This conceit is ingenious;—and that of Pandora and Prometheus more so. Less polished nations have vulgarly imitated the same fable. These inventions are the fancies of Eastern philosophy. All I can say is, that if by abusing your liberty you have done evil, you cannot say God will not punish you.

BIRTON.—I have tried to convince myself that he could not; but in vain. I confess I have abused my liberty, and that God may well punish me. But I cannot be punished when I have ceased to exist.

FREIND.—The best course is to do well, while you exist.

BIRTON.—To do well! Well, I confess I think you are right. It is the best course.

I wish, my dear friend, you had witnessed the effect of Freind's discourse on both the English and Americans. The light saucy Birton became thoughtful and modest. John fell at his father's feet, with tears in his eyes, and his father embraced him. I shall now proceed to relate the last scene of this interesting disputation.

BIRTON.—I conceive that the great master of the universe is eternal; but we, who are but of yesterday, may we presume to expect immortality? All beings around us perish, from the insect devoured by the swallow, to the elephant, eaten by worms.

FREIND.—Nothing perishes; but all things change. The genus of animals and vegetables subsist, develop, and multiply. Why can you not allow that God might preserve the principle which makes us act and think, of whatever nature it may be? God preserve me from making a system; but certainly there is in us something that wills and thinks. This something, formerly called a monad, is imperceptible. God has given it us, or, rather, God has given us to it. Are you sure he cannot preserve it in being? Can you give me any proof?

BIRTON.—No! I have sought for a proof in all the atheistical books within my reach; and especially in the third *Book of Lucrece;* but I never found anything but conjectures.

FREIND.—And shall we on simple conjecture give ourselves up to fatal passions, and live like brutes, with no other restraint upon us than the fear of men, rendered eternally cruel to each other by their mutual dread? For we always wish to destroy what we fear. Think, sir! think seriously, my son John. To expect neither reward nor punishment is the true spirit of atheism. What is the use of a God who has no power over you? As though one should say, "There is a very powerful king in China," I reply, "Success to him; let him keep in his territory,—I, in mine. I care no more for him than he cares for me. He has no more control over me than a canon of Windsor over a member of parliament." Then should I be a God to myself,—sacrificing the whole world to my caprice? And, recognizing no law, I should only consider myself? If others are sheep, I should become the wolf. If they choose to play the chicken, I should play the fox.

I will presume, (God forbid it,) that all Englishmen are atheists. I will allow that there may be some peaceable citizens, quiet by nature, rich enough to be honest, regulated by honor, and so attentive to demeanor, that they contrive to live together in society. They cultivate the arts which improve morals; they live at peace in the innocent gaiety of honest people. But the poor and needy atheist, sure of impunity, would be a fool if he did not assassinate or steal to get money. Then would all the bonds of society be sundered. All secret crimes would inundate the world, and, like locusts, though at first imperceptible, would overspread the earth. The common people would become hordes of thieves, like those of our day, of whom not a tenth part are hung at our sessions. They would pass their wretched lives in taverns, with bad women. They would fight together, and fall down drunk amidst the pewter pots with which they break each other's heads. Nor would they rise but to steal and murder again,—to recommence the same round of hideous brutality. Who, then, would restrain great kings in their fury? An atheist king is more dangerous than a fanatical Ravaillac.

Atheism abounded in Italy during the fifteenth century. What was the consequence? It was as common a matter to poison another, as to invite him to supper. The stroke of the stiletto was as frequent as an embrace. There were then professors of crime; as we now have professors of music and mathematics.

Faith, then, in a God who rewards good actions, punishes the bad. and forgives lesser faults, is most useful to mankind. It is the only restraint on powerful men, who insolently commit crimes on the public, and on others who skillfully perpetrate offences. I do not tell you to mingle, with this necessary faith, superstitious notions that disgrace it. Atheism is a monster that would prey on mankind only to satisfy its voracity. Superstition is another phantom, preying upon men as a deity. I have often observed that an atheist may be cured; but we rarely cure superstition radically. The atheist is generally an inquiring man, who is deceived; the superstitious man is a brutal fool, having no ideas of his own. An atheist might assault Ephigenia when on the point of marrying Achilles; but a fanatic would piously sacrifice her on the altar, and think he did service to Jupiter. An atheist would steal a golden vessel from the altar to feast his favorites, but the fanatic would celebrate in the same church, and sing hymns while he was causing Jews to be burned alive. Yes, my friends, superstition and atheism are the two poles of a universe in confusion. Tread these paths with a firm step; believe in a good God, and be good. This is all that the great philosophers, Penn and Locke, required of their people.

Answer me, Mr. Birton,—and you, my friends,—what harm can the worship of God, joined to the happiness of a virtuous life, do you? We might be seized with mortal sickness, even now while I am speaking; who, then, would not wish to have lived innocently? Read, in Shakespeare, the death of our wicked Richard III., and see how the ghosts of those he had murdered haunted his imagination.

Birton and his friends could contain themselves no longer. They fell at Freind's feet. "Yes," said Birton, "I believe in God, and I believe you."

X

RETURN TO ENGLAND. JOHN'S MARRIAGE

WE WERE already near Parouba's house; and we supped there. John could eat nothing. He sat apart in tears. His father went to console him.

"Ah!" said John, "I do not deserve such a father. I shall die of shame for yielding to the fascination of that wicked Clive-Hart. I am the cause of Miss Primerose's death; just now, when you talked of poison, I shuddered; for I thought I saw Clive-Hart presenting the horrible draught to Primerose. How could I have so far lost myself as to accompany so vile a creature? I was blind. I did not discover my error till she was taken by the savages. In a fit of rage she almost admitted her guilt. From that moment, I have loathed her; and, for a punishment, the form of Primerose is ever before me, and seems to say, 'I died because I loved you.'" His father said a blameless life could alone repair his past errors.

The next day we sailed for England, after giving presents to the Paroubas. Tears mingled with our adieus; and Birton, who had been only giddy, already seemed a reasonable person.

When we were out at sea, Freind said to John, in my presence: "Do you still cherish the memory of the amiable Primerose?" These words so wrung the heart of the young man, that I feared he would throw himself into the sea.

"Console yourself, then," said Freind. "Miss Primerose is alive, and loves you still."

Freind had received certain information on this subject from his servant, who had written to him punctually by every ship. Mr. Mead, who has since acquired so great a reputation by his skill in the counteraction of poisons, had saved the young lady's life. In a moment, John passed from despair to extreme joy. I will not attempt to describe the change. It was the happiest moment of his life. Birton and his friends shared his joy. What more shall I say? The worthy Freind was a father to all. The wedding was celebrated at Dr. Mead's. Birton, now another man, also married; and he and John are now among the best people in England.

Admit, that a wise man can instruct fools.

DEDICATION

INTRODUCTION

You wish that ancient history had been written by philosophers, because you are desirous of reading it as a philosopher. You seek for nothing but useful truths, and you say you have scarce found anything but useless errors. Let us attempt to mutually enlighten one another; let us endeavor to dig some precious monuments from under the ruins of ages.

We will begin by examining, whether the globe, which we inhabit, was formerly the same as it is at present.

Perhaps our world has undergone as many changes, as its states have revolutions. It seems incontestable that the ocean formerly extended itself over immense tracts of land, now covered with great cities, or producing plenteous crops.

You know that those deep shell-beds, which are found in Touraine and elsewhere, could have been gradually deposited only by the flowing of the tide, in a long succession of ages. Touraine, Brittany and Normandy, with their contiguous lands, were for a much longer time part of the ocean, than they have been provinces of France and Gaul.

Can the floating sands of the northern part of Africa, and the banks of Syria in the vicinity of Egypt, be anything else but sands of the sea, remaining in heaps upon the gradual ebbing of the tide? Herodotus, who does not always lie, doubtless relates a very great truth, when he says, that according to the relations given by the Egyptian priests, the Delta was not always land. May we not say the same of the sandy countries towards the Baltic Sea? Do not the Cyclades manifestly indicate, by all the flats that surround them, that they were formerly part of the continent?

The Straits of Sicily, that ancient gulf of Charybdis and Scylla, still dangerous for small barks, do they not seem to tell us that Sicily was formerly joined to Apulia, as the ancients always thought? Mount Vesuvius and Mount Ætna have the same foundations under the sea, which separates them. Vesuvius did not begin to be a dangerous volcano till Ætna ceased to be so, —one of their mouths casts forth flames, when the other is quiet. A violent earthquake swallowed up that part of this mountain, which united Naples to Sicily.

All Europe knows that the sea overflowed one half of Friesland. About forty years ago I saw the church steeples of eighteen villages, near Mordike, which still appeared above the water, but which have since yielded to the violence of the waves.

It is also reasonable to suppose that the sea sometimes recedes from its ancient bounds. Observe Aiguemorti, Frejus, and Ravenna, which were all seaports, but are no longer such. Observe Damietta, where we landed in the time of the Crusades, and which is now actually ten miles distant from the shore, in the midst of land. The sea is gradually retiring from Rosetta.

Nature everywhere presents evidence of these remarkable revolutions; and if stars have been lost in the immensity of space, if the seventh of the Pleiades has long since disappeared, if others have vanished from sight into the milky way, should we be surprised that this little globe of ours also undergoes perpetual changes?

I dare not, however, aver that the sea has formed or even washed all the mountains of the earth. The shells which have been found near mountains may have been left there by small testaceous fish, that inhabited the lakes; which lakes may have been moved by earthquakes, and formed into other lakes of inferior size. Ammon's horns, starry and lenticular stones, petrified fish-teeth, etc., appear to me as terrestrial fossils. It seems impossible that these petrifactions could be the tongues of sea dogs; and I am of the opinion of him who said one might as easily believe that thousands of women, moved by a common impulse, came regularly upon a certain shore, as to think that thousands of seadogs came there to deposit their tongues.

Let us beware how we blend doubt with certainty, and falsehood with truth. We have abundant proofs of the great changes and revolutions the globe has undergone, without appealing to tradition or fable.

The greatest of these revolutions would be the disappearance of the Atlantic land, if it were true that this part of the world ever existed. It is probable that this land consisted of nothing else than the island of Madeira, discovered by the Phœnicians (the most enterprising navigators of antiquity)—subsequently forgotten, and again discovered in the beginning of the fifteenth century of our vulgar era.

In short, it appears evident, by the sloping inclination of those parts of the earth washed by the ocean,—by those gulfs which the irruptions of the sea have formed,—by those archipelagos, scattered in the midst of the waters, that the two hemispheres have lost upwards of two thousand leagues of land on one side, which they have regained and added to the other.

THE PHILOSOPHY OF HISTORY

I

OF THE DIFFERENT RACES OF MEN

NOTHING can be more interesting to us than the sensible difference in the species of men, who inhabit the four known quarters of the world.

None but the blind can doubt that the Whites, the Negroes, the Albinos, the Hottentots, the Laplanders, the Chinese, and the Americans, are races entirely different.

No curious traveler ever passed through Leyden without seeing part of the *reticulum mucosum* of a Negro dissected by the celebrated Ruish. The remainder of this membrane is in the cabinet of curiosities at St. Petersburg. This membrane is black, and communicates to Negroes that inherent blackness which they do not lose but in such disorders as may destroy this texture, and allow the fat or mucus to issue from its cells and form white spots under the skin.

Their large round eyes, their broad flat noses, their thick coarse lips, their differently formed ears, and the measure of their intellects, show a great difference between them and other species of men; and what demonstrates, most clearly, that they are not indebted for this difference to their climate, is that Negro men and women, on being transported to the coldest climates, there produce beings of their own species, without apparent variation; and that Mulattoes are a mixed race of black men and white women, or white men and black women, as asses, specifically different from horses, produce mules when bred with mares.

The Albinos are, indeed, a very small and weak race, inhabiting the center of Africa. Their weakness prevents them from making excursions far from the caverns which they inhabit. The Negroes, however, sometimes capture some of them, and these we purchase to exhibit as curiosities. I have, myself, seen two of them, and so have probably thousands of other Europeans.

To pretend that they are dwarf Negroes, whose skin has been blanched by a kind of leprosy, is like saying that the blacks themselves are whites, whom an attack of leprosy has made black.

An Albino no more resembles a Negro from the coast of Guinea, than he does an Englishman or a Spaniard. Their whiteness is not like ours, it does not resemble flesh, it has no mixture of white and brown or red; it is the color of linen, or rather of bleached wax. Their hair and eyebrows are like the finest silk. Their eyes are unlike those of other races, and greatly resemble the eyes of a partridge. Their shape is like that of the Laplanders, but their heads differ from all other nations, and they have nothing that seems to belong to man but the stature of their bodies, with the faculty of speaking and thinking, but in a degree very different from ours.

The apron which nature has given to the Caffres, whose soft loose skin descends from the navel to the middle of the thighs; the black breasts of the women of Samoieda, the beard of the males of our continent, and the beardless chins of the native Americans, are such marked distinctions that it is scarce possible to imagine that they are not each of them different species of beings.

If it be asked, what is the origin of the Americans and whence do they come? Why not also enquire, from whence the inhabitants of the southern countries or Australia have come? And it has been already answered, that the same providence which placed men in Norway, also fixed some in America and in the southern polar circle; in the same manner as it has planted trees and shrubs, and causes the grass to grow there.

Many learned men have been of opinion that some of the various species of men, or of animals approaching to, or resembling men, have perished. The Albinos are now so few in number, so weak, and so ill-treated by the Negroes, that it is to be feared that this race of beings will in a short time become extinct.

Satyrs are spoken of by almost all ancient authors, and we cannot conceive their existence to have been impossible. In Calabria, even at the present time, it is said to be the custom to stifle all monstrous births; Herodotus, in his second book, describes the scenes he witnessed while traveling in the province of Mendes, and he appeals to all Egypt to substantiate the truth of his assertion; in the book of Leviticus it is forbidden to commit abomination.

With respect to the duration of the life of man (if we except that line of Adam's descendants, consecrated by the Jewish books) it is probable that all the races of men have enjoyed a life nearly as short as our own; as animals, trees, and all the productions of nature, have ever had the same duration.

We should, however, observe that as commerce did not always convey the productions and diseases of other nations to the human species, and as men were more industrious and robust when they lived in the simplicity of a rural life, for which nature designed them, they probably enjoyed a more regular state of health, and lived longer, than those who lead a life of luxury, or occupy themselves in the unhealthy trades of great cities; that is to say that if in Constantinople, Paris, or London, one man in twenty thousand attains the age of a hundred years, it is probable that twenty men in twenty thousand formerly attained that age. Such was the case in several parts of America, where mankind lived in a state of nature.

The plague and small pox, which the Arabian caravans at length brought to Europe, were for a long time unknown. Thus in the fine climates of Europe and Asia, mankind more rapidly increased than elsewhere. Accidental disorders and wounds were not, indeed, cured with such facility as at present, but the exemption from other diseases amply compensated for this want of skill, and all things considered, it is believed that the human species formerly lived longer, and enjoyed a healthier and happier state of existence, than since the foundation of great empires.

II

OF THE ANTIQUITY OF NATIONS

ALMOST every people, but particularly those of Asia, reckon a succession of ages, which terrifies us. This conformity among them should at least induce us to enquire whether their ideas of antiquity were destitute of all probability.

It certainly requires an immense period of time for a nation to unite as one body of people, to become powerful, warlike, and learned. Look at America. There were but two kingdoms in that quarter of the globe when it was discovered; and the art of writing was not yet invented in either of those kingdoms. All the other parts of this vast continent were divided into small societies to whom arts were unknown. All the colonies live in huts; they cover themselves with the skins of animals in the cold climates, and go almost naked in those that are temperate. The first live by hunting, the others subsist, principally, upon roots. They have not sought after any other kind of life, because we never desire what we are unacquainted with. Their industry has not extended beyond their most pressing wants. The Samoiedes, the Laplanders, the inhabitants north of Siberia, and those of Kamchatka, have made still less progress than the people of America. The greater part of the Negroes, and all the Kaffirs, are plunged in the same barbarous ignorance.

A favorable concurrence of circumstances must continue for ages to form a great society of men, united under the same form of government and laws. And the same concurrence of favorable circumstances is even necessary to form a language. Men would not articulate sounds, if they were not taught to pronounce words; they would utter nothing but a confused noise, and could not be understood but by signs. A child speaks after some time only by imitation, and it would pronounce words with great difficulty if it remained tongue-tied in its early years.

More time was perhaps necessary for men endowed with special talents, to teach others the first rudiments of an imperfect and barbarous language, than was afterwards needed to perfect the establishment of human society. There are even now whole nations who have never been able to form a regular language and a distinct pronunciation. Such are still the Trogolites according to Pliny, and such are also those who inhabit some parts of the Cape of Good Hope. But what a space still remains between this barbarous jargon, and the art of painting our grandest thoughts into the sublimest of words! The distance is indeed immense.

The brutal life which was, for a long time, led by mankind, must have tended to diminish their number in all climates. Men could hardly supply their wants, and, before the invention of language, could not assist each other. Carnivorous beasts having a stronger instinct than men, must have covered the earth, and devoured a portion of the human species.

Man could not defend himself against ferocious animals, but with stones and branches of trees; and from thence, perhaps, arose that confused notion of antiquity, that the first heroes combated lions and wild beasts with clubs.

The most populous countries were doubtless in warm climates, where man found a plentiful subsistence in corn, nuts, dates, figs, pineapples and rice, which grew spontaneously. And hence, it is probable that India, China, the banks of the Euphrates and the Tigris, were very populous, when the other regions were almost desolate. On the other hand, in our northern climates, it was, no doubt, easier to meet with a pack of wolves, than with a society of human beings.

III

OF THE KNOWLEDGE OF THE SOUL

WHAT notion had the first people of the soul? The same as our peasants entertain before reading their catechism, or even after they have learned it. They only acquire confused ideas, which they never reflect upon. Nature has been too kind to them to make them metaphysicians: that nature which is always and everywhere the same. She made the first societies sensible that there was a being superior to man, when they were afflicted with uncommon misfortunes. She in the same manner taught them that there is something in man, that acts and thinks. They did not distinguish this faculty from that of life.

By what degrees can one arrive at imagining, in our physical being, another metaphysical being? Men, entirely occupied with their wants, were certainly not philosophers.

In the course of time societies somewhat polished were formed, in which a small number of men were at leisure to think. It must have happened that a man sensibly affected with the death of his father, his brother, or his wife, saw the person whose loss he regretted in a dream. Two or three dreams of this sort must have caused uneasiness throughout a whole community. Behold a dead person appearing to the living, and yet the worms eating him! This, then, that wanders in the air, is something that was in him. It is his soul, his shade, his manes,—it is a superficial figure of himself.

Such is the natural reasoning of ignorance which begins to reason. This is the opinion of all primitive known times, and must consequently have been that of those unknown. The idea of something being purely immaterial could not have presented itself to the imagination of those who were acquainted with nothing but matter. Smiths, carpenters, masons, laborers, were necessary, before a man was found who had leisure to meditate. All manual arts, doubtless, preceded metaphysics by many ages.

We should here remark that in the middle age of Greece, in the time of Homer, the soul was nothing more than an aerial image of the body. Ulysses saw shades and manes in hell. Could he see spirits?

We shall in the sequel consider how the Greeks took from the Egyptians the idea of hell and the Apotheosis of the dead, how they believed, as well as other people, in a second life without suspecting the spirituality of the soul; on the contrary, they could not imagine that an incorporeal being could be susceptible of either good or evil: and I do not know whether Plato was not the first who spoke of a being purely spiritual. This, perhaps, is one of the greatest efforts of human knowledge. But we do not belong to those early times; and we consider that, as yet, the world has scarcely emerged from Chaos, and still remains in but a rude and unfinished state.

IV

OF THE RELIGION OF THE FIRST MEN

WHEN, after a number of ages, several societies were formed, it is credible that there was some religion,—a kind of rustic worship. Man, at that time entirely occupied in gaining the necessaries of life, could not soar to the Author of his being. He could not be acquainted with the connections of the various parts of the universe,—those innumerable causes and effects which, to the wise, proclaim an eternal architect.

The knowledge of a God, creator, requiter, and avenger, is the fruit of cultivated reason, or of revelation.

All people were, therefore, for ages, what the inhabitants of the several coasts of Africa, of several islands, and half the Americas, are at present. These people have no idea of one only God, creator of all things, omnipresent, and self-existent to all eternity. They should not, however, be called atheists in the usual sense; for they do not deny a supreme being; they are not acquainted with him; they have no idea of him. The Kaffirs take an insect for their protector, the Negroes a serpent. Among the Americans, some adore the moon, others a tree. Several have no worship whatever.

The Peruvians, when they became polished, adored the sun. Either Mango Capac had made them believe that he was the son of that planet, or a dawn of Reason made them think they owed some acknowledgment to the planet which animated nature.

In order to know how these different doctrines and superstitions gained ground, it seems to me necessary to follow the career of the human mind left alone without a guide. The inhabitants of a village, who are little better than savages, see the fruits perish which should nourish them; an inundation carries away some cabins; others are destroyed by lightning. Who has done them this mischief? It could not be their fellow citizens, for all have equally suffered. It is therefore some secret power which has afflicted them, and must therefore be appeased. How is it to be effected? by using it as they do those whom they are desirous of pleasing; by making it some small presents. There is a serpent in the neighborhood,—it is very likely the serpent. They offer him milk near the cavern to which he retires. From that time he becomes sacred. He is invoked when they are at war near the neighboring village, who, on their side have chosen another protector.

Other little colonies find themselves in the same situation. But there being no object near them to excite their terror and adoration, they call the being whom they suspect has done the mischief, the master, the lord, the chief, the god.

This idea being more conformable than the others to the dawn of reason, which increasing and strengthening with time, possesses every one's mind when the nation becomes more numerous. Thus we find that many nations have had no other god than their master, their lord. Such was Adonai among the Phœnicians, Baal, Milkom, and Adad, with the people of Syria. All these names signify nothing more than the Lord, the Powerful, the Almighty!

Every state had, then, in the course of time its tutelar divinity, without even knowing what was meant by a god, or without in the least suspecting that the neighboring state had not, as well as itself, a real protector. For how could they think, when they had a Lord, that others had not one also? The only thing in doubt was which among so many masters, lords, or gods, would be victorious, when the nations fought against each other.

This was doubtless the origin of the opinion, which so generally and so long prevailed, that every people was really protected by the divinity they had chosen. This idea was so prevalent among men, that in process of time it was also adopted by the Jews. Jeptha said to the Ammonites, "Do you not possess by right, what your lord Chamos has given you? Suffer us, then, to possess the land which our lord Adonai has promised unto us."

There are two other passages, not less expressive, to be found in the books of Jeremiah and Isaiah, where it is said, "What right had the Lord Melkom to seize the land of Gad?"

It is evident from these expressions that the Jews, though servants to Adonai, acknowledged, nevertheless, the gods Melkom and Chamos.

Still further. Nothing was more common than to adopt strange gods. The Greeks adopted those of the Egyptians. Perhaps not the ox Apis, and the dog Anubis, but certainly Ammon and the twelve great Gods. The Romans worshipped all the Gods of the Greeks. Jeremiah, Amos, and St. Stephen assure us that the Jews for forty years in the desert acknowledged only Moloch, Remphan, and Kium; that they made no sacrifice, and presented no offering to the lord Adonai, whom they afterwards adored.

It is true that the Pentateuch speaks of nothing but the golden calf, which no prophet mentions; but this is not the place to clear up this great difficulty. It is sufficient that they equally revered Moses, Jeremiah, Amos, and St. Stephen, who seem to contradict each other, and yet are reconciled.

I shall observe only, that, except in time of war and bloody fanaticism, which extinguished all humanity, and which rendered the manners, laws and religion of a people, the objects of horror to another people, all nations were very well satisfied that their neighbors should have their own particular gods, and that they frequently imitated the worship and ceremonies of strangers.

The Jews themselves, though they looked with horror upon the rest of men, which detestation increased with time, imitated the circumcision of the Arabs and Egyptians. Like the last, they accustomed themselves to make a distinction of meats, borrowed from them ablutions, processions, and sacred dances, the goat Hazael, and the red calf. They often adored the Baal and Belphegor of their neighbors; so much do nature and custom prevail over law, particularly when that law is not generally known to the people. Thus Jacob, grandson to Abraham, made no difficulty of wedding two sisters, who were what we call idolaters, and daughters of an idolatrous father. Moses himself espoused the daughter of an idolatrous Midianite.

Those same Jews, who made such an outcry against strange worships, called, in their sacred books, Nebuchadnezzar, the anointed of the lord. One of their prophets was sent to the idolatrous city of Nineveh! Elisha allowed the idolatrous Naaman to worship in the temple of Rimmon. But to avoid anticipation; we know well enough that men by their manners constantly run counter to the laws. Let us not lose sight of the subject we were considering, but continue to observe how different religions were established.

The most polished people of Asia, on this side the Euphrates, adored the stars. The Chaldeans, before the time of Zoroaster, paid homage to the sun; as did afterwards the Peruvians in another hemisphere. This error must be very natural to man, as it has had so many followers in Asia and America. A small and half savage nation has but one protector. As it becomes more numerous, the number of its gods is increased. The Egyptians began by adoring Isheth or Iris, and they at last adored cats. The first homage the rustic Romans paid was to Mars; that of the Romans, when masters of Europe, was to the goddess of marriage and the god of thieves. Nevertheless, Cicero, all the philosophers, and the initiated, acknowledged a supreme and omnipotent God. They were all brought back to that point of reason, from whence savage men had departed by instinct.

The apotheosis, or deification of the dead, could not have been devised till long after the first kinds of worship. It is not natural to deify a man immediately after his death, whom we know was born like ourselves, was subject to the same humiliating wants and miseries of humanity, and whom we have seen die and become food for worms. But this deification is what happened in almost all nations, after the revolutions of several ages.

A man who had done great actions, who had been serviceable to the human race, could not in truth be looked upon as a god, by those who had seen him tremble with the ague and suffer with fever; but enthusiasts persuade themselves that those possessing eminent qualities must have inherited them from God, and are the sons of God. In the same manner gods produced children all over the world, for without enumerating the dreams of so many people who preceded the Greeks, Bacchus, Perseus, Hercules, Castor and Pollux, were sons of gods. Romulus was a son of God, Alexander was proclaimed a son of God in Egypt. Among the northern nations, Odin was a son of God; Mango Capac was son of the sun in Peru. Abulgazi, the historian of the Moguls, relates that one of the grandmothers of Gengiscan, named Alanku, when a girl, became pregnant with celestial rays. Gengiscan himself, passed for the son of a god; and when Pope Innocent sent brother Ascelin to Batoukan, the grandson of Gengis, this monk, who could not be presented but to one of the viziers, said he came from the vicar of God. The minister replied, "Is this vicar ignorant of the reverence, homage, and tribute due to the son of God, the great Batoukan, his master?"

With men fond of the marvelous, there is no great distance between a son of God and God. After two or three generations, the son partakes of the father's dominion. Thus temples were raised to all those who were supposed to be the offspring of the gods, by the supernatural commerce of the divinity with the wives and daughters of men.

Volumes might be written upon this subject, but all these volumes may be reduced to two words—the ignorance and imbecility of mankind; and perhaps the most ignorant and imbecile of all these writers were those who endeavored to put a rational construction upon those absurd fables, and to engraft the simple logic of reason upon the supernatural narrations of folly.

V

Customs and Opinions of Ancient Nations

Nature being everywhere the same, men must necessarily have adopted the same truths, and fallen into the same errors, in regard to those things which are the immediate objects of sense, and the most striking to the imagination. They must have attributed the noise and effects of thunder to some superior being inhabiting the air. The people bordering upon the ocean, seeing great tides inundate their coasts at the time of full moon, must naturally have imputed to the moon the various effects which attended her different phases.

Among animals, the serpent must have appeared to them endowed with superior intelligence; because, seeing it sometimes cast its skin, they had reason to think it became young again. It might, then, by repeating this change, always remain youthful, and it was therefore believed immortal: so in Egypt and Greece it was the symbol of immortality. The larger serpents which were found near fountains terrified the timorous from approaching them; and hence they were soon imagined to be the guardians of hidden treasures. Thus a serpent was the fabled guardian of the golden apples of the Hesperides; another watched over the golden fleece; and in celebrating the mysteries of Bacchus, the image of a serpent was carried, which seemed to guard a bunch of golden grapes.

The serpent thus passing for the most subtile of animals, thence arose that ancient Indian fable, that God having created man, gave him a drug, which insured him a healthful and long life; but that man loaded this divine present upon his ass, who, upon the road, becoming thirsty, was seduced to a neighboring fountain by a serpent, who pretended to hold his burden while he was drinking; thus it was that man by his negligence lost immortality, and the serpent gained it by his subtility. Hence innumerable tales of asses and serpents.

Serpents were found, indeed, to be mischievous animals; but as they were supposed to possess something divine, nothing less than a deity was imagined capable of destroying them. Thus the serpent Python was killed by Apollo, and the great serpent Ophioneus waged war for a length of time against the gods, before the Greeks had invented their Apollo. We find it related in a fragment of Phericidus, that this fable of the great serpent, the enemy to the gods, was one of the most ancient among the Phœnicians.

We have already found that dreams must have introduced the same superstitions all over the earth. If while awake, I am uneasy for my wife or son's health, and in my sleep I see them in the agonies of death; should they die a few days after, it is not to be doubted that the gods sent me this warning. Is my dream not accomplished? it was a fallacious representation, which the gods were pleased to terrify me with. Thus in Homer, Jupiter sends a fallacious dream to Agamemnon, chief of the Greeks. Indeed, all dreams, true or false, the superstitious supposed to come from heaven. In the like manner oracles were supposed to be ordained upon earth.

Does a woman apply to the magi to know whether her husband will die within the year or not? one of them answers yes, the other no. It is certain that one of them must be in the right; if her husband lives, she says nothing of the matter; if he dies, she proclaims all over the city that the magi, who foretold his death, was a divine prophet. There are men in all countries who prognosticate events, and who discover the most hidden things. With the Egyptians these men were called seers, as Manethon relates after Josephus, in his discourse against Apion.

There were seers in Chaldea and Syria. Every temple had its oracles; those of Apollo gained such great credit, that Rollin, in his *Ancient History*, records the oraculous predictions of Apollo to Crœsus. The god divines that the king will dress a tortoise in a brass pan; and replies to the question Crœsus puts to him concerning the length of his reign, that it will end when a mule mounts the throne of the Persians. Rollin does not enquire whether these predictions, worthy only of Nostradamus, were not made after the predicted event had happened. He does not in the least question the foreknowledge of the priests of Apollo, but believes that God allowed Apollo to speak truth. This probably was to confirm the Pagans in their religion.

The origin of good and evil is a more philosophical question, which all great polished nations have agreed in, from Judea to Greece.

The first theologues of all nations must have put the same question which we do from the age of fifteen: Why is there any evil upon earth?

It was taught in India, that Adimo, the daughter of Brama, brought forth from the navel. the just from her right side and the unjust from her left; and that it was from this left side that we originally deduced physical and moral evil. The Egyptians had their Typhon, who was the enemy of Osiris. The Persians imagined that Ariman pierced the egg, which Oromasus laid, and communicated sin into it. We know of the Pandora of the Greeks. This is the finest of all the allegories which antiquity has handed down to us.

The allegory of Job was certainly written in Arabic, as the Hebrew and Greek versions have retained several Arabic terms. This book, which is of great antiquity, represents Satan, who is the Arimanes of the Persians, and the Typhon of the Egyptians, as wandering over the earth and asking permission of the Lord to afflict Job. Satan seems indeed to be in subordination to the Lord; but it afterwards appears that Satan is a very powerful being, capable of inflicting disorders, and destroying the animal world.

So many people really agreed, without knowing it, in the belief of two principles, that so much of the universe as was then known was in some measure Manichean.

Every people must have allowed expiations, for where was the man who had not been guilty of great injuries against society? and where was the man whose natural instinct did not prompt him to remorse? Water cleanses the body and the clothes we wear, fire purified metals; it was therefore necessary that water and fire should purify souls: nor were there any temples without holy water and sacred fire.

Men plunged themselves into the Ganges, into the Indus, and into the Euphrates, when it was new moon, and particularly during the eclipses. This immersion expiated their sins. If they did not purify themselves in the Nile, it was only for fear that the penitents might have been devoured by crocodiles. But the priests who purified themselves for the people, plunged themselves into large tubs of water, where they also bathed those criminals who came to ask pardon of the gods.

The Greeks had in all their temples sacred baths, as well as sacred fires, which were universal symbols with all men of the purity of souls. In a word, superstition seems to have been established in all nations and among all people, except the men of letters in China.

VI

OF SAVAGES

Do you understand by savages, those rustics who live in cabins with their females, and some animals, incessantly exposed to all the inclemency of the seasons; acquainted with nothing but the earth that nourishes them; the market where they sometimes repair to sell their commodities, in order to purchase some coarse raiments; speaking a jargon which is unintelligible in cities; furnished with few ideas, and consequently few expressions; subjected, without knowing why, to some chief, to whom they carry every year half of what they have earned by the sweat of their brow; meeting upon certain days in a kind of barn, to celebrate ceremonies which they no way comprehend; listening to a man dressed differently from themselves, whom they do not in the least understand; sometimes quitting their cottages at the beat of a

drum, and engaging to go and fight in a foreign land, to slay their own likenesses, for a quarter of what they would earn by working at home? There are
such savages as these all over Europe. It must certainly be agreed that the people
of Canada, and the Kaffirs, whom we have been pleased to style savages, are
infinitely superior to our own. The Huron, the Algonquin, the Kaffir, the
Hottentot, have the art of fabricating everything that is needful for them; this
art our rustics are wanting in. The colonies of America and Africa are free,
and our savages have not even the idea of freedom.

The supposed savages of America receive ambassadors from our colonies,
which avarice and imprudence have transplanted near their territories. They
are also acquainted with honor, which none of our European savages ever
heard mentioned. They have a country, they love it and defend it; they
make treaties, they fight courageously, and often speak with heroic energy.
Is there a finer reply from all Plutarch's great men than that of a Canadian chief
from whom a European nation desired to purchase their patrimony: "We
were born upon this land, our fathers were buried here, can we say to our
father's bones, Rise up and come with us into a foreign land?"

These Canadians are Spartans, in comparison to our rustics, who vegetate in
our villages, and the Sybarites who enervate themselves in our cities.

We are, if I mistake not, in the foremost rank (if it is allowable to be said) of
animals living in herds, like bees, ants, beavers, geese, fowls, sheep, &c. If we
meet with a straggling bee, is it to be concluded that it is in a state of pure
nature, and that those who work in the hive are degenerated?

Has not every animal his peculiar instinct, which he is necessarily compelled to obey? What is this instinct? The disposition of the organs, the motion of which time discovers. This instinct cannot display itself immediately,
because the organs have not acquired their greatest perfection.

> Their principles a sacred instinct moves
> And truth's unvaried law their power improves:
> But these th' unconscious infant cannot feel,
> Till strength and ripen'd thought such powers reveal.
> Can the young fibres of the unfeathered dove)
> So soon confess the soft alarms of love? }
> Or dare the new-born fox through forests rove?)
> The changeling worm that spins the silken clue,
> The bee who sips the flower's ambrosial dew,
> Whose wonderous art and industry might vie
> With the fair sisters of the peopled sky;
> Do they, first springing from their parent soil,
> While yet untaught, attempt their curious toil?
> Not so! All nature's children grow with time,
> Age ripens every fruit in every clime.
> Each being here with fittest power
> Has still its object at the appointed hour:
> Improv'd by strength and gradually refin'd,
> Moves and attains the goal by heaven design'd.

Do you understand by savages two-footed animals, walking occasionally upon their hands, wandering alone in forests, *falvatici, felvagi,* associating at a venture, forgetting the females to whom they were united, equally unacquainted with their fathers and their children, living like brutes, without the instinct and resources of brutes? Writers have averred this to be the true state of man, and that we have only miserably degenerated, since we have changed. I do not think this solitary life, which our forefathers led, is in human nature.

Do we not really see that all animals, as well as every other being, invariably execute that law which nature has prescribed to their species? The bird builds its nest, as the stars perform their course, by a principle which can never alter. Why should man only have changed? Had he been destined to pursue a solitary life, like the other carnivorous animals, could he so far counteract the law of nature as to live in society? And if he were made to live in herds like domesticated animals, could he immediately have perverted his destiny to that degree, as to live for ages in solitude? He is in a state of amelioration, and from thence it is concluded that his nature has been perverted; but why may it not be inferred that he has arrived at that degree of perfection which nature has limited to humanity?

All mankind live in society; can we from thence deduce that they were not in the same state formerly? Would this not be like concluding that bulls were not formerly possessed of horns, because they do not now exist without them?

Men in general have ever been what they now are: by this I would not mean to say that they always had fine cities, large cannon, comic operas, and religious convents; but man always had the same instinct, which prompted him to love himself, in the companion of his pleasures, in his children, in his grandchildren, in the works of his hands.

This law is immutable over the entire universe. The basis of society ever existing, there has therefore ever been some society, and we were consequently not made to live like bears.

Strayed children have sometimes been found in woods, living like brutes; but sheep and geese have also been found in the same state. This does not disprove that geese and sheep were destined to live in herds. Some fakirs in India live all alone loaded with chains. Even so, and they live in this manner that passengers may admire them, and bestow alms upon them. They perform through a kind of vain fanaticism, what our beggars do, who lame themselves to excite compassion. These dregs of human society are only proofs how far that society may be abused.

It is very probable that men were in a state of rusticity for many thousand ages, as an infinite number of peasants are to this very hour. But man could not live like badgers and hares.

By what law, by what secret ties, by what instinct, could men always have lived like a family, without the assistance of art, and without having yet formed a language? It must have been by their own nature, by the desire, which prompts them to a union with females; by the attachment which a Laplander, or a Hottentot, feels for his mate, when he hopes of seeing born of his blood a being like himself; by the reciprocal aid which this man and this woman furnish each other; by the love which nature inspires them with for the little one as soon as he is born; by the habitual love they have for him; by the habitual obedience which the child necessarily pays to his father and mother; by the assistance which he gives them when he has attained his fifth or sixth year; by the successive children they produce; in a word, because they see with pleasure, in an advanced age, their sons and daughters produce other children, who have the same instinct as their fathers and mothers. I acknowledge this is a very unpolished society of men: but is it believed that the colliers in the forests of Germany, the inhabitants of the North, and a hundred different people of Africa, live at this very time in a manner that is extremely different?

What language will these savage and barbarous families speak? they will, doubtless, be for a long time without speaking: they will understand each other very well by sounds and gestures. All nations have thus been savages, taking the word in this sense; that is to say, there must have been, for a great length of time, wandering families in forests, disputing their food with other animals, arming themselves against them with stones and thick branches, feeding upon wild roots, fruits of various kinds, and at length even upon animals.

There is a mechanical instinct in man, which we see every day produces great effects in men of very confined intellects. We see machines invented by the inhabitants of the mountains of Tyrol and the Vosges which astonish the learned. The most ignorant peasant knows how to raise the heaviest burdens by the assistance of a lever, not doubting that equilibrium power is in the weight, as the distance from the point of support to the weight is at the same distance from this point of support to the power. If it had been necessary that this knowledge should have preceded the use of levers, what a number of ages would have elapsed before a large stone could have been moved from its place!

Let it be proposed to any children to jump over a ditch, they will all mechanically take their spring, by retiring a little backward, in order to have a run. They are certainly ignorant that their strength is in this case the product of their mass being multiplied by their swiftness.

It is then evinced that nature only inspires us with useful ideas, which precede all our reflection. It is the same in morality. We are all possessed of two sentiments, which form the basis of society, pity and justice. If a child should see his companion torn to pieces, he would be seized by sudden agonies, which he would testify by his cries and tears; and he would, if it were in his power, succor the sufferer.

Ask a child who has had no education, who begins to speak and reason, if the grain which a man has sown belongs to him, and if the robber who has slain its proprietor has a legal right to that grain; you will find whether the child does not reply in the same manner as would all the legislators of the earth.

God has implanted in us a principle of reason that is universal, as he has given feathers to birds and skins to bears: and this principle is so immutable, that it subsists in despite of all the passions which oppose it, in despite of those tyrants who would down it in blood, in despite of those impostors who would annihilate it by superstition. It is for this reason that the most unpolished people constantly judge very well in the end of those laws by which they are governed, because they are sensible whether those laws are agreeable or opposite to the principles of pity and justice, which are implanted in their hearts.

But before a numerous society, a people, or a nation can be formed, it is necessary that some language should be established: this is the greatest difficulty to be surmounted. Without the gift of imitation, it would never have been overcome: they must doubtless have begun by sounds, which must have expressed their first wants; afterwards the most ingenious man, born with the most flexible organs, must have formed some articulations, which their children repeated, and their mothers must have particularly untied their tongues. Idioms in their first state must have consisted of monosyllables, being the most easy to form and retain.

We really find that the most ancient nations, who have preserved anything of their primitive tongue, still express by monosyllables the most familiar things which most immediately strike the senses. Chinese to this very hour is founded upon monosyllables.

Consult the ancient Tuscan, and all the northern idioms, you will scarce find any useful things in common, expressed by more than one articulation. It is all monosyllables; *zon* the sun, *moun* the moon, *ze* the sea, *flus* a flood, *man* man, *bof* the head, *boum* a tree, *drink* drink, *march* march, *shlaf* sheep, &c.

This brevity of expression was used in the forests of Gaul and Germany and all the north. The Greeks and Romans had no words more compound, till a long time after they were united as a body of people.

But what wisdom was necessary to distinguish the different senses? How came we to express the different graduations *I would, I should have willed*, the positive things and those that are conditional? It could only have happened among those nations that were already most polished, that in process of time they expressed with compound words those secret operations of the human mind; so we find among the Barbarians there are but three or four tenses: the Hebrews made use of only the present and future tenses. And after all, notwithstanding all the efforts of man, no language comes near to perfection.

VII

OF AMERICA

CAN it still be asked from whence came the men who people America? The same question might be asked with regard to the Terra Australis. They are much farther distant from the port which Columbus set out from, than the Antilles. Men and beasts have been found in all parts of the earth that are inhabitable. Who placed them there? We have already answered that He caused the grass to grow in the fields; and it is no more surprising to find men in America than it is to find flies there.

It is pleasant enough to read the Jesuit Lafiteau in his preface to the *History of the American Savages*, where he says that none but atheists can pretend to say that God created the Americans.

Maps of the ancient world are still engraven, where America appears under the title of the Atlantic Island. The Cape Verde Islands are there called the Gorgades, and the Caribbees the Hesperides. This is only founded upon the discovery of the Canary Islands, and probably that of Madeira, whither the Phœnicians and the Carthaginians sailed; they are almost close to Africa, and perhaps, they were not so far distant from it formerly as they are at present.

Let Father Lafiteau make the inhabitants of the Caribbees descend from Caria, by reason of the affinity of the name, and because the women of both served their husbands for cooks; let him imagine that Caribbeans produce red children, and Negro women black, because their forefathers accustomed themselves to paint their skins black or red.

It happened, says he, that the Negro women observing their husbands' complexions painted black, their imaginations were so much struck therewith that their race ever after felt the effects of it. The same thing happened to the Caribbean women, who by the same strength of imagination brought forth red children. He supports his argument with the example of Jacob's lambs, who were born with spotted skins, by the art of that patriarch, who put in their view branches of trees half peeled; these branches appearing at some distance of two different colors, communicated their color to the lambs of this patriarch. But the Jesuit should know that what happened in the time of Jacob does not happen now.

If Laban's kinsmen had been asked why his flocks, constantly seeing grass did not produce green herds, he would have been somewhat embarrassed what to reply.

Lafiteau at length makes the Americans descend from the ancient Greeks, for which opinion he assigns the following reasons. The Greeks had their fables, the Americans have also fables; the first Greeks went a hunting, the Americans also hunt; the first Greeks had oracles, the Americans have their sorcerers; there were dances performed at the feasts of the Greeks, the Americans dance. It must be allowed that these are very convincing reasons.

A reflection might be made upon the nations of the new world, which Father Lafiteau has omitted, which is, that the people distant from the tropics have always been invincible; and that those people who were nearest the tropics have almost always been subdued by monarchs. It was for a long time the same on our continent; but we do not find that the people of Canada have ever attempted to subjugate Mexico, in the manner that the Tartars spread themselves over Asia and Europe. It should seem that the Canadians were never sufficiently numerous to detach colonies into other parts.

America in general could never have been so populous as Europe and Asia; it is covered with vast marshes, which render the air very unhealthy. Innumerable poisons are the produce of the earth; arrows steeped in the juice of these venomous herbs always occasion mortal wounds. Nature, in fine, had given the Americans much less industry than the inhabitants of the ancient world: these causes united may have been greatly prejudicial to population.

Among the various physical observations which may be made upon this fourth part of our universe so long unknown, the most remarkable, perhaps, is that there is but one people who have any beards: these are the Esquimaux; they are situated about the fifty-second degree of northern latitude, where the cold is more intense than in fifty-six of our continent; their neighbors are all beardless. Here then are two races of men absolutely different, bordering upon each other.

Towards the Isthmus of Panama is the race of the Dariens almost similar to the Albinoes, who shun light, and vegetate in caverns, a feeble race, and consequently not numerous.

The American lions are small and timorous; the sheep are large and so vigorous that they are used to carry burdens. All the lakes are at least ten times as large as ours; in a word, the natural productions of the earth are not like those of our hemisphere. Thus are all things variegated, and the same providence which produced the elephant, the rhinoceros, and Negroes, has given birth in other regions to elks, deer, swine with navels upon their backs, and men with dispositions quite different from ours.

VIII

OF THEOCRACY

IT APPEARED that the greater part of the ancient nations were governed by a kind of theocracy. To begin with India, you there find the Brahmans have long been sovereigns. In Persia, the Magi have the greatest authority. The story of *The Ears of Smerdis* may very probably be a fable; but it will still follow that he was a Magi upon the throne of Cyrus.

Several of the Egyptian priests had so great a dominion over their kings that they went so far as to prescribe to them how much they should eat and drink; took charge of their infancy, sat in judgment upon them after their death, and often made themselves kings.

If we come down to the Greeks, however fabulous their history may be, do we not learn therefrom that the prophet Calcas had sufficient power in the army to sacrifice the daughter of the king of kings? Come still lower to the savage nations since the Greeks, we find the Druids governing the Gauls, and other nations.

It hardly seems possible that in the early ages there could have been any other than a theocratic government; for as soon as a nation has chosen a tutelar god, this god has priests; these priests reign over the minds of the people. They cannot govern but in the name of God! They therefore always make Him speak; they retail His oracles, and it is by an express order from God that everything is performed.

Hence the sacrifices of human blood which have drenched almost all the earth. What father, what mother, would ever have adjured nature to that degree as to present their son or daughter to a priest, in order to be slain upon an altar, if they had not felt certain that the God of their country had commanded the sacrifice?

Theocracy did not only reign for a long time, but it extended tyranny to the most shocking excesses that human falsehood can attain,—and the more this theocratical government was called divine, the more it became cruel and corrupt.

Almost every people have sacrificed children to their gods; they must therefore have believed that they received this unnatural mandate from the gods whom they adored.

Among the people who have improperly been called civilized, the Chinese alone appear not to have practiced these horrible cruelties. China is the only one of all the ancient states which has not been under sacerdotal subjection. As to the Japanese, they submitted to the laws imposed upon them by a priest six hundred years before we were in being. In almost every other nation, Theocracy has been so firmly established and so deeply rooted, that our first histories are those of the gods themselves, who became incarnate, to preside over the destinies of men. The gods, said the people of Thebes and Memphis, have reigned twelve thousand years in Egypt. Brahma incarnated himself to reign in India, Samonocodom at Siam, the god Adad governed Syria, the goddess Cybele had been sovereign of Phrygia, Jupiter of Crete, and Saturn of Greece and Italy. The same spirit runs through all these fables; it consists in a confused idea which everywhere prevailed, that the gods formerly came upon earth, to govern men.

IX

OF THE CHALDEANS

THE most ancient of polished nations appear to me to have been the Chaldeans, the Indians, and the Chinese. We have a certain epoch of the science of the Chaldeans: it was in the year 1903 of celestial observations sent from Babylon by Callisthenes to the preceptor of Alexander. These astronomical tables form an exact retrospect to the year 2234, before our vulgar era. It is true that this epoch borders upon the time when according to the Vulgate the deluge took place. But let us not enter here into the depths of the different chronologies of the Vulgate, the Samaritan, and the Septuagint, which we equally revere. The universal deluge is a great miracle, which has no connection with our inquiries. We are reasoning here only according to natural opinions, constantly submitting the weak feelings of our shallow understandings to the enlightened ideas of a superior order of beings.

Ancient authors, quoted by George le Sincelle, say that in the time of a Chaldean king named Xixoutrou, there happened a dreadful inundation. The Tigris and the Euphrates overflowed their banks, probably more than usual. But the Chaldeans could not have known otherwise than by revelation that such a scourge had submerged all the habitable world. Once more let it be observed I consider here only the usual course of nature.

It is certain that the Chaldeans had not existed upon earth more than 1900 years before our era: this short space would not have been sufficient for them to discover the true system of our universe; an amazing thought, which however, the Chaldeans at length compassed. Aristarchus of Samos tells us that the sages of Chaldea were acquainted with the impossibility of the earth's occupying the center of the planetary world, and that they had assigned to the sun this station, which belonged to him; that they made the earth and the other planets revolve around him, each in a different orbit.

The progress of the mind is so slow, the illusion of our eyes so powerful, the submission to receive ideas so tyrannical, that it is not possible for a people who had existed only nineteen hundred years to have arrived at that summit of philosophy which contradicts the sight, and which requires the most profound theory. So did the Chaldeans reckon 470,000 years. Again, this knowledge of the true system of the world was not the lot but of a small number of philosophers. This is the fate of all great truths; and the Greeks, who came afterwards, adopted nothing but the common system, which is the system of children.

Four hundred and seventy thousand years sound immense to us, who were born only yesterday; but this is a very little time for the whole universe. I know that we cannot adopt this reckoning, that Cicero made a joke of it, that it is extravagant, and moreover that we should rather give credit to the Pentateuch, than to Sanchoniathon or Berosus: but once more, it is impossible (humanly speaking) that men should in nineteen hundred years arrive at the knowledge of such astonishing truths. The first of all arts is that of providing sustenance, which formerly was more difficult for men than brutes; the second, to form a language, which certainly requires a very considerable space of time; the third, to build some huts; the fourth, to provide clothing. Then the forging of iron, or the supplying the want of it; these require so many lucky accidents, so much industry, so many ages, that it is surprising how men could any way compass them. What a leap from this state to the sublime science of astronomy!

The Chaldeans for a long time engraved their observations and their laws upon bricks in hieroglyphics: these were speaking characters, a custom which the Egyptians acquired after several ages had elapsed. The art of transmitting ideas by alphabetical characters could not have been invented but very late in that part of Asia.

It may be supposed that when the Chaldeans built cities, they began to make use of the alphabet. How did they manage before? Will it be answered, as we do in our village, and in twenty thousand other villages of the world, where no one can either write or read. and where nevertheless people understand each other very well, where all the necessary arts are cultivated, and even some-times with genius?

Babylon was probably a very ancient hamlet, before it was formed into an immense and superb city. But who built this city? was it Semiramis? was it Belus? was it Nabonassar? There never was in Asia any woman called Semira-mis, nor any man called Belus. It is like our giving to Greek cities the names of Armagnac and Abbeville. The Greeks, who changed all the barbarous termi-nations into Greek words also changed all the Asiatic names. Moreover, the history of Semiramis resembles in all respects an oriental tale.

Nabonassar, or rather Nabon-Assor, was probably the person who em-bellished and fortified Babylon, and at length rendered it so superb a city. He was a real monarch, known in Asia by the era which bears his name. This incontestable era did not begin till 1747 years before our own; so that it is very modern when compared to the number of ages necessary to have estab-lished great dominions. It appears even by the name of Babylon, that it existed long before Nabonassar. It was the city of Father Bel. Bab in Chaldean signifies father, as Herbelot acknowledges; *Bel* is the name of the Lord. The Orientals never knew it by any other name than *Babel*, the city of the Lord, the city of God, or according to others the door of God.

Neither was there such a person as Ninus, the founder of Ninvah, which we call Nineveh, any more than there was a Belus the founder of Babylon. Never did the name of any Asiatic prince terminate in *us*.

The circumference of Babylon might have been twenty-four of our middling leagues; but that one Ninus should have erected upon the Tigris at the distance of only forty leagues from Babylon, a city named Nineveh, of so great an extent, is what does not seem credible. Three powerful empires are said to have existed at the same time, namely, that of Babylon, that of Assyria or Nineveh, and that of Syria or Damascus: this has but very little the air of probability; it is like saying that there were at the same time in a part of Gaul three powerful empires, the capitals of which were Paris, Soissons, and Orleans, each being twenty-four leagues in circumference. Besides, Nineveh was not built, or at least was of very little importance at the time when it was said that the prophet Jonah was appointed to exhort the people to perform penance, and was swallowed up on his way by a fish, which kept him in his stomach three nights and three days.

The imaginary empire of Assyria was not yet in existence at the time that Jonah is introduced; for he prophesied, it is said, under the petty Jewish viceroy Joash; and Phul, who is looked upon in the Hebrew books as the first king of Assyria, did not reign, according to them, till about fifty-two years after the death of Joash. By confronting the dates in this manner, contradic-tions are everywhere discovered, and uncertainty necessarily follows.

I acknowledge I do not comprehend anything about the two empires of Babylon and Assyria. Several sages who were desirous of throwing some light upon these obscurities, have affirmed that Assyria and Chaldea were one and the same empire, sometimes governed by two princes, one residing at Babylon, the other at Nineveh; and this reasonable opinion may be adopted, till such time as we discover one still more reasonable.

What contributes to give great probability to the antiquity of this nation, is that famous tower erected to observe the planetary world. Almost all the commentators, unable to dispute the existence of this monument, think themselves obliged to suppose that it was the remains of the tower of Babel, which men wanted to erect unto heaven. What the commentators mean by heaven is not very evident. Is it the moon? is it the planet Venus?—they are very distant from us.

Be this as it may, if Nebonassar erected this edifice to serve for an observatory, it must at least be acknowledged that the Chaldeans had an observatory upwards of 2,400 years before us. Let us now consider how many centuries were necessary for the slowness of human wit to arrive at that pitch, which the erection of such a monument to the sciences must require.

The Zodiac was invented in Chaldea, and not in Egypt. There appears to me three testimonies of weight: the first is, that the Chaldeans were an enlightened people before Egypt, ever inundated by the Nile, could have been habitable; the second, that the signs of the Zodiac correspond with the climate of Mesopotamia, and not with that of Egypt. The Egyptians could not have the sign of the bull in the month of April, since they do not work in this season; they could not in the month which we call August figure a sign by a maid laden with heads of corn, as their harvest is not at this time. They could not represent January by a pitcher of water, as it seldom rained in Egypt, and never in the month of January. The third reason is, that the ancient signs of the Chaldean Zodiac were one of the articles of their religion. They were governed by twelve secondary gods, twelve mediating gods; each of them presiding over a constellation, as we are told by Diodorus Siculus (lib. 2). The religion of the ancient Chaldeans was Sabaism, that is to say, the adoration of one supreme God, and the veneration of the stars, and the celestial intelligences which presided over the stars. When they prayed, they turned themselves towards the northern star: so much analogy had their worship to astronomy.

Vitruvius in his ninth book, where he treats of solar quadrants, of the elevation of the sun, of the length of shadows, of the reflected light of the moon, constantly quotes the ancient Chaldeans, and not the Egyptians. This seems to me a proof sufficiently strong, that Chaldea and not Egypt was considered as the cradle of that science; so that nothing is truer than the old Latin proverb.

Tradidit Ægyptis Babylon Ægyptus Achivis.

X

OF THE BABYLONIANS BECOME PERSIANS

THE Persians were situated to the east of Babylon. They carried their arms and religion to Babylon, when Koresh, whom we call Cyrus, took the city.

with the assistance of the Medes, who were established to the northward of Persia. We have two capital fables relating to Cyrus, that of Herodotus and that of Xenophon, which are in every respect contradictory, and which, nevertheless, a thousand writers have copied.

Herodotus supposes a king of the Medes, that is to say, a king of Hyrcania, whom he calls Astyages, a name derived from the Greek. This Hyrcanian orders his grandson Cyrus to be drowned in his cradle, because he saw in a dream his daughter Mandane, mother to Cyrus, inundate all Asia, as if by a miracle. The rest of this adventure is nearly in the same style; this is a history of Gargantua, seriously written.

Xenophon makes the life of Cyrus a moral romance, nearly resembling our Telemachus. He begins by supposing, in order to recommend the masculine and robust education of his hero, that the Medes were voluptuaries sunk in effeminacy.

All that can be positively averred with respect to Cyrus is that he was a great conqueror, and consequently a scourge of the earth. The basis of his history is very true: the episodes are fabulous: all histories are the same.

Rome existed in the time of Cyrus: her territories extended between four and five leagues, and she pillaged her neighbors as much as possible; but I would not support the battle of three Horatius's, the adventure of Lucretia, the bucklers descending from Heaven, nor the stone being cut with a razor. There were Jewish slaves in Babylon and elsewhere; but humanly speaking, one might doubt that the angel Raphael had come down from Heaven to conduct young Tobit on foot towards Hercania, in order to receive some money, and to drive away the devil Asmodeus with the smoke of a pike's liver.

I shall take care not to touch upon the romance of Herodotus, or that of Xenophon, with respect to the life of Cyrus; but I shall observe that the Persis, or Persians, pretended to have among them, for 6,000 years, an ancient Zerdust, a prophet, who had taught them to be just, and to revere the sun, as the ancient Chaldeans had revered the stars.

I shall take care not to affirm that these Persians and these Chaldeans were so just, or that I know so precisely at what time came their second Zerdust, who rectified the worship of the sun, and taught them to adore only the God, author of the sun and the stars. He wrote, or rather commented upon, as it is said, the book of the Zend, which the Persians circulated over Asia, now revered as their Bible. This book is, perhaps, the oldest in the world, after that of the five kings of the Chinese; it is written in the ancient sacred language of the Chaldeans; and Mr. Hyde who has given us a translation of the Sadder would have procured us that of the Zend, had he been able to have defrayed the expense of such a search. I mean at least the Sadder, that extract of the Zend which is the catechism of the Persians. I there find that these Persians believed, for a long series of time, in a god, a devil, a resurrection, a paradise, a hell. They were, without contradiction, the first who framed these ideas: this was the most antique system, and which was not adopted by other nations, till after many ages, since the Pharisees among the Jews did not strongly maintain the immortality of the soul, and the dogma of rewards and punishments after death, till about the time of Herod.

This, perhaps, is the most important circumstance in the ancient history of the world. Here is a useful religion established upon the dogma of the immortality of the soul, and upon a knowledge of the creative being. Let us continue to observe how many degrees are necessary for the human understanding to pass through, in order to conceive such a system. Observe again that baptism and immersion into water, to purify the soul by the body, is one of the precepts of the Zend.

The origin of all rites is, perhaps, derived from the Persians and Chaldeans, and extended to the extremities of the west. I shall not enter into an enquiry here, why and how the Babylonians had their secondary gods in acknowledging a sovereign god. This system, or rather this chaos, was that of all nations, except the tribunals of China. We everywhere find extreme folly united to a little wisdom in the laws, the worships, and customs. Mankind is led more by instinct than reason; the divinity is everywhere adored and dishonored. The Persians revered statues as soon as they could procure sculptors; but even in these figures the symbols of immortality are discovered; we see heads soaring with wings to heaven, symbols of the passage of a transitory life to that of immortality.

Let us now observe those customs which are entirely human. I am astonished that Herodotus should say before all Greece, in his first book, that all the Babylonian women were compelled by the law to visit, once at least in their lives, the temple of Melita, or Venus. I am still more astonished that in all the histories which are compiled for the instruction of youth, this same tale is constantly preserved. This certainly must have been an elegant festival, a curious devotion, to see the dealers in camels, horses, oxen, and asses, repairing to church, and there to associate on equal terms with the principal ladies of the city. Could such enormities be really practiced by a people who were esteemed polished? Is it possible that the magistrates of one of the greatest cities of the world should frame such a statute? that the husbands should consent to such associations for their wives? that the fathers should abandon their daughters to the company of the riff-raff of Asia? What is not in nature can never be true; I would as soon believe Dion. Cassius, who avers that the grave senators of Rome debated upon a decree whereby Cæsar should be allowed the privilege of marrying all the women he chose.

Should not those who are at present employed in compiling ancient history, and copy so many authors without examining any of them, have perceived that either Herodotus related fables, or rather that his text was corrupted? In a word, when we read history, we should constantly be upon our guard not to adopt fables.

XI

OF SYRIA

BY ALL the monuments which remain for our inspection, I find that the country which extends from Alexandretta or Scanderoon, nearly to Bagdat, was always called Syria; the alphabet used by this people was always Syriac; that the ancient cities of Zobah, Balbec, and Damascus, were here situated, and afterwards those of Antioch, Seleucia, and Palmyra. Balk was so ancient, that the Persians pretend that their Bram or Abraham came from Balk amongst them. Where then could that ancient empire of Assyria, of which so much has been said, be situated if it were not in the land of fables?

The Gauls sometimes extended themselves as far as the Rhine; at other times, they were more confined; but who could ever think of placing a vast empire between the Rhine and the Gauls? Or that the nations bordering upon the Euphrates were called Assyrians, when they extended themselves towards Damascus; and the people of Syria were called Assyrians, when they approached the Euphrates? The difficulty may be reduced to the discussion of this single point. All the neighboring nations have intermingled; they were each of them at war and exchanged their limits. But when once capital cities are founded, these cities establish a certain distinction between the two nations. Thus the Babylonians, whether conquerors or conquered, were always a different people from that of Syria: the ancient characters of the Syriac language were not the same as those of the ancient Chaldeans.

The worship, the superstition, the laws, whether good or bad, the extravagant customs, were none of them similar. The goddess of Syria, of such great antiquity, was in no way related to the worship of the Chaldeans. The Magi of the Chaldeans, the Babylonians, and the Persians, never made themselves eunuchs, as did the priests of the goddess of Syria.

The priests of Cybele in Phrygia made themselves eunuchs in the same manner as those of Syria. It cannot be doubted but that it was an ancient custom for men to sacrifice to the gods what was dearest to them, and not to expose themselves before beings whom they thought pure, to accidents they judged were impure.

The city, which has been called the holy city, and by the Greeks Hierapolis, was by the Syrians named Magog. The word Mag has a great affinity with the ancient Magi; it seems to have been commonly applied to all those who were in those climates consecrated to the service of the divinity. Every people had a holy city. We know that Thebes in Egypt was the city of god; Babylon was the city of god; and Apamea, in Phrygia, was also the city of god.

The Hebrews, a long time after, make mention of the people of Gog and Magog; they might by these names signify the people of the Euphrates and the Orontes; they might also signify the Scythians, who ravaged Asia, before the time of Cyrus, and who made devastations in Phœnicia. But it is of little importance to know what idea a Jew framed to himself when he uttered the words Gog or Magog.

I do not, in other respects, hesitate believing that the Syrians were much more ancient than the Egyptians, for this evident reason, that the lands which are most easily cultivated, are necessarily the first peopled, and are the earliest in a flourishing state.

XII

OF THE PHŒNICIANS, AND OF SANCHONIATHON

THE Phœnicians were probably united as a body of people, as early as the other inhabitants of Syria. They may not be so ancient as the Chaldeans, because their country is not so fertile: Sidon, Tyre, Joppa, Berith, and Ascalon, are barren lands. Maritime trade has constantly been the last resource of every people. They began by cultivating their land before they built ships, to go in search of other countries beyond the sea. But those who are compelled to yield to maritime trade are soon possessed of that industry, the daughter of necessity, which does not animate other nations. There is no mention made of any maritime expeditions, either among the Chaldeans or the Indians. Even the Egyptians looked with horror upon the sea; the sea was their Typhon, an evil disposed being; and this makes the four hundred ships that were fitted out by Sesostris for the conquest of India very questionable; but the enterprises of the Phœnicians are real. Carthage and Cadiz were founded by them, the discovery of England, their trade to India conducted by Ezion-gaber, their manufactures of valuable stuffs, their art of dyeing purple, testify their abilities, and those abilities caused their grandeur.

The Phœnicians were with respect to antiquity what the Venetians were in the fifteenth century, and what the Dutch have since been, compelled to enrich themselves by industry.

Commerce necessarily required registers, which supplied the place of our account books, with easy and lasting signs to fix those registers. The opinion which supposes that the Phœnicians were the authors of the written alphabet, is therefore very probable. I shall not aver that they invented such characters before the Chaldeans; but their alphabet was certainly the most complete and useful, as they expressed the vowels, which the Chaldeans did not. The word Alphabet itself, composed of their first two characters, is an evidence in favor of the Phœnicians.

I do not find that the Egyptians ever communicated their letters or their language to any other people: on the other hand, the Phœnicians imparted their language and their alphabet to the Carthaginians, who afterwards changed them. Their letters were transformed into those of the Greeks; what a decided proof in favor of the antiquity of the Phœnicians!

Sanchoniathon, the Phœnician, who wrote long before the Tuscan war the history of the first ages, some of whose fragments, translated by Eusebius, have been handed down to us by Philo de Biblos; Sanchoniathon, I say, informs us that the Phœnicians had sacrificed from time immemorial to the elements and the winds; this indeed agrees with the dispositions of a maritime people. He was desirous in his history to trace things to their origin, like all the primitive writers. He was animated with the same ambition as the authors of the Zend and Vedam, the same ambition as Manethon in Egypt, and Hesiod in Greece.

What proves the prodigious antiquity of the book of Sanchoniathon is, that the first lines of it were read in the celebration of the mysteries of Isis and Ceres, a homage which the Egyptians and Greeks would not have paid to a foreign author, had he not been one of the first sources of human knowledge.

Sanchoniathon wrote nothing of himself, he consulted all the ancient archives, and particularly the priest Jerombal. The name of Sanchoniathon signifies, in the ancient Phœnician, *A lover of truth*. Porphyrus, Theodorus, and Eusebius, acknowledge it. Phœnicia was called the country of the Archives. Kirjath Sepher. When the Hebrews settled in a part of this country, they gave him this testimony, as we find in Joshua and the book of Judges.

Jerombal, whom Sanchoniathon consulted, was a priest of the supreme God, whom the Phœnicians named Jaho, Jehovah, a reputed sacred name, adopted by the Egyptians, and afterwards by the Jews, as we find by the fragments of this ancient record, which is of such antiquity that Tyre, which had so long existed, had not yet become a powerful city.

The word El, signifying God among the first Phœnicians, has some analogy to the Alla of the Arabians; and it is probable, that the Greeks composed their Elios from this monosyllable El. But what is most observable, is, that we find the ancient Phœnicians had the word Eloa, Eloim, which the Hebrews for a very long time afterwards retained, when they settled in Canaan.

The Jews derived all the names they gave to God, Eloa, Iaho, Adonai, from Phœnicia: this cannot be otherwise, as the Jews in Canaan did not for a great while speak anything but the Phœnician tongue.

The word Iaho, that ineffable word with the Jews, and which they never pronounced, was so common in the East, that Diodorus in his second book, speaking of those who feigned conversations with the gods, says, that "Minos boasted of having communed with the god Zeus, Zamolxis with the goddess Vesta, and the Jew Moses with the god Iaho, &c."

What deserves particular observation, is that Sanchoniathon, in relating the ancient cosmology of his country, speaks at first of the chaos enveloped in dark air, *Chaut-Ereb*. Erebus, Hesiod's night, is derived from the Phœnician word, which the Greeks preserved. From chaos came Muth or Moth, which signified matter. Now who controlled this matter? It was Colpi Iaho, the spirit of God, the wind of God, or rather the voice of God, by which animals and men were created.

We may easily be convinced that this cosmogony is the origin of almost all the others. The more ancient people are always imitated by those who succeed them. They acquire their language, they follow part of their rites, and they adopt their antiquities and fables. I am sensible how obscure are all the origins of the Chaldeans, the Syrians, the Phœnicians, the Egyptians, and the Greeks. What origin is not so? We can know nothing certain concerning the formation of the world, but what the Creator of the world has deigned to teach us himself. We walk with security, till we reach certain limits; we know that Babylon existed before Rome; that the cities of Syria were powerful before Jerusalem was known; that there were kings of Egypt before Jacob or Abraham: but to know with precision which was the first people, revelation is absolutely necessary.

We are at least allowed to weigh probabilities, and to make use of our reason in what does not relate to our sacred dogmas, which are superior to all reason.

It is very strongly attested that the Phœnicians inhabited for a long time their country, before the Hebrews made their appearance there. Could the Hebrews learn the Phœnician tongue when they were wandering at a distance from Phœnicia, in the desert, in the midst of some Arabian bands?

Could the Phœnician tongue have become the common language of the Hebrews, and could they have written in that language in the time of Joshua, amidst continual devastations and massacres? Did not the Hebrews after Joshua, when they had been for a long while in a state of bondage, in the very country they had sacked and burned; did they not then acquire some small knowledge of the language of their masters, as they did a little of the Chaldean, when they were slaves at Babylon?

Is it not highly probable that a trading, industrious, and learned people, settled from time immemorial, and who were the reputed inventors of letters, should write long before a wandering people, newly settled in their country, without any knowledge, without any industry, without any trade, subsisting solely by rapine?

Can the authenticity of Sanchoniathon, quoted by Eusebius, be seriously denied? or can it be imagined with the learned Hewit that Sanchoniathon borrowed from Moses? When all the remains of the monuments of antiquity intimate that Sanchoniathon lived about the time of Moses, nothing can be determined; the intelligent and judicious reader is to decide between Hewit and Vandale, who refuted him. We are in search of truth and not disputation.

XIII

Of the Scythians and Gomerians

Let us leave Gomer just after coming out of the ark to go and subjugate Gaul, and in a few years people it: let us leave Tubal to go into Spain, and Magog into the north of Germany, about the time that the son of Cham produced an amazing number of children completely black, towards the coast of Guinea and Congo. These disgusting impertinences have been obtruded in so many books, that they are not worth mentioning; children begin to ridicule them. But by what secret malignity, or by what affectation to display ill-placed

eloquence, have so many historians made such great eulogiums upon the Scythians, whom they knew nothing of?

Why does Quintus Curtius, in talking of the Scythians, who were situated to
the north of Sogdiana, beyond the Oxus (which he mistakes for the Tanais,
fifty leagues distant) why, I say, did Quintus Curtius put a philosophical
harangue into the mouth of those barbarians? why does he imagine that they
reproached Alexander with his thirst of conquest? why does he make them say,
that Alexander is the most famous robber upon the earth, those who had practiced rapine all over Asia, so long before him? why, in fine, does Quintus
Curtius represent those Scythians as the most just of men? The reason is, that
placing the Tanais towards the Caspian Sea, like a bad geographer, he speaks
declamatorily of the supposed disinterestedness of the Scythians. If Horace, in
contrasting the manners of the Scythians to those of the Romans, gives an
harmonious panegyric upon those barbarians. If he says,

> Happy the Scythians, houseless train!
> Who roll their vagrant dwellings o'er the plain;

it is that Horace speaks as a poet somewhat satirical, who is willing to honor
strangers at the expense of his own country.

For the same reason Tacitus exhausts himself in the praise of the barbarous
Germans, who pillaged the Gauls, and immolated men to their abominable
Gods. Tacitus, Quintus Curtius, and Horace, are like those pedagogues, who,
in order to excite an emulation in their disciples, are lavish of their praises before them of strange children, however unworthy of their applause.

The Scythians are those same Barbarians, whom we have since called Tartars:
they are the same who long before Alexandria repeatedly ravaged Asia, and
have been the depredators of a great part of the continent. At one time bearing the name of Mongols or Huns, they subjected China and Judea; at another,
under the name of Turks, they drove out the Arabs, who had conquered part
of Asia. From these extensive plains the Huns went forth in order to reach
Rome. These are the disinterested and just men, whose equity our compilers so
highly celebrate when they copy Quintus Curtius. In this manner are we
pestered with ancient histories, without choice and without judgment; they are
read with nearly the same kind of taste as they are written, and the natural
offspring of this sort of erudition must be error.

The modern Russians now inhabit the ancient European Scythia: this people
have furnished history with some very astonishing facts. There have been
revolutions upon earth much more striking to the imagination; but there are
none that give so much satisfaction to the human mind, and do it so much
honor as this. Conquerors and devastations have made their appearance; but
that a single man should, in the course of twenty years, change the manners, the
laws, and the sentiments of the greatest empire upon earth;—that all the arts
should have flocked together to embellish deserts, is really worthy of admiration. A woman, who could neither read nor write, brought to perfection the

work which Peter began; another woman, named Elizabeth, extended still farther those noble essays. Another empress has gone beyond either of the two former; her subjects have imbibed her genius; the revolutions of the palace have not retarded a single moment the progress of the empire towards felicity. In a word, half a century has more enlightened the court of Scythia than ever were those of Greece and Rome.

XIV

OF ARABIA

THOSE who are curious about such monuments as those of Egypt, need not, I imagine, go in search of them to Arabia. Mecca, it is said, was built about the time of Abraham; but it is situated in so sandy and barren a soil, that it does not appear this city could have been settled before those which were founded near rivers, in fertile countries. Above half of Arabia is a vast desert, either sandy or stony; but Arabia Felix deserved that name, as, being surrounded with thick woods and a tempestuous sea, it was sheltered from the rapacity of robbers, who, till the time of Mahomet, were called conquerors; or rather, as it was the boundaries of his victories. This advantage is far above its aromatics, its incense, its cinnamon (which is of inferior quality) or even its coffee, which now creates its riches.

Arabia Deserta is that unhappy country inhabited by some Amalekites, Moabites, and Midianites; a shocking country, which does not now contain above nine or ten thousand wandering Arabian robbers, and which could not furnish subsistence for more. It was in these deserts that, it is said, two millions of Hebrews remained for forty years. This is not the true Arabia; and this country is often called the desert of Syria.

Arabia Petræa is thus called only from the name of Petra, a small fortress, to which the Arabs certainly did not give this name, but which received it from the Greeks, about the time of Alexander. This Arabia Petræa is very small, and may, without doing it prejudice, be confounded with Arabia Deserta: they have each been constantly inhabited by bands of vagabonds.

As to that extensive part called Happy, half of it consists also in deserts; but upon advancing some miles into the interior parts, either to the east of Mocha, or to the east of Mecca, there is found the most pleasant country in the world. The air is continually perfumed, during a perpetual summer, by the odor of the aromatic plants which nature spontaneously produces. Thousands of streams flow from the mountains, and preserve an incessant coolness, which moderates the heat of the sun beneath the evergreen shades. It was particularly in this country that the words garden and paradise implied celestial favor.

The gardens of Saana, towards Aden, were more famous among the Arabians than were those of Alcinous among the Greeks. And this Aden or Eden was called the place of delights. An ancient Shedad is still spoken of, whose gardens were not in less renown. Shade in those scorching regions was considered as happiness.

This vast country of Yemen is so fine, its ports are so happily situated upon the Indian Ocean, that it is said Alexander was desirous of conquering Yemen, in order to make it the seat of his empire, and the emporium of trade for the whole world. He would have preserved the ancient canal of the kings of Egypt, which joined the Nile to the Red Sea; and all the treasures of India would have been transplanted from Aden or Eden, to his city of Alexandria. Such an enterprise bears no resemblance to those insipid and absurd fables with which all ancient history is replete. He must indeed have subjugated all Arabia: if any one could have done it, it must have been Alexander. But it seems that this people did not fear him; they did not even send deputies to him, when Egypt and Persia had submitted to his yoke.

The Arabians whose defense are their deserts and their courage, have never submitted to a foreign yoke. Trajan conquered only a small part of Arabia Petræa: they to this time brave the power of the Turk. This great people have always been as free as Scythians, and more civilized.

Care should be taken not to confound these ancient Arabs with that banditti, who said they were descended from Ishmael. The Ishmaelites or Agarians, or those who called themselves the children of Cethura, were foreign tribes, who never set foot in Arabia Felix. Their bands wandered in Arabia Petræa towards the country of Midian; they afterwards intermingled with the true Arabians in the time of Mahomet, when they embraced his religion.

Those may be properly called the people of Arabia, who were the real aborigines, that is to say, who from time immemorial inhabited this fine country, without intermixing with any other nation, without having even been conquered or conquerors. Their religion was the most natural and simple of any; it consisted in worshipping a God, and venerating the stars, which seemed, under so fine and clear a sky, to set forth the grandeur of God with more magnificence than any other part of nature. They considered the planets as mediators between God and men: they followed this religion to the time of Mahomet. I believe they were addicted to many superstitions, as they were men; but detached from the rest of the world by seas and deserts, in the possession of a delicious country, above every want and fear, they must necessarily have been less prone to wickedness, and not so superstitious as other nations.

They were never known to invade the property of their neighbors, like famished carnivorous animals; nor to devour the weak under pretence of divine ordinances; nor to pay court to the powerful by flattering them with false oracles. Their superstition was neither absurd nor barbarous.

They are not mentioned in our universal histories, fabricated in our western part of the globe. I really believe they had no connection with that little Jewish nation, which is become the object and foundation of our pretended universal histories, wherein a certain kind of authors copy one from the other, whilst they all forget three-fourths of the earth.

XV

OF BRAM, ABRAM, OR ABRAHAM

IT SEEMS that the name of Bram, Abram, Abraham, or Ibrahim, was one of the most common names with the ancient people of Asia. The Indians, whom we look upon as one of the first of the nations, make their Bram a son of God, who taught the Brahmans the manner of adoring him. This name came gradually into veneration. The Arabians, the Chaldeans, the Persians, all used it, and the Jews looked upon him as one of their patriarchs. The Arabs, who traded with the Indians, were perhaps the first who had some confused idea of Brama, whom they called Abrama, and from whom they afterwards boasted of being descended. The Chaldeans adopted him as a legislator; the Persians called their ancient religion, "Millat Ibrahim," and the Medes called theirs "Kish Ibrahim." They supposed that this Ibrahim, or Abraham, was born in Bactriana, and that he resided near the city of Balk. They revered in him a prophet of the religion of Zoroaster, but he belonged doubtless only to the Hebrews, as they acknowledge him for their father in their sacred books.

Some of the learned have thought that it was an Indian name, because the Indian priests called themselves Brahmans or Brachmans, and that several of their sacred institutions have a near affinity with this name: whereas, among the western Asiatics no institution can be traced which derives its name from Abram or Abraham. There never was any Abramic society—no rite or ceremony of this name; but as the Jewish books say that Abraham was of the stock of the Hebrew race, they should be credited without hesitation.

The Alcoran quotes the Arabian histories with regard to Abraham, but very little is said about him. They, however, allege that he was the founder of Mecca.

The Jews assert that he came from Chaldea, and not from India or Bactriana. They were in the neighborhood of Chaldea; India and Bactriana were unknown to them. Abraham was a stranger to all these people, and Chaldea being a country long famed for arts and sciences, it was an honor, humanly speaking, for a small nation, enclosed in Palestine, to reckon among the number of their ancestors an ancient sage—a reputed Chaldean.

If we are allowed to examine the historical part of the Jewish books, by the same rules as are followed in the examination of other histories, it must be agreed with all commentators, that the recital of the adventures of Abraham, as it is found in the Pentateuch, would be liable to many difficulties, if it were found in another history.

According to Genesis, Abraham came out of Haran at the age of seventy-five, after the death of his father.

But it is said in the same Genesis that Thareus, his father, having had children at the age of seventy, he lived to be two hundred and five years old, so that Abraham was an hundred and thirty-five years old when he came from Chaldea. It appears strange, that at such an age he should abandon the fertile country of Mesopotamia, to go three hundred miles from thence, in the barren and rocky country of Sichem, where no trade was carried on. He is made to go . from Sichem to Memphis, which is about six hundred miles distant, to purchase corn; and upon his arrival, the king of Memphis becomes enamored with his wife, who is seventy-five years old.

I do not enter upon the divine part of this history, I keep close to my researches into antiquity. It is said that Abraham received considerable presents from the king of Egypt. This country was from that time a powerful state; the monarchy was founded, and arts were cultivated: the flood was stopped; canals were dug on every side to receive its inundations, without which that country would not have been habitable.

Now, I ask any reasonable man whether ages are not required to establish such an empire in a country which had been for a length of time inaccessible and laid waste by the very waters which rendered it fertile?

Abraham, according to Genesis, arrived in Egypt two thousand years before our vulgar era. We can, therefore, excuse Manethon, Herodotus, Diodorus, and Eratosthenes, and many other authors for the very great antiquity which they ascribe to the kingdom of Egypt. And yet this antiquity is of modern date, in comparison with that of the Chaldeans and Syrians.

May it be allowable to examine a passage in the history of Abraham? He is represented upon his going out of Egypt, as a wandering shepherd traveling between Mount Carmel and the Lake Asphaltide; and this is the most barren desert of all Arabia Petræa. His tents are conveyed thither by three hundred and eighteen domestics, and Lot, his nephew, is settled in the borough of Sodom. A king of Babylon, a king of Persia, a king of Pontus, and kings of several other nations, league together to wage war against Sodom, and four other small neighboring boroughs. They take these boroughs, including Sodom. Lot is taken prisoner.

It is not easy to conceive how five such great and powerful kings should league together to make an attack, in that manner, upon a band of Arabs, in such a sterile portion of the earth; or how Abraham defeated such powerful monarchs with only three hundred and eighteen country valets, or how he could pursue them beyond Damascus. But Dan did not exist in the time of Moses, much less in the time of Abraham. Lake Asphaltides, where Sodom was situated, was more than three hundred miles distant from Damascus.

This is all above our comprehension. Everything is miraculous in the history of the Hebrews; we have already said it, and we again repeat it, that we believe these prodigies, and all the others, without examining them.

XVI

OF INDIA

IF CONJECTURES are allowable, the Indians toward the Ganges are, perhaps, the men who were the most anciently united into a body of people. It is certain that the soil, where animals most easily find pasture, is soon covered with that species, which it is fit to nourish.

Now there is no country in the world where the human species have within their reach more wholesome and agreeable aliments, or in greater plenty, than towards the Ganges; rice grows spontaneously; pineapples, cocoa, dates, and fig trees, offer on every side delicious regales; the orange and lemon trees at once yield refreshing liquor and some nourishment; sugar canes are under their very hand; the palm and broadleaf fig trees spread the thickest shade. There is no occasion in this country to skin herds, to defend their children against the inclemency of the season; they are to this hour brought up to the age of puberty quite naked. Life was here never risked for the means of preserving it, by attacking animals in order to feed upon their dismembered joints, as has been practiced everywhere else.

Men would of themselves have united into society in this happy climate; no contest would have arisen for a parched country to rear bands of Negroes; war would not have been waged for a well or a fountain, as with the Barbarians of Arabia Petræa.

I shall make no mention here of the ancient monuments of which the Brahmans boast: it is sufficient to know that the most antique rarities which the Emperor of China, Cam-hi, had in his palace, were Indian: he displayed to our mathematical missionaries, Indian specie in coin of much earlier date than any of the copper money of the Chinese emperors, and it was, probably, from the Indians that the kings of Persia acquired the art of coining.

The Greeks, before the time of Pythagoras, traveled into India for instruction. The signs of the seven planets, &c., are still almost all over the earth, such as the Indians invented: the Arabians were obliged to adopt their arithmetical characters. Those games, which do the greatest honor to the human faculties, incontestably come from India; as elephants, for which we have substituted towers, in the game of Chess, evince. In fine, the people who were the earliest known, the Persians, Phœnicians, Arabians, Egyptians, went from time immemorial to traffic in India, in order to bring home spices, which nature has given to those climates alone; but the Indians never went to ask anything from other nations.

One Bacchus is mentioned, who is said to have set out from Egypt, or a country west of Asia, to conquer India. This Bacchus, whoever he was, must therefore have known that there was, at the end of our continent, a nation more valuable than his own. Want created the first robbers; they invaded India for no other reason but because it was rich; and surely a rich people is united, civilized, and polished, long before a society of thieves.

What strikes me the most in India is that ancient opinion of the transmigration of souls, which in time extended itself as far as China, and into Europe. Not that the Indians knew what a soul was; but they imagined that this principle, whether it was aerial or igneous, successively animated different bodies. Let us attentively observe that system of philosophy which relates to morals. The dread of being condemned by Vishnu and Brama, to become the most vile and unhappy of animals, was a great constraint upon those of a perverse disposition. We shall presently find that all the great people had an idea of another life, though their notions of it were different. I meet with very few among the ancient empires, except the Chinese, who did not establish the doctrine of the immortality of the soul. Their first legislators promulgated only moral laws; they thought it sufficient to exhort men to virtue, and to compel them by a strict and severe policy.

The doctrine of the Metempsychosis imposed another constraint upon the Indians; the dread of killing their father or their mother, in slaying men and animals, inspired them with horror for murder and all violence, which became amongst them a second nature. Thus all the Indians, whose families are not allied, either to the Arabians or the Tartars, are to this hour the mildest of men. Their religion, and the temperature of their climate, rendered these people entirely similar to those peaceable animals which we rear in our folds and dovehouses, to destroy them at pleasure. All ferocious nations who descended from the mounts Caucasus, Taurus, and Immaus, to subjugate the inhabitants of the coasts of the Indies, the Hydaspes, and the Ganges, conquered them by only appearing.

The same thing would happen now to those primitive Christians who are called Quakers, who are as pacific as the Indians; they would be devoured by other nations if they were not protected by their warlike countrymen. The Christian religion, which these alone strictly follow, is as much an enemy to blood as that of the Pythagorians. But the Christian people have never observed their religion, and the ancient Indian casts always practiced theirs; because Pythagorism is the only religion in the world which could render the horror of murder part of filial piety, and a religious sentiment. The transmigration of souls is a system so simple and even so probable to the eyes of ignorant people; it is so easy to believe that what animates one man may afterwards animate another, that all those who adopted this religion imagined that they saw the souls of their relations in all the men that surrounded them: they believed that they were all brothers, fathers, mothers, and children of one another. This idea necessarily inspired universal charity, a man trembled at wounding a being who was of the same family: in a word, the ancient religion of India, and that of the literary men in China, are the only ones wherein men have not been barbarous. How could it afterwards happen that these same men, who looked upon killing an animal as a crime, should allow the women to burn themselves upon their husbands' dead bodies, in the vain hope of being born again in bodies that should be more beautiful and more happy? Because fanaticism and contradiction are the appendages to human nature.

It should be particularly observed that abstinence from the flesh of animals is a necessary consequence of the climate; meat is soon corrupted by its extreme heat and humidity, and is therefore a very bad aliment. Strong liquors are also forbidden by the necessity of drinking cooling liquors in India. The Metempsychosis reached indeed our northern countries. The Celtæ thought that they should regenerate in other bodies; but if the Druids had subjoined to this doctrine a prohibition of eating flesh, they would not have been obeyed.

We scarce know anything of the rights of the ancient Brahmans, which are still preserved. The books of the Sanscrit, which they have still in this ancient sacred language, gives us but very little insight into them. Their Vedams have been as long unknown as the Zend of the Persians, and the Five Kings of the Chinese. It is scarce six score years since the Europeans had the first notion of the Five Kings; and the Zend was never seen but by the celebrated Dr. Hyde, who had not wherewithal to purchase it, nor to pay the interpreter; and by the trader Chardin, who would not give the price asked for it. We had no other extract of the Zend but the Sadder, which I have already spoken of.

The library of Paris has, by a mere lucky accident, procured an ancient book of the Brahmans: this is the Ezourvedam, written before the expedition of Alexander into India, with a recital of all the ancient rites of the Brahmans, entitled the Cormo-Vedam. This manuscript, which is translated by a Brahman, is not really the Vedam itself, but is a summary of the rites and opinions contained in that law. We may, therefore, flatter ourselves that we have some knowledge of the three most ancient writings in the world.

We can never hope to have anything from the Egyptians, their books are lost, their religion is annihilated; they no longer understand their own vulgar tongue, still less the sacred one: so that which was nearer to us, more easily preserved, and deposited in immense libraries, is lost forever; and we have found, at the end of the world, monuments not less authentic, which we had no reason to expect finding.

The truth and authenticity of this ritual of the Brahmans, of which I am speaking, cannot be doubted. The author certainly does not flatter his sect; he does not attempt to disguise their superstitions, or to give them an air of probability, by feigned explanations, or to excuse them by allegories. He gives an account of the most extravagant laws, with simplicity and candor; human understanding appears then in all its misery. If the Brahmans observed all the laws of their Vedam, there is no monk who would submit to such a state; scarce is the son of a Brahman born before he is the slave of ceremonies: his tongue is rubbed with rosin mixed with flour; the word *Oum* is pronounced; twenty divinities are invoked before his navel skin is cut; but these words are repeated to him, "Live to command Men"; and as soon as he can speak, he is taught the dignity of his being. The Brahmans were, in effect, for a long time sovereigns of India; and theocracy was established in that vast country more than in any country in the world.

The infant is soon exposed to the moon; the Supreme Being is implored to efface those sins which the child may have committed, though he has been born only eight days; anthems are sung to fires; the child, after a hundred ceremonies, is called *Chormo*, which is the honorary title of the Brahmans.

As soon as the child can walk, his life is passed in bathing and repeating prayers. He sacrifices for the dead; and this sacrifice is instituted, that Brama may give to the souls of the child's ancestors an agreeable abode in other bodies.

The five winds that may issue from the openings of the human body are prayed to. This is not more strange than the prayers which are repeated to the god Pet, by the good old women of Rome.

There is no function of nature, no action among the Brahmans, without prayers. The first time that the child's head is shaved, the father says to the razor, very devoutly, "Shave my son as thou hast shaved the sun and the god Indro." It is possible that the god Indro might formerly have been shaved; but as to the sun's undergoing that operation, this is not very easy to comprehend, unless the Brahmans have had our Apollo, whom we still represent without a beard.

The recital of all these ceremonies would be as tedious as they appear ridiculous; and in their blind state, they say as much of ours: but there is a mystery amongst them, which should not be passed over in silence: that is, the Matricha Machom; this mystery gives fresh being and new life.

The soul is supposed to be in the breast, and this, indeed, is the sentiment of almost all antiquity. The hand is moved from the breast to the head, in pressing upon the nerve which we imagine communicates from one of these organs to the other; and in this manner the soul is conducted to the brain. When it is certain that the soul is well hung, the young man then calls out, that his soul and body are united to the Supreme Being, and says, "I am myself part of the divinity."

This opinion was that of the most respectable philosophers of Greece, of those Stoics who have raised human nature above itself, that of the divine Antonines; and it must be owned that nothing was more capable of inspiring great virtues: to believe one's self part of the divinity, is to impose a law of doing nothing that is not worthy of God himself.

We find in this law the Brahmans' ten commandments, and these are ten sins to be avoided; they are divided into three species, the sins of the body, those of the word, and those of the will. To strike or kill one's neighbor, to rob him, and violate a woman, these are bodily sins; dissimulation, lying, and scandal, are the sins of the word; those of the will consist in evil-wishing, in being envious of others' good, in not being affected with others' misfortunes. These ten commandments make us forgive all the ridiculous rites. We evidently find that morality is the same with all civilized nations; and that the most sacred customs amongst one people, appear to others as extravagant or detestable. Established rites at present divide mankind, and morality reunites them.

Superstition never prevented the Brahmans from acknowledging an only God. Strabo, in his fifteenth book, says that they adore a Supreme God; that they remain silent for several years, before they dare speak; that they are sober, chaste, and temperate; that justice guides their life, and they die without remorse. This is corroborated by St. Clement of Alexandria, Apulius, Porphyrus, Palladius, and St. Ambrose. We should constantly remember that they enjoyed a terrestrial paradise, and that those who abused God's bounties were driven out of that paradise.

The fall of degenerated man is the foundation of the theology of almost all nations. The natural bias of man to complain of the present, and praise the past, has made it universally believed, that there was a golden age, to which the iron ages have succeeded. What is still more extraordinary, is, that the Vedam of the ancient Brahmans taught that the first man was Adimo and the first woman Procriti: Adimo signified lord, and Procriti meant life; as Heva, among the Phœnicians and the Hebrews, signified also life, or the serpent. This conformity deserves great attention.

XVII

OF CHINA

DARE we speak of the Chinese without having recourse to their own annals? They are confirmed by the unanimous opinion of our travelers of different sects, Jacobins, Jesuits, Lutherans, Calvinists, all interested in contradicting them. It is evident that the empire of China was formed upwards of four thousand years ago. The people of antiquity never heard any mention made of those physical revolutions, of those inundations, those fiery devastations, the slight remembrance of which is preserved and changed in the fables of the deluge of Deucalion, and the fall of Phæton. The climate of China was therefore preserved from these scourges, as it always was from the plague, literally speaking, which has made such frequent ravages in Africa, Asia, and Europe.

If any annals carry with them the stamp of certainty, they are those of China, which have united, as has been already said, the history of Heaven with that of earth. Singular from every other people, they have constantly marked their epochs by eclipses, and the conjunctions of the planets; and our astronomers, who have examined their calculations, have been surprised to find them almost all just. Other nations invented allegorical fables, and the Chinese wrote their history with the pen and the astrolabe in their hand, with such simplicity as cannot be equalled in the rest of Asia.

Each reign of their emperors was written contemporary; there are no different methods of reckoning amongst them, no contradictory chronologies. Our traveling missionaries candidly relate, that when they spoke to the wise emperor Cam-hi, of the chronology of the Vulgate, of the Septuagint, and the Samaritan, Cam-hi replied to them, Is it possible that the books that you believe in are at variance?

The Chinese wrote upon thin tablets of bamboo, when the Chaldeans did not yet write upon anything but bricks; and they have still some ancient tablets, which their varnishes have preserved from rotting. These are perhaps the most ancient monuments in the world. They have no history before that of their emperors, no fictions, no prodigies, no inspired men, who called themselves demi-gods, as with the Egyptians and Greeks. When these people write they write reasonably.

They particularly differ from other nations in the history, making no mention of a college of priests, who ever controlled their laws. The Chinese do not refer to those savage times, when it was necessary for men to be cheated in order to be guided. Other people began their history by the origin of the world; the Zend of the Persians, the Vedam of the Indians, Sanchoniato, Manetho; in fine, down to Hesiod, they all trace things back to their origin and the formation of the world. The Chinese have not been guilty of this folly; their history comprehends no other than historical times.

In this place above all others, we should apply our great principle, that a nation whose first chronicles attest the existence of a vast empire, powerful and wise, must have been assembled as a body of people for antecedent ages. Here is a people who for upwards of four thousand years daily write annals. Again, would it not be madness to disbelieve that to be expert in all the arts necessary to society, even so far as to write, and to write well, more time was necessary than the Chinese empire has subsisted, in reckoning only from the emperor Tohi, till now? None of the literati of China doubt that the Five Kings existed two thousand three hundred years before our vulgar era. This monument, then, is four hundred years anterior to the first Babylonian observations sent into Greece by Callisthenes. Does it really become the literati of Paris to contest the antiquity of a Chinese book, considered as authentic by all the tribunals of China?

The first rudiments of every kind are always slower in their progress than the more advanced stages. Let us constantly remember that five hundred years ago scarce anyone knew how to write, either in the North, in Germany or France. Those tallies which bakers still use were the hieroglyphics, and our books of account. There is no other kind of arithmetic used in collecting the taxes; and the name of tallies are still a proof of it in the country. Our capricious customs, which were not revised by writing till within these four hundred and fifty years, sufficiently teach us how scarce the art of writing then was. There are no people in Europe who have not latterly made more progress within half a century in all the arts than they had made from the time of the invasion of the Barbarians till the fourteenth century.

I shall not here examine why the Chinese, who were arrived at the knowledge and practice of everything that was useful in society, did not go as far as we do at present in the sciences: they are, I allow, as bad physicians as we were two hundred years ago, and as the Greeks and Romans; but they brought morality to perfection, which is the first of the sciences.

Their vast and populous empire was already governed like a family, whose monarch was the father; and forty of whose legislative tribunals were considered as the elder brothers, whilst we were wandering in the forests of the Ardennes.

Their religion was simple, wise, august, free from all superstition and all barbarity, ere we had yet Theutats, to whom the Druids sacrificed the children of our ancestors, in great osier baskets.

The Chinese emperors themselves offered to the God of the Universe, to Chang-ti, to the Tien, to the principle of all things, the first fruits of their harvest twice a year, and even of those harvests which they had sown with their own hands. This custom was kept up for upwards of forty centuries, in the midst of revolutions, and even the most horrid calamities.

Never was the religion of the emperors and of the tribunals dishonored with impostures; never was it troubled with quarrels between the priests and the empire; never was it burdened with absurd innovations, which are supported one against the other by arguments as absurd as themselves, the rage of which has at length placed the poignard in the hands of fanatics led on by the factious. Here the Chinese are particularly superior to all the nations of the universe.

Their Confucius framed neither new opinions nor new rites. He neither pretended to be an inspired man, nor a prophet. He was a magistrate, who taught the ancient laws. We sometimes say, very improperly, "the religion of Confucius"; he had no other than that of the first sages; he recommends nothing but virtue, preaches no mysteries; he says, in his first book, that in order to learn to govern, we should pass our whole life in correcting ourselves; in the second he proves that God has himself graven virtue in the heart of man; he says that man is not born wicked, and that he became so by his own fault; the third is a collection of pure maxims, where we can meet with nothing that is mean, nor any ridiculous allegories. He had five thousand disciples, he might have put himself at the head of a powerful party; but he rather chose to instruct men, than to govern them.

The temerity we have shown, at the extremity of the west, of judging of this eastern court, and imputing atheism to them, has been vehemently attacked in an *Essay upon General History*. What, in fact, must have been the rage of some amongst us, to call an empire atheistical, when almost all its laws are founded upon the knowledge of a Supreme Being, Requiter, and Avenger? The inscriptions of their temples, of which we have authentic copies, are, "To the First Principle, without beginning and without end: He has done all, and governs all; He is infinitely good, infinitely just: He enlightens, He supports and regulates all nature."

The Jesuits, who are disliked in Europe, are reproached with flattering the atheists of China. A Frenchman, named Maigret, Bishop of Conon, who did not understand a word of Chinese, was deputed by a pope to go and try causes upon the spot; he treated Confucius as an atheist, upon these words of that great man, "Heaven has given me virtue, man cannot hurt me." The greatest of our saints never uttered a more celestial maxim. If Confucius was an atheist, so were Cato and the Chancellor L'Hospital.

Let us here repeat and put calumny to the blush; that the same man who opposed Bayle by asserting that a society of atheists was impossible, at the same time advanced, that the most ancient government upon earth was a society of atheists. We cannot be too much ashamed of our contradictions.

Let us again repeat that the literati of China, adorers of one only God, abandoned the people to the superstition of the Bonzes. They tolerated the sect of Laokium, that of Fo, and several others. The magistrates conceived that the people might have different religions from that of the state, as they live upon grosser aliment; they tolerated the Bonzes, and protected them. In almost every other country, those who carried on the trade of Bonzes had the principal authority.

It is true that the laws of China do not mention rewards and punishments after death; they did not choose to affirm what they did not know. This difference between them and all the great polished people is very astonishing. The doctrine of hell was useful, and the government of the Chinese never admitted it. They imagined, that an exact policy, constantly exercised, would have greater effect than opinions, which might be opposed; and that the people would fear a law always present more than one in future. We shall, in the proper place, mention a people infinitely less considerable, who had nearly the same idea, or who rather had no idea, but which was propagated by means unknown to other men.

Let us resume here, only to add that the empire of China subsisted with splendor, when the Chaldeans began the course of those nineteen hundred years' astronomical observations, which were sent into Greece by Callisthenes. The Brahmans then reigned in a part of India; the Persians had their laws; the Arabians to the south, and the Scythians to the north, had no other habitation than tents. Egypt, which we are now going to speak of, was a powerful kingdom.

XVIII

OF EGYPT

IT APPEARS evident to me that the Egyptians, ancient as they undoubtedly are, could not have been united into a civilized, polished, industrious body, till very long after all the nations that have passed in review. The reason whereof is clear. Egypt, as far as the Delta, is inclosed by two chains of rocks, between which is the fall of the Nile, in descending from Ethiopia in the south to the north. From the cataracts of this river to its entrance, in a straight line, the distance is only one hundred and sixty leagues, of three thousand geometrical feet each; and its breadth is only from ten to fifteen and twenty leagues, till it washes the Delta, a low part of Egypt, which embraces an extent of fifty leagues from east to west.

On the right of the Nile are the deserts of Thebaid, and on the left are the uninhabitable sands of Lybia, which extend as far as that small and restricted country where the temple of Ammon was erected.

The inundations of the Nile must for ages have prevented the colonization of a land which was under water for four months in the year; and these stagnant waters, continually increasing, must for a long time have made all Egypt one continued morass.

This is not the case upon the shores of the Tigris, the Indus, the Ganges, and other rivers, which also overflow their banks almost every year, at the annual melting of the snow. Their inundations are not, however, so great, and the extensive plains which surround them enable the cultivators to abundantly profit by the fertility of the soil.

We should particularly observe that the plague, that inherent scourge of humanity, breaks out at least once in ten years in Egypt. It must have been much more destructive when the waters of the Nile, by stagnating upon the land, added their infection to that horrid contagion. And thus the population of Egypt must have been very small for many ages.

The natural order of things seems then clearly to demonstrate that Egypt was one of the last of the inhabited lands. The Troglodites, born upon those rocks, which are washed by the Nile, were compelled to perform labors as continual as they were difficult; to dig canals for the reception of this river; to erect cabins, and to raise them twenty-five feet above the earth. This was, however, necessary before Thebes, with its hundred gates, could be built; before Memphis could be erected, or the construction of the Pyramids could be thought of. It is very strange that no ancient historian has made so natural a selection.

We have already observed that in those times, wherein Abraham's travels are placed, Egypt was a powerful kingdom: its kings had already erected some of those pyramids, which still astonish the eyes of the imagination of travelers. The Arabs have written that the greatest was erected by Saurid, many ages before Abraham. The time of building the famous Thebes, with its hundred gates, is not known. It seems that in those obscure times, great cities bore the name of the cities of God, like Babylon. But who can believe, that from each of the hundred gates of Thebes, two hundred chariots, armed in a warlike manner, and a hundred thousand warriors, issued? They would amount to twenty thousand chariots, and a million of soldiers; and if there was one soldier among every five persons, this number must make us suppose five millions of inhabitants for a single city, in a country that is not so large as Spain or France, and which, according to Diodorus Siculus, contained no more than three millions of inhabitants and but one hundred and sixty thousand soldiers for its defense. Diodorus says (book 1st) that Egypt was so well peopled, that it formerly contained seven millions of inhabitants; and that even in his time there were three millions.

You do not give greater credit to the conquests of Sesostris than to the millions of soldiers that issued from the hundred gates of Thebes. Do you not imagine that you are reading the history of Picrocoles, when those who copy Herodotus tell you that the father of Sesostris, founding his hopes upon a dream, and an oracle, destined his son to conquer the world; that he brought up all the children that were born the same day as this son in his own court, to the trade of arms; that they had no victuals allowed them till they had run the length of eight of our longest leagues; that at length Sesostris appeared with his six hundred thousand men, twenty-seven thousand warlike cars, and set out to conquer all the earth, from the Indus to the Euxine Sea; and that he subjugated Mingrelia, and Georgia, then called Colchis. Herodotus does not in the least doubt that Sesostris left colonies in Colchis, because he saw tawny men with frizzled hair, who resembled Egyptians, at Colchis. I would much sooner believe that this species of Scythians, upon the banks of the Black and Caspian seas, came to renounce the Egyptians, when they ravaged, for such a length of time, Asia before the reign of Cyrus. I should believe they carried with them slaves from Egypt, that true country of slaves, whose descendants Herodotus might see, or thought he saw in Colchis. If these Colchians had, indeed, the superstition to be circumcised, they probably retained that custom from Egypt, as it always happened that the people of the North adopted the rites of those civilized nations whom they had conquered.

The Egyptians were never, at any known period, a formidable people; they were never attacked by any enemy without being conquered. The Scythians began; after the Scythians came Nabucodonoser, who conquered Egypt without opposition. Cyrus had nothing more to do than to send thither one of his lieutenants; when they revolted under Cambyses, one campaign was sufficient to make them submit; and this Cambyses so much despised the Egyptians, that he killed their god Apis in their presence. Ochus reduced Egypt to a province of his kingdom. Alexander, Cæsar, Augustus, and the Caliph Omar conquered Egypt with equal facility. This same people of Colchis, under the name of Mamelukes, returned again to seize upon Egypt in the time of the Crusades; at length Selim conquered Egypt in a single campaign, like all those who had made their appearance. There never were any other but our Crusaders, who suffered themselves to be beaten by those Egyptians, the most dastardly of mankind, as has been elsewhere observed; but this was owing to their being governed by the Mamelukes of Colchis.

It is true that an humbled people might formerly have been conquerors, as the Greeks and Romans testify. But we are more certain of the ancient grandeur of the Romans and Greeks, than that of Sesostris.

I do not deny that he whom we call Sesostris might have carried on a fortunate war against some Ethiopians, some Arabs, and some people of Phœnicia. This was sufficient, in the language of some exaggerators, to make him the conqueror of the earth. There is no subjugated nation who does not pretend formerly to have subjugated others. The glory of ancient superiority, administers consolation for present humiliation.

Herodotus ingenuously related to the Greeks what the Egyptians had told him; but how comes it that in speaking to him of nothing but prodigies, they gave him no intimation of the famous plagues of Egypt; of that magical battle between the sorcerers of Pharaoh, and the minister of the God of the Jews; and of a whole army swallowed up in the Red Sea, under waters which rose like mountains to the right and left to let the Hebrews pass, and which, by their fall, drowned the Egyptians? This certainly was the greatest event in the history of the world. Neither Herodotus, Manethon, or Eratosthenes, nor any of the Greeks, who were so fond of the marvelous, and who kept a regular correspondence with Egypt, mention these miracles, which should employ the attention of all generations. I certainly do not make this reflection to invalidate the testimony of the Hebrew books, which I revere as I ought to do. I wonder only at the silence of the Egyptians and the Greeks. Was God unwilling that so divine a history should be transmitted to us by any profane hand?

XIX

The Egyptian Language and Symbols

The language of the Egyptians had no affinity with that of the nations of Asia. You do not find among this people the word *Adonai* or *Adinijah*, nor *Bal*, nor *Baal*, terms which signify *The Lord;*—nor *Mitra*, which, with the Persians, was *The Sun*, nor *Melch*, or *Melk*, which signifies *King*, in Syria; nor *Shak*, *Schach*, or *Shah*, which signifies the same thing among the Indians and the Persians. On the contrary you find that *Pharaoh* was the Egyptian name that answers to *King*, *Oshireth* (Osiris), corresponded to the *Mitra* of the Persians; and the common word *On*, signified the Sun.

The Chaldean priests were called *Mag—Magi;* those of the Egyptians *Choen*, as Diodorus Siculus relates. The Hieroglyphics and alphabetic characters of Egypt, which time has spared, and which we still find engraven upon the obelisks, have no relation to those of any other people.

Before men had invented hieroglyphics, they had doubtless representative signs, for the fact. What could the first men do, besides what we do, when we are in their place? Let a child be in a country ignorant of its language, and he will talk by signs; if he is not understood, he will draw upon a wall, with a piece of charcoal, the things that he wants, if he has the least sagacity.

They therefore, at first, painted in a very clumsy style what they wanted to communicate; and the art of drawing, doubtless, preceded that of writing. Thus it was that the Mexicans and Peruvians wrote. They had not made any further progress in the art. Such was the method of all the first polished people. In time, they invented symbolical figures; two hands united signified peace; darts represented war; an eye signified the divinity; a scepter implied royalty; and lines, uniting these figures, expressed short phrases.

The Chinese at length invented characters, to express each word of their language. But what people invented the alphabet, which, in placing before our eyes the different sounds that can be articulated, facilitates the combination of all possible words by writing? Who could teach men to engrave thus easily their thoughts? I shall not here repeat all the stories of the ancients upon this art—which eternizes all arts—I shall only say that many centuries were necessary to accomplish it.

The Choens, or priests of Egypt, continued for a long time to write in hieroglyphics, which is forbidden by the second article of the Hebrew laws; and when the people of Egypt had alphabetical characters, the Choens, or priests, adopted different ones, which they called sacred; and in order to keep a constant barrier between them and the people, the Magi and the Brahmans made use of the same kind of characters; so necessary has the art of disguise appeared, in order to govern mankind.

Those Choens not only had characters peculiar to themselves, but they had still preserved the ancient language of Egypt, when time had changed the vulgar tongue.

Manethon, who is quoted by Eusebius, speaks of two columns engraved by Thaut, the first Hermes, in the characters of the sacred language. But who knows the period of time when this ancient Hermes lived?

The Egyptians were particularly careful in preserving their first symbols. It is curious to observe upon their monuments, a serpent biting his own tail, to represent the twelve months of the year, and each of these months expressed by animals which are not the signs of the Zodiac, known to us. We again see the five days added to the twelve months, under the form of a little serpent, with five figures upon it; these are the sparrow-hawk, a man, a dog, a lion, and a stork. We see them as drawn by Kirker, after the monuments preserved at Rome. Thus we find that almost everything in antiquity was symbolical and allegorical.

XX

EGYPTIAN MONUMENTS

IT IS certain that after the ages in which the Egyptians fertilized the soil, by the draining of the flood; after those time when villages began to be changed into opulent cities, then the necessary arts, having arrived at perfection, the ostentatious arts began to be in esteem. Sovereigns were then found who employed their subjects, and some Arabs, in the neighborhood of Lake Sirbon, to build them palaces and pyramidical tombs, to cut enormous stones in the quarries of Upper Egypt, and bring them afloat upon rafts as far as Memphis; to erect upon massive columns great flat stones, without either taste or proportion. They were acquainted with the great, but not with the beautiful. They taught the first Greeks; but the Greeks, after they had built Alexandria, became their masters in everything.

It is melancholy to think, that in Cæsar's wars half of the famous library of the Ptolemies was burnt; and that the other half heated the baths of Mussulmen, when Omar subdued Egypt. We should have known at least the origin of the superstitions with which that people were infected, the chaos of their philosophy, and some of their antiquities and sciences.

They must certainly have been at peace for several ages for their princes to have had time and leisure to raise all those prodigious buildings, the greatest part of which still exist.

Their pyramids must have been the produce of many years and much expense; a great number of inhabitants, together with foreign slaves, must have been for a long time employed in these immense works. They were erected by despotism, vanity, servitude, and superstition; in fact none but a despotic king could thus have constrained nature. England, for example, is more powerful than Egypt was. Could a king of England employ his people to raise such monuments?

Vanity, doubtless, had its share; it was the ambition of the ancient kings of Egypt, who should raise the finest pyramid to his father, or to himself. Servitude procured the laboring hand; and as to superstition, we know that these pyramids were tombs; we know that the Chocamatins, or Choen, of Egypt, that is to say the priests, had persuaded the people that the soul returned into its own body at the expiration of a thousand years. They chose that the body should be a thousand years entirely free from all corruption: for which reason it was so very carefully embalmed; and to secure it from all accidents, it was inclosed in a large stone that had no opening. The kings and great people erected tombs for themselves, in such forms as they judged would be the least exposed to the injuries of time. The preservation of their bodies surpasses all human hopes. There are now Egyptian mummies, which have been buried upwards of four thousand years. Carcasses have endured as long as pyramids.

The opinion of a resurrection, after ten centuries, was afterwards adopted by the Greeks, who were disciples of the Egyptians, and the Romans, who were disciples of the Greeks. We find it in the sixth book of the Æneid, which is only a description of the mysteries of Isis and Ceres of Eleusina.

> But when a thousand rolling years are past,
> (So long their punishments and penance last,)
> Whole droves of minds are, by the driving god,
> Compelled to drink the deep Lethæan flood:
> In large forgetful draughts to steep the cares
> Of their past labors, and their irksome years.

It was afterwards introduced amongst the Christians, who established the reign of a thousand years; the sect of the Millenarians has handed it down to our time. Thus have many opinions passed all over the world. This is sufficient to point out the design of erecting those pyramids. We shall not repeat what has been said upon their architecture and dimensions; I examine only the history of the human understanding.

XXI

Of the Greeks

THEIR DELUGES, THEIR ALPHABET, AND GENIUS

GREECE is a small hilly country, intersected by the sea, of much the same extent as Great Britain. Everything in this country testifies the physical revolutions it has undergone. The islands which surround it sufficiently show, by the continued shoals near their shores, by the shallowness of the sea, by the herbs and roots which grow under the water, that they were detached from the continent. The Gulfs of Eubœa, Chalcis, Argos, Corinth, Actium, and Messina, demonstrate that the sea has made passages through the earth. The seashell beds, with which are covered those mountains that surround the famous vale of Tempe, are ocular proofs of an ancient inundation; and the deluges of Ogyges and Deucalion, which have produced so many fables, are historically true. This may probably be the reason why the Greeks are so modern a people. These great revolutions sunk them once more in barbarity, at the time that the nations of Asia and Egypt were flourishing.

I shall leave to men more learned than myself the trouble of proving that the three children of Noah, who were the only inhabitants of the globe, divided the whole of it amongst them; that they separated from each other two or three thousand leagues, laying everywhere the foundation of powerful empires; and that Javan, his grandson, peopled all Greece, in passing through Italy; that from thence the Greeks derived the name Ionians, Ion having detached colonies upon the coasts of Asia Minor; that Ion plainly appears to be Javan, by changing the *I* into *Ja*, and the *on* into *van*. Such tales are told to children, and children do not believe them:

Nec pueri credunt nisi qui nondum œre lavantur.

The deluge of Ogyges is usually placed about twelve hundred years before the first Olympiad: the first who speaks of it is Acesilas, quoted by Eusebius, in his *Evangelical Preparation,* and by George le Sincelle. Greece, it is said, remained a desert two hundred years after the sea had made this eruption into the country. It is, nevertheless, asserted, that a government was at the same time established in Sicyon and in Argos; the names of the first magistrates of these little provinces are even mentioned, and they are called Basiloi, which answers to Princes. But let us not lose time in penetrating these useless obscurities.

There was another inundation in the time of Deucalion, the son of Prometheus. The fable adds that there remained no other inhabitants than Deucalion and Pyrrha, who made fresh men, by throwing stones behind them, through their legs. By which method the world was stocked with men faster than a warren is with rabbits.

If very judicious men, like the writer Petau, are to be believed a single son of Noah produced a race, which, at the end of twenty-eight years amounted to six hundred and twenty-three thousand billions, six hundred and twelve millions of men. The calculation is a little high. We are so unhappy at present, that in twenty-six marriages there are usually but four which produce children that become fathers. This calculation is formed upon the accounts of the registers of the greatest cities. Of a thousand children that are born the same year, there are scarce six hundred remaining at the end of twenty years. Let us suspect the veracity of Petau, and such, who, like him, create children with the stroke of a pen, as well as those who relate that Deucalion and Pyrrha peopled Greece by throwing stones.

Greece, we know, was the country of fables, and almost every fable was the origin of a doctrine, of a temple, and of a public feast. By what excess of madness, by what absurd obstinacy, have so many compilers endeavored to prove, in so many enormous volumes, that a public feast, established in commemoration of an event, is a demonstration of the truth of that event? What, because young Bacchus is celebrated in a temple issuing from Jupiter's thigh, Jupiter really had concealed Bacchus in his thigh? What, Cadmus and his wife were changed into serpents, in Bœotia, because the Bœotians commemorated such an event in their ceremonies! Did the temples of Castor and Pollux, at Rome, demonstrate that those gods descended upon earth, in favor of the Romans?

Much rather assure yourself, when you see an ancient feast, or an antique temple, that they are the works of error. This error gains credit at the end of two or three centuries; it afterwards becomes sacred, and temples are erected to chimeras.

On the contrary, in historical times, the most noble truths have but few sectaries; the greatest men die without honor. The Themistocles, the Cimons, the Miltiades, the Aristides, the Phocions, are persecuted; whilst Perseus, Bacchus, and other fantastical personages, have temples erected to them.

Credit may be given to a people with regard to what they say of themselves to their own disadvantage, when these accounts are attended with probability, and are no way contradictory to the common order of nature.

The Athenians, who were dispersed in a very barren land, inform us themselves that an Egyptian, named Cecrops, who was driven out of his country, gave them their first institutions. This appears surprising, because the Egyptians were not navigators; but it might have happened that the Phœnicians, who traveled throughout all nations, carried Cecrops into Attica. It is very certain that the Greeks did not adopt the Egyptian letters, which theirs no way resemble. The Phœnicians carried them their first alphabet, which then consisted of only sixteen characters, and are evidently the same. The Phœnicians afterwards added eight letters, which the Greeks still retain.

I look upon an alphabet as an incontestible monument of the country from whence a nation derived its first knowledge. It appears very probable, again that these Phœnicians discovered the silver mines, which were in Attica, as they worked those of Spain. Merchants were the first preceptors of these same Greeks, who afterwards instructed all other nations.

These people, all barbarous as they were in the time of Ogyges, seem to have been born with organs more favorable to the fine arts than any other people. They had something in their nature more refined and subtile. Their language evinces it; for even before they knew how to write, we find they had a more harmonious mixture of soft consonants and vowels in their language than any other people of Asia were acquainted with.

The name of Knath, which signifies the Phœnicians, according to Sanchoniathon, is certainly not so harmonious as that of Helienos, or Graius. Argos, Athens, Lacedæmon, the Olympia, sound better than Reheboth city.

Sophia, wisdom, is softer than Shochemath in Syriac, and Basileus, in Hebrew. Roy sounds better than Melk or Shack. Compare the names Agamemnon, Diomedes, and Idomeneus, with those of Mardokempad, Simordak, Sohasduch, and Niricassolahssar.

Josephus, himself, in his book against Apion, acknowledges that the Greeks could not pronounce the barbarous name of Jerusalem, because the Jews pronounced it Hershalaïm. This word grated in the ear of an Athenian; and it was changed by the Greeks from Hershalaïm to Jerusalem.

The Greeks transformed all the harsh Syriac, Persian and Egyptian names. Of Coresh they made Cyrus; of Istheth and Oshireth, they made Isis and Osiris; of Moph, they made Memphis, and at length brought the barbarians to pronounce in the same manner, so that in the time of the Ptolomies, the Egyptian cities and gods had no other than Grecian names.

The Indus and Ganges had their names from the Greeks. The Ganges, in the language of the Brahmans, was called Sannoubi, and the Indus Sombadipo. Such are the ancient names that we find in the Vedam.

The Greeks, in extending themselves along the coasts of Asia Minor, carried harmony with them. Their Homer was probably born at Smyrna.

Fine architecture, perfect sculpture, painting, and good music, genuine poetry, real eloquence, the method of writing good history, and in short, philosophy itself, although rude and obscure, were transmitted to other nations by the Greeks, who excelled their predecessors in almost everything.

Egypt had never any fine statues but by Grecian hands. Ancient Balbec in Syria, ancient Palmyra in Arabia, were indebted for their palaces and their magnificently constructed temples, to the Grecian artists whom their sovereigns employed. We find nothing but the remains of barbarism (as has been before observed, in the ruins of Persepolis, built by the Persians; whilst the monuments of Balbec and Palmyra are still, under their ruins, master-pieces of architecture.

XXII

OF THE JEWS, WHEN FIRST KNOWN

WE SHALL touch as little as possible upon what is divine in the history of the Jews; or, if compelled to speak of it, shall go no farther than as their miracles seem to have a connection with the usual course of events.

We have all the respect that is due to the continual prodigies which signalized the progress of that nation. We believe in them with all the reasonable faith that is required by the church, which has been substituted for the synagogue. We do not examine them, but confine ourselves to history.

We shall write of the Jews as we spoke of the Scythians and the Greeks, in weighing the probabilities and discussing the facts. As no other persons than themselves have written their history, before the Romans destroyed their city, it is only necessary to consult their own annals.

The Jews rank only among the most modern nations, if we consider them from the time they first formed a settlement and possessed a capital. They seemed to have been of but little consideration to their neighbors until the time of Solomon, which was about the time of Hesiod and Homer, and the first Archons of Athens.

The name of Solomon, or Soleiman, is well known to the Eastern people; but that of David is not, and Saul still less. The Jews, before Saul, appeared only like a band of Arabs of the Desert, of so little power that the Phœnicians treated them nearly the same as the Lacedemonians treated the Iliots; that is, as slaves, who were not allowed arms. They had not the privilege of forging iron, not even to sharpen their plow-shares and the edge of their hatchets. This is set forth in the book of Samuel, and they add that they had neither sword nor javelin in Saul and Jonathan's battle at Bethaven against the Philistines—an action in which Saul made an oath of sacrificing to the Lord those who should eat during the conflict.

It is true that before this battle, won without arms, it is said in 1 Kings, chap. ii., that Saul, with an army of three hundred and thirty thousand men, entirely defeated the Ammonites; which does not seem to agree with the confession that they had neither sword nor javelin, nor any other arms. Moreover, the greatest princes have seldom had at one time three hundred and thirty thousand effective warriors. How could the Jews, who appear wandering and oppressed in this little country, which has not a single fortified city, no arms, not so much as a sword, be able to bring thirty-three thousand soldiers in the field? Such a force was adequate to the conquest of all Asia and Europe.

Let us leave the task of reconciling these apparent contradictions, which superior intellects remove, to learned and celebrated authors: let us respect what we were obliged to respect; and let us recur to the history of the Jews according to their own writings.

XXIII

Of the Jews in Egypt

According to the annals of the Jews, this nation inhabited the confines of Egypt in those remote times of which history furnishes no account. They resided in the little country of Gossen, or Goshen towards Mount Cassius and Lake Sirbon. The Arabians, who in winter repair with their herds to graze in lower Egypt, still remain there.

This nation was composed of no more than a single family, who, in the space of two hundred years, produced a race of two millions of people; for to furnish six hundred thousand warriors, who according to Genesis came out of Egypt, they must have consisted of at least two millions of souls.

This multiplication, contrary to the order of nature, is one of those miracles which God deigned to operate in favor of the Jews.

It is in vain for a multitude of learned men to be astonished that the king of Egypt should have commanded the two midwives to destroy all the male children of the Hebrews,—that the king's daughter, who resided at Memphis, should go and bathe herself at a great distance from Memphis, in a branch of the Nile where nobody ever bathed on account of crocodiles; it is in vain for them to make objections to the age of eighty, which Moses had already attained, before he undertook to conduct a whole people out of bondage.

They dispute about the ten plagues of Egypt. They say that the magicians of the kingdom could not perform the same miracles as the messenger of God; and that if God gave them this power, he seems to have acted against himself. They suppose that as Moses had changed all the waters into blood, there remained no more water for the magicians to perform the same metamorphosis upon.

They ask how could Pharaoh pursue the Jews with a great number of horsemen, after all the horses had died, by the fifth and sixth plagues? They ask why six hundred warriors should run away when God was at their head, and they might have engaged the Egyptians to advantage, all the first born of whom being struck dead? They ask again, why God did not give fertile Egypt to his cherished people, instead of making them wander forty years in shocking deserts?

There is but a single answer to all these innumerable objections; and this answer is, God would have it so. The Church believes it, and we should believe it. It is in this respect that this history differs from others. Every people have their prodigies; but everything is prodigious with the Jewish nation; and it should have been so, as this people were conducted by God himself. It is plain that the history of God should not resemble that of man. Wherefore we shall not relate any of those supernatural facts, which should be mentioned only in the holy Scripture. Still less should we dare attempt their explanation. Let us only examine those few that may be subject to criticism.

XXIV

Of Moses as Chief of a Nation

THE master of nature only gives strength to the arm he deigns to choose. Moses is supernatural in everything. More than one learned man has looked upon him as a very able politician. Others have considered him only as a weak reed, which the divine hand deigned to use, to frame the destiny of empires.

What can we think of an old man of eighty years of age, who by himself alone undertakes to conduct a whole people over whom he had no authority? His arm cannot fight nor his tongue articulate. He is described as a cripple and a stammerer. He conducts his followers for forty years successively through horrid deserts. He wants to give them a settlement, but he gives them none.

If we were to pursue his steps in the deserts of Sur, Sin, Horeb, Sinai, Pharan, and of Cades-Barnea, and observe his retrograde motions towards the very spot from which he set out, could we believe that he was a great commander? It is stated that he was at the head of six hundred thousand warriors, and he could neither provide clothing nor subsistence for them. God does everything. God remedies everything. He nourishes, He clothes the people, by working miracles. Moses, then, is nothing of himself, and his impotence shows that he can be guided by nothing but the hand of the Almighty. We therefore consider him as a man, and not the minister of God. His personality, in this capacity, is an object of interesting enquiry.

He wants to go into the country of the Canaanites, on the west of the river Jordan, in the land of Jericho, which is in fact the only fruitful spot in the whole province; and instead of taking this road, he turns eastward, towards Esion-gaber and the Black Sea, a savage barren country on which not a single shrub or bush grows, and which is without a rivulet, without springs, save a few small wells of brackish and unwholesome water.

When the news of this irruption of a foreign people reached the Canaanites or Phœnicians, they came and gave them battle in these deserts of Cades-Barnea. How could Moses permit himself to be defeated at the head of six hundred thousand soldiers, in a country which does not now contain three thousand inhabitants? At the expiration of thirty-nine years he gains two victories, but he does not fulfill a single object of his legislation. He and his people die before he sets foot in the country which he hoped to conquer.

A legislator, according to our common notions, should make himself beloved and feared. He should not push severity to barbarity. He should not, instead of inflicting by the ministers of the law some punishments upon the criminal, make a foreign nation murder the greatest part of his own people.

Could Moses at near the age of a hundred and twenty years, could he, actuated only by his own feelings, have been so inhuman, so hardened in bloodshed, as to command the Levites to massacre indiscriminately their brothers to the number of twenty-three thousand, to screen his own brother, who ought rather to have died, than to have made a golden calf to be adored? And, strange to relate, his brother is, after this shameful action, made high pontiff, and twenty-three thousand men are massacred.

Moses had espoused a Midianitish woman, the daughter of Jethro, the high priest of Midian, in Arabia Petræa. Jethro had conferred numerous favors upon him; and permitted his son to accompany him as a guide in the wilderness. Now, by what cruelty, so contrary to all policy (to judge only by our feeble notions) must Moses have been actuated with, to command the massacre of twenty-four thousand of his countrymen, under the pretext that a Jew had been discovered with a woman of Midian? And how can it be said, after such astonishing butchery, that "Moses was the most meek and gentle of men?"

We must acknowledge, humanly speaking, that these horrid deeds revolt against reason and nature. But if we consider Moses as the minister of God's designs and vengeance, the aspect is entirely changed. He is not a man that acts as a man; he is the instrument of the divinity, whom we should not call to account. We should offer up silent adoration.

If Moses had of himself instituted his religion, like Zoroaster, Thauth, the first Brahmans, Numa, Mahomet, and many others, we might ask him, why he did not avail himself of the most useful and efficacious means of restraining lust and sin? Why he did not expressly preach the immortality of the soul, rewards and punishments after death; dogmas long before received in Egypt, in Phœnicia, in Mesopotamia, in Persia, and in India?

"You have been instructed," we should tell him, "in the wisdom of the Egyptians, you are a legislator, and you absolutely neglect the principal dogma of the Egyptians, the most necessary dogma to man, a belief so salutary and holy, that your own Jews, barbarous as they were, embraced it a long time after you; it was, at least, partly adopted by the Essenes and the Pharisees, at the end of a thousand years."

This perplexing objection against a common legislator falls to the ground, and loses, as we find, all its force, when a law given by God himself, who condescended to be the king of the Jewish people, temporarily rewarding and punishing them, and who would not reveal the knowledge of the immortality of the soul, and hell's eternal torments, but at the time appointed by his decrees. Almost every event merely human among the Jews is the summit of horror. Everything divine is above our feeble comprehension. We are constantly silenced by them both.

There have been men of extensive knowledge, who have carried their skepticism so far as to question the existence of such a person as Moses; whose whole life, which is a series of prodigies from his cradle to his grave, appeared to them an imitation of the ancient Arabian fables, and particularly that of the ancient Bacchus. They do not know at what period to fix Moses. Even the name of Pharaoh, king of Egypt, is unknown. No monument, no vestige, remains in the country in which he is said to have traveled. It seems impossible that Moses should have governed two or three millions of men for forty years in uninhabitable deserts, where we can scarce meet at present with two or three wandering tribes, who do not number altogether more than between three and four thousand men. For our own part, we are far from adopting this bold opinion, which would sap the very foundations of the ancient history of the Jewish people.

Neither shall we adhere to the opinion of Eben-Esra, of Maimonides, Nugens, or the author of the *Jewish Ceremonies*, though the learned Le Clerc, Middleton, the eminent men known as the theologians of Holland, and even the great Newton, have added weight to the doctrine. These illustrious scholars imagine that neither Moses nor Joshua could have written the books that are attributed to them. They say that their histories and laws would have been engraven on stone, had they in fact ever existed,—that this art requires great labor and perseverance, and that it is not possible to engrave histories in deserts. They found their opinion upon various assertions and contradictions. In opposition to these learned men, we embrace the common opinion, which is that of the synagogue and the church, whose infallibility we acknowledge.

Not that we dare accuse the Le Clercs, the Middletons, or the Newtons of impiety. God forbid! We are convinced that if the books of Moses and Joshua do not appear to them as if coming from the hands of those heroes of Israel, they are still of the opinion that these books were inspired. They acknowledge the finger of God in every line of Genesis, in Joshua, in Sampson, and Ruth. The Jewish writer was merely the secretary of God—that God who has dictated all things. Newton could not think otherwise, as we already know. God keep us from those perverse hypocrites who, on every pretence, accuse great men of irreligion, just as they formerly accused them of magic! We do not assert that the most learned men, and the greatest geniuses on earth are not true Christians. The more we respect the church, to which we submit, the more we think that this church tolerates, with that charity which forms its real character, the honest opinions of all virtuous scholars.

XXV

Of the Jews from Moses to Saul

I do not endeavor to discover why Joshua or Josuah, captain of the Jews, in making his tribe pass from the east of the river Jordan to the west, towards Jericho, should want God to suspend the course of this river, which is not at that place forty feet wide, when it was so easy to throw a bridge over it, and which it was still more easy to ford. There were several fords to this river, which is proved by the Israelites slaying at one of them the forty-two thousand Jews who could not pronounce the word *Shiboleth*.

I do not ask why the walls of Jericho should fall at the sound of trumpets. These are strange prodigies which God thought fit to operate in favor of the people whose king he had declared himself to be, and miracles of this kind do not belong to historical research. I shall not examine what right Joshua had to come and destroy villages, where his name had never been heard of before. The Jews claimed that they were descended from Abraham. Abraham traveled in this country about four hundred years ago. Therefore, said Joshua, your country belongs to us, and we ought to cut the throats of your mothers, wives, and children.

On this point, Fabricius and Holstenius have made the following objection. What should we say if a Norwegian came into Germany with some hundreds of his countrymen, and told the Germans that about four hundred years ago a countryman of ours, who was the son of a potter, traveled near Vienna; therefore, Austria belongs to us, and we are come to sacrifice you all in the name of the Lord?

The same authors consider that the time of Joshua is not ours; that it is not for us to cast a profane eye upon things divine; and particularly that God had a right to punish the sins of the Canaanites by the hands of the Jews.

We are told that no sooner was Jericho defenceless, than the Jews sacrificed to their God all the inhabitants, old men, aged women, husbands, wives, sons, daughters, nursing infants, and even all domestic animals.

The only exception to this indiscriminate slaughter was a famous courtezan, who had concealed the Jewish spies in her house,—spies that were quite useless, as the walls of the city were to fall at the sound of the trumpets. And why were all the domestic animals killed, which certainly were of great use and value?

With regard to the disreputable woman, before mentioned, it is probable that she afterwards led a more virtuous life, as she is acknowledged to have been one of King David's grandmothers, and in the Vulgate is called *Meretrix*.

All these events are so many figures, or prophecies, which foretold from afar the law of grace. Once more, we repeat, these are mysteries, as sacred as they are incomprehensible.

From the book of Joshua we learn that this chief, having made himself master of part of the land of Canaan, had thirty-one of their petty kings hanged, that is to say, thirty kings and one of the principal burgesses, who had dared to defend their firesides, their wives and their children. We should here prostrate ourselves to Providence, who chastised the sins of these kings by the sword of Joshua.

It is not at all astonishing that the neighboring people should unite against the Jews, who in their eyes could only appear as a band of execrable robbers and depredators; and not as the sacred instruments of divine vengeance, and the future salvation of the human race. They were reduced to slavery by Cushan, king of Mesopotamia. It is true that Mesopotamia and Jericho are at a great distance apart. Cushan must then have conquered Syria, and part of Palestine. Be this as it may, they were in bondage eight years, and remained afterwards fifty-two years upon the same spot. These fifty-two years were a space of servitude, as they were commanded by the law to take all the country from the Mediterranean to the Euphrates,—all this vast extent of country being promised to them; and they would doubtless have been tempted to seize upon it, if they had been at liberty. They were also in bondage for eighteen years to Eglon, king of the Moabites, who was assassinated by Ehud, or Aod; they were afterwards for twenty-eight years slaves to a people of Canaan, whom they do not name, till the warlike prophetess Deborah delivered them. Gideon held them afterwards for seven years in bondage.

They were for eighteen years slaves to the Phœnicians, whom they call Philistines, till the time of Jephtha. And were, for forty years more, slaves to the same people, till the time of Saul. What perplexes our judgment is that they remained slaves at the time of Sampson, when Sampson only required the jawbone of an ass to kill a thousand Philistines, and when God performed, by the hands of Sampson, such wonderful prodigies.

Let us stop a moment to observe how many Jews were exterminated by their own brothers, or by the order of God himself, from the time that they wandered in the desert till the time they elected a king by drawing lots.

Slaughtered by the Levites, after the worship of the Golden Calf, made by
Aaron, the brother of Moses 23,000
Destroyed by fire, at Korah's revolt 250
Put to death for the same revolt 14,700
Slaughtered for correspondence with Midianitish women 24,000
Slain at ford of Jordan for not correctly pronouncing *Shiboleth* 42,000
Killed by the tribe of Benjamin who were attacked 40,000
Benjaminites killed by other tribes 45,000
When the Ark was taken by the Philistines, and God having afflicted them
with emerods, they returned the Ark to Bethshemeth, and make an offering
of five golden emerods, and five golden rats. There were slaughtered of
the Bethshemites for looking into the Ark 50,700
                                                                    ———
. Total number 239,650

Here we have two hundred and thirty-nine thousand six hundred and fifty
Jews, exterminated either by the command of God himself or in their civil
wars; without reckoning those who fell in the different battles with the
Canaanites, &c.

If we were to judge of the Jews as of other nations, we could not conceive
how the children of Jacob could have produced a race sufficiently numerous
to sustain such a loss. But God who conducted and watched over them, God
who tried and punished them, rendered that nation so different and distinct
from all others that we should not look upon them with the same eyes, nor
judge their actions by the same standard that seems applicable to ordinary
mortals.

These children of Abraham, these favorites of Omnipotence, these chosen
people of Israel, have always claimed special rights, special privileges, and
special rewards.

XXVI

Of the Jews, after Saul

The Jews do not appear to have enjoyed a happier lot under their Kings
than under their Judges. Their first king, Saul, was obliged to put himself
to death. Ishbosheth, and Mephibosheth, his sons, were assassinated.

David delivers up to the Gibeonites seven of Saul's grandsons, who were
cruelly murdered. He also orders his son Solomon to put to death Adonijah,
his other son, and Joab his general. Their king Asa destroys a considerable
number of the people in Jerusalem, and Baasha assassinates Nadab, the son of
Jeroboam, and all his family and kindred. Jehu assassinates Jaram and
Ochosias, Ahab's seventy sons, forty-two brethren of Ochosias, and all their
kindred. Athaliah assassinates all her grandsons except Joash and she, in her
turn, is assassinated by the high priest, Johoiada. Joash is assassinated by his
servants, and his son Amaziah meets with the same fate. Zachariah is slain by
Shallum, who, after a short reign, is slain by Menahem. Of this last wretch,

the Scriptures assert "that he ripped up all the women that were with child, in Tipshah." Pekahiah, the son of Menahem, is assassinated by Pekah, the son of Remaliah, and Pekah himself is assassinated by Hoshea, the son of Elah. Of Manasseh, it is said, that he "shed innocent blood, till he had filled Jerusalem from one end to another." And Amon, son of Manasseh, is also assassinated, &c.

In the midst of these massacres ten tribes, who are carried off by Salmanazar, king of Babylon, are enslaved and dispersed forever, except some husbandmen, who were left to till the land.

There yet remained two tribes, who were also carried into captivity, and continued in a state of bondage seventy years; when they obtained permission from their conquerors to return to Jerusalem. These two tribes, with the few Jews still remaining in Samaria, were finally subjected to the kings of Persia.

When Alexander became master of Persia, Judea was comprised in his conquests. After Alexander, the Jews remained in subjection, at one time to the Selucidæ, his successors in Syria, at another, to the Ptolemies, his successors in Egypt; constantly in a state of subjection, and obtaining a livelihood, by acting as brokers in different parts of Asia. They obtained some favors from Ptolemy Epiphanes, king of Egypt. A Jew named Joseph became farmer-general of the imposts in Lower Syria and Judea, which belonged to this Ptolemy. This was the most fortunate state of the Jews, for it was at this time that they built the third part of their city, afterwards called the inclosure, or the wall of the Maccabees, because they finished and completed the work.

From the yoke of King Ptolemy, they passed under that of Antiochus. The courage and greatness of the Maccabees at this period are celebrated by the Jews of Alexandria; but the Maccabees could not prevent the general Antiochus Eupater, son to Antiochus Epiphanes, from razing to the ground the temple, leaving only the sanctuary standing, or from cutting off the head of Onias, the high priest, who was considered as the instigator of the revolt.

Never were the Jews more attached to their law than under the kings of Syria; they no longer adored foreign divinities, and it was at this time that their religion was irrevocably fixed. They were, nevertheless, more unhappy than ever, always in expectation of being delivered by the promises of their prophets—by the assistance of their gods—but they were abandoned by Providence, whose decrees are unknown to man.

They had sometimes a period of tranquillity, by the intestine wars of the kings of Syria. But the Jews soon armed themselves one against another. As they had no kings, and as the first dignity was that of the sacrificing priest, violent parties arose in order to obtain it. There was no method of obtaining the dignity of high priest but by sword in hand, and the path to the sanctuary was often obstructed with the dead bodies of the slain.

Hircan, of the race of the Maccabees, being made high priest, but still in subjection to the Syrians, caused David's sepulchre to be opened, in which the exaggerator, Josephus, pretends that he found three thousand talents. This imaginary treasure should have been sought for at the time of rebuilding the temple under Nehemiah. This Hircan obtained from Antiochus Sidetes the privilege of coining money; but as there never was any Jewish money, it is very probable that the treasure found in David's tomb was not very considerable.

It is remarkable that this high priest, Hircan, was a Sadducean, and that he neither believed in the immortality of the soul nor in angels,—a fresh subject of altercation, which began to divide the Sadducees and the Pharisees. These latter conspired against Hircan, and would have condemned him to be whipped and imprisoned. He avenged himself of them and governed despotically.

His son, Aristobulus, was daring enough to create himself king during the troubles of Syria and Egypt. This was a more cruel tyrant than any who had oppressed the Jewish people. Aristobulus, who indeed prayed very regularly in the temple, and never ate any pork, starved his mother to death, and had his brother, Antigonus, slain. His successor was named John, or Johannes, and was as wicked as himself.

This Johannes, overwhelmed with crimes, left two sons, who waged war against each other. These two sons were named Aristobulus and Hircan. The Romans at that time were subjugating Asia. Pompey arrives, puts things in order, and teaches the Jews reason. He took the Temple, had the seditious hanged at the gates, and loaded the pretended king, Aristobulus, with irons.

This Aristobulus had a son, who was insolent enough to take upon himself the name of Alexander. He stirred up a revolt, raised some troops, and was hung by order of Pompey.

At length Mark Anthony gave to the Jews for king an Idumean Arab of the country of those Amalekites so much cursed by the Jews. It was this same Herod, of whom St. Matthew relates that he had all the little children put to death in the neighborhood of Bethlehem, upon being informed that a king of the Jews was born in that village; and that three Magi conducted by a star came to offer him presents.

Thus were the Jews almost constantly subjugated or enslaved. We know how they revolted against the Romans, and how Titus had them sold in the open market, at the price of that animal, whose flesh they would not touch.

They met with a still more wretched fate under the emperors Trajan and Adrian, and they deserved it. An earthquake happened in the time of Trajan, which swallowed up the finest cities of Syria. The Jews thought this was the signal of God's wrath against the Romans. They assembled and armed themselves in Africa and in Cyprus. They were animated with such rage, that they devoured the limbs of the Romans whom they had slain. But soon after, all the guilty were executed. Those who remained were animated with the same rage under Adrian, when Barcochebas, who called himself their Messiah, commanded them. This fanaticism was stifled by torrents of blood.

It is surprising that there should remain any Jews. The famous Benjamin of Tudela, a very learned Rabbin, who traveled in Europe and Asia, in the twelfth century, computed there were three hundred and eighty thousand Jews and Samaritans. For we must not mention the imaginary kingdom of Thema, near Tibet, where this Benjamin, either deceived or deceiving, asserts that there were three hundred thousand Jews of the ancient tribes assembled under one sovereign. The Jews never had any country to themselves since the time of Vespasian, except some hamlets of Arabia Felix towards the Red Sea.

Mahomet was at first obliged to keep terms with them. But he at length destroyed the little dominion which they had established in the north of Mecca. It is from the time of Mahomet that they have actually ceased to exist as a body of people.

In following simply the historical account of the little Jewish nation, we see that they could have no other end. They boast of having issued from Egypt like a band of robbers, carrying away everything they had borrowed from the Egyptians. They glory in having spared neither age, sex, nor infancy, in the villages and boroughs they subdued. They have the effrontery to display an irreconcilable hatred against other nations—they revolt against all their masters—ever superstitious—ever envious of others' good—ever barbarous—and ever servile in misfortune, and insolent in prosperity. Such were the Jews in the opinion of the Greeks and Romans, who could read their books; but in the eyes of Christians, enlightened by the faith which they persecuted, they prepared the way for us. They have even been considered by some as the heralds of Providence.

The two other nations who are wanderers like the Jews in the East, and who, like them, do not unite with any other people are Banians and the Guebres, of the race of the Parsees, or Persians. These Banians, whose talent consists in trade, like the Jews, are the descendants of the first peaceable inhabitants of India. They do not intermarry with other nations, and in this respect resemble the Brahmans. The Parsees are the same people we now call Persians, who were formerly rulers of the East and sovereigns of the Jews. They have been dispersed since the time of Omar, and cultivate in peace part of the land where they formerly reigned,—still faithful to the ancient religion of the Magi,—adoring one only God, and preserving the sacred fire, which they look upon as the work and emblem of the divinity.

I do not write of that remnant of the Egyptians, the secret worshippers of Isis, who now no longer exist, save as strolling and wandering bands, that will soon, no doubt, be totally annihilated.

XXVII

OF THE ROMANS, THEIR EMPIRE, RELIGION AND TOLERATION

THE Romans cannot justly be reckoned among the primitive nations. Rome has existed only seven hundred and fifty years before our vulgar era. When they had rites and laws, they adopted them from the Etruscans and Greeks. The Etruscans communicated to them the superstition of Augeries; a superstition, nevertheless, founded upon physical observations—upon the passage of birds, from whence they foretold the changes of the atmosphere. It appears that many superstitions have something natural for their principle, and that many errors are derived from truth that is misunderstood and abused.

The Greeks furnished the Romans with the law of the twelve tables. Now, a people who apply to another nation for laws and gods must be a small and barbarous people; and such, undoubtedly, were the first Romans. Their territory in the time of the kings and first consuls was not so extensive as that of Ragusa. We must not by this title of king, understand a monarch such as Cyrus and his successors. The chief of a little people living by rapine can never be despotic. The spoils are divided in common, and each one defends his liberty as his own property.

The first kings of Rome were the captains of freebooters.

If we are to credit the Roman historians, this warlike people began by out-raging the females, and plundering the property of their neighbors. They should have been exterminated; but the ferocity and want that led them on to rapine crowned their unjust enterprises with success. They maintained themselves by being always at war; and at length, after about four centuries had elapsed, being more warlike than other people, they made them all submit, one after another, from the extremity of the Adriatic Gulf to the Euphrates.

In the midst of rapine, the love of their country always predominated, till the time of Sylla. This love of country consisted for upwards of four hundred years in bringing something to the common stock of what had been pillaged from other nations. This is the virtue of robbers. Patriotism was with them, murdering and fleecing other men. But great virtues existed in the heart of the republic. The Romans, improved by time, polished all the barbarians they conquered, and became at length the legislators of the western world.

The Greeks appeared in the early days of their republic as a nation superior to the Romans. The latter sallied forth from their retreat in the Seven Mountains, with handfuls of hay (*Manipli*) which served them for standards, with a view of robbing the neighboring towns and villages. The Greeks, on the contrary, were employed only in defence of their liberty. The Romans rob hundreds of miles in circumference, the Æqui, the Volsci, and the Antii. The Greeks repulse the immense armies of the great king of Persia, and triumph over him by sea and land. The victorious Greeks cultivated and improved all the fine arts, and the Romans were entirely ignorant of them till about the time of Scipio Africanus.

With respect to the religion of the Romans I shall here remark that they adopted or allowed the doctrine of every other people, after the example of the Greeks: and that in reality the senate and the emperors always acknowl-edged one supreme God, in acccordance with the greatest part of the philoso-phers and poets of Greece.

The toleration of all religions was a law of nature engraven on the hearts of all men. For what right can one created being have to compel another to think as he does, and exercise the same form of worship? Now, the Romans by their laws adopted all the Gods of the Greeks, who themselves had altars erected *To the Unknown Gods.*

The twelve tables ordained, *Separatim nemo habessit deos neve advenas nisi publice adscitos,* "That no one should have foreign or new gods without the public sanction." This sanction was given to many doctrines; and all the others were tolerated. This association of all the divinities of the world—this kind of divine hospitality—was the law of nations from all antiquity, with one or two slight exceptions.

As there were no dogmas, there was no religious war. It was enough that ambition and rapine should shed human blood, without religion accomplishing the extermination of the race.

It is also remarkable that amongst the Romans no one was ever persecuted for his way of thinking. There is not a single example from the time of Romulus down to Domitian; and among the Greeks, Socrates is the only exception.

It is also incontestable that the Romans, as well as the Greeks, adored one supreme God. Their Jupiter was the only one that was looked upon as the God of Thunder,—the only one that was styled the most great and the most good God, *Deus optimus maximus.* Thus from Italy to India and China, you find the doctrine of one supreme God, and free toleration granted by all the civilized nations.

With this knowledge of a Supreme Being, and to this universal indulgence —the fruits of cultivated reason—were blended innumerable superstitions—the offspring of faith and ignorance. We know that the sacred fowls, and the goddesses Pertunda and Cloacina are ridiculous.

Why did not the conquerors and legislators of so many nations abolish such nonsense? Because, being ancient, it was dear to the people, and was in no way prejudiced to the government. The Scipios, the Paulus Emelius's, the Ciceros, the Catos, the Cæsars, had other employment than that of combating popular superstitions. When an ancient error is established, policy uses it as a bit which the vulgar have put into their mouths, until another superstition arises to supersede it, when policy profits by the second error as it did by the first.

THE IGNORANT PHILOSOPHER

I

The First Doubt

Who art thou? From whence dost thou come? What is thy employment? What will become of thee? These are questions that should be put to every being in the universe, but to which no one replies. I ask of plants by what virtue they grow, and how the same earth produces such a diversity of fruits? These insensible and mute beings, though enriched with a divine faculty, leave me to my own ignorance and to vain conjectures.

I interrogate that herd of different animals, all which have the power of motion and communication, who enjoy the same sensations as myself, whose passions are accompanied with an extent of ideas and memory. They are still more ignorant than myself what they are, wherefore they exist, and what they shall become.

I suspect, I have even some reason to believe that the planets, the innumerable suns which replenish space, are peopled with sensible and thinking people; but an eternal barrier separates us, and no inhabitant of the other globes ever communed with us.

The Prior, in Nature Displayed, says to the Knight that the stars were made for the earth, and the earth as well as animals for man. But as the little globe of earth revolves with the other planets round the sun; as the regular and proportionate motions of the stars may eternally subsist without men; as there are in our little planet an infinitely greater number of animals than human beings; I imagine that the Prior was actuated by too great a share of self-love, in flattering himself that every thing had been made for him. I find that man in his life-time will be devoured by every kind of animal, if he be defenceless, and that they all devour him after his death. Wherefore I have had some difficulty in conceiving that the Prior and the Knight were the sovereigns of nature. A slave to every thing that surrounds me, instead of being a king; chained to a single point, and environed with immensity; I will begin by searching into myself.

II

Our Weakness

I am a weak animal; at my birth I have neither strength, knowledge, nor instinct; I cannot even crawl to my mother's breast, like every quadruped; I only acquire a few ideas, as I acquire a little strength, and as my organs begin to unfold themselves. This strength increases in me, till such time as having attained my full growth it daily decreases. This power of conceiving ideas increases in the same manner during its term, and afterwards by degrees insensibly vanishes.

What is that mechanism which momentarily increases the strength of my members, as far as the prescribed boundaries? I am ignorant of it; and those who have passed their whole lives in the research, know no more than myself.

What is that other power, which conveys images into my brain, and which preserves them in my memory? Those who are paid for knowing have only made fruitless enquiries; we are all in the same state of ignorance, with regard to the first principles of our infant state.

III

How Am I to Think?

HAVE the books which have been written for these two thousand years taught me anything? We have sometimes a desire of knowing in what manner we think, though we have seldom any desire of knowing how we digest, how we walk. I have questioned my reason, and asked what it is? This question has always confounded me.

I have endeavored to discover by it, if the same springs that make me digest, which make me walk, are the same whereby I receive ideas. I never could conceive how and wherefore these ideas fled when my body languished with hunger, and how they were renovated after I had eaten.

I discovered such a wide difference between thought and nourishment, without which I should not think, that I believed there was a substance in me that reasoned, and another substance that digested. Nevertheless, by constantly endeavoring to convince myself that we are two, I materially felt that I was only one: and this contradiction gave me infinite pain.

I have asked some of my own likenesses who cultivate the earth, our common mother, with great industry, if they felt that they were two? if they had discovered by their philosophy that they possesed within them an immortal substance, and nevertheless formed of nothing, existing without extent, acting upon their nerves, without touching them, sent expressly into them six weeks after their conception? They thought that I was jesting, and pursued the cultivation of their land without making me a reply.

IV

Is It Necessary for Me to Know?

FINDING then that a prodigious number of men had not even the slightest idea of the difficulties that disturb me, and had no doubts of what is taught in schools, of being, in general, matter and spirit, &c., finding that they often ridiculed my desire of being acquainted with these things; I suspected that it was not in the least necessary that we should know them; I imagined that nature has given to every being a portion that is proper for him; and I thought those things which we could not attain, did not belong to us. But notwithstanding this despair, I cannot divest myself of a desire of being instructed; and my baffled curiosity is ever insatiable.

V

ARISTOTLE, DESCARTES, AND GASSENDI

ARISTOTLE begins by saying that incredulity is the source of wisdom; Descartes has carried this sentiment still farther, and they have both taught me to believe nothing they say. This Descartes, particularly, after pretending to doubt, speaks in such an affirmative manner of what he does not understand; he is sure of the fact, when he is grossly mistaken in physics; he has built such an imaginary world; his whirlwinds and three elements are so prodigiously ridiculous, that I ought to suspect everything he says upon the soul, after he has imposed upon me with respect to bodies.

He believes, or affects to believe, that we are born with metaphysical ideas. I would as soon aver that Homer was born with the Iliad in his head. It is very true, that Homer, at his birth, had a brain so constructed that having afterwards acquired poetical ideas, sometimes fine, sometimes incoherent, or sometimes exaggerated, he at length composed the Iliad. We bring into the world at our birth the seed of what afterwards displays itself in us; but we have really no more innate ideas than Raphael and Michael Angelo had at their birth pencils and colors.

Descartes endeavors to unite his scattered chimeras, by supposing men always to think; I would as soon imagine that birds never cease flying, or dogs running, because they are endowed with these abilities.

We need only consult a little of our experience and that of human nature to be thoroughly convinced of the contrary; there is no man mad enough to firmly believe he has thought all his life, night and day, without interruption, from the time of his being a fœtus till his last illness. The only resource of those who have defended such a romance has been to say that we always think, but we do not always perceive that we think. It might be as well asserted that we drink, eat, and ride on horseback without knowing it. If you don't perceive that you possess any ideas, how can you affirm that you have any? Gassendi ridiculed this extravagant system as it deserved. Do you know what was the consequence? Gassendi and Descartes were pronounced atheists.

VI

BEASTS

MAN being supposed to have continually possessed ideas, perceptions, and conceptions, it naturally follows, that beasts were likewise always in possession of them; for it is incontestable that a hunting dog has the idea of the master he obeys, and of the game that he brings him. It is evident that he has memory, and that he combines some ideas. Thus then if the thought of man be the essence of his soul, that of the dog is the essence of his soul, and if man had always ideas, animals must necessarily have had them also. To remove this difficulty, the manufacturer of whirlwinds and chamfered matter dared to say that beasts were pure machines, who sought for food without appetite, who had constantly had the organs of sensation without ever having the least sensation, who cried without pain, who testified joy without pleasure, who possessed a brain incapable of receiving the slightest idea, and who were therefore a perpetual contradiction.

This system was as ridiculous as the other; but instead of exposing its extravagance, it was treated as impious. It was pretended that this system was repugnant to the Holy Scriptures, which says in Genesis, "And surely your blood of your lives will I require; at the hand of every beast will I require it"; which manifestly supposes in beasts a knowledge of, and acquaintance with, good and evil.

VII

EXPERIENCE

LET us never introduce the Holy Scriptures into our philosophical disputes; these are things too heterogeneous, and which have no relation to it. The point here is to examine what we can know by ourselves, and this is reduced to a very narrow compass. We must give up all pretensions to common sense not to agree, that we know nothing in the world but by experience; and certainly, if it is only by experience, and by a succession of groping and long reflection, that we obtain some feeble and slight ideas of body, of space, time, infinity, and God himself; it would not be worth while for the author of nature to put these ideas into the brain of every fœtus, in order that only a very small number of men should make use of them.

We are all, with respect to the objects of our knowledge, like the ignorant lovers Daphnis and Chloë, whose amours and innocence Longus has depicted. They required much time to learn how to satisfy their desires, they having no experience. The same thing happened to the emperor Leopold, and to a son of Louis XIV.; it was necessary to instruct them. If they had been born with innate ideas, we should believe that nature would not have refused them the knowledge necessary for the preservation of the human species.

VIII

SUBSTANCE

AS WE can have no notion, but by experience, it is not impossible that we can ever know what matter is. We touch, we see the properties of this substance;

but this very expression "substance which is beneath,' sufficiently acquaints us that this thing beneath will ever be unknown to us; whatever we may discover of its appearance, there will always remain this *beneath* to discover. For the same reason, we can never know by ourselves what is *spirit*. It is a word which usually signifies breath, and by which we endeavor to express vaguely and grossly that which gives us thoughts. But when, even by a prodigy, which is not to be supposed, we should acquire some slight idea of the substance of this spirit, we should be no farther advanced; and we could never guess how this substance received sentiments and thoughts. We know very well that we have some small intellectual faculty; but how do we obtain it? This is a secret of nature, which she has not divulged to any mortal.

IX

Narrow Limits

Our intellects are very confined as well as the strength of our body. Some men are more robust than others: there are also Hercules's with respect to thought, but, at the bottom, this superiority is a very trivial thing. One shall lift ten times as much matter as myself; another can do in his head and without paper a division of fifteen figures, whilst I can only divide three or four, with much difficulty; here then is the extent of that vaunted strength; its limits are very confined; and therefore in games of combination, no man after having trained himself with great application and long practice, will, with all his efforts, get beyond that degree of perfection allotted him: this is the goal of his intellect. It is absolutely necessary that it should be so, otherwise we should gradually go on to infinity.

X

Impossible Discoveries

In this narrow circle by which we are circumscribed, let us see what we are condemned to be ignorant of, and what we gain a little knowledge of. We have already found that no first resource, no first principle, can be traced by us.

Why does my arm obey my will? We are so accustomed to this incomprehensible phenomenon, that very few pay attention to it; and when we want to trace the cause of so common an effect, we find that there is infinity between our will and the obedience of our limb; that is to say, there is no proportion between them, no reason, no apparent cause; and we feel that we might think to eternity, without being able to discover the least glimpse of probability.

XI

The Foundation of Despair

Thus stopped at the very first onset, and vainly relying upon ourselves, we are dismayed from seeking after ourselves, as we can never discover ourselves. To ourselves we are inexplicable.

We know pretty nearly, with the assistance of triangles, that the sun and earth are about thirty millions of geometrical miles distant; but what is the sun? and wherefore does it turn upon its axis and why in one sense more than another? and why do Saturn and we revolve round this planet sooner from west to east than from east to west? This question will not only ever remain unsatisfied, but we shall never discover the least possibility to devise a physical cause for it. Wherefore? because the first knot of this difficulty is in the principle of things.

It is the same with respect to what acts within us, as to what actuates the immense spaces of nature. There is in the arrangement of the planets, and in the formation of a handworm, and of man, a first principle, the avenue to which must necessarily be barred against us. For if we could be acquainted with the cause of our first origin, we should be its masters, we should be gods. Let us illustrate this idea, and see if it be just.

Suppose that we found, in effect, the cause of our sensations, of our thoughts, and our motions, as we have only discovered in the planets the reason of eclipses and of the different phases of the moon and Venus; it is evident we could then foretell our sensations, our thoughts, and our desires resulting from these sensations, as we predict the phases and the eclipses. Being then acquainted with what would happen to-morrow within us, we should clearly see by the play of this machine, whether we should be affected in a fatal or auspicious manner. We have, it is agreed, a will that directs our interior motions in various circumstances. For example, I find myself disposed to wrath, my reflection and will suppress its growing exhibition; I shall see if I know my first principles, all the affections to which I am disposed for to-morrow, all the successive ideas that wait for me; I could have the same power over this succession of ideas and sentiments, as I sometimes exert over actual sentiments and thoughts, which I divert and repress. I should find myself precisely in the same case with every man who can retard and accelerate, according to his will, the motion of a watch, a ship, or any other well-known machine.

Being master of the ideas that are destined for me to-morrow, I should be also of those for the following day, and even the remainder of my life; I could then be ever powerful over myself, I should be the God of myself. I am very sensible that this state is incompatible with my nature; it is therefore impossible that I can know anything of the first principle which makes me think and act.

XII

Doubt

is THAT which is impossible for my weak limited nature of so short a duration, equally impossible in other globes, in other species of beings? Are there any superior intelligences, masters of all their ideas, who think and feel all that they choose? I know nothing of the matter; I am only acquainted with my own weakness, I have no idea of the powers of others.

XIII

Am I Free?

LET us not yet quit the circle of our existence; let us examine ourselves as far as we are able. I remember one day before I had put all the foregoing questions, a reasoner wanted to make me reason. He asked me if I was free? I replied that I was not in prison, that I had the key of my chamber, that I was perfectly free. That is not what I ask you, he replied, do you believe your will is at liberty of disposing or not disposing you to throw yourself out of the window? Do you think with the scholastic angel that the free agent is an appetitive power, and the free agent is lost by sin? I fixed my eyes upon the querist, in order to read in his, if he was not out of his mind; and I answered, that I did not understand the least of his gibberish.

Nevertheless, this question, upon the freedom of man, greatly interested me; I read scholastics, and, like them, I was in the dark; I read Locke, and I discovered some rays of light; I read Collins's treatise, which appeared to me an improvement upon Locke; and I have never read any thing since that has given me additional instruction. This is what my weak reason hath conceived, with the assistance of these two great men, the only two, who have, in my opinion, understood themselves in writing upon this subject, and the only two who have made themselves understood to others.

There is nothing without a cause. An effect without a cause are words without meaning. Every time that I have a will, this can only be in consequence of my judgment, good or bad; this judgment is necessary, consequently, so is my will. In effect, it would be very singular that all nature, all the planets, should obey eternal laws, and that there should be a little animal five feet high, who, in contempt of these laws, could act as he pleased, solely according to his caprice. He would act by chance; and we know that chance is nothing. We have invented this word to express the known effect of all unknown causes.

My ideas necessarily enter into my brain, how then can my will, which depends upon them, be free? I feel upon various occasions that this will is not free; thus when I am overwhelmed with illness, when I am transported with passion, when my judgment cannot comprehend objects that present themselves to me, &c. I should think, therefore, that the laws of nature being always the same, my will is not more free in things that appear to me the most indifferent, than in those in which I find myself compelled by an invincible force.

To be really free is to have power. My liberty consists in doing what I choose: but I must necessarily choose what I will; otherwise it would be without reason, without cause, which is impossible. My liberty consists in walking when I have a mind to walk, and I have not the gout.

My liberty consists in not doing a bad action when my mind necessarily represents it as a bad action; to subdue a passion, when my mind points out to me the danger of it, and the horror of the act powerfully combats my desire. We may suppress our passions (as I have already said, No. IV.) but then we are not freer in suppressing our desires than by letting ourselves be carried away by our inclination; for in both cases we irresistibly pursue our last idea; and this last idea is necessary: wherefore I necessarily perform what this dictates to me. It is strange that men should not be content with this measure of liberty, that is to say, the power which they have received from nature of doing what they choose; the planets have it not; we possess it, and our pride makes us sometimes believe that we possess still more. We figure to ourselves that we have the incomprehensible and absurd gift of election, without reason, without any other motive than that of free-will. See No. XXIX.

No, I cannot forgive Dr. Clarke for having sophistically opposed these truths, the force of which he felt, but which did not well agree with his systems. No, it is not allowed to such a philosopher as him to attack Collins as a sophist, by changing the state of the question, and reproaching Collins with calling man "a necessary agent." Agent or patient, what doth it signify? An agent when he voluntarily moves, a patient when he receives ideas. What doth the name to the thing? Man is in everything a dependent being, as nature is throughout dependent, and he cannot be excepted from other beings.

The preacher in Samuel Clarke stifles the philosopher; he distinguishes the physical from the moral necessity. And what is a moral necessity? It appears probable to you that a queen of England, whose coronation ceremony is performed in a church, will not cast off her regal robes to throw herself quite naked upon the altar, though a similar adventure is related of a queen of Congo. You call this a moral necessity in a queen of our climate; but it is at the bottom a physical and eternal necessity, blended with the constitution of things. It is as certain this queen will not be guilty of such a folly, as that she will one day die. Moral necessity is but a phrase: all that is done is absolutely necessary. There is no medium between necessity and chance; and you know there is no chance: wherefore all that happens is necessary?

To embarrass the thing still more, it has been devised to distinguish again between necessity and constraint; but constraint, in fact, is nothing but necessity that is perceived, and necessity is a constraint, that is unperceived. Archimedes is equally necessitated to remain in his chamber when shut in, as when he is deeply engaged with a problem, and the idea of going out does not accur to him.

Ducunt volentem fata, nolentum trahunt.

The ignoramus who thinks in this manner did not always think the same; but he is at length compelled to yield.

XIV

Is Every Thing Eternal?

SUBJECT to eternal laws like every sphere that replenishes space, as the elements, animals, and plants, I view with astonishment every thing that surrounds me; I search for my author, and the author of that immense machine, of which I am scarce a perceptible wheel.

I am not derived from nothing; for the substance of my father and mother, who bore me nine months in her womb, is something. It is evident to me that the sperm which produced me could not be produced from nothing; for how can nothing produce existence? I find myself subdued by this maxim of all antiquity, "nothing arises from nought, nothing can return to nought."

This axiom carries with it such dreadful power, that it bears down all my understanding, without my being able to contend with it. No philosopher has ever lost sight of it. No legislator whatsoever has contested it. The Cahut of the Phœnicians, the Chaos of the Greeks, the Tohu-bohu of the Chaldeans and the Hebrews, all evince that the eternity of matter has ever been believed. My reason, perhaps, deceived by so ancient and general an idea, tells me—matter must necessarily be eternal, because it exists: if it was in being yesterday, it was before.

I cannot perceive any probability of its having begun to be, any cause why it had not been, any cause wherefore it received existence at one time more than at another. I therefore yield to this conviction, whether well or ill founded, and I list myself under the banner of the whole world, till such time as having made some progress in my researches, I discover a luminary superior to the judgment of all mankind, which compels me to retract against my will.

But if, according to the opinion of so many philosophers of antiquity, the eternal being has always acted, what becomes of the Cahut and Erebus of the Phœnicians, the Tohu-bohu of the Chaldeans, the Chaos of Hesiod? they will remain fables. Chaos is an impossibility in the eyes of reason; for it is impossible that intelligence being eternal, there should ever have been any thing contrary to the laws of that intelligence: now the Chaos is precisely contrary to all the laws of nature. Enter into the most horrid caverns of the Alps, under those ruins of rocks, ice, sand, waters, unfashioned crystals, and minerals, they all submit to gravitation. Chaos never existed anywhere but in our heads, and has only served to assist Hesiod and Ovid in the composing of some elegant verses.

If our Holy Scripture says Chaos did exist, if it had adopted the Tohu-bohu, we doubtless believe it, and with the most ready faith. We are, in this place, speaking only of the deceitful lights of our reason. We have confined ourselves, as we have said, to what we may suspect by ourselves. We are children who endeavor to go a few steps without leading-strings.

XV

INTELLIGENCE

BUT in perceiving the order, prodigious skill, mechanical and geometrical laws, that reign in the universe, their causes, the innumerable ends of all things, I am seized with admiration and respect. I immediately judge that if the works of man, even my own, compel me to acknowledge an intelligence within us, I should acknowledge one far more superior, actuating the multitude of so many works. I admit of this supreme intelligence, without fearing that I shall be obliged to change my opinions. Nothing staggers me with respect to this axiom, every work demonstrates a workman.

XVI

ETERNITY

Is THIS intelligence eternal? Doubtless, for whether I admit or reject the eternity of matter, I cannot reject the eternal existence of its supreme artisan; and it is evident that if it exists at present, it ever has existed.

XVII

INCOMPREHENSIBILITY

I HAVE as yet advanced only two or three steps in this vast career; I want to know if this divine intelligence is something absolutely distinct from the universe, nearly as the sculptor is distinguished from the statue; or whether this soul of the world is united to the world, and still penetrates it nearly in the same manner, as what I call my soul is united to me, and according to that of antiquity so well expressed in Virgil and Lucan:

> *Mens agitat molem & magno se corpore miscet,*
> *Jupiter est quodcumque vides quocumque moveris.*

I find myself suddenly interrupted in the prospect of my vain curiosity. Miserable mortal, if I cannot fathom my own intelligence, if I cannot know by what I am animated, how can I have any acquaintance with that ineffable intelligence which visibly presides over matter entirely? There is one, as everything demonstrates, but where is the compass that will direct me towards its secret and eternal abode?

XVIII

İNFINITY

Is THIS intelligence infinite in power and immensity, as it is incontestably infinite in duration? I can know nothing of this by myself. It doth exist, wherefore it hath ever existed, that is clear. But what idea can I have of an infinite power? How can I conceive an infinity actually existing? How can I suppose that the supreme intelligence is in the vacuum? An infinity of extent is not the same as an infinity of duration. An infinity of duration is elapsed, the instant that I am speaking of it; it is certain, that I can add nothing to past duration, but I can always add to that space which I conceive, in the same manner that I can add to the numbers that I conceive. Infinity in numbers and extent is beyond the sphere of my understanding. All that can be said can give me no insight into this abyss. I happily feel that my difficulties and my ignorance can be no way pernicious to morality; we may very well be incapable of perceiving neither immensity of space replenished, nor infinite power which has created every thing, and which may nevertheless be still able to perform; this will only serve to prove still more the weakness of our understanding; and this weakness will render us only still more submissive to that eternal Being, whose work we are.

XIX

MY DEPENDENCE

WE ARE his work. This is an important truth for us to know; for to know philosophically at what time he made man, what he did before, if he exists materially, or in vacuum, if he is at one point, if he constantly acts or not, if he acts everywhere, if he acts without or within himself; these are researches which strengthen the conviction of my profound ignorance.

I even see that there has been scarce a dozen men in Europe who have written upon these abstracted things with any kind of method; and if I could suppose that they had spoken in an intelligible manner, what would be the consequence? We have already found (No. IV.) that things which so few persons can flatter themselves with understanding, are useless to the rest of mankind. We certainly are the work of God, this is useful for me to know; and the proof is also clear. All things in my body are causes and effects; that is, spring, pulley, moving power, hydraulic machine, equilibrium of fluids, and chemical laboratory. It is therefore arranged by an intelligence (No. XV.). I am not indebted for this arrangement to the intelligence of my parents, for

they certainly did not know what they did when they produced me: they were
only the blind instruments of this eternal manufacturer, who animates the
worm of the earth, and makes the sun turn upon its own axis.

XX

ETERNITY AGAIN

BORN from seed, produced by other seed, has there been a continual succession,
an unfolding without end of these seeds, and has all nature ever existed by a
necessary succession from that Supreme Being, who existed of himself? If I
were to believe only my feeble understanding, I should say, it seems to me,
that nature has always been animated. I cannot conceive that the cause which
continually and visibly actuates her, being at all times able to act, has not alway∎
acted. An eternity of idleness in the active and necessary being appears to me
incompatible. I am inclined to believe that the world has ever issued from that
primitive and necessary cause, as light emanates from the sun. By what a concatenation of ideas do I find myself led to believe the works of the eternal
being eternal? My conception, pusillanimous as it is, has strength enough to
rise to a being necessarily existing by himself; but has not the strength to conceive nought. The existence of a single atom proves to me the eternity of
existence, but nothing proves to me a mere void. What? is that space filled
that was once a vacuum? This appears absurd and contradictory. I cannot allow
of this *nothing*, this *void*, unless revelation assists me in fixing my ideas, which
carry me beyond time.

I am sensible that an infinite succession of beings without origin is equally
absurd: this is the opinion of Samuel Clarke: but he does not undertake to
affirm that God has not held this chain from all eternity; he dare not say that it
was impossible for a Being eternally active so long to display his works. It is
evident that he could, and if he could, who will be bold enough to tell me that
ne did not? I say, once more, that nothing but revelation can teach me the
contrary. But we have not yet attained that revelation which destroys all
philosophy, that light before which all other lights are eclipsed.

XXI

MY DEPENDENCE AGAIN

THIS eternal being, this universal cause, gives me my ideas; for I don't receive
them from object. Unshaped matter cannot communicate any thoughts to me;
my thoughts do not come from myself, for they occur against my will, and
frequently escape the same. We know very well there is no resemblance, no
connection between objects, our ideas, and sensations. There was certainly

something sublime in that Mallebranche, who dared to imagine that we see everything in God himself. But was there not something sublime in the Stoics, who thought that God acted within us, and that we possess a ray of his substance? Where shall we find truth between the dreams of Mallebranche and the Stoics? I sink again (No. II.) into ignorance, which is the appendage of our nature, and I adore that God by whom I think, without knowing how I think.

XXII

A Fresh Doubt

Convinced by my small share of reason, that there is a necessary eternal Being, from whom I receive my ideas, without being able to divine how or wherefore, I ask what is this being? If it hath the form of those intelligent and active species superior to ours in other globes? I have already said I knew nothing of the matter. (No. I.) Nevertheless, I cannot affirm it to be impossible; for I perceive planets very superior to ours in extent, surrounded with more satellites than the earth. It is not improbable that they may be peopled with intelligences far superior to me, with bodies more robust, more active and more durable. But their existence having no connection with mine, I shall leave it to the poets of antiquity, to make Venus descend from her imaginary third heaven, and Mars from the fifth. My enquiries should be confined to the action of the Being necessarily presiding over myself.

XXIII

A Sole Supreme Artist

A great part of mankind observing the physical and moral evil diffused through this globe, imagined there were two powerful beings, one of which produced all the good, and the other all the evil. If they existed they were necessary; they therefore necessarily existed in the same place; there is no reason that what exists by its own nature should be excluded any place; they therefore penetrated each other—this is absurd. The idea of these two powerful enemies can derive its origin only from examples that strike us upon earth; we there observe gentle and ferocious men, useful and obnoxious animals, good masters and tyrants. There were two opposite powers devised, who presided over nature; this is only an Asiatic romance. There is throughout nature a manifest unity of design; the laws of motion and gravity are invariable; it is impossible that two supreme artists, in opposition to each other, could have followed the same laws. This alone has, in my opinion, overturned the Manichean system, and voluminous writings are superfluous to explode it.

There is then a sole eternal Power, to whom everything is united, on whom all depends; but whose nature is to me incomprehensible. St. Thomas tells us,

"That God is a pure act, a form that has neither gender nor predicament, that he is nature and the agent, that he exists essentially, participatively, and noncupatively." When the Dominicans were masters of the inquisition, they would have burned a man who would have denied these fine things—I should not have denied them, but I should not have understood them.

I am told that God is simple; I acknowledge that I do not understand any more the value of this word. It is true that I should not attribute to him gross parts that I could separate; but I cannot conceive that the principal and master of all that is in the extent, should not be in the extent. Simplicity, strictly speaking, appears to me to resemble too much a nonentity. The extreme weakness of my understanding has no instrument nice enough to lay hold of this simplicity. Shall I be told that the mathematical point is simple; but the mathematical point does not really exist.

It is again said that an idea is simple, but I do not understand this a whit better. I perceive a horse, I have the idea of it, but I see in him only an assemblage of things. I see a color, I have the idea of color; but this color is extent. I pronounce the abstracted names of color in general; of vice, virtue, truth, in general; but the reason is, that I have had a knowledge of things colored, of things that have appeared to me virtuous or vicious, true or false. I express all this by a word; but I have no clear knowledge of simplicity. I know no more of it than I do of an infinity in numbers actually existing.

I am already convinced that not knowing what I am, I cannot know what is my author. I am every instant overwhelmed with my ignorance, and I console myself by incessantly reflecting that it is of no consequence to me to know, whether my master is or is not in the extent, provided I do nothing against that conscience he has given me. Of all the systems which men have invented upon the Divinity, which, then, shall I embrace? Not one, without it be that of adoring him.

XXIV

SPINOZA

AFTER being immersed with Thales in the water, of which his first principle consisted; after glowing before Empedocles's fire; after running in a straight line in the vacuum, with Epicurus's atoms; after having calculated numbers with Pythagoras, and heard his music; after having paid my respect to the Androgines of Plato, and having passed through all the regions of metaphysics and madness; I was at length desirous of being acquainted with the system of Spinoza.

He is not new; he has imitated some ancient Greek philosophers, and even some Jews; but Spinoza has done what no Greek philosopher, and much less a Jew, ever did. He has used an imposing geometrical method to calculate the net produce of his ideas. Let us see if he has not methodically wandered with the thread that conducts him.

He at first establishes a clear and incontestable fact. There is something, consequently there has eternally existed a necessary Being. This principle is so true, that the profound Samuel Clarke has availed himself of it, to prove the existence of God.

This Being must be found in all places where there is existence; for who can limit it?

This necessary being is then everything that exists: wherefore there is only one substance in the universe.

This substance cannot create another; for as it fills everything, where can a new substance be placed, and how can something be created from nothing? How can extent be created without placing it in extent itself, which necessarily exists?

There are in the world thought and matter; that necessary substance which we call God is therefore thought and matter. All thought and all matter are then comprehended in the immensity of God; there can be nothing out of him; they can only act within him; he comprehends everything, he is everything.

Wherefore everything we call different substances is, in fact, nothing but the universality of the different attributes of the Supreme Being, who thinks in the brain of man, enlightens in the light, moves upon the winds, darts in the lightning, revolves in the planets, and exists in all nature.

He is not like a vile king of the earth confined to his palace, separated from his subjects; he is intimately united with them; they are essential parts of himself; if he were distinguished from them, he would be no longer universal, he would not fill all space, he would be a side being like another.

Though all the variable modifications in the universe are the effect of his attributes, nevertheless, according to Spinoza, he hath no parts; for, says he, Infinity has none, properly speaking. In fine, Spinoza pronounces that we must love this necessary, infinite, eternal God. These are his words

"With regard to the love of God, this idea is so far from weakening it, that I think no other is so fit to increase it, since it teaches me that God is intimate with my being, that he gives me existence and all my properties,—that he gives them to me liberally, without reproach, without interest, without subjecting me to anything but my own nature. It banishes fear, uneasiness, diffidence, and all the defects of a mean and sordid love. It teaches me that it is a good I cannot lose, and which I the more advantageously possess, as I know and love it."

These ideas seduced many readers; there were even some, who having at first written against him, afterwards embraced his opinion.

The learned Bayle is upbraided with having severely attacked Spinoza, without understanding him. Severely, I agree to; but I do not think unjustly. He easily discovered the weak side of this enchanted castle: he saw that Spinoza, in fact, composed his God of parts, though he found himself compelled to retract, terrified at his own system. Bayle saw his frenzy in making God a star and a pumpkin, thought and smoke, beating and beaten. He saw that this fable is much beneath that of Proteus. Perhaps Bayle should have confined himself to the word modalities, and not parts, as Spinoza always makes use of the word modalities. But, if I am not mistaken, it is equally impertinent, whether the excrement of an animal is a modality or a part of the Supreme Being.

He did not indeed attack the reasons by which Spinoza maintains the impossibility of the creation; but the reason is, that the creation, properly speaking, is an object of faith, and not of philosophy: because this opinion is no way peculiar to Spinoza, and all antiquity have thought like him. He attacks only the absurd idea of a simple God, composed of parts, of a God that eats and digests himself, who loves and hates the same thing at the same time, &c. Spinoza constantly makes use of the word God, and Bayle takes him according to his own expressions.

But at the bottom, Spinoza does not acknowledge any God; he has probably made use of this expression, he has said that we should serve and love God, only that he might not startle mankind. He appears to be an atheist, according to the full extent of the epithet; he is not such an atheist as Epicurus, who acknowledged useless and lazy gods; he is not like the greater part of the Greeks and Romans, who ridiculed the gods of the vulgar; he is such, because he acknowledges no providence whatever, because he admits only of eternity, immensity, and the necessity of things; like Stratonius, like Diagoras; he does not doubt like Pyrrho, he affirms, and what does he affirm? That there is only a single substance, that there cannot be two, that this substance is extended and pendant, and this is what none of the Greek or Asiatic philosophers ever said, as they admitted of a universal soul.

He nowhere mentions in his book specified designs, which are manifested in all beings. He does not examine whether eyes were made to see with, ears to hear, feet to walk, or wings to fly; he neither considers the laws of motion in animals and plants, nor their structure adapted to those laws, any more than the depth of mathematics, which governs the course of the stars: he is afraid to perceive that everything which exists attests a divine providence; he does not rise from effects to their cause, but immediately placing himself at the head of the origin of things, he builds his romance in the same manner as Descartes constructed his, upon a supposition. He supposes, with Descartes, a plenum, though it has been strictly demonstrated that all motion is impossible in a plenum. This was his principal reason for looking upon the universe as one single substance. He was the dupe to his geometrical genius. How came it that Spinoza, who could not doubt that spirit and matter existed, did not at least examine whether providence had not arranged everything? How came it that he did not give a single glance towards those springs, those means, each of which hath its design, and enquired whether they evinced a supreme artist? He must either have been a very ignorant physician, or a sophist swelled up with a very stupid kind of pride, not to acknowledge a providence every time he breathed and felt his heart beat; for this respiration and this motion of the heart are the effects of a machine so industriously complicated and arranged with such powerful art, depending upon so many springs, all concurring to the same end, that it is impossible to be imitated, and impossible for a man of good sense not to admire it.

The modern Spinozists reply, Do not terrify yourselves at these consequences, which you impute to us; we find, as you do, a succession of admirable effects in the organized bodies, and in all nature. The eternal cause is in the eternal intelligence, which we admit, and which, with matter, constitutes the universality of things, which is God. There is but one single substance, which acts by the same modality of its thought upon the modality of matter, and which thus constitutes the universe, which forms but one whole inseparable thing.

To this reply we answer: How can you prove to us that the thought which gives motion to the stars, which animates man, which doth everything, can be a modality, and that the excrements of a toad and a worm should be a modality of the same sovereign Being? Will you dare to say that so strange a principle is demonstrated to you? Do you not cloak your ignorance beneath words that you do not understand? Bayle has thoroughly unfolded the sophisms of your master in all the windings and all the obscurities of the style of a pretended and really much confused geometrician, which is that of this master. I refer you to him; philosophers should not exclaim against Bayle.

Be this as it may, I shall observe of Spinoza that he very honestly deceived himself. It seems to me he did not suppress in his system those ideas which might be troublesome to him, only because he was too full of his own; he went on in his own road, without observing anything that might interrupt him, and this is what very often happens to us. Moreover, he inverted all the principles of morality, though he was himself a rigid moralist; so particularly sober, that he scarce drank a pint of wine in a month; so disinterested as to transfer to the heirs of the unfortunate John de Wit a pension of two hundred florins, which this great man had granted him: so generous as to give away his fortune; ever patient in his illness and in his poverty, ever consistent in his conduct.

Bayle, who has so ill treated him, had nearly the same character. Each of them sought after truth all their lives by different roads. Spinoza frames a specious system in some respects, and very erroneous in the foundation. Bayle has combated all systems: what became of their writings? They have prevented the idleness of some readers, and this is the full scope of all writings; and from Thales down to the professors of our universities, and the most chimerical reasoners, as well as their plagiarists, no one philosopher has influenced the manner of the very street he lived in. What is the reason? Because men are led by custom, not by metaphysics.

XXV

ABSURDITIES

THERE are many voyages made in unknown countries productive of no advantage. I am in the situation of a man, who having wandered upon the ocean, and perceiving the Maldivian Islands with which the sea of India is interspersed, is desirous of visiting them all. My long voyage has been of no avail to me; let me see if I can reap any benefit by my observations upon these little islands, which seem only to interrupt the passage.

In a hundred courses of philosophy, such things are explained to me, of which nobody can frame the least idea. By this I am taught to comprehend the Trinity physically; it says that it resembles three dimensions of matter. Go on, and so will I. That pretends to communicate to me transubstantiation by the touch, by showing me according to the laws of motion how an accident may exist without a subject, and how one single body may be in two places at the same time. I shut my ears, and retire with still greater precipitation.

Pascal, Blaise Pascal himself, the author of the Provincial Letters, utters these words: "Do you believe that it is impossible that God may be infinite and without parts? I will then show you a thing indivisible and infinite; this is a point moving everywhere with infinite swiftness, for it is in every place, and everywhere, quite entire."

A mathematical point that moves of itself! just heaven! a point that exists nowhere but in the head of a geometrician, which is everywhere at the same time, of infinite swiftness, as if actual infinite swiftness could exist! Every word is frenzy, and he was a great man that uttered these frenzies!

Your soul, says another, is simple, incorporeal, intangible; and, as no body can touch, I shall prove, according to the physics of Albert the Great, that it will be physically burnt, if you be not of my opinion: this is the way I prove it to you à priori, in strengthening Albert with the syllogisms of Abeli.

I reply to him, I do not understand his priori; that I think his compliment is very harsh; that revelation, which we have nothing to do with, can alone teach me a thing so incomprehensible; that I allow him to differ from me in opinion, without threatening him: and I get a good distance from him for fear of an accident, for he seems to me to be a dangerous man.

A multitude of sophists of all countries overwhelm me with unintelligible arguments upon the nature of things; upon my own, upon my past, present, and future state. If one talks to them of eating and clothing, lodging, the necessaries of life, money by which they are procured, they are perfectly conversant in these things; are there a few pistoles to be got, each of them is eager to obtain them, and they do not make a mistake of a farthing; but when the question is concerning our being, they have not one clear idea about it. Common sense deserts them. From hence I return to my first conclusion (No. IV.) that what cannot be of universal use, what is not within the reach of common men, what is not understood by those who have most exercised their faculty of thinking, is not necessary to mankind.

XXVI

Of the Best of Worlds

In my various peregrinations in search of instruction I met with some disciples of Plato. Come along with me, said one of them, you are in the best of worlds; we have far surpassed our master. There were in his time only five possible worlds, because there are but five regular bodies; but now there are an infinity of possible universes; God has chosen the best; come and you will be satisfied with it.

I humbly replied, The worlds which God might create were either better, perfectly equal, or inferior. He could not choose the worst. Those which were equal, supposing such to be, could have no preference; they were ever completely the same; there could have been no choice amongst them; to fix upon one or the other was just the same. It was therefore impossible that he could avoid choosing the best. But how could the others be possible, when it is impossible they can exist?

He made some very curious distinctions, incessantly assuring me, without knowing what he said, that this world is the best of all really possible worlds. But being just then tortured with the stone, which gave me an almost insupportable pain, the citizens of the best of worlds conducted me to the neighboring hospital. In the way two of these perfectly happy inhabitants were carried off by two creatures of their own likeness. They were loaded with irons, the one for debt, the other upon mere suspicion.

I know not whether I was conducted into one of the best possible hospitals; but I was crowded amongst two or three thousand wretches like myself. Here were many defenders of their country, who informed me that they had been trepanned and dissected alive; that they had had arms and legs cut off; and that many thousands of their generous fellow-countrymen had been massacred in one of the thirty battles fought in the last war, which is about the hundredth million war since we have been acquainted with wars.

One might also meet in this house about a thousand persons of both sexes, who resembled hideous spectres, and who were rubbed with a certain metal, because they had followed the law of nature, and nature had, I know not how, taken the precaution of poisoning in them the source of life. I thanked my two conductors.

After a very sharp iron had been thrust into my bladder, and some stones were extracted from this quarry,—when I was cured, and I had no further complaints than a few disagreeable pains for the rest of my days, I made my representations to my guides.

I took the liberty of telling them there was some good in this world. as the surgeons had extracted four flints from my torn entrails; but that I would much rather that bladders had been lanterns than quarries. I spoke to them of the innumerable calamities and crimes that were dispersed over this excellent world. The bolder of the two, who was a German and my countryman, told me that all this was a mere trifle.

Heaven was peculiarly propitious to man when Tarquin violated Lucretia and she stabbed herself, because the tyrants were thereupon driven out, and rapes, suicides and war laid the foundation of a republic which conferred happiness upon those they vanquished.

I had some difficulty in agreeing to this happiness. I did not immediately conceive the felicity of the Gauls and Spaniards, of whom it is said Cæsar put three millions to the sword.

Devastation and rapine appeared to me things somewhat disagreeable, but the defender of optimism did not quit his hold; he persevered in telling me, like Don Carlos's jailer, "Peace, peace, it is for your good."

Having, however, at length run him pretty hard, he said, that "we should not consider this mere globule, where every thing is jarring; but that in the star Sirius, in Orion, the Ox's-Eye and elsewhere, everything is perfect."

"Let us, then, go thither," said I.

A little theologist then took me by the arm. He told me, in confidence, that "those folks were very dreamers; that it was not in the least necessary that there should be any evil upon earth; that it was expressly formed that there never should be any thing but good; and in order to prove this, you must know that things formerly went on in this manner in Eden for ten or twelve days."

"Alas!" I replied to him, "it is a great pity, reverend father, that things did not continue so."

XXVII

OF MONADS

THE same German then laid hold of me again. He tutored me, and clearly taught me the nature of my soul.

"Every thing in nature," said he, "consists of monads. Your soul is a monad, and as it is united with all the others, it necessarily has ideas of all that passes in them. These ideas are confused, which is very necessary; and your monad, as well as mine, is a concentrical mirror of the universe.

"But believe not that you act in consequence of your thoughts. There is a pre-established harmony between the monad of your soul and the monads of your body, so that when your soul hath an idea, your body has a motion, without the one being the result of the other. They are two pendulums that go together; or, if you will, the one resembles a man who preaches, whilst another makes gesticulations. You easily conceive that this must necessarily be so in the best of worlds; for——

XXVIII

Of Plastic Forms

As i had no comprehension of these admirable ideas, an Englishman, named Cudworth, discovered my ignorance and my embarrassment by my fixed eyes and downcast look.

"These ideas," he said, "appear deep to you, because they are well sifted. I will give you a concise notion of the manner in which nature acts. First, there is nature in general, then, there are plastic natures, which form all animals and all plants.—You understand me?"

"Not a word, Sir."

"Let us go on, then."—

"A plastic nature is not a corporeal faculty; it is an immaterial substance, which acts without knowing what it does, being entirely blind and insensible to reason and to vegetation. But the tulip has its plastic form, which makes it vegetate; the dog has also its plastic form, which makes it pursue the chase, and man has his, which makes him reason. These forms are immediate agents of the divinity. There are no ministers in the world more faithful; for they yield everything, and keep nothing for themselves.

"You see very well that these are the true principles of things, and that plastic natures are at least equal to pre-established harmony and monads, which are the concentrical mirrors of the universe." I acknowledged to him that the one was as good as the other.

XXIX

Of Locke

After so many unfortunate excursions, fatigued, harassed, ashamed of having sought after so many truths, and found so many chimeras, I returned to Locke, like the prodigal son who returned to his father. I threw myself into the arms of a modest man, who never pretends to know what he is really ignorant of; who, in fact, is not possessed of immense riches, but whose security is always good, and who enjoys the most permanent wealth without ostentation.

He confirms me in the opinion I always entertained, that nothing obtains a place in our understanding but through our senses:

That there are no innate ideas:

That we can neither have the ideas of infinite space nor infinite number:

That I do not always think, and consequently that thought is not the essence, but the action of my understanding:

That I am free when I can do what I please:

That this liberty does not consist in my will, since when I remain voluntarily in my chamber, the door of which is locked, without my having the key, I am

not at liberty to go out; as I suffer when I am not willing to suffer; as I frequently cannot recall my ideas when I am disposed to recall them.

It is therefore, in fact, absurd to say that the will is free, as it is absurd to say
I will such a thing; for this is precisely as if one were to say, I desire to desire it,
I fear to fear it. In a word, the will is no more free than it is blue or square.
(See Article XIII.)

That I can only form a will in consequence of ideas received in my brain;
that I am necessitated to determine in consequence of those ideas, as I should
otherwise determine without reason, which would be an effect without a cause:

That I cannot have a positive idea of infinity, as I am absolutely finite.

That I cannot know any substance, as I can have no ideas but of their qualities, and that a thousand qualities of a thing cannot communicate the intimate
nature of this thing, which may possess a hundred thousand other qualities that
I am unacquainted with:

That I am no longer the same person after I have lost my memory; for not
having the smallest part of my body which belonged to me in my infancy,
and not having the least remembrance of the ideas that affected me at that
age, it is clear that I am no longer that same child any more than I am Confucius or Zoroaster.

I am reputed the same person by those who have observed me grow, and who
have always resided with me; but I have in no respect the same existence; I am
no longer my former self; I am a new identity; and what singular consequences must hence arise!

That, in fine, agreeable to my profound ignorance, of which I am convinced,
according to the principles of things, it is impossible that I can know what are
the substances to which God deigns to grant the gifts of feeling and thinking.
In fact, are there any substances the essence of which is to think, that always
think, and which think by themselves? In this case these substances, whatever
they be, are gods; for they have no occasion for the eternal Being and Creator,
as they possess their essences without him—as they think without him.

Secondly.—If the eternal Being has communicated the gifts of feeling and
thinking to these beings, he has given them what did not essentially belong to
them; he could therefore have given this faculty to all beings whatever.

Thirdly.—We are unacquainted with the inward recesses of any being; wherefore it is impossible for us to know whether a being is susceptible or insuscep-
tible of sensation and thought.

The words matter and spirit are mere words. We have no complete idea of
these two things. Wherefore, in fact, it would be as bold to say that a body
organized by God himself cannot receive thought from God himself, as it
would be ridiculous to urge that spirit could not think.

Fourthly.—I imagine there are substances purely spiritual, which never had
any idea of matter and motion; would it be thought proper for them to deny
that matter and motion may exist?

I suppose that the learned congregation who condemned Galileo for impiety
and absurdity—for having demonstrated the motion of the earth round the

sun, had obtained some knowledge of the ideas of Chancellor Bacon, who proposed to examine whether attraction be given to matter. I suppose that he who made the report of this great tribunal remonstrated to these great personages, that there were people mad enough to suspect that God could communicate to all matter from Saturn down to our little lump of earth, a tendency towards a center,—attraction, gravitation,—which would be absolutely independent of all impulse; as impulse acts upon surfaces, and this gravitation actuates solids.

Do you not find these judges of human reason, and of God himself, immediately dictate their sentences, anathematize this gravitation (which Newton has since demonstrated) pronounce it impossible for God to perform, and that gravitation towards a center is blasphemy?

I am, methinks, guilty of the same temerity, when I dare aver that God cannot make any organized being whatever feel and think.

Fifthly.—I cannot doubt that God has granted sensations of the memory, and consequently ideas, to the organized matter in animals. Wherefore, then, should I deny that he may make the same present to other animals? It has already been observed, that the difficulty consists less in knowing whether organized matter can think, than in knowing how any being whatever can think.

Thought is something divine; yes, doubtless, and therefore I never shall know what a thinking being is. The principal motion is divine; I shall never know the cause of this motion, the laws whereof all my members execute.

Aristotle's child being at nurse, attracted into his mouth the nipple which he sucked, forming with his tongue, which he drew in, a pneumatic machine, pumping the air, and causing a vacuum: whilst his father, quite ignorant of this, said at random, that "nature abhors a vacuum."

The child of Hippocrates, at four years of age, proved the circulation of the blood by passing his finger over his hand; and Hippocrates did not know that the blood circulated.

We are all, great as we may be, like those children; we perform admirable things, and there is not a single philosopher who knows how they are done.

Sixthly.—These are the reasons, or rather the doubts, produced by my intellectual faculty upon Locke's modest assertion. Once more, I do not say that it is matter which thinks within us. I say with Locke, that it does not belong to us to assert that it should be impossible for God to make matter think; that it is absurd to declare it; and that it is not for worms of the earth to limit the power of the Supreme Being.

Seventhly.—I add that this question is absolutely foreign to morality: because whether matter can, or cannot think, whoever thinks must be just; because the atom to which God shall have given thought may be worthy or unworthy, be punished or recompensed, and exist eternally, as well as the unknown being formerly called *breath* and at present *spirit*, of which we have a less idea than even an atom.

I know very well that those who thought the being called breath could alone by susceptible of feeling and thinking, have persecuted those who have followed the sagacious Locke, and who have not dared to limit the power of God to animating only this breath. But when the whole universe believed that the soul was a light body, a breath, a substance of fire, would it have been just to persecute those who came to teach us that the soul is immaterial?

All the fathers of the church who thought the soul an extended body, would they have done right to persecute the other fathers who communicated to man the idea of perfect immateriality?

No, doubtless; because a persecutor is an abominable character. Wherefore those who allow of perfect immateriality, without comprehending it, should have tolerated those who rejected it, because they did not comprehend it.

Those who have refused God the power of animating the unknown being called matter, should also have tolerated those who have not dared to divest God of his power; for it is very scandalous to hate one another for syllogisms.

XXX

What Have I Thus Far Learned?

I have then reckoned with Locke and with myself, and I find myself possessed of four or five truths, abstracted from a hundred errors, and loaded with an immense quantity of doubts. I said to myself afterwards,—These few truths which I have acquired by my reason, will be but barren land in my hands, if I can find no principle of morality in them. It is very fit for such an insignificant animal as man to raise himself up to the knowledge of the master of nature. But this will be of no more service to me than the science of algebra, if I do not derive from it some rule for the conduct of my life.

XXXI

Is There Any Morality?

The more I have observed men differ by climate, manners, languages, laws, doctrine, and the measure of their understanding, the more I have observed they have the same fund of morality. They have all a barbarous notion of justice and injustice, without knowing a word of theology. They have all acquired this notion at an age when reason begins to unfold itself: as they have naturally acquired the art of raising burdens with poles, and passing a rivulet upon a piece of wood, without having learned the mathematics.

It therefore appeared to me that this idea of justice and injustice was necessary for them, because they all agreed in this point, as soon as they could act and reason.

The supreme intelligence which formed us has then been pleased that there should be justice upon earth, that we might live there for a certain time.

It appears to me, that having neither instinct to nourish ourselves like animals, nor natural arms like them, and vegetating for several years in the imbecility of infancy, exposed to every danger, the few men that would have escaped from the jaws of ferocious animals, from famine and misery, would have been employed in wrangling for a little nourishment and a few skins of animals; and they would have been destroyed like the children of the dragon of Cadmus, as soon as they would have been able to have used any arms.

At least, there would have been no society, if men had not conceived the idea of some justice, which is the tie of all society.

How would the Egyptians, who raised pyramids and obelisks, and the wandering Scythians, who were even unacquainted with a cabin, have had the same fundamental notions of justice and injustice, if God had not given to each of them, from the beginning of time, that reason which, in unfolding itself, made them perceive the same necessary principles, in the same manner as he gave them affections and passions, which having attained the degree of their development, necessarily perpetuate in the same manner the race of the Scythian and the Egyptian?

I perceive a barbarous, ignorant, superstitious herd, a bloody and a furious people, who had not even a term in their jargon to signify geometry and astronomy. This people hath nevertheless, the same fundamental laws as the wise Chaldean, who was acquainted with the course of the stars, and the Phœnician, still more learned, who availed himself of the knowledge of the stars to go and lay the foundation of colonies at the extremity of the hemisphere, where the ocean mingles with the Mediterranean. All these people aver that they should respect their father and mother; that perjury, calumny, and homicide are abominable crimes: they therefore derive the same consequences from the same principles of their unfolded reason.

XXXII

Real Utility. The Notion of Justice

The notion of something just appears to me so natural, so universally received by all men, that it is independent of all law, of all compact, of all religion.

Let me ask a Turk, a Guebrian, or a Malabarian, for the money I lent him, to enable him to eat and clothe himself, and he will never think of replying: "Wait till I learn if Mahomet, Zoroaster, or Brahma commands me to restore your money."

He will acknowledge that it is just that he should pay me, and if he doth not perform it, either his poverty, or his avarice, predominates over the justice which he acknowledges.

I assert it as a fact, that there are no people who maintain, that it is either just, right, proper, or honest, to refuse nourishment to one's father or mother, when it is practicable to bestow it.

That no community has ever considered calumny as a good action, not even a sect of bigoted fanatics.

The idea of justice appears to me so much a truth of the first order, to which the whole universe has given its assent, that the greatest crimes which afflict society are all committed under the false pretence of justice. The greatest of all crimes, at least that which is the most destructive, and consequently the most opposite to the design of nature, is war; but there never was an aggressor who did not gloss over his guilt with the pretext of justice.

The Roman depredators had all their invasions declared just, by priests named FECIALS.

Every free-booter, who finds himself at the head of an army, begins his foray by a manifesto, and implores the God of armies.

Petty thieves themselves, when united in a society, take care not to say, "let us go and rob, let us go and despoil the widow and the orphan of their scanty pittance," but they say, "let us be just, let us recover our fortune from the hands of the rich, who have deprived us of it."

They have even a dictionary among them, which has been printed since the sixteenth century, and in this vocabulary, which they call ARGOT, the words theft, robbery, rapine, are not to be met with. They make use of terms which correspond with gaining, reimbursing, etc.

The word injustice is never uttered in a council of state, where the most unjust murder is proposed. Even the most bloody conspirators have never said, "let us commit a crime." They have ever said, "Avenge our country for the crimes of a tyrant; let us punish what appears to us unjust."

In a word, servile flatterers, barbarous ministers, odious conspirators, the most infamous robbers, all pay homage against their will, to that virtue they trample upon.

I have been greatly astonished that amongst the French who are enlightened and polished, maxims have been repeated upon the stage which are equally as shocking as false.

La justice et le droit font des vaines idées,
Le droit des rois consiste à rien epargner.

"Justice and right are vain ideas, the right of kings consists in sparing nothing."

And this abominable speech is put in the mouth of Phocian, minister to young Ptolemy. But it is precisely because he is a minister that he should say the contrary; he should represent the death of Pompey as a necessary and just misfortune.

I believe, then, that the ideas, just and unjust, are as clear and universal as the ideas of health and sickness, truth and falsehood, convenience and inconvenience.

The limits of justice and injustice are very difficult to fix; as the middle state between health and disease, between the convenience and the inconvenience of things, between falsehood and truth, is difficult to specify. They are shades that are interwoven; but glaring colors strike every eye.

For example, all men agree that we should restore what we have borrowed; but if I know that the person to whom I am indebted two millions will make use of it to enslave my country, should I put such fatal arms into his hands? Here are sentiments that are divided; but in general I should observe my oath when no evil results from it. This is what no one ever doubted.

XXXIII

Is Universal Consent a Proof of Truth?

It may be objected that the consent of men at all times, and in all countries, is not a proof of truth. All people believed in the Magi, in sorcery, demons, apparitions, planetary influence, and a hundred other such like follies. Might it not be the same with respect to justice and injustice?

It appears to me not. First, it is false that all men believed these chimeras. They were, in fact, aliment to the weakness of the vulgar; but a great number of sages constantly ridiculed them. These numerous wise men, on the contrary, always admitted of justice and injustice, as much and even more than the people.

The belief in sorcerers, demons, etc., is far from being necessary to mankind; the belief in justice is absolutely necessary, because it is an unfolding of that reason given by God; and the idea of sorcerers, people possessed, etc., is, on the contrary, a perversion of this same reason.

XXXIV

Against Locke

Locke, who instructs and teaches me to mistrust myself, does he not sometimes impose upon himself like many others? He wants to prove the falsity of innate ideas; but does he not add a very bad reason to several good ones? He acknowledges it is not just to boil one's neighbor in a cauldron and eat him. He nevertheless says there have been nations of Anthropophagi; and that these thinking beings would not have eaten men, if they had possessed the ideas of justice and injustice, which I suppose is necessary for the preservation of the human species. (See No. XXXVI.)

Without entering into a disquisition, whether there were in fact any nations of Anthropophagi,—without examining the relations of the traveler Dampier, who traversed all America, and who never saw any, but who, on the contrary, was received amongst all the savages with the greatest humanity: I reply as follows:

Conquerors have eaten their slaves taken in war. They imagined they did a very just action. They imagined they had a right over their life and death; and, as they had but few good meats for their table, they thought they were allowed to feed upon the fruit of their victory.

They were in this more just than the Romans, who, without reaping any advantages, strangled the captive princes that were chained to their triumphal cars.

The Romans and the savages had a very false idea of justice, I allow; but they, however, both thought they acted justly. And this is so true, that the same savages, when they had admitted these captives into their society, looked upon them as their children; and the same ancient Romans have given a thousand examples of admirable justice.

XXXV

AGAINST LOCKE

I AGREE with the sagacious Locke, that there is no innate idea—no innate principle of practice. This is such an incontrovertible truth, that it is evident that all children would have a clear notion of God if they were born with this idea, and all men would then agree with this same notion—an agreement that has never been known.

It is also evident that we are not born with innate principles of morality, as we do not see how a whole nation could reject a principle of morality which had been engraven on the heart of every individual of that nation.

I suppose that we are all born with the moral principle well understood, that no person should be persecuted for his manner of thinking. How could whole communities become persecutors? I suppose that every man carries within himself that evident law whereby he is commanded to be faithful to his oath. How could all men, united in a body, have enacted that no faith should be kept with heretics?

I repeat again, that instead of these chimerical innate ideas, God has given us reason, which is strengthened with age, and which teaches us all, when we are attentive without prejudice, that there is a God, and that we should be just. But I cannot grant Locke the consequences he draws from thence. He seems to approach too near Hobbes' system, though, in fact, he is very distant from it.

These are his words in the first book of his *Essay upon the Human Understanding*.

"View but an army at the sacking of a town, and see what sense of moral principles or what touch of conscience they exhibit for all the outrages they do."

No, they have no remorse, and why? Because they believe they act justly.

Not one amongst them imagines the cause of the Prince for whom they are fighting to be unjust. They risk their life for their cause—they fulfill the bargain they have made. They might have been killed in the assault, they therefore think they have a right to kill; they might have been plundered, they therefore think they may plunder.

Add to this, that they are intoxicated with fury, which does not reason. And to convince you that they have not divested themselves of the idea of justice and honesty, propose to these same soldiers much more money than the plunder of the city, handsomer women than those they have violated, upon condition only that instead of murdering in their rage three or four thousand enemies, who still make resistance, and who may kill them, they go and cut the throats of their king, his chancellor, his secretaries of state, and his high almoner, you will not find a single soldier who does not reject your proposal with horror: and yet you propose but six murders, instead of four thousand, and you present them with a very valuable recompense.

Why do they refuse you? Because they think it is just to kill four thousand enemies; but the murder of their sovereign, to whom they are bound by a solemn oath, appears to them abominable.

Locke continues his argument, and to prove the better that no rule of conduct is innate, he speaks of the Mengrelians, who out of sport, he says, bury their children alive; and of the Caribbees, who fatten them, in order to eat them.

It has already been observed that this great man was too credulous in relating these fables. Lambert, who alone imputes to the Mengrelians the interment of their children alive, through wantonness, is not an author of sufficient credit to be quoted.

Chardin, who passes for a traveler of veracity, and who was ransomed in Mengrelia, would have spoken of this horrible custom if it had existed; and his affirming it would not have been sufficient to give it credit. Twenty travelers of different nations and religions should agree to confirm such a strange custom, in order to obtain an historical certainty of it.

It is the same with the women of the Antilles islands, who raised their children to eat them. This is not in the nature of a mother. The human heart is not thus framed.

Amongst the wealthy and the great, who were perverted by the excesses of luxury and jealousy, the refinement was practiced of having eunuchs to wait upon and guard their wives and concubines. Eunuchs were also in demand in Italy, and were employed at the Pope's Chapel, in order to have voices finer than those of women.

Locke's assertion regarding the saints of the Mahometan religion and their useful quadrupeds, should be placed with Prince Maurice's story of the parrot, who kept up such a fine conversation in the Brazilian language, which Locke is simple enough to relate, without considering that the prince's interpreter may have related a joke to him.

In this manner the author of the *Spirit of Laws* amuses himself in quoting the imaginary laws of Tonquin, Bantam, Borneo, and Formosa, upon the report of some travelers, or romancers, or persons misinformed.

Locke and Montesquieu are two great men, in whom such simplicity appears to me inexcusable.

XXXVI

NATURE EVERYWHERE THE SAME

IN GIVING up Locke at this point, I say with the great Newton, *Natura est semper sibi consona*, Nature everywhere resembles herself. The law of gravitation, which acts upon a star, acts upon all stars, upon all matter. Thus the fundamental law of morality equally acts upon all civilized nations. There are a thousand differences in the interpretation of this law in a thousand circumstances; but the basis ever remains the same, and this basis is the idea of justice and injustice. Innumerable acts of injustice are committed in the fury of passion, as reason is lost in drunkenness; but when the intoxication is over, reason returns; and this, in my opinion, is the only cause of human society subsisting,— a cause subordinate to the wants of each other's assistance.

How then have we acquired the idea of justice? As we acquired that of prudence, of truth, of convenience, by sentiment and reason. It is impossible for us to avoid thinking it a very imprudent action for a man to throw himself into the fire, in order to be admired, and who should hope afterwards to escape injury. It is impossible for us to avoid thinking a man very unjust for killing another in his passion. Society is founded entirely upon these notions, which can never be torn from the heart, and it is for this reason that all society subsists, whatever extravagant and horrible superstition it may be subject to.

At what age are we acquainted with what is just and unjust? At the age when we know that two and two make four.

XXXVII

OF HOBBES

THOU profound and extravagant philosopher, thou good citizen, thou enemy of Descartes, who deceivedst thyself like him, thou whose physical errors are great but pardonable, because thou camest before Newton, thou who hadst told truths that do not obliterate thy mistakes, thou who didst first display the chimeras of innate ideas, thou who wert the forerunner of Locke in many things, as well as of Spinoza, in vain dost thou astonish thy readers by almost succeeding to prove to them that there are no laws in the world but the laws of conventions; that there is no justice or injustice but what has been agreed upon as such in a country.

If thou hadst been alone with Cromwell in a desert island, and Cromwell would have killed thee for having been a partisan of thy king in the island of England, would not such an attempt appear to thee as unjust in thy new island as in thine own country?

Thou sayest in thy *Law of Nature,* "That every one having a right to all things, each has a right over the life of his own likenesses."

Dost thou not confound power with right?

Dost thou think that, in fact, power conveys right? and that a robust son has nothing to reproach himself with for having assassinated his old and decrepit father?

Whoever studies morality should begin by refuting thy book in his heart; but thine own heart refuted it still more; for thou wert virtuous as well as Spinoza,—and thou wert only wanting, like him, in teaching the principles of virtue, which thou didst practice and recommend to others.

XXXVIII

UNIVERSAL MORALITY

MORALITY appears to me so universal, so calculated by the universal Being that formed us, so destined to serve as a counterpoise to our fatal passions, and to solace the inevitable troubles of this short life, that from Zoroaster down to Lord Shaftesbury, I find all philosophers teaching the same morality, though they have all different ideas upon the principles of things.

We find that Hobbes, Spinoza, and Bayle himself, who either denied the first principles, or at least doubted of them, have, nevertheless, strongly recommended justice, and all the virtues.

Every nation had peculiar religious rights, and very often absurd and revolting opinions in metaphysics and theology. But the point in question is to know whether we should be just. In this the whole universe agrees, as we said in No. XXXVI., and this statement cannot be too often repeated.

XXXIX

ZOROASTER

I SHALL not examine at what time Zoroaster lived, whom the Persians allowed to have existed nine thousand years before them, as well as Plato and the ancient Athenians.

I find that his moral precepts, which were translated from the ancient language of the Magi into the vulgar language of the Guebrians, have been preserved till the present time; and it evidently appears, from the puerile allegories, the ridiculous observations, the fantastic ideas with which this collection is filled, that the religion of Zoroaster is of the highest antiquity.

The word Garden is there used to express the recompense of the just; we there meet with the evil principle under the word Satan, which the Jews also adopted. We there find the world formed in six times or seasons. It is there commanded to recite an *abunavar* and an *ashim vuhu*, for those who sneeze.

But, in fine, in this collection of a hundred subjects or precepts taken from the book of Zend, and in which the very words of the ancient Zoroaster are repeated, what moral duties are prescribed?

That of loving and succoring one's father and mother, that of giving alms to the poor, that of never breaking one's word, that of abstaining when doubtful whether the action to be performed is just or not. (Subject XXX.)

I shall confine myself to this precept, because no legislator could ever go beyond it; and I am confirmed in the opinion that though Zoroaster established ridiculous superstitions in matters of doctrine, the purity of his morals proves that he was not corrupt, and that the more he gave way to errors in his dogmas, the more impossible was it for him to err in teaching virtue.

XL

OF THE BRACHMANS

IT IS probable that the Brahmans, or Brachmans, existed long before the Chinese had their five kings; and what gives rise to this great probability is, that in China the antiquities most sought after are Indian, and that in India there are no Chinese antiquities.

Those ancient Brahmans were doubtless as bad metaphysicians and ridiculous theologists as the Chaldeans and Persians, and all the nations that are to the east of China. But what a sublime morality! According to them, life was only a death of some years, after which they were to live with the divinity. They did not confine themselves to being just towards others, but they were rigorous towards themselves. Silence, abstinence, contemplation, the renouncing of all pleasures, were their principal duties. Likewise, from the sages of other nations, they were to learn what was called Wisdom.

XLI

OF CONFUCIUS

THE Chinese could not reproach themselves with any superstition, any quackery, like other nations. The Chinese government displayed to men upwards of four thousand years ago, and still displays to them, that they may be ruled without being cheated; that the God of truth is not served by falsehood; that superstition is not only useless, but destructive to religion.

Never was the adoration of God so pure and holy as at China, about the time of the Revelation.

I do not speak of the sects of the people, I speak of the religion of the prince of that of the tribunals, and above all of the populace.

What has been the religion of all men of sense in China for many ages? It was this: "Adore heaven and be just." No emperor ever had any other.

The great Confutse, whom we call Confucius, is often placed among the ancient legislators—amongst the founders of religion; but this is a great mistake. Confucius is very modern; he lived only six hundred and fifty years before our era. He never instituted any doctrine, any rite. He neither called himself inspired nor a prophet; he only united in one body the ancient laws of morality.

He invites men to forgive injuries, and to remember nothing but good deeds.

To incessantly watch over themselves, and to correct to-day the faults of yesterday.

To suppress the passions, and to cultivate friendship—to give without ostentation, and not to receive but in extreme necessity, without meanness.

He does not say that we "should not do unto others, what we would not they should do unto us." This is only forbidding evil. He does more—he recommends good. "Treat others as thou wouldst thyself be treated."

He does not only teach modesty, but even humility. He recommends all the virtues.

XLII

Of the Grecian Philosophers and First of Pythagoras

ALL the Greek philosophers have talked nonsense in physics and metaphysics. They are all excellent in morality; they are all equal to Zoroaster, Confucius, and the Brahmans. Read only the golden verses of Pythagoras: they are the essence of his doctrine. It is immaterial from what hand they came. Tell me only if a single virtue is omitted.

XLIII

Of Zaleucus

UNITE the common-place arguments of all the Greek, Italian, Spanish, German, French, and other preachers; extract the essence of all their declamations, and see whether it will be purer than the exordium of the laws of Zaleucus?

"Gain the dominion over your own soul, purify it, drive away all criminal thoughts, believe that God cannot be well served by the perverse; believe that he does not resemble those weak mortals who are seduced by praises and presents. Virtue alone can please him."

This is the substance of all morality and all religion.

XLIV

Of Epicurus

College pedants and seminary fops have believed from some pleasant strokes of Horace and Petronius that Epicurus had taught voluptuousness by precept and example. Epicurus was, during his life, a wise, temperate, and just philosopher. He showed his wisdom at twelve or thirteen years of age; for when the grammarian who instructed him, recited this verse of Hesiod:

Chaos was produced the first of all beings,

"Aye," said Epicurus, "who produced it, since it was the first?"
"I cannot tell," said the grammarian; "none but philosophers know."
"I will apply to them for instruction," said the child; and from that time till the age of seventy-two, he cultivated philosophy.

His will, which Diogenes of Laertes has preserved to us entire, displays a tranquil and just soul.

He gave such slaves liberty as he thought deserved such favor. He recommends to his testamentary executors to give those their liberty who are worthy of it.

Here is no ostentation, no unjust preference. It is the last will of a man, who never had any but what was reasonable.

Singular from most philosophers, all his disciples were his friends, and his sect was the only one which taught to love, and which did not divide itself into various others.

It appears after having examined his doctrine, and what has been written for and against him, that it is all confined to the dispute between Mallebranche and Arnaud. Mallebranche acknowledged that pleasure made us happy, while Arnaud denied it.

This was an altercation upon words, like many other disputes wherein philosophy and theology assist, each on their part, with their uncertainties.

XLV

Of the Stoics

If the Epicureans rendered human nature amiable, the Stoics rendered it almost divine. Resignation to the Being of beings, or rather the elevation of the soul to that being; contempt of life, and even death; inflexibility in justice; such was the character of the real Stoics; and what could be said against them is, they discouraged the rest of men.

Socrates, who was not of their sect, demonstrated that virtue could not have been carried to such a height without being of some party; and the death of this martyr to divinity is an eternal opprobrium to Athens, though she afterwards repented of it.

The Stoic Cato is, on the other hand, the eternal honor of Rome. Epictetus in slavery is, perhaps, superior to Cato, inasmuch as he is contented with his misery. I am, said he, in that place for which providence designed me; therefore to complain is offending him.

Shall I say that the emperor Antoninus is still superior to Epictetus, because he triumphed over more seductions,—and it was much more difficult for an emperor to avoid corruption, than it was for a poor fellow not to murmur! Read the thoughts of both, the emperor and the slave will appear to you equally great.

Dare I mention here the emperor Julian? He erred with respect to his dogmas, but certainly not with respect to morality. In a word, there was no philosopher of antiquity that was not desirous of making men better.

There have been people amongst us, who have said, that all the virtues of their great men were nothing but illustrious sins. Can this earth be covered with such criminals?

XLVI

Philosophy Is Virtue

There were philosophers who were with respect to sophists what men are to monkeys. Lucian ridiculed them, they were despised. They nearly resembled mendicant monks in universities. But let us never forget that philosophers have set great examples of virtue; and that the sophists and even the monks have all respected this virtue in their writings.

XLVII

Of Aesop

I shall place Aesop amongst those great men, and even at the head of these great men. Whether he was the Pilpay of the Indians, the ancient forerunner of Pilpay, or the Lokman of the Persians, or the Akkim of the Arabians, or the Hacam of the Phœnicians, it matters not. I find that his fables were in vogue amongst all the eastern nations, and that his origin is lost in such a depth of antiquity that the abyss cannot be fathomed.

What is the tendency of these fables, equally deep, and ingenious,—these apologues, which seem to have been written at a time when it was not questioned whether or not beasts had a language?

They have instructed almost our whole hemisphere. They are not collections of pompous sentences, which are more tedious than instructive,—they are truth itself, in the attractive garb of fable.

This ancient wisdom is simple and naked in its primitive form. All that ha.
been added is only embellishment in modern languages. The natural grace
which have been given in France have not concealed the original elegance.
What is the great lesson taught by these apologues and fables? To be just!

XLVIII

OF PEACE, THE OFFSPRING OF PHILOSOPHY

As ALL philosophers had different dogmas, it is evident that dogma and virtue
are entirely heterogenous. Whether they believed or not that Thetis was the
goddess of the Sea, whether or no they were convinced of the war of the giants,
and the golden age; of Pandora's-box, and the death of the serpent Pytho, &c.,
these doctrines were in no way connected with morality. It is an admirable
thing in antiquity that theogeny never disturbed the peace of nations.

XLIX

QUESTIONS

OH! IF we could but imitate,—if we could at length do with respect to theological disputes, what we have already done, at the end of seventeen hundred years,
with respect to the *Belles Lettres!*

We have returned to the pure taste of antiquity, in regard to literature, after
being immersed in the barbarisms of our schools.

The Romans were never so absurd as to imagine a man could be persecuted
because he believed in a vacuum or a plenum,—because he thought that accidents could not subsist without a subject,—because he explained the words of an
author in a sense differing from others.

We recur every day to the Roman jurisprudence, and when we are in want
of laws (which often happens) we consult the Code and the Pandects.

Why do we not also imitate our masters in their wise toleration?

Of what importance is it to the nation whether our opinions agree with the
Reals or the Nominals?—whether we join with Scotus or Thomas for Oecolam-
pade or for Melancthon,—whether we are of the party of a bishop of Ypres,
whom we have not read, or a Spanish monk, whose writings we have still less
perused? is it not evident that all this should be as indifferent to the true state of
a nation, as a good or bad translation of a passage of Lycrophon or Hesiod?

L

Other Questions

I KNOW that men have disorders in their brain. We have seen a musician die mad, because his music did not appear good enough. Some folks have imagined that their noses were made of glass; but if any were so violently afflicted as to fancy, for instance, that they were always in the right, would there be helebore enough for such a strange disorder?

And if these patients, in order to maintain that they were always in the right, should threaten with immediate death any who thought them in the wrong,— if they appointed spies to discover those who were refractory,—if they condemned a father upon the testimony of his son, a mother upon that of her daughter, to perish in flames,—should not these people be confined, and treated like bedlamites?

LI

Ignorance

You ask me what avails all this moralizing, if man be not free? I immediately reply, I did not tell you man was not free. I told you that his liberty consisted in his power to act, and not in the chimerical power of willing to will. I shall now tell you that everything being connected in nature, eternal providence predestined me to pen these reveries, and predestined five or six readers to profit by them, and five or six others to contemn them, and throw them aside amongst that immense multitude of useless writings.

If you tell me that I have taught you nothing, remember that I set out by informing you that I was ignorant.

LII

Other Kinds of Ignorance

I AM so ignorant as to be unacquainted with those ancient facts with which children are rocked to sleep. I am constantly in fear of deceiving myself, perhaps seven or eight hundred years, more or less, when I enquire at what time those ancient heroes lived, who are said to have first practiced robbery and free-booting through a vast extent of country, and those first sages, who adored stars, fishes, serpents, dead carcasses, or fantastic beings.

Who was he that first invented the six Gahambers, the bridge of Tshinavar, Dardaroth, and the lake of Charon? At what period did the first Bacchus, the first Hercules, and the first Orpheus exist?

All antiquity is so obscure till the time of Thucydides and Xenophon, that

I am almost debarred from knowing a word of what passed upon the globe which I inhabit, before the short space of about thirty centuries; and in these thirty centuries, how many obscurities, how many uncertainties, how many fables!

LIII

GREATER IGNORANCE

MY IGNORANCE is of far greater weight with me, when I see that neither I, nor any of my fellow countrymen, absolutely know anything about our country.

My mother has told me that I was born upon the banks of the Rhine. I am willing to believe it.

I asked my friend the learned Apedeutes, a native of Courland, if he had any knowledge of the ancient people of the North, his neighbors, and of his unfortunate little country?

He told me he had no more knowledge concerning them than the fish in the Baltic Sea.

As for me, all I know about my country is what Cæsar said, about one thousand eight hundred years ago, that we were free-booters, who were accustomed to sacrifice men to I know not what Gods, to obtain from them many victims; and that we never went hunting without taking with us some old witches, who made these fine sacrifices.

Tacitus, a century later, said a few words about us without having even seen us.

He considers us as the most honest people in the world, at least, when compared with the Romans; and he avers that, as we had nobody to rob, we passed nights and days in our cabins, getting drunk with bad beer.

From the time of our "golden age" to the time of Charlemagne, there is an immense void.

When I have come to these known times, I find in Golstad a charter of Charlemagne, dated at Aix la Chapelle, wherein this learned emperor thus expresses himself:

"You know that hunting one day near this city, I found the hot baths, and the palace which Granus, brother to Nero and Agrippa, had formerly built."

This Granus and this Agrippa, brothers to Nero, show me that Charlemagne was quite as ignorant as myself. This comforts me.

LIV

RIDICULOUS IGNORANCE

THE history of the church of my country resembles that of Granus, brother to Nero and Agrippa, and is still more marvelous. There are little boys risen from the dead; dragons taken with a mole, like rabbits with a snare; hosts, which bleed at the stroke of a knife given them by a Jew; saints that run after their heads when decapitated.

One of the best authenticated legends, in our German Ecclesiastical History, is that of the fortunate Peter of Luxemburg, who in the one thousand three hundred eighty-eighth and eighty-ninth year after his death, operated two thousand four hundred miracles; and the years following, three thousand clearly enumerated; amongst which there were, however, but forty-two dead persons brought to life.

I have made enquiry whether the other states of Europe have ecclesiastical histories equally marvelous and authentic and have everywhere found the same wisdom and the same certainty.

LV

Worse than Ignorance

I afterwards discovered the cause of these unintelligible follies for which men heaped imprecations upon each other—detested each other—persecuted each other—cut the throats of each other—hung, racked and burned each other—and I said if there had been a single wise man in those abominable times, he must have lived and died in a desert.

LVI

The Dawn of Reason

I find to-day, in this age, which is the dawn of reason, some heads of that Hydra, fanaticism, again appearing, but its poison seems less mortal, and its jaws less devouring.

There has not been in recent years as much blood shed for versatile grace, as there formerly was for plenary indulgences, which were publicly sold in the open market; but the monster, fanaticism, still exists, and whoever seeks after truth will run the risk of being persecuted.

Must we therefore remain idle in darkness, or must we light a flambeau, at which envy and calumny will rekindle their torches?

For my part, I think that truth should no more be hidden before these monsters, than that we should abstain from taking nourishment, lest we should be poisoned.

DIALOGUES

I

THE CHINESE CATECHISM

Or, Dialogues between Cu-su, *a Disciple of Confucius, and Prince* Kou, *Son of the King of Lou, tributary to the Chinese Emperor, Gnenvan, four hundred and seventeen years before the common Era.*

Kou. What is meant by my duty to worship heaven? (Chang-ti?)

Cu-su. Not the material heaven, which we see; for this heaven is nothing but the air, and the air is composed of every kind of earthly exhalation. Now, what a folly it would be to worship vapors.

Kou. It is, however, what I should not much wonder at. Men, in my opinion, have gone into greater follies.

Cu-su. Very true; but you, being born to rule over others, it becomes you to be wise.

Kou. There are whole nations who worship heaven and the planets.

Cu-su. The planets are only so many earths, like ours. The moon, for instance, might as well worship our sand and dirt, as we to prostrate ourselves before the moon's dirt and sand.

Kou. What is the meaning of what we so often hear, HEAVEN AND EARTH; *to go up to heaven;* to be *deserving of heaven?*

Cu-su. It is talking very silly. There is no such thing as heaven. Every planet is environed by its atmosphere as with a shell, and rolls in space around its sun; every sun is the centre of several planets, which are continually going their rounds. There is neither high nor low, up nor down. Should the inhabitants of the moon talk of going up to the earth, of making one's self deserving of the earth, it would be talking madly; and we are little wiser in talking of deserving heaven. We might as well say, a man must make himself deserving of the air—deserving of the constellation of the dragon—deserving of space.

Kou. I believe I understand you. We are only to worship God alone. But in saying that he made heaven and earth, however devout our meaning may be, it is talking very silly, for if, by heaven, we mean the prodigious space in which God kindled so many suns and set so many worlds in motion, it is much more ridiculous to say, "heaven and earth," than it is to say, "the mountains and a grain of sand." Our globe is infinitely less than a grain of sand, in comparison to those millions of ten thousands of millions of worlds, among the infinitude of which we are lost. All that we can do is to join our feeble voice to that of the innumerable beings, who, throughout the abyss of expansion, ascribe homage and glory to their adorable Creator.

Kou. It was, then, a great imposition to tell us that Fo came down among us from the fourth heaven, assuming the form of a white elephant.

These are tales which the bonzes tell to old women and children. The Eternal Author of all things is alone to be worshiped.

Kou. But how can one being make the other beings?

Cu-su. You see yonder star. It is fifteen hundred thousand millions of *Lis* from our globe, and emits rays which, on your eyes, form two angles equal at the top; and, the like angles, they form on the eyes of all animals. Is not this manifest design? Is not this an admirable law? and is it not the workman who makes the work? and, who frames laws but a legislator? Therefore, there is an eternal Artist, an eternal Legislator.

Kou. But who made this Artist? and what is he like?

Cu-su. My dear Prince, as I was yesterday afternoon walking near the magnificent palace, so lately built by the king, your father, I overheard two crickets. One said to the other, "What a stupendous fabric is here"; "Yes," said the other; "and though I am not a little proud of my species, he who has made this prodigy must be something above a cricket; but I have no idea of that being. Such a one, I see there must be; but what he is I know not."

Kou. You are a cricket of infinitely more knowledge than I, but what I particularly like in you is, your not pretending to know what you really do not understand.

Second Dialogue

Cu-su. You allow, then, that there is an Almighty Being, self-existent, supreme Creator and Maker of all nature.

Kou. Yes; but if he be self-existent, he is unlimited; consequently, he is everywhere. He exists throughout all matter and in every part of myself.

Cu-su. Why not?

Kou. I should then be a part of the Deity.

Cu-su. Perhaps that may not be the consequence. Behold this piece of glass; you see the light penetrates it everywhere; yet, will you say it is light? It is mere sand, and nothing more. Unquestionably everything is in God; that, by which everything is animated, must be everywhere. God is not like the emperor of China, who dwells in his palace, and sends his orders by koloas. As existing, he must necessarily fill the whole of space, and all his works, and since he is in you, this is a continual monition never to do anything to raise shame or remorse.

Kou. But for a person serenely to consider himself before the Supreme Being without shame or disgust, what must he do?

Cu-su. Be just.

Kou. And what further?

Cu-su. Be just.

Kou. But Laokium's sect says, "There is no such thing as just or unjust, vice or virtue."

Cu-su. And does Laokium's sect say, "There is no such thing as health or sickness?"

Kou. No, to be sure; what egregious nonsense that would be!

Cu-su. And let me tell you, that to think there is neither health nor sickness of soul, virtue nor vice, is as egregious an error, and much more mischievous.

They, who have advanced that every thing is alike, are monsters. Is it alike, to carefully bring up a son, or, at his birth, to dash him against the stones—to relieve a mother, or to plunge a dagger into her heart?

Kou. That is horrible. I detest Lakium's sect. But *just* and *unjust* are oftentimes so interwoven, that one is at a loss. Who can be said precisely to know what is forbidden, and what is allowed? Who can safely set limits to good and evil? I wish you would give me a sure rule for this important distinction.

Cu-su. There can be no better than that of Confucius, my master: "*Live as thou wouldst desire to have lived, when thou comest to die; use thy neighbor as thou wouldst have him use thee.*"

Kou. Those maxims, I own, should be mankind's standing law. But what am I the better for my good life, when I come to die? What great advantage shall I get for my virtue? That clock goes as well as ever clock did; but, when it comes to be worn out, or should it be destroyed by accident, will it be happy for having struck the hours regularly?

Cu-su. That clock is without thought or feeling, and incapable of remorse, which you sharply feel on the commission of any crime.

Kou. But what if, by frequent crimes, I come to be no longer sensible of remorse?

Cu-su. Then it is high time an end should be put to your being; and, take my word for it, that as men do not love to be oppressed, should you be guilty, one or another would stop you in your career, and save you from committing other crimes.

Kou. At that rate, God, who is in them, after allowing me to be wicked, would allow them likewise to be so.

Cu-su. God has endowed you with reason; neither you nor they are to make a wrong use of it; as, otherwise, you will not only be unhappy in this life, but how do you know but that you may likewise be so in another?

Kou. And who told you there is another life?

Cu-su. The bare uncertainty of it should make you behave as if it were an undoubted certainty.

Kou. But what if I be sure there is no such thing?

Cu-su. That I defy you to make good.

Third Dialogue

Kou. You urge me home Cu-su. My being rewarded or punished after death requires that something, which feels and thinks in me, must continue to subsist after me. Now, as no part in me had any thought or sense before my birth, why should it possess them after my death? What can this incomprehensible part of myself be? Will the humming of that bee continue after the end of its existence? or the vegetation of this plant, when plucked up by the roots? Is not *vegetation* a word made use of to express the inexplicable mode appointed by the Supreme Being, for the plants imbibing the juices of the earth? So the *soul* is an invented word, faintly and obscurely denoting the spring of human life. All animals have a motion, and this ability to move is called active force; but this force is no distinct being whatever. We have passions, memory, and reason; but these passions, this memory, and this reason, are surely not separate things; they are not beings existing in us; they are not diminutive persons of a particular existence; they are generical words, invented to fix our ideas. Thus the soul itself, which signifies our memory, our reason, our passions, is only a bare word. Whence, then, motion in nature? from God. Whence vegetation in that plant? from God. Whence motion in animals? from God. Whence cogitation in man? from God.

Were the human soul a diminutive person, inclosed within our body, to direct its motions and ideas, would not that betray, in the eternal maker of the world, an impotence and an artifice quite unworthy of him? He, then, must have been incapable of making automata, having the gift of motion and thought in themselves. When I learned Greek under you, you made me read Homer, where Vulcan appears an excellent smith, when he makes golden tripods, going of themselves to the council of the gods; but had this same Vulcan concealed within those tripods one of his boys, to make them move without being perceived, I should consider him but a bungling cheat.

Some obscure dreamers have been charmed with the fancy of the planets being rolled along by genii, as something very grand and sublime; but God has not been reduced to such a paltry shift. In a word, wherefore put two springs to a work when one will do? That God can animate that inanimate substance called matter, you cannot deny, why then should he make use of another agent to animate it?

Further, what may that soul be which you are pleased to give to our body? From whence did it come? When did it come? Must the Creator of the universe be continually observing human beings and animals, and providing the former with souls at birth?

This is really a strange employment for the Sovereign of the world, and it is not only on the passions of the human species that he must be intent, but must also observe the like vigilance and celerity with all animals whatever; for, like us, they have memory, ideas, and passions; and, if a soul be necessary for the formation of these sentiments, these ideas, these passions, and this memory, God must be perpetually at work about souls for elephants and flies, for fish and for bonzes.

What idea does such a notion give of the Architect of so many millions of worlds, thus obliged to be continually making invisible props for perpetuating his work?

These are some, though a very small sample, of the reasons for questioning the soul's existence.

Cu-su. You reason candidly; and such a virtuous turn of mind, even if mistaken, cannot but be agreeable to the Supreme Being. You may be in error, but as you do not endeavor to deceive yourself, your error is excusable. But consider what you have proposed to me are only doubts, and melancholy doubts. Listen to probabilities of a solacing nature. To be annihilated is dismal;

hope then for life. A thought, you know, is not matter, nor has any affinity with it. Why, then, do you make such a difficulty of believing that God has put a divine principle into you, which, being indissoluble, cannot be subject to death? Can you say that it is impossible that you should have a soul? No, certainly. And, if it be possible that you have one, is it not also very probable? How can you reject so noble a system—so necessary to mankind? Shall a few slender objections withhold your assent?

Kou. I would embrace this system with all my heart, on its truth being proved to me. But it is not in my power to believe without evidence. I am always struck with this grand idea, that God has made everything—that he is everywhere—that he penetrates all things, and gives life and motion to all things; and, if he be in all parts of my being, as he is in all parts of nature, I do not see that I have any need of a soul.

Where is the use or importance of this little subaltern being to me, who am animated by God himself? Of what improvement can it be? It is not from ourselves that we derive our ideas; they generally obtrude themselves on us against our wills; we have them when locked up in sleep; everything passes in us without our intervention. What would it signify to the soul, were it to say to the blood and animal spirits, "Be so kind as to gratify me in running this way?" They will still circulate in their natural course. Let me be the machine of a God, whose existence all things proclaim aloud, rather than of a soul, whose existence, to say the least, is a very great uncertainty.

Cu-su. Well, if God himself *animates* you, be very careful of committing any crime, as defiling that God, who is within you; and, if he *has* given you a soul, never let it offend him. In both systems you have a volition, you are free; that is, you have a power of doing what you will. Make use of this power in serving that God who gave it to you. If you are a philosopher, so much the better; but it is necessary for you to be just; and you will be more so, when you come to believe that you have an immortal soul. Please to answer me, Is not God sovereign and perfect justice?

Kou. Doubtless, and should he cease to be so, (which it is blasphemy to think) I would myself act equitably.

Cu-su. Will it not be your duty, when on the throne, to reward virtue and punish vice? and can you think of God's not doing what is incumbent on yourself to do? You know that there are, and ever will be, in this life, good men *distressed*, while bad men *prosper*; therefore, good and evil must be finally judged in another life. It is this, so simple, so general, and so natural an opinion, which has induced and fixed among so many nations the belief in the immortality of our souls, and of their being judged by divine justice, on their quitting this mortal tenement. Is there, can there be, a system more rational, more suitable to the Deity, and more beneficial to mankind?

Kou. Why, then, have so many nations rejected this system? You know that, in our province, we have about two hundred families of the old Sinous, who formerly dwelt in part of Arabia Petræa; and neither they, nor their ancestors, ever believed anything of the immortality of the soul. They have their five books, as we have our five *Kings*. I have read a translation of them. Their laws, which necessarily correspond with those of all other nations, enjoin them to respect their parents, not to steal nor lie, and to abstain from adultery and bloodshed; yet these laws are wholly silent, as to the rewards and punishments in another life.

Cu-su. If this truth has not as yet been made known to those poor people, unquestionably their eyes will some day be opened. But what signifies a small obscure tribe, when the Babylonians, the Egyptians, the Indians, and all polished nations, have subscribed to this salutary doctrine? If you were sick, would you decline making use of a remedy, approved by all the Chinese, because some barbarous mountaineers had expressed a dislike to it? God has endowed you with reason, and this reason tells you that the soul must be immortal; therefore, it is God himself who tells you so.

Kou. But how can I be rewarded or punished when I shall cease to be myself?—when nothing which had constituted my person shall be remaining? It is only by my memory that I am always myself: now, my memory, I lose in my last illness; so that, after my death, nothing under a miracle can restore it to me, and thus replace me in my former existence.

Cu-su. That is as much as to say, should a prince, after making his way to the throne by the murder of all his relatives, play the tyrant over his subjects, he need only say to God, "It is not I; I have totally lost my memory; you mistake, I am no longer the same person." Think you God would be pleased with such a sophism?

Kou. Well, I acquiesce. I was for living irreproachable for my own sake, now I will do so to please the Supreme Being. I thought the whole matter was for my soul to be just and virtuous in this life; but I will now hope that it will be happy in another.

This opinion, I perceive, makes for the good of both subjects and sovereigns. Still, the worship of the Deity perplexes me.

Fourth Dialogue

Cu-su. Why, what is there that can offend in our Chu-king, the first canonical book, and which all the Chinese emperors have so greatly respected? You plough a field with your own royal hands by way of example to the people; and the first fruits of it you offer to the Chang-ti, to the Tien, to the Supreme Being, and sacrifice to him four times every year. You are king and high-priest; you promise God to do all the good which shall be in your power. Is there anything in this which you cannot digest?

Kou. I am very far from making any exceptions. I know that God has no need either of our sacrifices or prayers, but the offering of them to him is very needful for us. His worship was not instituted for himself, but on our account. I am very much delighted with praying, and am particularly careful that there be nothing ridiculous in my prayers; for, were I to cry out till my throat was sore, "That the mountain of Chang-ti is a fat mountain, and that fat mountains are not to be looked upon";—though I should have put the sun to flight, and dried up the moon, will this rant be acceptable to the Supreme Being, or of any benefit to my subjects or to myself?

Especially, I cannot bear with the silliness of the sects about us. On one side is Laotz, whom his mother conceived by the junction of heaven and earth, and was for fourscore years pregnant with him. I as little believe his doctrine of universal deprivation and annihilation, as of his being born with white hair, or of his going to promulgate his doctrine, riding on a black cow.

The god *Fo* I put on the same footing, notwithstanding he had a white elephant for his father, and promises immortal life. One thing, at which I cannot forbear taking great offence, is that the bonzes continually preach such chimeras, thus deceiving the people, in order the better to sway them. They gain for themselves respect by mortification, at which, indeed, nature shudders. Some deny themselves, during their whole lives, the most salutary foods, as if there were no way of pleasing God but by a bad diet. Others carry a pillory about their necks, and sometimes they richly deserve it. They drive nails into their thighs, as into boards, and for this fanaticism, the people follow them in crowds. On the king's issuing any edict which does not suit their humor, they coolly tell their auditors, that this edict is not to be found in the commentary of the god Fo, and that god is to be obeyed in preference to men. Now, how am I to remedy this popular distemper, which is extravagant in the highest degree, and not less dangerous?

Toleration, you know, is the principle of the Chinese, and, indeed, of all Asiatic governments, but such an indulgence must be owned to be highly mischievous, as exposing an empire to be overthrown on account of some fanatical notions.

Cu-su. God forbid that I should go about to extinguish in you the spirit of toleration, that quality so eminently respectable, and which, to souls, is what the permission of eating is to bodies. *By the law of nature, every one may believe what he will, as well as eat what he will.* A physician is not to kill his patients for not observing the diet he has prescribed to them; neither has a sovereign a right to hang his subjects for not thinking as he thinks; but he has a right to prevent disturbances, and, with prudent measures, he will very easily root out superstitions of all kinds.

Do you know what happened to Daon, the sixth king of Chaldea, about four thousand years ago?

Kou. No. I pray you oblige me with an account of it.

Cu-su. The Chaldean priests had taken it into their heads to worship the pikes of the Euphrates, pretending that a famous fish called *Oannes,* had formerly taught them divinity; that this fish was immortal, three feet in length, and a small crescent was on the tail. In veneration of this *Oannes,* no pikes were to be eaten. A violent dispute arose among the divines, whether the fish *Oannes* had a soft or hard roe. Both parties not only fulminated excommunications, but, at several times, they came to blows.

To put an end to such disturbances, King Daon made use of this expedient.

He ordered a strict fast for three days to both parties, and at the expiration of it, sent for the sticklers of the hard-roed pike, who, accordingly, were present at his dinner. A pike was brought to him, three feet in length, and on the tail, a small crescent had been put.

"Is this your god?" said he, to the doctors.

"Yes, sir," answered they; "we know him by the crescent on the tail, and make no question but he is hard-roed."

On this, the king ordered the pike to be opened. It was found to have the finest melt that could be.

"Now," said the king, "you see that this is not your god, it being soft-roed"; and the king and his nobles ate the pike.

The hard-roed divines were not a little pleased that the god of their adversaries had been fried.

Immediately after, the doctors of the opposite side were sent for, and a pike of three feet, with a crescent on his tail, being shown to them, they, with great joy, assured his majesty that it was the god *Oannes*, and that he had a soft roe; but, behold! on being opened, it was found hard-roed.

At this, the two parties, equally out of countenance, and still fasting, the good-natured king told them, that he could only give them a dinner of pikes; and they greedily fell to eating both hard and soft-roed, indiscriminately.

This closed the war with great distinction for King Daon's wisdom and goodness, and since that time the people have been allowed to eat pikes as often as they pleased.

Kou. Well done, King Daon! and I give my word that I will follow his example on every occasion, and as far as I can, without injuring any one, and without worshiping *Fo's* or pikes.

I know that in the countries of Pegu and Tonquin there are little gods and little Tapolins, which bring down the moon, when in the wane, and clearly foretell what is to come; that is, they clearly see what is not. I will take care that the Tapolins shall not come within my reach, to make futurity present, and bring down the moon.

It is a shame that there should be sects rambling from town to town, propagating their delusions, as quacks do their medicaments. What a disgrace it is to the human mind for petty nations to think that truth belongs to them alone, and that the vast empire of China is given up to error.

Is then, the Eternal Being only the god of Formosa or Borneo? Has he no concern for the other parts of the universe? My dear Cu-su, he is a father to all men; he allows every one to eat pike. The most acceptable homage which can be paid to him is being virtuous. The finest of all his temples, as the great emperor Hiao used to say, is a pure heart.

Fifth Dialogue

Cu-su. Since you love virtue, in what manner do you propose to practice it, when you come to be king?

Kou. In not being unjust to my neighbors, or my subjects.

Cu-su. To do no harm, does not come up to virtue. I hope my prince will do good; will feed the poor by employing them in useful labor, and not endow sloth; mend and not embellish the highways, dig canals, build public edifices, encourage arts, reward merit of every kind, and pardon involuntary faults.

Kou. This I call not being unjust: those things are plain duties.

Cu-su. Your way of thinking becomes a king; but there is the king and the man—the public life and the private life. You will be married: how many wives do you think of having?

Kou. Why, a dozen, I think will do; a greater number might prove to be a hindrance from business. I do not approve of kings, like Solomon, with three hundred wives and seven hundred concubines and thousands of eunuchs to wait on them. This custom of having eunuchs, especially, appears to me a most execrable insult and outrage to human nature. What is the use of their being thus mutilated? It improves their voices: the Dela-i Lama has fifty of them to sing purely in his pagoda. Let him tell me whether the Chang-ti is much delighted with the clear pipes of these fifty emasculated beings.

Another most ridiculous thing is the bonzes not marrying. They boast of being wiser than the other Chinese; well, then, let them prove their wisdom by getting married, and becoming the happy fathers of intelligent children. An odd manner, indeed, of worshiping the Chang-ti, to deprive him of worshipers; and, to be sure, they must have a great affection for mankind, who lead the way to extinguish the species!

The good little Lama, called Stelca Isant Erepi, used to say, "That every priest should marry, and rear as many children as possible." What this Lama taught, he practised, and was very useful in his generation.

For my part, I shall marry all the Lamas and Bonzes, and Lamasses and Bonzesses, who shall appear to have a call to the holy work. Besides making them better patriots, I shall think it no small service to my dominions.

Cu-su. What an excellent prince shall we have in you! I cannot forbear weeping for joy. But you will not be satisfied with having wives and subjects, for after all, one cannot be perpetually drawing up edicts, and caring for children; you will likewise make yourself some friends.

Kou. I am not without some already, and those good ones; putting me in mind of my faults, and I allow myself the liberty of reproving theirs. We likewise mutually comfort and encourage one another. Friendship is the balm of life. It excels that of the chemist Eruil; and even all the nostrums of the great Ranoud are not comparable to it. I think friendship should have been made a religious precept. I have a good mind to insert it in our ritual.

Cu-su. By no means. Friendship is sufficiently sacred of itself. Never enjoin it: the heart must be free; besides, were you to make a precept, a mystery, a rite, a ceremony, of friendship, it would soon become ridiculous through the fantastical preachings and writings of the bonzes. Let it not be exposed to such profanation.

But how will you deal with your enemies? Confucius, I believe, in no less than twenty places, directs us to love them. Does not this appear somewhat difficult to you?

Kou. Love one's enemies! Oh, dear doctor! nothing is more common.

Cu-su. But what do you mean by love?

Kou. Mean by it! what it really is. I was a volunteer under the prince of Decon, against the prince of Visbrunk; when a wounded enemy fell into our hands, we took as much care of him as if he had been our brother. We have even parted with our beds to them, and we lay by them on tigers' skins spread on the bare ground. We have tended and nursed them ourselves. Is not this loving our enemies?

Cu-su. I am greatly pleased with your discourse, and wish that all nations could have heard you, for I have been informed of some, so very ignorant and impertinent as to assert that we know nothing of true virtue—that our good actions are only specious sins—and that we stand in need of their Talapoins to instruct us in right principles! Poor creatures! A few years ago there was no such thing as reading or writing among them; and now they are for teaching their masters!

Sixth Dialogue .

Cu-su. I shall not repeat to you the common phrases, which, for these five or six thousand years past, have been retailed among us, relating to all the several virtues. Some there are which only concern ourselves, as prudence in the guidance of our souls; temperance in the government of our bodies; but these are rather dictates of policy, and care of health. The real virtues are those which promote the welfare of society, as fidelity, magnanimity, benefi-cence, toleration, etc., and, thank Heaven, these are the first things which every woman, among us, teaches her children. They are the rudiments of the rising generation, both in town and country; but, I am sorry to say there is a great virtue which is sadly on the decline among us.

Kou. Quickly name it, and no endeavor of mine shall be wanting to revive it.

Cu-su. It is hospitality; for, since inns have been established among us, this social virtue—this sacred tie of mankind—becomes more and more relaxed.

That pernicious institution, the hotel, we have borrowed, I am told, from those western savages, who probably have no houses to entertain travelers. My heart melts with delight when I have the happiness of entertaining, in the vast city of Lou, in Honcham, that superb square, or my delicious seat at Ki, some generous stranger from Samarcand, to whom, from that moment, I be-come sacred, and who, by all laws human and divine, is bound to entertain me on any call I may have into Tartary; and to be and remain my cordial friend.

The savages I am speaking of do not admit strangers into their huts, filthy as they are, without their paying, and dearly too, for such sordid reception; and yet these wretches, I hear, think themselves above us; and that our morality is nothing in comparison to theirs—that their preachers excel Confucius himself.

In a word, they alone know what true justice is, and as a proof of their claim, they allow the sale of deleterious compounds for wine in public places, and permit their women, as if mad, to dance, and rove about the streets, whilst ours are breeding silk-worms.

Kou. I much approve of hospitality, and the practice of it gives me pleasure; but I am afraid it will be much abused. Near Tibet dwells a people, who, besides the poverty of their habitations, being of a roving disposition, will, for any trifle, go from one end of the world to the other; and, on your visiting Tibet, so far from returning your hospitality, they have nothing to set before you, nor so much as a bed for you to lie on. This is enough to put one out of conceit with courtesy.

Cu-su. These disappointments may easily be remedied, by entertaining such persons only as come well recommended. Every virtue has its difficulties, and dangers, and, without them, the practice of virtue would want much of its glory and excellence. How wise and holy is our Confucius! There is not a virtue that he does not inculcate. Every sentence is pregnant with the happiness of mankind. One at present recurs to me; I think it is the fifty-third:

"Kindnesses acknowledge with kindness, and never revenge injuries."

What a maxim! what a law! Can the western people bring any thing in competition with such exalted morality? Then, in how many places, and how strongly, does he recommend humility! Did this amiable virtue prevail among men, there would be an end to all quarrels and broils.

Kou. I have read all that Confucius and the sages before him have said about humility; but none of them, I think, have been sufficiently accurate in their definition of it. There may, perhaps, be but little humility in presuming to censure them; but with all due deference, I own that they are beyond my comprehension. What is your idea of humility?

Cu-su. Humility, I take to be mental modesty; for, as to external modesty, it is no more than civility. Humility cannot consist in denying to one's self that superiority which we may have acquired above another. An able physician cannot but be sensible that he is possessed of a knowledge infinitely beyond that of his delirious patient. The teacher of astronomy must necessarily think himself more learned than his scholar; but they must not pride themselves on their superior acquirements. Humility is not debasement, but a corrective of self-love, as modesty is the corrective of pride.

Kou. Well, *it is in the practice of all these virtues, and the worship of one simple and universal God, that I propose to live, far from the chimeras of sophists, and the illusions of false prophets. The love of mankind shall be my virtue, and the love of God my religion.*

As to the god Fo, and Lao-Tse, and Vishnu, who has so often become incarnate among the Indians; and Sammonocodom, who came down from heaven to fly a kite among the Siamese, together with the Camis, who went from the moon to visit Japan,—I cannot endure such impious fooleries.

How weak, and at the same time how cruel, is it for a people to conceive that there is no God but with them alone! It is downright blasphemy. The light of the sun irradiates all nations, but the light of God shines only in a little insignificant tribe, in a corner of this globe! It is appalling that such a thought could enter the mind of man! The Deity speaks to the heart of all men of all nations, and they should, from one end of the universe to the other, be linked together in the bonds of charity.

Cu-su. O wise Kou! you have spoken like one inspired by the great Chang-ti himself! You will make a worthy prince. From being my pupil, you have become my teacher.

II

The Japanese Catechism; or, An Indian and Japanese Dialogue

Indian. Is it so, that formerly, the Japanese knew nothing of cookery; that they had submitted their kingdom to the great Lama; that this great Lama arbitrarily prescribed what they should eat and drink; that he used, at times, to send to you an inferior Lama for receiving the tributes, who, in return, gave you a sign of protection, which he made with his two forefingers and thumb?

Japanese. Alas! It is but too true; nay, all the places of the Canusi, or chief cooks of our island, were disposed of by the Lama, and the love of God was quite out of the question. Further, every house of our seculars paid annually an ounce of silver to this head cook of Tibet, whilst all the amends we had, were some small plates of *relics*, and these none of the best tasted; and, on every new whim of his—as making war against the people of Tangut—we were saddled with fresh subsidies. Our nation frequently complained, but all we got by it, was to pay the more for presuming to complain. At length, love, which does every thing for the best, freed us from this galling thraldom. One of our emperors quarreled with the great Lama, about a woman; but it must be owned that they who, in this affair, did us the best turn, were our Canusi, or Pauxcospies. It is to them that, in fact, we owe our deliverance; and it happened in this manner. The great Lama, forsooth, insisted on being always in the right. Our Dairi and Canusi would have it, that sometimes, at least, they might not be in the wrong. This claim the great Lama derided as an absurdity; on which, our gentry, being as stiff as he was haughty, broke with him forever.

Indian. Well, ever since you have had golden days, I suppose?

Jap. Far from it: for nearly two hundred years, there was nothing but persecution, violence, and blood shed among us; and though our Canusi pretend to be in the right, it is but a hundred years since they have had their proper reason; but, from that time, we may boldly esteem ourselves one of the happiest nations on earth.

Indian. How can that be, if, as reported, you have no less than twelve different sects of cookery among you? Why you must always be at daggers-drawing?

Jap. Why so? If there be twelve cooks, and each have a different recipe, shall we, instead of dining, cut each other's throats? No, each one may regale himself at that cook's table whose manner of dressing victuals he likes best.

INDIAN. True; tastes are not to be disputed about. Yet people will make them a matter of contention, and all sides grow warm.

JAP. After long disputing, men come to see the mischiefs of these wranglings, and at length agree upon a reciprocal toleration; and, certainly, they can do nothing better.

INDIAN. And pray, what are those cooks, who make such a stir in your nation about the art of eating and drinking?

JAP. First, there is the Breuxehs, who never allow any pork or pudding. They hold with the old-fashioned cookery; they would as soon die, as lard a fowl; then they deal much in numbers, and if an ounce of silver is to be divided between them and the eleven other cooks, they instantly secure one-half to themselves, and the remainder take who will.

INDIAN. I fancy you do not often foul a plate with these folks.

JAP. Never. Then there are the Dispates, who will, on some days of the week, and even for a considerable time of the year, gormandize on turbot, trout, salmon, sturgeon, be they ever so dear, yet would not, for the world, touch a sweetbread of veal, which may be had for a groat.

As for us Canusi, we are very fond of beef and a kind of pastry ware, in Japanese called pudding. Now, all the world allows our cooks to be infinitely more knowing than those of the Dispates. Nobody has gone farther than we, in finding out what was the garum of the Romans. We surpass all others in our knowledge of the onions of ancient Egypt, the locust paste of the primitive Arabs, the Tartarian horse-*flesh;* and there is always something to be learned in the books of those Canusi, commonly known by the name of Pauxcospies.

I shall omit those who eat only in Tarluh, those who observe the Vincal diet, the Bastistans, and others; but the Quekars deserve particular notice. Though I have very often been at table with them, I never saw one get drunk, or heard him swear an oath. It is a hard matter to cheat them, but then they never cheat you. The law of loving one's neighbor as one's self, seems really peculiar to them; for, in truth, how can an honest Japanese talk of loving his neighbor as himself, when, for a little pay, he goes as a hireling, to blow his brains out, and to hew him with a four-inch broad sabre, and all this in form; then he, at the same time, exposes himself to the like fate, to be shot or sabred: so he may, with more truth, be said to hate his neighbor as himeslf.

This is a frenzy the Quekars were never possessed with. They say, and very justly, that poor mortals are earthen vessels, made to last but a very short time, and that they should not wantonly go and break themselves to pieces one against another.

I own that were I not a Canusi, I should take part with the Quekars; for you see that there can be no wranglings nor blows with such peaceable cooks.

There is another, and a very numerous branch of cooks, called Diestos; with these, every one, without distinction, is welcome to their table, and you are at full liberty to eat as you like. You have larded or barded fowls, or neither larded nor barded, egg sauce, or oil; partridge, salmon, white or red wines;

these things they hold as matters of indifference, provided you say a short prayer before and after dinner, and even without this ceremony before break-fast:—and with good-natured, worthy men, they will banter about the great Lama, the Turlah, Vincal and Memnon, &c.; only these Diestos must acknowledge our Canusi to be very profound cooks; and, especially, let them never talk of curtailing our incomes: then we shall live very easily together.

INDIAN. But still there must be cookery, by law established, or the king's cookery.

JAP. There must, indeed; but when the king of Japan has regaled himself plentifully, he should be cheerful and indulgent, and not hinder his good and loyal subjects from having their repasts.

INDIAN. But, should some hot-headed people take on themselves to eat sausages close to the king's nose, when the king is known to have an aversion to that food; should a mob of four or five thousand of them get together, each with his gridiron, to broil their sausages, and insult those who are against eating them?

In such a case, they ought to be punished, as turbulent drunkards. But we have obviated this danger; none but those who follow the royal cookery are capable of holding any employment: all others may, indeed, eat as they please, but this humor excludes them from some emoluments. Tumults are strictly forbidden, and instantly punished without mercy or mitigation. All quarrels at table are carefully restrained by a precept of our Japanese cook, who has written, in the sacred language, "*Suti raho, cus flat, natus in usum lœtita scyphis pugnare tracum est:*" that is, "the intent of feasting is a sober and decent mirth; but to throw glasses at one another is savage."

Under these maxims we live very happily. Our liberty is secured by our Taicosemas. We are every day growing more and more opulent. We have two hundred junks of the line, and are dreaded by our neighbors.

INDIAN. Why, then, has the pious rhymer, Reen, (son of the justly celebrated poet, Reen,) said, in a didactic work, entitled *Grace*, and not *the Graces*,

> "*Le Japon ou jadis brilla tante de lumiere,*
> *N'est plus qu'un triste amas de felles visions.*"

> Japan, once famed for intellectual light,
> Lies sunk in vision, chimera, and night.

JAP. The poet Recna is himself an arrant visionary. Does not this weak Indian know, that it is we who have taught his countrymen what light is? that it is to us India owes its knowledge of the course of the planets? and that it is we who have made known to man the primitive laws of nature?

To descend to things of more common use: by us his countrymen were taught to build Junks in mathematical proportion; they are beholden to us for those coverings of their legs, which they call woven stockings. Now, is it possible, that, after such admirable and useful inventions, we should be madmen? And, if he have rhymed on the follies of others, does that make him the only wise man? Let him leave us to our own cookery, and, if he must be versifying, I would advise him to choose more poetical subjects.

This Recna, trusting to the visionaries of his country, has advanced, "That no good sauces were to be made, unless Brahma himself, out of his gracious favor, taught, or inspired his particular favorites to make the sauce; that there was an infinite number of cooks, who, with the best intentions and most earnest endeavors, were quite unable to serve a ragout; Brahma, from mere ill will, disabling them." Such stuff will not be credited in Japan, where the fol-lowing quotation is esteemed as an indisputable truth:

"God never acts by partial, but by general laws."

INDIAN. What can be said? He is full of his country's prejudices, those of his party, and his own.

JAP. A world of prejudices indeed!

III

THE GARDENER'S CATECHISM

A DIALOGUE BETWEEN BASHAW TUCTAN, AND KARPOS THE GARDENER

TUCTAN. You sell your fruit, friend Karpos, very dear; however, it is pretty good. Pray, what religion do you profess now?

KARPOS. Why, indeed, my Lord Bashaw, I cannot very well tell you. When our little island (Samos) belonged to the Greeks, I remember that I was ordered to say, that *Agiou pneuma* (the sacred spirit) proceeded only from *tou patrou* (the father). I was told to pray to God, standing upright, with my arms across, and was prohibited eating milk in Lent. When the Venetians came, our new Italian curate ordered me to say, that *Agiou pneuma* proceeded both from *tou patrou* and from *tou uiou* (the son), permitting me to eat milk, and making me pray on my knees. On the return of the Greeks, and their expelling the Venetians, I was obliged again to renounce *tou uiou* and milk porridge. You have, at length, expelled the Greeks, and I hear you cry out, as loud as you can, "*Allah illa Allah!*" For my part, I no longer know what I am; but I love God with all my heart, and sell my fruit very reasonably.

TUCT. You have some fine figs there.

KARP. At your service, my lord.

TUCT. They say you have a fine daughter too.

KARP. Yes, my lord Bashaw; but she is not at your service.

TUCT. Why so? Wretch!

KARP. Because I am an honest man. I may sell my figs, if I please; but I may not sell my daughter.

TUCT. And, pray, by what law are you allowed to sell one kind of fruit and not the other?

KARP. By the law of all honest gardeners. The honor of my daughter is not my property, but hers. It is not, with us, a marketable commodity.

TUCT. You are, then, disloyal to your Bashaw.

KARP. Not at all. I am his faithful servant in every thing that is just, so lon͜ᶜ as he continues my master.

TUCT. And so, if your Greek patriarch should form a plot against me, and should order you, in the name of *tou patrou*, to enter into it, you would not have devotion enough to turn traitor? Ha!

KARP. Not I.

TUCT. And, pray, why should you refuse to obey your patriarch, on such an occasion?

KARP. Because I have taken an oath of allegiance to you, as my Bashaw; and I know that *tou patrou* does not command any one to engage in plots and conspiracies.

TUCT. I am glad of that, at least. But what, if the Greeks should retake the isle, and expel your Bashaw; would you be faithful to me still?

KARP. What! when you are no longer my Bashaw?

TUCT. What, then, would become of your oath of allegiance?

KARP. Something like my figs: you would not be, any more, the better for it. Craving your honor's pardon, it is certain, that if you were now dead, I should owe you no allegiance.

TUCT. The supposition is a little impolite; but, however, your conclusion is true.

KARP. And would it not be the same, my lord, if you were expelled? for you would have a successor, to whom I must take a fresh oath of allegiance. Why should you require fidelity of me, when it would be no longer of use to you? That would be just as if you could not eat my figs yourself, and yet you would prevent my selling them to any body else.

TUCT. You are a reasoner, I see, and have your principles of action.

KARP. Aye, such as they are. They are but few, but they serve me; and, even, had I more, they would only puzzle me.

TUCT. I should, indeed, much like to know your principles, and the rules that govern your conduct.

KARP. They are—to be a good husband, a good father, a good neighbor, and a good gardener. I go no further, and hope for the rest, that God will take every thing in good part, and have mercy on me.

TUCT. And do you think he will show the same mercy to me, who am governor of this island of Samos?

KARP. And, pray, how do you think I should know that? Is it for me to conjecture how God Almighty behaves to Bashaws? That is an affair between you and him, which I do not intermeddle with in any shape. All that I believe of the matter is, that if you be as good a Bashaw as I am a gardener, God will be very good to you.

TUCT. By Mahomet, I like this idolator very well! Farewell friend: *Allah* be your protection!

KARP. Thank you, my lord Bashaw! God have mercy upon you.

IV

LIBERTY

A DIALOGUE BETWEEN A PHILOSOPHER AND HIS FRIEND

PHIL. A battery of cannon is playing close by your ears; are you at liberty to hear or not to hear it?

FRIEND. Unquestionably, I cannot but hear it.

PHIL. Would you have those cannon balls carry off your head, and your wife's and daughter's, who are walking with you?

FRIEND. What a question! In my sober senses, it is impossible, that I should will any such thing. It cannot be.

PHIL. Well: you necessarily hear the explosion of those cannon, and you necessarily are against being, with your family, cut off by a cannon-shot, as you are taking the air. You have not the power not to hear, nor the power of willing to remain there.

FRIEND. Nothing more evident.

PHIL. Accordingly, you have come thirty paces to be out of the cannon's way: thus you have had the power of walking that little space with me.

FRIEND. That also is clear.

PHIL. And, if you had been paralytic, you could not have avoided being exposed to this battery. You would not have had the power of being where you are; you would necessarily not only have heard the explosion, but have received a cannon-shot; and thus you would undoubtedly have been killed.

FRIEND. Very true.

PHIL. In what, then, consists your liberty? if not in the power which your body has made use of to do, what your volition, by an absolute necessity, required.

FRIEND. You put me to a stand. Liberty, then, is nothing but the power of doing what I will?

PHIL. Think of it, and see whether liberty can have any other meaning.

FRIEND. At this rate, my greyhound is as free as I am. He has necessarily a will to run at the sight of a hare, and likewise the power of running, if not lame: so that, in nothing am I superior to my dog. This is leveling me with the beasts.

PHIL. Such are the wretched sophisms of those who have tutored you. Wretched! to be in the same state of liberty as your dog? And are you not like your dog in a thousand things? In hunger, thirst, waking, sleeping: and your five senses, are they not also possessed by him? Are you for smelling otherwise than through the nose? of hearing, except through the ears? of seeing, without eyes? Why, then, are you for having liberty in a manner different from him?

FRIEND. How! am I not at liberty to will what I will?

PHIL. Your meaning?

FRIEND. I mean what all the world means. Is it not a common saying, Will is free?

PHIL. A proverb is no reason. Please to explain yourself more clearly.

FRIEND. I mean that I have the liberty of willing as I please.

PHIL. By your leave, there is no sense in that. Do you not perceive, that it is ridiculous to say, I will will. You will necessarily, in consequence of the ideas occurring to you. Would you marry? yes, or no.

FRIEND. What, were I to say, I neither will the one nor the other?

PHIL. That would be answering like him, who said: Some think that Cardinal Mazarine is dead, others believe him to be still living, but I believe neither the one nor the other!

FRIEND. Well I have a mind to marry.

PHIL. Good. That is something of an answer. And why have you a mind to marry?

FRIEND. Because I am in love with a young lady, who is handsome, of a sweet temper, well bred, with a tolerable fortune, sings charmingly, and her parents are people of good credit. Besides, I flatter myself, that my addresses are very acceptable, both to herself, and to her family.

PHIL. Why, there is a reason. You see you cannot will without a reason, and I declare you have the liberty of marrying; that is, you have the liberty of signing the contract.

FRIEND. How! not will without a reason! What, then, becomes of another proverb, *"Sit pro ratione voluntas?"* my will is my reason. I will, because I will.

PHIL. My dear friend, under favor, that is an absurdity. There would then be in you an effect without a cause.

FRIEND. What! when I am playing at even and odd, is there a reason for my choosing even, rather than odd?

PHIL. Yes, to be sure.

FRIEND. Pray, let me hear that reason.

PHIL. Because the idea of odd presented itself to your mind before the contrary notion. It would be strange, indeed, that in some cases you will because there is a cause of volition; and that, in other cases, you will without any cause. In your willing to be married, you evidently perceive the determining reason; and, in playing at even and odd, you do not perceive it; and yet one there must be.

FRIEND. But again, am I not then free?

PHIL. Your will is not free, but your actions are. You are free to act, when you have the power of acting.

FRIEND. But all the books I have read on the liberty of indifference—

PHIL. Are nonsense. There is no such thing as the liberty of indifference. It is a word void of sense, and was coined by those who were not overloaded with it.

PHILOSOPHIC CRITICISMS

OF THE EGYPTIAN RITES

IN THE first place, did the Egyptians acknowledge one supreme God? If this question had been propounded to the commonalty of that people themselves, they would not have known what to reply: if to the young students in Egyptian theology, they would have harangued for a long time, without understanding themselves: if to any one of the sages consulted by Pythagoras, Plato, or Plutarch, he would ingenuously have replied that he adored only one God. which answer would be founded upon the ancient inscription of the statue of Isis, "*I am what is*"; and this other, "*I am all that has been and shall be; no mortal can raise my veil.*" He would have pointed out the globe, placed upon the temple-gate at Memphis, which represented the unity of the divine nature, under the word *Knef*.

The most sacred name amongst the Egyptians, was that of *Y-ha-ho*, which the Hebrews adopted. It is variously pronounced; but Clement of Alexandria assures us, in his *Stromates*, that those who entered into the temple of Serapis were obliged to wear the inscription of the name *I-ha-ho*, or *I-ha-hou*, which signified the God eternal. The Arabians have retained only the syllable *hou*, afterwards adopted by the Turks, who pronounce it with still greater respect than the word *Allah*, for they use *Allah* in conversation, and they never use *hou* but when at prayer. Let us observe here, en passant, that when the Turkish ambassador, Said Effendi, saw the representation of the *Bourgeois Gentilhomme*, or *Tradesman Turned Gentleman*, and that ridiculous ceremony in which he is made a Turk, and hearing the sacred word *hou* pronounced with derision and extravagant gestures, he looked upon this diversion as the most abominable profanation.

But to resume. The Egyptian priests fed a sacred ox, a sacred dog, and a sacred crocodile it is true; and the Romans had also their sacred geese. They had gods of every kind, and the devotees had, among their household deities, the god of the open-chair, *Deum Stercutium*, and the god Pet, *Deum crepitum;* but did they the less acknowledge the *Deum optimum maximum*—the master of gods and men?

Which is the country that has not abounded with superstitious bigots, and a small number of reasonable people?

What should be particularly observed with respect to Egypt and all other nations, is, that they never had any invariable opinions, any more than laws, that were always uniform, notwithstanding the attachment which men have to their ancient customs.

There is nothing immutable but Geometry, all things else undergo incessant variation.

The learned dispute, and will dispute. One asserts that the ancient people were all idolators, another denies it; one says that they adored only one God without an image; another says that they adored several gods in several images. They are all right; nothing more is requisite than to distinguish the times and men which have changed; there never was any agreement. When the Ptolomies and the principal priests made a joke of Apis's bull, the people prostrated themselves before it.

Juvenal says that the Egyptians adored onions; but we do not find it in any history. There is a great deal of difference between a sacred onion and an onion that is a god. Every thing is not adored that is placed, that is consecrated, upon the altar. We read in Cicero that those men who have drained every kind of superstition have not yet arrived at that of eating their gods; and that this is the only absurdity they are deficient in.

Is circumcision derived from the Egyptians, the Arabians, or the Ethiopians? I am ignorant. Let those who know speak. All I know is, that the priests of antiquity imprinted upon their bodies marks of their consecration, as the Roman soldiers were afterwards marked with a hot iron. There, the sacrificing priests slashed the bodies, as did afterwards the priests of Bellona: Here, they made themselves eunuchs, in imitation of the priests of Cybele.

The Jews adopted circumcision from the Egyptians, with part of their ceremonies. They have always retained it, as well as the Arabians and the Ethiopians; the Turks have submitted to it, though it is not ordered in the Alcoran. It is only an ancient usage which was introduced by superstition, and which has been preserved by custom.

Mysteries of the Egyptians

I am far from knowing what nation first invented these mysteries, which have gained so much credit from the Euphrates to the Tiber. Egyptians make no mention of the author of the mysteries of Isis. Those established in Persia are attributed to Zoroaster, those of Greece to Cadmus and Inachus, those of Thrace to Orpheus, and those of Crête to Minos.

It is certain that all these mysteries intimate a future state; for Celsus says to the Christians, "You boast of believing in eternal punishments, and do not all the ministers of mysteries declare them to the initiated?"

The Greeks, who borrowed so many things from the Egyptians; their Tartharoth, of which they made Tartarus: the lake, of which they made their Achèron; the boatman Charon, of whom they made the ferryman of the dead, framed their famous mysteries of Eleusinia only upon those of Isis. But no one can affirm that the mysteries of Zoroaster did not precede those of the Egyptians. They are both of the greatest antiquity, and all the Greek and Latin authors, who have made mention of them, agree that the unity of God, the immortality of the soul, rewards and punishments after death, were announced in these sacred ceremonies.

It is very probable that the Egyptians, having once established these mysteries, preserved their rites; for notwithstanding their extreme levity, they were invariable in their superstitions. The prayer, which we meet with in Apuleïus, when Lucius is initiated into the mysteries of Isis, must have been the ancient form of prayer:

"The celestial powers serve thee, the infernal regions are in submission to thee, the universe turns beneath thy hand, thy feet bear down Tartarus, the stars harken to thy voice, the seasons return at thy command, the elements obey thee," &c.

Can we possibly have stronger evidence than this, that the ancient Egyptians, in the midst of all their contemptible superstitions, yet acknowledge both the existence and the unity of one only God?

OF ZALEUCUS

EVERY moralist and legislator may be challenged to produce anything more beautiful and useful than the exordium of the laws of Zaleucus, who lived before the time of Pythagoras, and was the first magistrate of the Locrians.

"Every citizen should be persuaded of the existence of the divinity. It is only necessary to observe the order and harmony of the universe, to be convinced that accident could not have formed it. We should subdue the soul, purify it, and cleanse it from all evil, from a conviction that God cannot be well served by those of a perverse disposition; and that he does not resemble those wretched mortals, who suffer themselves to be influenced by magnificent ceremonies and sumptuous offerings. Virtue alone, and a constant desire to do good, can please him. Let us then endeavor to be just in our principles and practice, and we shall thereby become dear to the divinity. Every one should dread more what leads to ignominy than what leads to poverty. He should be looked upon as the best citizen, who gives up his fortune for justice; but those whose violent passions lead them to evil, men, women, citizens and strangers, should be cautioned to remember the gods, and to think of the severe judgments which they exercise against the wicked; let them call to remembrance the hour of death—the fatal hour which awaits us all—the hour when the remembrance of faults brings on remorse, and the vain regret of not having regulated all our actions by the rules of equity.

"Every one should so conduct himself during each moment of his life, as if that moment were his last; but if an evil genius prompts him to crimes, let him fly to the foot of the altar, and implore heaven to drive from him this evil genius; let him, above all, seek the society of just and virtuous men, whose counsels will bring him back to virtue, by representing to him God's goodness and his vengeance."

No; there is nothing in all antiquity that should obtain a preference to this simple but sublime moral, dictated by reason and virtue, stripped of all enthusiasm, and of that extravagant coloring, which good sense disowns.

Charondas, a disciple of Zaleucus, expressed himself in the same manner. The Platos, Ciceros, and divine Antonines, have never since held any other language. Thus did Julian, who had the misfortune to give up the Christian religion, but who did so much honor to that of nature, also express himself; that Julian, who was the scandal of our church and the glory of the Roman Empire.

"The ignorant," says he, "should be instructed and not punished; they should be pitied, and not hated. The duty of an Emperor is to imitate God; to imitate him, is to have the fewest wants, and to do all the good that is possible."

Let those who insult antiquity learn to be acquainted with it; let them not confound wise legislators with fabulists; let them learn how to distinguish between the laws of the wisest magistrates and the ridiculous customs of the people; let them not say that superstitious ceremonies were invented by intelligent rulers, and that they originated false oracles and false prodigies without number, and therefore all the magistrates of Greece and Rome, who tolerated these absurdities, were blind deceivers and deceived. This would be like saying that there are bonzes in China, who have abused the populace, and that therefore the wise Confucius was a wretched impostor.

Men should, in so enlightened an age as this, blush at those declamations, which ignorance has so often promulgated against sages, who should be imitated and not calumniated. Do we not know that in every country the vulgar are imbecile, superstitious, and insensible? Are there not Methodists, Millinarians, Moravians, and fanatics of every kind, in that country which gave birth to the chancellor Bacon, to those immortal geniuses Newton and Locke, and to a multitude of great men?

OF BACCHUS

EXCEPTING those fables which are clearly allegorical, such as those of the Muses, of Venus, the Graces, Zephyrus, Love and Flora, with a few others of the same species, all the rest are a collection of idle stories, which have no other merit than that of having furnished Ovid and Quinaut with materials for some beautiful verses, and of having exercised the pencils of our best painters. But there is one, however, which seems to deserve the attention of those who delight in the researches of antiquity, and this is, *The Fable of Bacchus.*

Was this Bacchus, or Back, or Backos, or Dionisios, a son of God, a real personage? Many nations mention him, as well as Hercules. Indeed, so many different Herculeses and Bacchuses have been celebrated, that it may reasonably be supposed that there was, in fact, one Bacchus as well as one Hercules.

It is certain, that in Egypt, Asia, and Greece, Bacchus as well as Hercules was acknowledged for a demi-god; that their feasts were celebrated; that miracles were attributed to them; and that mysteries were instituted in the name of Bacchus before the Jewish books were known.

We know that the Jews did not communicate their books to foreigners till the time of Ptolemy Philadelphus, about two hundred and thirty years before our era. Now, before that time, the East and West re-echoed with the orgies of Bacchus. The verses that are attributed to hte ancient Orpheus celebrated the conquests and good actions of this supposed demi-god. His history is so ancient that the fathers of the church suppose Bacchus to have been Noah, because Bacchus and Noah are both reputed to have cultivated the vine.

Herodotus, in relating the ancient opinions, says that Bacchus was *in*

Egyptian, brought up in Arabia Felix. The Orphic verses say that he was saved from the waters in a small box, which was called Misem, in remembrance of this adventure; that he was instructed in the secrets of the gods; that he had a wand, which he changed into a serpent at will; that he passed through the Red Sea dry-shod, as Hercules subsequently did, in his goblet, through the straits of Abila and Calpe; and that, when he went into India, he and his army enjoyed the light of the sun during the night. Moreover, it is said, that he touched with his magic wand the waters of the rivers Orontes and Hydaspes; and that these waters then separated and left him a free passage. It is even said that he arrested the course of the sun and moon. He wrote his laws upon two tables of stone: and was anciently represented with horns, or rays, issuing from his head.

After this it is not surprising that several learned men, and particularly Bochart and Huet in modern times, should suppose that Bacchus was a copy of Moses and Joshua. Indeed, everything concurs to favor the resemblance; for Bacchus was, amongst the Egyptians, called Arsaph, and amongst the names which the fathers have given to Moses, we find that of Osasirph.

Between these two histories, which appear similar in so many respects, it is not to be doubted that the history of Moses is the real one, and that of Bacchus only the fable. But it appears that this fable was known to several nations long before the history of Moses had reached them. No Greek author before Longinus, who lived under the emperor Aurelian, had quoted Moses; but all had previously celebrated Bacchus.

It appears impossible that the Greeks could have taken their ideas of Bacchus from the book of the Jewish laws, which they did not understand, and of which they had not the least knowledge,—a book, moreover, so scarce, even amongst the Jews, that in the reign of King Josias but one copy could be found,—a book that was almost entirely lost during the slavery of the Jews, who were transported into Chaldea, and other parts of Asia,—a book that was afterwards restored by Esdras in the flourishing times of Athens, and the other Grecian republics—times when the mysteries of Bacchus were already instituted.

God then allowed that the spirit of untruth should reveal the absurdities of the life of Bacchus to a hundred nations, before the spirit of truth divulged the life of Moses to any other people than the Jews.

The learned bishop of Avranches, struck with this surprising resemblance, did not hesitate to contend that Moses was not only Bacchus, but the Thaut, the Osiris of the Egyptians. He even adds, to remove any contradiction, that Moses was also their Typhon, that is to say, that he was at the same time the good and the bad principle, the protector and the enemy, the God and the Devil of the Egyptians.

Moses, according to this learned man, is the same as Zoroaster. He is Esculapius, Amphion, Apollo, Faunus, Janus, Perseus, Romulus, Vertumnus, and finally, Adonis and Priapus. The proof that he was Adonis is that Virgil says,

"Et formosus oves ad flumina pavit Adonis."
"And the beautiful Adonis was a keeper of sheep."

Now Moses watched the sheep towards Arabia. The proof of his being Priapus is still better. Priapus was sometimes represented with an ass, and the Jews were supposed to adore an ass. Huet adds, to complete the confirmation, that the rod of Moses might very well be compared to the sceptre of Priapus:

"Sceptrum Priapo tribuitur, virga Mosi."

This is what Huet calls his demonstration. It is not in truth very geometrical. There is even reason to believe that he blushed at it in the latter part of his life; and that he remembered this demonstration when he wrote his *Treatise on the Weakness of the Human Mind, and the Uncertainty of Its Knowledge.*

GRECIAN METAMORPHOSES

THE opinion of the transmigration of souls naturally leads to metamorphoses, as we have already seen. Every idea that strikes the imagination, and amuses it, presently spreads throughout the world. As soon as you have persuaded me that my soul can enter into the body of a horse, it will not be difficult for you to make me believe that my body may be also changed into a beast.

The compilation of Metamorphoses by Ovid, of which we have already spoken, would not in the least astonish a Pythagorian, a Brahman, a Chaldean, or an Egyptian. The gods were transformed into animals in ancient Egypt. Dorceto, or Dercetis was changed into a fish in Syria; and Semiramis into a dove, at Babylon. The Jewish records, in earlier times, claim that Nabucodonosor was changed into an ox, while Lot's unfortunate wife was transformed into a pillar of salt. Are not the apparitions of gods and genii in human shape real, if transitory, metamorphoses?

A god cannot well commune with us unless he appears in a human form. It is true that Jupiter took upon himself the figure of a beautiful swan, to entice Leda. But instances of this kind are now extremely rare; and in every religion, the divinity has always assumed the human form when he came to give orders. It would be difficult to understand the voice of the gods, if they appeared in the shape of bears or crocodiles.

In fine, the gods metamorphosed themselves almost everywhere; and as soon as we became acquainted with the secrets of magic, we, also, metamorphosed ourselves. Several persons worthy of credit changed themselves into wolves. The word *were-wolf* is still a proof to us of this metamorphosis.

What gives weight to the belief in all these prodigies and transmutations is, that no formal proof can be given of their impossibility. There is no argument to be opposed, if a person should aver that a god came yesterday to my house in the figure of a handsome young man, who wooed and wed my daughter, who will in time become the mother of a beautiful child that the god had deigned to confer upon her. My brother who was so daring as to doubt the divinity of this pretender, was, it is said, turned into a wolf. It is certain that he went into the woods and howled. The only recourse is to summon before a judge the young man who counterfeited a god, and married the young lady—to watch the uncle, the *were-wolf*, and get evidence of the imposture. But the family will not expose themselves to this examination. They will maintain with the priests of the Canton that you are a profane, ignorant man—they will show you that since a caterpillar can be changed into a butterfly, a man with equal facility may be changed into a beast; and, if you dispute, you will be impeached at the Inquisition of the country, as an impious wretch, who neither believes in *were-wolves* nor in gods endowed with the passions and frailties of the human race.

OF IDOLATRY

AFTER having read all that has been written upon idolatry, there is nothing that communicates a precise idea of it. It seems that Locke was the first who taught men to define the words they used, and not to speak at random.

The term that answers to idolatry is not to be found in any ancient language; it is an expression of the Greeks of the last ages, which was never in use before the second century of our era. It signifies the adoration of images. It is a term of reproach—an expression of abuse. No people ever took upon themselves the title of idolators—no government ever ordained that the people should adore an image as the supreme God of nature.

The ancient Chaldeans, the ancient Arabians, the ancient Persians, had, for a long time, neither images nor temples. How could those who venerated the emblems of divinity in the sun, the stars, and fire, be called idolators? They revered what they saw. But revering the sun and the stars is surely not adoring a graven image, made by a workman. It is, undoubtedly, an erroneous doctrine, but it is not idolatry.

Suppose that the Egyptians really adored the dog Anubis, and the bull Apis—that they were ignorant enough to consider them not as animals consecrated to the divinity, and as an emblem of the good which their Isheth and their Isis did unto man, but that they really believed that a celestial ray had animated the consecrated ox and dog, still it is evident that this belief was not adoring a statue. A beast is not an idol.

Men had, no doubt, objects of devotion before they had sculptors; and it is clear that those men who were so ancient could not be called idolaters. It remains then to ascertain if those who afterwards placed statues in the temples, and who ordained the reverence of those statues, were called "worshipers of images," and their people, also, "worshipers of images." This certainly is not to be found in any monument of antiquity.

But without taking upon themselves the title of idolaters, were they really so in fact? Was it ordained that they should believe that the brazen statue, which represented the fantastical figures of Bel and Babylon, was the master, the God, the creator of the world? Was the figure of Jupiter, Jupiter himself?

Is it not (if it be allowable to compare the customs of our holy religion with the customs of antiquity) like saying that we adore the figure of the eternal Father with a long beard, the figure of a woman and a child, the figure of a dove? these forming the emblematical ornaments in our temples. We adore them so little, that if these images happen to be of wood, and begin to decay, we use them for firewood, and erect others in their places. They are merely significant emblems appealing to the eyes and the imagination. The Turks, and those of the reformed church, think that the Catholics are idolaters, but the Catholics loudly protest against the accusation.

It is impossible really to adore a statue, or to believe that any statue can be the supreme God. There was but one Jupiter, but there are a thousand statues of him. Now, this Jupiter, who was supposed to dart his lightning, was thought to inhabit the clouds, or Mount Olympus, or the planet which bears his name. His emblems did not dart lightning, and were neither in a planet, in the clouds, nor upon Mount Olympus. All prayers were dedicated to the immortal Gods, and, assuredly, the statues were not immortal.

Knaves and impostors have asserted, and the superstitious have believed that statues have spoken. The ignorant are almost invariably credulous; but these absurdities were never, amongst any people, the religion of the state. Some credulous old woman may not have distinguished the statue from the god; but this is no reason for maintaining that the government thought like this old woman. The magistrates were willing that the representation of the gods they adored should be revered, and that the attention of the people should be fixed by these visible signs. If the ancients were idolaters for having statues in their temples, one half of Christendom are also idolaters; and, if the latter were not so, neither were the nations of antiquity.

In a word, there is not in all antiquity a single poet, a single philosopher, a single man of any rank, who has said that stone, marble, brass, or wood should be adored; but there are innumerable testimonies to the contrary. Idolatrous nations are then like sorcerers; they are frequently spoken of, but they never existed.

A commentator has concluded that the statue of Priapus was really adored, because Horace, in making this bug-bear speak, causes it to say—"I was formerly the trunk of a tree; the artisan undetermined whether he should make a god, or a joint-stool of me, finally resolved to make me a god," &c. This commentator cites the prophet Baruch, to prove that in the time of Horace, the statue of Priapus was worshiped as a real divinity. He does not perceive that Horace is making a jest, both of the pretended god and his statue. It may be possible that, one of the servant-maids, in seeing this enormous figure, might conceive there was something divine in it; but it will not, assuredly, be pretended, that all those wooden figures of Priapus, with which the gardens were filled for the purpose of driving away the birds, were regarded as the Creators of the world!

It is said that Moses, notwithstanding the divine law which forbade the making of images of men or animals, erected a brazen serpent, which was an imitation of the silver serpent carried by the Egyptian priests in procession; but though this serpent was made to cure the bites of real serpents, it was not, however, adored. Solomon placed two cherubims in the temple, but these cherubims were not looked upon as gods. If, then, in the temple of the Jews, and in our temples, statues have been respected without idolatry, why should other nations be so greatly reproached? We should either absolve them, or they should accuse us.

OF ORACLES

IT IS evident we cannot be acquainted with futurity, because we cannot be acquainted with what does not exist; but it is also clear that conjectures may be formed of an event.

You see a numerous and well disciplined army, conducted by a skillful chief, advancing in an advantageous place, against an imprudent captain, followed by only a few troops, badly armed, badly posted, and half of whom you know to be traitors. You foretell that this captain will be defeated.

You have observed that a young man and a young woman are desperately fond of each other; you saw them meet at an appointed rendezvous; you announce that in a short time they will be married. You cannot be much mistaken. All predictions are reduced to the calculation of probabilities: there is therefore no nation in which some predictions have not been made that have come to pass. The most celebrated and best attested is that which the traitor Flavian Josephus made to Vespasian and Titus his son, the conquerors of the Jews. He saw Vespasian and Titus adored by the Roman armies in the East, and Nero detested by the whole empire. He had the audacity, in order to obtain the good graces of Vespasian, to predict to him, in the name of the God of the Jews, that he and his son would become emperors. They, in effect, were so; but it is evident that Josephus ran no risk. If the day of Vespasian's overthrow had come, he would not have been in a situation to punish Josephus: if he obtained the imperial throne, he must recompense his prophet; and till such time as he reigned, he was in hopes of doing it. Vespasian informed this Josephus, that if he were a prophet, he should have foretold him the loss of Jotapat, which he had ineffectually defended against the Roman army: Josephus replied, that he had in fact foretold it, which was not very surprising. What commander, who sustains a siege in a small place against a numerous army, does not foretell that the place will be taken?

It was not very difficult to discover that respect and money might be drawn from the multitude by playing the prophet, and the credulity of the people must be a revenue for any who knew how to cheat them. There were in all places soothsayers; but it was not sufficient to foretell in their own name, it was necessary to speak in the name of the divinity; and from the time of the prophets of Egypt, who called themselves seers, till the time of Ulpius, who was prophet to the favorite of the empire, Adrian, who became a god, there was a prodigious number of sacred quacks, who made the gods speak, to make a jest of man. It is well known how they might succeed; sometimes by an ambiguous reply, which they afterwards explained as they pleased; at othen times by corrupting servants, and thereby penetrating the secrets of those devotees who came to consult them. An idiot was greatly astonished that a cheat should tell him of what he had done in the most hidden manner.

These prophets were supposed to know the past, the present, and the future: this is the eulogium which Homer makes upon Calchas. I shall add nothing in this place to what the learned Vandale and the judicious Fontenelle his reviser, have said of oracles; they have sagaciously convicted the ages of imposture; and the jesuit Balthus displayed very little sense, or much malignity, when he supported, in opposition to them, the truth of the Pagan oracles, upon the principles of the Christian religion. It was really doing God an injury, to suppose this God of goodness and truth had left loose the devils from hell, to come upon earth, and there perform what he does not exercise himself, in order to produce oracles.

Either these devils uttered truths, and in that case it was impossible not to believe them, and God himself supporting every kind of false religion by daily miracles, gave the world up to his enemy's will; or else they spoke false; and in this case, God must have unfettered the devils to deceive all mankind. There never was, perhaps, a more absurd opinion.

The most famous oracle was that of Delphos. They at first chose innocent young girls, as more proper than any other to be inspired; that is to say, to utter with faith all the nonsense the priests dictated to them. The young Pythia mounted a tripod, fixed in the opening of a cavity, from whence her prophetic utterances issued; but a young Pythia having been run away with by a devotee, an old woman supplied the young one's place to carry on the trade; and I believe that upon this account the oracle of Delphos began to lose much of its credit.

Divinations and auguries were a kind of oracles, and are, I believe, of higher antiquity; for many ceremonies were necessary, much time was required, to draw custom to a divine oracle, that could not do without a temple and priests; and nothing was easier than to tell fortunes in the cross-ways. This art was subdivided into a thousand shapes; predictions were extracted from the flight of birds, sheep's livers, the lines of the palm of the hand, circles drawn upon the ground, water, fire, small flints, wands, and, in a word, from every thing that could be devised, and frequently from enthusiasm alone, which supplied the place of all rules. But who invented this art? The first rogue that met with a fool.

The greatest part of the predictions were like those of the Liege Almanac; "A great man will depart this life." Storms will "arise." Does a village magistrate die within a twelve-month? this was the great man, with respect to that village, whose death was foretold. Is a fishing boat stranded? these are the violent storms predicted. The author of the Liege Almanac is a sorcerer, whether his predictions are or are not accomplished; for if any event favors them, his magic is demonstrated; if the events are opposite, the prediction is applied to a quite different thing, and he saves himself allegorically.

The Liege Almanac has told us that there would come a people from the North, who would destroy every thing; this people did not come, but a north wind froze up some vines, this was what was predicted by Matthew Lansberg. Does any one dare to doubt of his knowledge? the hawkers would as soon arraign him for a bad citizen, or the astrologers treat him as a man of shallow parts and little reason.

The Mahometan Sunnites have greatly availed themselves of this method, in their explanation of Mahomet's Koran. Aldebaran's star was in great veneration amongst the Arabians, it signifies the ox's eye; this meant that Mahomet's eye would enlighten the Arabians, and that, like an ox, he would strike his enemies with his horns.

The acacia tree was in esteem in Arabia; great hedges were made of it, to preserve the crops from the heat of the sun; Mahomet is the acacia, who is to cover the earth with his salutary form. The sensible Turks laugh at these subtle stupidities; the young women do not think about them; the old female devotees firmly believe them; and he who should say to a dervish that he teaches nonsense, would run the risk of being impaled. There have been learned men who have traced the history of their own times in the Iliad and Odyssey; but these learned men did not acquire the same fortune as the commentators of the Koran.

The most brilliant function of the oracles was to insure victory in war. Each army, each nation, had its own peculiar oracles, that promised triumphs. The oraculous intelligence of one of the parties was infallibly true. The vanquished, who had been deceived, attributed their defeat to some fault committed towards the gods, after the oracle had been consulted, and they hoped the oracle's prediction would eventually be accomplished. Thus is almost the whole earth fed with illusions. There were scarce any people who did not preserve in their archives, or who had not, by oral tradition, some prediction which insured them the conquest of the world, that is to say, of the neighboring nations. No conqueror ever gained a victory without its being predicted in form, as soon as the battle was over. Even the Jews, who were shut up in a corner of the earth, almost unknown, between Anti-libanus and Arabia Deserta and Petræa, hoped, like the other people, to be the masters of the universe, upon the foundation of a thousand oracles, which we explain in a mystical sense, but which they understood quite literally.

OF THE GREEK SIBYLS

WHEN almost the whole earth was filled with oracles, there were old maids, who, without belonging to any temple, thought proper to prophesy upon their own account. They were called Sibyls, a Greek word of the Laconian dialect, which signified "The Council of God." According to antiquity, there were ten principal Sibyls in different countries.

The story of the woman, who came tô Rome and brought the elder Tarquin the nine books of the ancient Sibyls of Cumæa, is well known. As Tarquin bargained too much, the old woman threw the first six books into the fire, and insisted upon as much money for the three remaining ones as she had asked for the nine all together. Tarquin paid her. They were, it is said, preserved at Rome, till the time of Sylla, when they were consumed in the conflagration of the Capitol.

But how could the prophecies of the Sibyls be dispensed with? Three senators were dispatched to Erythea, a city of Greece, where a thousand bad Grecian verses were carefully kept, because they were reputed to be the production of the Sibyl of Erythea. Every one was anxious to obtain copies of them; the Sibyl of Erythea had foretold every thing. Her prophecies were considered in the same light as those of Nostradamus with us. Upon every remarkable event, some Greek verses were forged, which were attributed to the Sibyl.

Augustus, who had just reason to fear that in these rhapsodies some verses would be met with that authorized conspiracies, forbade, upon pain of death, any Roman to keep Sibylline verses by him: a prohibition worthy of a suspicious tyrant, who, by address, preserved a power usurped by crimes.

The Sibylline verses were in greater esteem than ever when the reading of them was forbidden. They must needs have contained truth, as they were concealed from the people.

Virgil, in his eclogue upon the birth of Pollio, or Marcellus, or Drusus, failed not to cite the authority of the Sibyl of Cumæa, who had fairly foretold that the child, who should soon after die, would restore the golden age. The Sibyl of Erythea had, as it was then said, prophesied at Cumæa. The prediction of the new-born infant belonging to Augustus, or to his favorite, must necessarily have taken place. Besides, predictions are never made but for the great; the vulgar are unworthy of them.

These oracles of the Sibyls, being then always in great repute, the first Christians being too much carried away by false zeal, imagined that they might forge similar oracular predictions, in order to defeat the Gentiles with their own arms. Hermas and St. Justin are reputed the first who supported this imposture. St. Justin cites the oracles of the Sibyl of Cumæa, promulgated by a Christian, who had taken the name of Istapus, and pretended that his Sibyl had lived in the time of the deluge. St. Clement of Alexandria, in his Stromates, assures us that the apostle St. Paul recommends in his Epistles "the reading of the Sibyls, who have manifestly foretold the birth of the Son of God."

These epistles of St. Paul must necessarily be lost; for none of these words, nor any like them, are to be found in any of the epistles of St. Paul now extant. An infinite number of books, which we are now no longer possessed of, were then dispersed amongst the Christians, such as the prophecies of Jallabash, those of Seth, Enoch, and Kamla; Adam's Penances; the History of Zachariah, father to St. John; the evangelist of the Egyptians, the evangelist of St. Peter, of Andrew, of James, the evangelist, of Eve, Apocalypse of Adam, the letters of Jesus Christ, and a hundred other writings, of which scarce any fragments remain; and these are buried in books that are very rarely read.

The Christian religion was then divided into a Jewish society and a Non-jewish society. These two were subdivided into many others. Whoever was possessed of any degree of talents wrote for his party. There were upwards of fifty gospels till the Council of Nice; and at present there remain only those of the Virgin, of the Infancy, and of Nicodemus. Verses attributed to the Sibyls were frequently forged. Such was the respect the people paid to these Sibylline oracles, that this foreign support was judged necessary to strengthen the dawn of Christianity. Not only Greek Sibylline verses were made, which foretold Jesus Christ; but they were formed in acrostics, so that the letters of these words, "Jesous Christos iös Soter," followed each other at the beginning of every verse. Among these poems we meet this prediction:

"With five loaves and two fishes,
He will feed five-thousand men in the desert,
And in gathering up the fragments that remain,
He will fill twelve baskets."

They did not confine themselves to this: it was imagined that the sense of the verses of the fourth Eclogue of Virgil might be turned in favor of Christianity.

"Ultima Cumæi venit jam carminis ætas;
Jam nova progenies cœlo demittitur alto."

"The time of Sibyls are at last arrived,
A new progeny descends from above the skies."

This opinion was so current in the first ages of the church, that the emperor Constantine vehemently supported it. When an emperor spoke he was surely in the right. Virgil was, for a long time, considered as a prophet. The oracles of the Sibyls were at length so thoroughly believed, that in one of our hymns, which is not very ancient, we have these two remarkable verses:

"Solvet sæclum in favilla
Teste David cum Sibylla."

"The world to ashes he will reduce,
In proof—David and the Sibyl we adduce."

Amongst the productions attributed to the Sibyls, the Millennium was particularly esteemed, and which was adopted by the fathers of the church, till the time of Theodosius the Second.

This Millennium of Jesus Christ upon earth was at first founded on the prophecy of St. Luke (chap. xxi.) a prophecy that has been misunderstood "that Jesus would come in the clouds with great power and majesty, before the present generation was gone." The generation had passed; but St. Paul had also said in his first epistle to the Thessalonians, chap. iv., "For this we say unto you, by the word of the Lord, that we which are alive, and remain unto the coming of the Lord, shall not prevent them which are asleep. For the Lord

himself shall descend from heaven with a shout, with the voice of the arch-
angel, and with the trump of God: and the dead in Christ shall rise first. Then
we which are alive and remain shall be caught up together with them in the
clouds, to meet the Lord in the air: and so shall we ever be with the Lord."

It is very strange that Paul says that the Lord himself spoke unto him; for
Paul, so far from having been one of the disciples of Christ, had for a long time
been one of his persecutors. Though he might be one, the Apocalypse also said,
chap. xx. "that the just should reign upon earth for a thousand years with
Jesus Christ."

It was therefore every moment expected that Jesus Christ would descend
from heaven to establish his reign, and rebuild Jerusalem, wherein the Christians were to rejoice with the Patriarchs.

This new Jerusalem was foretold in the Apocalypse. "I John, saw the new
Jerusalem, which descended from heaven, decked out like a bride.—It had a
large and high wall, twelve gates, and an angel at each gate—twelve foundations—whereon are to be inscribed the names of the apostles of the lamb—He
that spake unto me had a golden fathom to measure—the city, the gates, and
the wall. The city is a square building, twelve thousand furlongs in circumference; its length, breadth, and height, are all equal.—He also measured with it
the wall, which is a hundred and forty-four cubits high—this wall was made of
jasper, and the city was made of gold, &c."

This prediction might have sufficed; but a voucher was thought necessary,
who was a Sibyl, and made to say nearly the same things. This belief was so
strongly imprinted on the people's minds, that St. Justin in his Dialogue against
Tryphon says, "he is convinced, and that Jesus is to come into that Jerusalem,
and drink and eat with his disciples."

St. Irenæus so completely adopted this opinion that he attributes these
words to St. John the Evangelist. "In the new Jerusalem every vine shall produce ten thousand branches, and every branch ten thousand buds, and every
bud ten thousand bunches, and every bunch ten thousand grapes, and every
grape ten thousand amphors of wine. And when any of the holy vintagers shall
gather a grape, the next grape shall say to him, take me, I am better than him."

It was not sufficient that the Sibyl had predicted those miracles,—there were
witnesses of their being fulfilled. Tertullian relates that the new Jerusalem was
seen forty successive nights to descend from heaven.

Tertullian expresses himself thus: "We confess that the kingdom is promised
to us for a thousand years upon earth, after the resurrection in the city of
Jerusalem brought down from heaven thither."

Thus has a love of the marvelous and a desire of hearing and relating extraordinary things, at all times, perverted common sense, and banished reason.
Thus has fraud been brought into play, when force could not be produced.
The Christian religion was, in other respects supported by such solid reasons,
that all this jumble of errors could not shake it. The pure gold was extracted
from this alloy, and the church, by degrees, arrived at the state where we now
see it.

OF MIRACLES

LET us never lose sight of the nature of man: it loves nothing but what is extraordinary, and this is so true, that as soon as the beautiful and sublime become familiar, they are no longer beautiful and sublime. We require uncommon things of every kind; and, in this pursuit, we break down the fences of possibility. Ancient history resembles the history of the cabbage, which was larger than a house, and of the pot, bigger than a church, in which it was to be boiled.

What idea have we affixed to the word *miracle*, which at first signified something admirable? We have said, that what nature cannot produce is contrary to all its laws. So the Englishman, who promised the people of London to get whole into a bottle, promised a miracle. And legend-makers would not formerly have been wanting to affirm the accomplishment of this prodigy, if it had produced anything to the convent.

We believe, without difficulty, the real miracles operated in our holy religion, and amongst the Jews, whose religion paved the way for ours. We speak in this place only of other nations, and we reason only according to the rules of good sense, ever subordinate to revelation.

Whoever is wanting in the light of faith, cannot consider a miracle as anything else than a contradiction to the eternal laws of nature. It does not appear possible to him that God should disturb his own work: he knows that everything in nature is concatenated by indissoluble chains. He knows that God being immutable, his laws are the same, and that no one wheel of the whole machine can be stopped without nature's self being disordered.

If Jupiter while visiting Alcmena makes a night of twenty-four hours, when it should consist of only twelve, the earth must necessarily be stopped in its course, and remain motionless twelve whole hours. But as the usual phenomena appeared the succeeding night, the moon and the other planets must consequently have been stopped in their course. This would have been a very great revolution in the celestial orbs, in favor of a woman of Thebes in Bœotia.

A dead man comes to life after being breathless for some days. All the imperceptible particles of his body, which were exhaled in the air, and which had been carried away by the wind, must have returned exactly to their former station, and the worms, birds, or other animals, which were nourished with the substance of this corpse, must each of them restore what he had taken from it. The worms, fattened with the entrails of this man, must have been eaten by swallows, these swallows by magpies, these magpies by falcons, and these falcons by vultures. Each one must restore precisely what belonged to the deceased, without which it could not be the same person. And all this is nothing, unless the soul returns to its former mansion.

If the Eternal Being, who has foreseen all things, arranged all things, who governs all things by immutable laws, acts contrary to his own design by subverting those laws, this can be supposed to take place only for the benefit of all nature. But it appears contradictory to suppose a single case, wherein the creator and master of all things could change the order of the universe for the benefit of the world; for he either foresaw the supposed necessity there would be before the change, or else he did not see it. If he did foresee, the necessary regulations were made in the beginning; if he did not foresee, he is no longer God.

It is averred that to please a nation, a city, or a family, the Supreme Being made Pelops, Hippolites, Heres, and some other famous personages rise from the dead; but it does not seem probable that the common master of the universe should forget the care of that universe, in favor of this Hippolites, or this Pelops.

The more incredible miracles are (according to our weak intellects) the more readily they have met with belief. Every people had so many prodigies, that they became very common things; nor did they think it prudent to deny those of their neighbors. The Greeks said to the Egyptians and Asiatic nations, "The gods spoke to you sometimes, they speak to us every day; if they have fought twenty times for you, they have put themselves forty times at the head of our armies. If you have metamorphoses, we have a hundred times more than you. If your animals speak, ours have made very elegant orations." There are no people, even down to the Romans, among whom beasts have not had the power of speech, to foretell future events. Titus Livius relates that an ox cried out in the public market-place when full of people, "Rome, take care of thyself." Pliny in his eighth book says, that a dog spoke, when Tarquin was driven from the throne. If Suetonius is to be credited, a crow cries out in the Capitol when Domitian was going to be assassinated, *Estai panta Kalos*, very well done, *all is well*. In the same manner one of Achilles's horses, named Xante, foretold to his master that he should fall before Troy. Before Achilles's horse, Phrixus's ram had spoken, as well as the cows upon Mount Olympus. So that instead of refuting fables, they were improved upon. This was like the council whose client had a bond forged upon him; he did not amuse himself with pleadings; he immediately produced a forged receipt.

It is true we do not meet with many resurrections amongst the Romans, they confined themselves chiefly to miraculous cures. The Greeks, more attached to the metempsychosis, had many resurrections. They had this secret from the people of the East, from whom all sciences and superstitions are derived.

Of all the miraculous cures, the best attested, and most authentic, are those of the blind man, whom the emperor Vespasian restored to sight, and the paralytic who by this monarch's aid recovered the use of his limbs. It is in Alexandria that this double miracle operates, before innumerable spectators, before Romans, Greeks, and Egyptians. It is upon his tribunal, that Vespasian operates these prodigies. He does not endeavor to gain esteem by imposture, which is unnecessary to a monarch who is firmly seated on his throne: but the two patients prostrated themselves at his feet, and conjure him to cure them; he blushes at their entreaties, ridicules them, saying that such cures are not in the power of mortals. They insist upon it: Serapis has appeared to them; Serapis has told them they shall be cured by Vespasian. He at length lets himself be prevailed upon; he touches them without being flattered with success. The Divinity, favoring his modesty and virtue, communicates to Vespasian his power; that instant the blind man sees, and the lame one walks. Alexandria, Egypt, all the empire, applaud Vespasian, favored by Heaven. The miracle is preserved in the archives of the empire, and in all the contemporary histories. This miracle has nevertheless in course of time been disbelieved by every one, because no one is interested in supporting its credit.

If we believe I know not what sort of a writer of our barbarous ages, named *Helgaut;* King Robert, son to Hugh Capet, also cured a blind man. This miraculous gift was probably given to Robert, to requite the charity wherewith he burnt his wife's confessor, and the canons of Orleans, who were accused of not believing the infallibility and absolute power of the pope, and consequently of being Manicheans; or if this was not the recompense of this good action, it was to indemnify him, for the excommunication which he suffered, for his attention to the queen, his wife.

Philosophers have made miracles in the same manner as emperors and kings. We are acquainted with those of Apollonius Tyannus. He was a Pythagorian philosopher, temperate, chaste and just, who is not reproached by history with any equivocal action, nor any of those weaknesses with which Socrates is stigmatized. He traveled amongst the Magi and the Brahmans; and was the more honored everywhere, on account of his modesty, always giving wise counsel, and seldom disputing. The constant prayer, which he preferred to the gods, was admirable: "Immortal gods, grant unto us what you think is needful, and which we are not unworthy of." He was no enthusiast; but his disciples were enthusiasts; they attributed miracles to him, which were collected by Philostrates. The Tyarnaens placed him amongst the demi-gods, and the Roman emperors approved of his apotheosis. But in time the apotheosis of Apollonius met the same fate as that which decreed to the Roman emperors. The chapel of Apollonius was equally deserted as that which had been erected by the Athenians to Socrates.

The kings of England from the time of St. Edward to the time of William III. daily performed a great miracle, which was to cure the evil, which physicians could not remove. But William III. would perform no miracles, and his successors have followed his example in abstaining from them. If England should ever undergo any great revolution whereby that nation will be sunk again in ignorance, the English will then have miracles performed every day.